READER'S DIGEST

BEST LOVED
BOOKS

FOR YOUNG
READERS

READER'S DIGEST

BEST LOVED
BOOKS

FOR YOUNG
READERS

selected and condensed by
the Editors of The Reader's Digest

❖

VOLUME EIGHT

THE READER'S DIGEST ASSOCIATION
PLEASANTVILLE, NEW YORK

Contents

Explanatory

In this book a number of dialects are used, to wit: the Missouri Negro dialect; the extremest form of the backwoods Southwestern dialect; the ordinary "Pike County" dialect; and four modified varieties of this last. The shadings have not been done in a haphazard fashion, or by guesswork; but painstakingly, and with the trustworthy guidance and support of personal familiarity with these several forms of speech.

I make this explanation for the reason that without it many readers would suppose that all these characters were trying to talk alike and not succeeding.

THE AUTHOR

The Adventures of

HUCKLEBERRY
FINN

A condensation of the book by **Mark Twain**

Illustrated by John Falter

Tom Sawyer's best friend was Huckleberry Finn, the envy of all his contemporaries because he smoked a pipe and never had to wash or go to school. But there were now too many well-intentioned grown-ups wanting to "sivilize" the irrepressible Huck, so he had no choice but to leave town, quietly. This book is his own ever-memorable account of what followed.

Down the Mississippi he floated on a log raft. And his experiences, recounted in his inimitably racy language, were legion: some hair-raising, some hilarious, some bittersweet and haunting. On the whole he was happy. "You feel mighty free and easy and comfortable on a raft," he decided.

Huck came to value freedom for others as well when he joined forces with Jim, a brave and generous runaway slave. Years ahead of his time (which was the early nineteenth century) Huck learned that the color of a man's skin has nothing to do with his worth as an individual or his right to freedom.

The Adventures of Huckleberry Finn is Mark Twain's masterpiece. Ernest Hemingway said of it that "all modern American literature stems from this one book," and for H. L. Mencken the discovery of *Huckleberry Finn* was "the most stupendous event of my whole life."

Mark Twain (whose real name was Samuel Clemens) grew up beside the "father of waters" and was for a time a steamboat pilot. He knew the river firsthand, and the ways of the river folk—both saints and scoundrels—who throng these pages. He has embodied in the one small raggedy figure of Huck all the toughness and tenderness, all the humor and independence of the American frontier spirit.

CHAPTER I

YOU DON'T KNOW ABOUT ME without you have read a book by the
name of *The Adventures of Tom Sawyer;* but that ain't no matter.
That book was made by Mr. Mark Twain, and he told the truth,
mainly. There was things which he stretched, but mainly he told
the truth.

Now the way that the book winds up is this: Tom and me found
the money that the robbers hid in the cave, and it made us rich.
We got six thousand dollars apiece—all gold. Well, Judge Thatcher
he took it and put it out at interest, and it fetched us a dollar a
day apiece—more than a body could tell what to do with. The
Widow Douglas she took me for her son, and allowed she would
sivilize me; but it was rough living in the house all the time, considering how dismal regular and decent the widow was in all her
ways; and so when I couldn't stand it no longer I lit out. I got
into my old rags again, and was free and satisfied. But Tom
Sawyer he hunted me up and said he was going to start a band
of robbers, and I might join if I would go back to the widow and
be respectable. So I went back.

The widow she cried over me, and called me a poor lost lamb,
a lot of other names, too, but she never meant no harm by it. She
put me in them new clothes again, and I couldn't do nothing but
sweat and sweat, and felt all cramped up. Well, then, the old thing

commenced again. The widow rung a bell for supper, and you had to come to time. When you got to the table you couldn't go right to eating, but you had to wait for the widow to tuck down her head and grumble a little over the victuals. After supper she got out her book and learned me about Moses and the Bulrushers, and I was in a sweat to find out about him; but by and by she let it out that Moses had been dead a considerable time; so then I didn't care no more about him, because I don't take no stock in dead people.

Pretty soon I wanted to smoke, and asked the widow to let me. But she wouldn't. She said it was a mean practice, and I must try to not do it anymore. And then her sister, Miss Watson, a tolerable slim old maid, with goggles on, who had just come to live with her, took a set at me with a spelling book. She worked me middling hard for about an hour, and then the widow made her ease up. I couldn't stood it much longer. Then for an hour it was deadly dull, and I was fidgety.

Miss Watson would say, "Don't put your feet up there, Huckleberry"; and "Set up straight, Huckleberry"; and "Don't gap and stretch like that, Huckleberry—why don't you try to behave?" Then she told me all about the bad place, and I said I wished I was there. She got mad then, but I didn't mean no harm. All I wanted was to go somewheres; all I wanted was a change, I warn't particular. She said it was wicked to say what I said; said she wouldn't say it for the whole world; *she* was going to live so as to go to the good place. Well, I couldn't see no advantage in going where she was going, so I made up my mind I wouldn't try for it. But I never said so, because it would only make trouble, and wouldn't do no good.

Miss Watson she kept pecking at me, and it got tiresome. By and by they fetched the niggers in and had prayers, and then everybody was off to bed. I went up to my room with a piece of candle, and put it on the table. Then I set down in a chair by the window.

I felt so lonesome I most wished I was dead. The stars were shining, and the leaves rustled in the woods ever so mournful;

and I heard an owl, away off, who-whooing about somebody that was dead; and the wind was trying to whisper something to me, and it made the cold shivers run over me. Pretty soon a spider went crawling up my shoulder, and I flipped it off and it lit in the candle; and before I could budge it was all shriveled up. I didn't need anybody to tell me that that was an awful bad sign and would bring me bad luck, so I was scared, and I got up and turned around in my tracks three times and crossed my breast; but I hadn't no confidence. I hadn't ever heard anybody say there was any way to keep off bad luck when you'd killed a spider.

I set down again, a-shaking all over, and got out my pipe for a smoke; for the house was all as still as death now, and so the widow wouldn't know. Well, after a long time I heard the clock in the town go *boom—boom—boom*—twelve licks; and all still again—stiller than ever. Pretty soon I heard a twig snap down in the dark, and I set still and listened. Directly I could just barely hear a *me-yow! me-yow!* That was good! Says I, "*Me-yow! Me-yow!*" soft as I could, and I put out the light and scrambled out the window onto the shed. Then I slipped down to the ground and crawled in among the trees, and, sure enough, there was Tom Sawyer waiting for me.

WE WENT TIPTOEING ALONG a path amongst the trees back toward the end of the widow's garden, stooping down so as the branches wouldn't scrape our heads. When we was passing by the kitchen I fell over a root and made a noise. We scrouched down and laid still. Miss Watson's big nigger, named Jim, was setting in the kitchen door; we could see him because there was a light behind him. He got up and said, "Who dah?" Then he listened some; then he came tiptoeing down and stood right between us. We could 'a' touched him, nearly.

For minutes and minutes there warn't a sound, and we all there so close together. There was a place on my ankle that got to itching, but I dasn't scratch it; and then my ear begun to itch; and next my back, right between my shoulders. Seemed like I'd die if I couldn't scratch. Well, I've noticed that thing plenty times since.

If you are with the quality, or at a funeral, or trying to go to sleep when you ain't sleepy—if you are anywheres where it won't do for you to scratch, why you will itch all over in upwards of a thousand places. Pretty soon Jim says:

"Say, who is you? Dog my cats ef I didn' hear sumf'n. Well, I know what I's gwyne to do: I'se gwyne to set down here and listen tell I hears it ag'in."

So he set down on the ground betwixt me and Tom, and he leaned his back up against a tree and stretched his legs out. Then my nose begun to itch. It itched till the tears come into my eyes and I reckoned I couldn't stand it a minute longer, but I set my teeth and got ready to try. Just then Jim begun to breathe heavy; next he begun to snore—and then I was pretty soon comfortable again.

Tom he made a sign to me—kind of a noise with his mouth—and we went creeping away on our hands and knees. When we was ten foot off Tom whispered to me, and wanted to tie Jim to the tree for fun. But I said no; he might wake and make a disturbance, and then they'd find out I warn't in. Then Tom said he hadn't got candles enough, and he would slip in the kitchen and get some more. I said Jim might wake up and come. But Tom wanted to resk it; so we slid in there and got three candles, and Tom laid five cents on the table for pay. Then we got out, and I was in a sweat to get away; but nothing would do Tom but he must crawl to where Jim was, on his hands and knees, and play something on him. I waited, and it seemed a good while, everything was so still and lonesome.

As soon as Tom was back we cut along the path, around the garden fence, and by and by fetched up on the steep top of the hill the other side of the house. Tom said he slipped Jim's hat off his head and hung it on a limb right over him, and Jim stirred, but he didn't wake. Afterward Jim said the witches bewitched him, and rode him all over the state, and then set him under the trees again, and hung his hat on a limb to show who done it. And next time Jim told it he said they rode him down to New Orleans; and, after that, every time he told it he spread it more and more, till by and by he said they rode him all over the world. Jim was monstrous proud about it. Niggers would come miles to hear him tell about it, and he was more looked up to than any nigger in that country. And he always kept that five-center piece round his neck with a string, and said it was a charm the devil give to him with his own hands. He was most ruined for a servant, because he got stuck up on account of having seen the devil and been rode by witches.

Well, when Tom and me got to the edge of the hilltop we looked away down into the village and could see three or four lights twinkling, where there was sick folks, maybe; and the stars over us was sparkling ever so fine; and down by the village was the river, a whole mile broad, and awful still and grand. We went down the hill and found Joe Harper and Ben Rogers, and two or three more of the boys, hid in the old tanyard. So we unhitched a skiff and pulled down the river two mile and a half, to the big scar on the hillside, and went ashore.

We went to a clump of bushes, and Tom made everybody swear to keep the secret, and then showed them a hole in the hill, right in the thickest part of the bushes. We lit the candles and crawled in. After we went about two hundred yards the cave opened up. Tom poked about amongst the passages, and pretty soon we went along a narrow place and got into a kind of room, all damp and cold, and there we stopped.

Tom says, "Now, we'll start this band of robbers and call it Tom Sawyer's Gang. Everybody that wants to join has got to take an oath, and write his name in blood."

Everybody was willing. So Tom got out a sheet of paper that he had wrote the oath on, and read it. It swore every boy to stick to the band, and never tell any of the secrets; and if anybody done anything to any boy in the band, whichever boy was ordered to kill that person and his family must do it, and he mustn't eat or sleep till he had killed them and hacked a cross on their breasts, which was the sign of the band. And nobody that didn't belong to the band could use that mark, and if he did he must be sued; and if he done it again he must be killed. And if anybody that belonged to the band told the secrets, he must have his throat cut, and then have his carcass burnt up and the ashes scattered, and his name blotted off the list with blood and never mentioned again by the gang, but have a curse put on it and be forgot forever.

Everybody said it was a real beautiful oath, and asked Tom if he got it out of his own head. He said some of it, but the rest was out of pirate books and robber books, and every gang that was high-toned had it.

Some thought it would be good to kill the *families* of boys that told the secrets. Tom said it was a good idea and wrote it in. Then Ben Rogers says:

"Here's Huck Finn, he hain't got no family; what you going to do 'bout him?"

"Well, hain't he got a father?" says Tom Sawyer.

"Yes, he's got a father, but you can't never find him. He used to lay drunk with the hogs in the tanyard, but he hain't been seen in these parts for a year or more."

They talked it over, and they was going to rule me out, because they said every boy must have a family or somebody to kill, or else it wouldn't be fair and square for the others. I was most ready to cry; but all at once I thought of a way, and I offered them Miss Watson—they could kill her. Everybody said, "Oh, she'll do. That's all right. Huck can come in."

Then they all stuck a pin in their fingers to get blood to sign with, and I made my mark on the paper.

"Now," says Ben Rogers, "what's the line of business of this Gang?"

"Robbery and murder," Tom said. "We are highwaymen. We stop stages and carriages on the road, with masks on, and kill the people and take their watches and money."

"Must we always kill the people?"

"Oh, certainly. It's best—except some you bring to the cave here, and keep them till they're ransomed."

"Ransomed? What's that?"

"I don't know. But that's what they do. I've seen it in books; and of course that's what we've got to do."

"But how can we do it if we don't know what it is?"

"Why, blame it all, we've *got* to do it. Don't I tell you it's in the books?"

"That's all very fine to *say*, Tom Sawyer, but how in the nation are these fellows going to be ransomed if we don't know how to do it to them? What do you *reckon* it is?"

"Per'aps if we keep them till they're ransomed, it means that we keep them till they're dead."

"Now, that's something *like*. That'll answer. Why couldn't you said that before? We'll keep them till they're ransomed to death; and a bothersome lot they'll be too—eating up everything and always trying to get loose."

"How you talk, Ben Rogers. How can they get loose when there's a guard over them, ready to shoot them down if they move a peg?"

"A guard! So somebody's got to set up all night and never get any sleep, just so as to watch them! Why can't a body take a club and ransom them as soon as they get here?"

"Because it ain't in the books so—that's why. Now, Ben Rogers, do you want to do things regular, or don't you?"

"All right. But, say, do we kill the women, too?"

"Ben Rogers, if I was as ignorant as you I wouldn't let on. Kill the women? No; nobody ever saw anything in the books like that. You fetch them to the cave, and you're always as polite as pie to them; and by and by they fall in love with you, and never want to go home anymore."

"Well, if that's the way I'm agreed, but mighty soon we'll have a cave so cluttered up with women, and fellows waiting to be ransomed, that there won't be no place for the robbers. But go ahead, I ain't got nothing more to say."

Little Tommy Barnes was asleep now, and when they waked him up he was scared and cried, and said he wanted to go home to his ma. So they all called him crybaby, and that made him mad, and he said he would go straight and tell all the secrets. But Tom gave him five cents to keep quiet, and said we would all go home and meet next week, and rob somebody and kill some people.

Then we elected Tom Sawyer first captain and Joe Harper second captain of the Gang, and so started home.

I clumb up the shed and crept into my window just before day was breaking. My new clothes was all greased up and clayey, and I was dog-tired.

CHAPTER II

WELL, I GOT A GOOD GOING-OVER in the morning from old Miss Watson on account of my clothes; but the widow she didn't scold, but only looked so sorry that I thought I would behave awhile if I could. Then Miss Watson she took me in the closet and prayed, but nothing came of it. She told me to pray every day, and whatever I asked for I would get it. But it warn't so. I tried it. Once I got a fishline, but no hooks. It warn't any good to me without hooks. I tried for the hooks three or four times, but somehow I couldn't make it work. By and by, one day, I told the widow about it, and she said the thing a body could get by praying for it was "spiritual gifts." This was too many for me, but she told me what she meant—I must help other people, and do everything I could for other people, and look out for them all the time, and never think about myself. I went out in the woods and turned it over in my mind a long time, but I couldn't see no advantage about it—except for the other people; so at last I reckoned I wouldn't worry about it anymore, but just let it go.

Pap he hadn't been seen for more than a year, and that was comfortable for me. He used to always whale me when he was sober and could get his hands on me; though I used to take to the woods most of the time when he was around. But I warn't comfortable long, because I judged the old man would turn up again by and by, though I wished he wouldn't.

We played robber now and then about a month, and then I resigned. All the boys did. We hadn't robbed nobody, hadn't killed any people, but only just pretended. We used to hop out of the woods and go charging down on hog drivers and women in carts taking garden stuff to the market, but we never hived any of them. Tom Sawyer called the hogs "ingots," and he called the turnips and stuff "julery," and we would go to the cave and powwow over what we had done, and how many people we had killed. But I couldn't see no profit in it.

One time Tom sent a boy to run about town with a blazing stick, which was the sign for the Gang to get together, and then he said he had got news by his spies that next day a whole parcel of Spanish merchants and rich A-rabs was going to camp in Cave Hollow with two hundred elephants, and six hundred camels, and a thousand "sumter" mules, all loaded down with di'monds, and so we would lay in ambuscade, as he called it, and kill the lot and scoop the things. He said we must slick up our swords and guns, and get ready.

I didn't believe we could lick such a crowd, but I wanted to see the camels and elephants, so I was on hand next day, Saturday, in the ambuscade; and when we got the word we rushed out of the woods and down the hill. But there warn't no Spaniards and A-rabs; it warn't anything but a Sunday-school picnic, and only a primer class at that. We busted it up, and chased the children; but we never got anything but some doughnuts and jam, and then the teacher charged in, and made us drop everything and cut. I didn't see no di'monds, and I told Tom Sawyer so. He said there was loads of them there, anyway; and he said there was A-rabs there, too, and elephants and things. I said, why couldn't we see them, then? He said if I warn't so ignorant, I would know without asking it was all done by enchantment; but we had enemies which he called magicians, and they had turned the whole thing into an infant Sunday school, just out of spite. I said, all right; then the thing for us to do was to go for the magicians. Tom Sawyer said I was a numskull.

"Why," said he, "a magician could call up a lot of genies, and they would hash you up like nothing. They are as tall as a tree and as big round as a church."

"Well," I says, "s'pose we got some genies to help *us*—can't we lick the other crowd then?"

"How you going to get them?"

"I don't know. How do *they* get them?"

"Why, they rub an old tin lamp, and then the genies come tearing in, with the thunder and lightning a-ripping around, and the smoke a-rolling, and everything they're told to do they up and do it. Whoever rubs the lamp, they've got to do whatever he says. If he tells them to build a palace forty miles long out of di'monds, and fill it full of chewing gum, or whatever you want, they've got to do it."

"Well," says I, "I think they are a pack of flatheads for not keeping the palace themselves. And what's more—if I was one of them I would see a man in Jericho before I would drop my business and come to him for the rubbing of an old tin lamp."

"How you talk, Huck Finn. Why, you'd *have* to come when he rubbed it."

"What! And I as high as a tree and as big as a church? Shucks, it ain't no use to talk to you, Huck Finn. You don't seem to know anything—perfect saphead."

I thought all this over for two or three days, and then I reckoned I would see if there was anything in it. I got an old tin lamp, and went out in the woods and rubbed and rubbed till I sweat like an Injun, calculating to build a palace and sell it; but it warn't no use, none of the genies come.

So then I judged that all that stuff was only just one of Tom Sawyer's lies. I reckoned he believed in the A-rabs and the elephants, but as for me I think different. It had all the marks of a Sunday school.

WELL, THREE OR FOUR MONTHS run along this way, and it was well into the winter now. I had been to school most all the time and could spell and read and write just a little, and could say the multiplication table up to six times seven is thirty-five. At first I hated the school, but by and by I got so I could stand it. I was getting sort of used to the widow's ways, too, and they warn't so raspy on me. Living in a house and sleeping in a bed pulled on me pretty tight mostly, but before the cold weather I used to slide out and sleep in the woods sometimes, and so that was a rest to me. The widow said I was coming along slow but sure, and doing very satisfactory. She said she warn't ashamed of me.

One morning I happened to turn over the salt at breakfast. I reached for some of it to throw over my left shoulder and keep off the bad luck, but Miss Watson was in ahead of me. She says, "Take your hands away, Huckleberry; what a mess you are always making!" So I started out, after breakfast, feeling worried and shaky, and wondering where the bad luck was going to fall on me, and what it was going to be.

I went down to the front garden and clumb over the stile where you go through the high board fence. There was an inch of new snow on the ground, and I seen somebody's tracks. They had come up from the quarry and stood around the stile awhile, and then went on around the garden fence. It was funny they hadn't come in, after standing around so. I couldn't make it out, and I stooped down to look at the tracks. I didn't notice anything at first, but next I did. There was a cross in the left bootheel made with big nails, to keep off the devil.

I was up in a second and shinning down the hill to Judge Thatcher's as quick as I could get there. He said:

"Why, my boy, you are all out of breath. Did you come for your interest?"

"No, sir," I says. "Is there some for me?"

"Yes, a half-yearly is in—a hundred and fifty dollars. Quite a fortune. You had better let me invest it along with your six thousand, because if you take it you'll spend it."

"No, sir," I says. "I don't want to spend it. I don't want it at all—nor the six thousand, nuther. I want you to take it; I want to give it to you—the six thousand and all."

He looked surprised, and then he says, "Why, what can you mean, my boy? Is something the matter?"

"Please take it," says I, "and don't ask me nothing—then I won't have to tell no lies."

He studied awhile, and then he says, "Oh-o! I think I see. You want to *sell* your property to me—not give it. That's the correct idea." Then he wrote something on a paper, and says, "There; you see it says 'for a consideration.' That means I have bought it and paid you for it. Here's a dollar for you. Now you sign it."

So I signed it, and left.

Miss Watson's nigger, Jim, had a hair ball as big as your fist, which had been took out of the fourth stomach of an ox, and he used to do magic with it. He said there was a spirit inside of it, and it knowed everything. So I went to him that night and told him Pap was here again, for I found his tracks in the snow. What I wanted to know was, what he was going to do, and was he going to stay? Jim got out his hair ball and said something over it, and then he dropped it on the floor. It fell pretty solid, and only rolled about an inch.

Jim got down on his knees, and put his ear against it and listened. But it warn't no use; he said it wouldn't talk. He said sometimes it wouldn't talk without money. I told him I had an old slick counterfeit quarter that warn't no good because the brass showed through the silver, but maybe the hair ball would take it, because it wouldn't know the difference. Jim smelt it and bit it and rubbed it, and said he would manage so the hair ball would think it was good.

Jim put the quarter under the hair ball, and got down and listened again. This time he said the hair ball was all right. He said it would tell me my whole fortune if I wanted it to. I says, go on. So the hair ball talked to him, and Jim told it to me. He says:

"Yo' ole father doan' know yit what he's a-gwyne to do. Sometimes he spec he'll go 'way, en den he spec he'll stay. De bes' way is to res' easy en let de ole man take his own way. Dey's two angels hoverin' roun' 'bout him. One uv 'em is white en shiny, en t'other one is black. De white one gits him to go right a little while, den de black one sails in en bust it all up. A body can't tell yit which one gwyne to fetch him at de las'. But you is all right. You gwyne to have considerable trouble in yo' life, en considerable joy. Dey's two gals flyin' 'bout you in yo' life. One uv 'em's light en t'other one is dark. One is rich en t'other is po'. You's gwyne to marry de po' one fust en de rich one by en by. You wants to keep 'way fum de water, en don't run no resk, 'kase it's down in de bills dat you's gwyne to git hung."

When I lit my candle and went up to my room that night there sat Pap—his own self!

CHAPTER III

I HAD SHUT THE DOOR TO. Then I turned around, and there he was.

He was most fifty, and he looked it. His hair was long and tangled and greasy. It was all black, no gray; so was his long whiskers. There warn't no color in his face, where his face showed; it was white—fish-belly white. As for his clothes—just rags, that was all. The boot on one foot was busted, and two of his toes stuck through. His hat was laying on the floor—an old black slouch with the top caved in, like a lid. He sat there a-looking at me, with his chair tilted back. I set the candle down. I noticed the window was up; so he had clumb in by the shed.

By and by he says, "Starchy clothes—very. Think you're a big-bug, *don't* you?"

"Maybe I am, maybe I ain't," I says.

"Don't give me none o' your lip," says he. "I'll take you down a peg before I get done. You're educated, too, they say—can read and write. Think you're better'n your father, now, don't you, because he can't? *I'll* take it out of you. Who told you you might meddle with such hifalut'n foolishness, hey? Who told you you could?"

"The widow. She told me."

"The widow, hey? I'll learn her to meddle! Looky here—you drop that school, you hear? I'll learn people to bring up a boy to put on airs over his own father and let on to be better'n what *he* is. I ain't the man to stand it—you hear? Say, lemme hear you read."

I took up a book and begun something about General Washington. When I'd read about a half minute, he fetched the book a whack and knocked it across the house. He says:

"It's so. You can do it. Now looky here; you stop that putting on frills. I'll lay for you, smarty; and if I catch you about that school I'll tan you good. First you know you'll get religion, too. I never see such a son."

He sat there a-mumbling and a-growling a minute, and then he says, "*Ain't* you a sweet-scented dandy, though? A bed, and a look'n-glass, and a piece of carpet on the floor—and they say you're rich. Hey—how's that?"

"They lie—that's how."

"Looky here—don't gimme no sass. I've been in town two days, and I hain't heard nothing but about you bein' rich. I heard about it down the river, too. That's why I come. You git me that money tomorrow—I want it."

"I hain't got no money."

"It's a lie. Judge Thatcher's got it. You git it."

"I hain't got no money, I tell you. You ask Judge Thatcher."

"All right; I'll ask him. Say, how much you got in your pocket? I want it."

"I hain't got only a dollar, and I want that to—"

"It don't make no difference what you want it for—shell it out."

He took it, and then he said he was going down to town to get some whiskey; said he hadn't had a drink all day. Then he went out over the shed.

Next day he was drunk, and he went to Judge Thatcher's and bullyragged him, and tried to make him give up the money; but he couldn't, and then he swore he'd make the law force him.

The judge and the widow went to law to get the court to take me away from him and let one of them be my guardian; but it was a new judge that had just come, and he didn't know the old man; so he said courts mustn't interfere and separate families if they could help it. So Judge Thatcher and the widow had to quit on the business.

That pleased the old man till he couldn't rest. He said he'd cowhide me till I was black and blue if I didn't raise some money for him. I borrowed three dollars from Judge Thatcher, and Pap took it and got drunk, and went a-blowing around and whooping and carrying on; and he kept it up all over town, with a tin pan, till most midnight; then they jailed him, and the next day they had him before court, and jailed him for a week.

When he got out the new judge said he was a-going to make a man of him. So he took him to his own house, and dressed him up clean and nice, and had him to breakfast and dinner and supper with the family, and was just old pie to him, so to speak. And after supper he talked to him about temperance and such things till the old man cried, and said he'd been a fool, and fooled away his life; but now he was a-going to turn over a new leaf. And he rose up and held out his hand, and says:

"Look at it, gentlemen and ladies all; take a-hold of it; shake it. There's a hand that was the hand of a hog; but it ain't so no more; it's the hand of a man that's started in on a new life. It's a clean hand now; shake it—don't be afeard."

So they shook it, one after the other, all around, and cried. The judge's wife she kissed it. Then the old man he signed a pledge— made his mark. The judge said it was the holiest time on record, or something like that. Then they tucked the old man into a beautiful room, which was the spare room, and in the night sometime he got powerful thirsty and clumb out onto the porch roof and slid down a stanchion and traded his new coat for a jug of forty-rod, and clumb back again and had a good old time; and towards daylight he crawled out again, drunk as a fiddler, and rolled off the porch and broke his left arm in two places, and was most froze to death when somebody found him after sunup. And when they come to look at that spare room they had to take soundings before they could navigate it.

The judge he felt kind of sore. He said he reckoned a body could reform the old man with a shotgun, maybe, but he didn't know no other way.

WELL, PRETTY SOON THE OLD MAN was up and around again, and then he went for Judge Thatcher in the courts to make him give up that money, and he went for me, too, for not stopping school. He catched me a couple of times and thrashed me, but I went to school just the same; I didn't want to go to school much before, but I reckoned I'd go now to spite Pap. That law trial was a slow business—appeared like they warn't ever going to get started on it; so every now and then I'd borrow two or three dollars off of the judge for him, to keep from getting a cowhiding. Every time he got money he got drunk, and raised Cain; and every time he raised Cain he got jailed.

Then he got to hanging around the widow, and she told him at last that if he didn't quit she would make trouble for him. Well, *wasn't* he mad? He said he would show who was Huck Finn's boss. So he watched out for me one day in the spring, and catched me, and took me up the river alone three mile in a skiff, and crossed over to the Illinois shore where it was woody and there warn't no houses but an old log hut.

He kept me with him all the time, and I never got a chance to run off. We lived in that old cabin, and he always locked the door and put the key under his head nights. He had a gun, and we fished and hunted. Every little while he locked me in and went down to the store, three miles, to the ferry, and traded fish and game for whiskey, and fetched it home and got drunk. The widow she found out where I was by and by, and she sent a man to get me; but Pap drove him off with the gun, and it warn't long after that till I was used to being where I was, and liked it—all but the cowhide part.

It was kind of lazy and jolly, laying off all day, smoking and fishing, and no books nor study. Two months or more run along, and my clothes got to be all rags, and I didn't see how I'd ever got to like it so well at the widow's, where you had to wash, and eat on a plate.

But by and by Pap got too handy with his hick'ry, and I couldn't stand it. He got to going away so much, too, and locking me in. Once he locked me in and was gone three days. I judged he had got drowned, and I wasn't ever going to get out anymore. I was scared. I made up my mind I would fix up some way to leave there.

I had tried to get out of that cabin many a time, but I couldn't find no way. There warn't a window to it big enough for a dog to get through, and the door was thick oak slabs. Pap was pretty

careful not to leave a knife or anything in the cabin when he was away; I reckon I had hunted the place over as much as a hundred times. But this time I found something at last: I found an old rusty wood saw without any handle; it was laid in between a rafter and the roof. I greased it up and went to work. There was an old horse blanket nailed against the logs at one end of the cabin behind the table, to keep the wind from blowing through the chinks and putting the candle out. I got under the table and raised the blanket, and went to work to saw out a section of the big bottom log. Well, it was a good long job, but I was getting towards the end of it when I heard Pap's gun in the woods. I got rid of the signs of my work, and pretty soon Pap came in.

Pap warn't in a good humor; he said he was down to town, and everything was going wrong. His lawyer said he reckoned he would win his lawsuit and get the money if they ever got started on the trial; but then there was ways to put it off a long time, and Judge Thatcher knowed how to do it. And he said people allowed there'd be another trial to get me away from him and give me to the widow, and they guessed it would win this time. This shook me up considerable, because I didn't want to go back to the widow's anymore and be so cramped up and sivilized. Then the old man said he would like to see the widow get me; he said if they tried to come any such game on him he knowed of a place six or seven mile off to stow me in, where they might hunt till they dropped and not find me. That made me pretty uneasy again, but only for a minute; I reckoned I wouldn't stay on hand till he got that chance.

The old man made me go to the skiff and fetch the things he had got. There was a fifty-pound sack of cornmeal, and a side of bacon, ammunition, and a four-gallon jug of whiskey. I toted up a load, and went back and sat down on the bow of the skiff to think it all over. I reckoned I would walk off with the gun, and take to the woods when I run away. I guessed I would tramp right across the country, mostly nighttimes, and hunt and fish to keep alive, and so get so far away that the old man nor the widow couldn't ever find me anymore. I judged I would saw out and leave that night if Pap got drunk enough. I got so full of it I didn't notice how long I was staying till the old man hollered and asked me whether I was asleep or drownded.

I got the things all up to the cabin, and then it was about dark. While I was cooking supper the old man took a swig or two and got sort of warmed up, and went to ripping again. He had been drunk over in town, and laid in the gutter all night, and he was a sight to look at, all mud. Whenever his liquor begun to work he most always went for the govment. This time he says:

"Call this a govment! Why, just look at it and see what it's like. Here's the law a-standing ready to take a man's son away from him—a man's own son, which he has had all the trouble and all the expense of raising. Yes, just as that man has got that son raised at last, and ready to go to work and begin to do suthin' for *him*, the law up and goes for him. And they call *that* govment! That ain't all, nuther. The law backs that old Judge Thatcher up and helps him to keep me out o' my property. The law takes a man worth six thousand dollars and up'ards, and jams him into an old trap of a cabin like this, and lets him go round in clothes that ain't fittin for a hog. They call that govment? Why, a man can't get his rights in a govment like this. Oh, yes, this is a wonderful govment, wonderful. Why, looky here. There was a free nigger there in town from Ohio. He had the whitest shirt on you ever see, and the shiniest hat; and a gold watch and chain, and a silver-headed cane. And what do you think? They said he was a p'fessor in a college, and could talk all kinds of languages, and knowed everything. And that ain't the wust. They said he could *vote* when he was at home. Well, that let me out. Thinks I, What is the country a-coming to? It was 'lection day, and I was just about to go and vote myself if I warn't too drunk to get there; but when they told me there was a state in this country where they'd let that nigger vote, I drawed out. I says the country may rot for all me—I'll never vote ag'in as long as I live!"

After supper Pap took the jug, and said he had enough whiskey there for two drunks and one delirium tremens. That was always his word. I judged he would be blind drunk in about an hour, and then I would steal the key, or saw myself out, one or t'other. He drank and drank, and tumbled down on his blankets by and by; but luck didn't run my way. He didn't go sound asleep, but groaned and moaned and thrashed around this way and that. At last I got so sleepy I couldn't keep my eyes open, and so before I knowed what I was about I was sound asleep, and the candle burning.

I don't know how long I was asleep, but all of a sudden there was an awful scream and I was up. There was Pap looking wild, and skipping around and yelling about snakes. I couldn't see no snakes, but he said they was crawling up his legs; and then he would give a jump and scream, and say one had bit him on the cheek. I never see a man look so wild. Pretty soon he was all fagged out, and fell down panting; then he rolled over and over, screaming and saying there was devils a-hold of him. He wore out by and by, and laid still awhile, moaning. Then he laid stiller, and didn't make a sound. I could hear the owls and the wolves away off in the woods, and it seemed terrible still. He was laying over by the corner. By and by he raised up partway and listened, with his head to one side. He says, very low:

"Tramp—tramp—tramp; that's the dead; tramp—tramp—tramp; they're coming after me; but I won't go. Oh, they're here! Don't touch me—don't! Hands off—they're cold; let go. Oh, let a poor devil alone!"

He rolled himself up in his blanket and went to crying. But by and by he rolled out and jumped up to his feet looking wild, and he see me and went for me. He chased me round and round the place with a clasp knife, calling me the Angel of Death, and saying he would kill me, and then I couldn't come for him no more. I begged, and told him I was only Huck; but he laughed *such* a screechy laugh, and roared and cussed, and kept on chasing me. Once when I turned short and dodged under his arm he got me by the jacket between my shoulders, and I thought I was gone; but I slid out of the jacket and saved myself. Pretty soon he was all tired out, and dropped down with his back against the door, and said he would rest a minute and then kill me. He put his knife under him, and pretty soon he dozed off.

By and by I got the old split-bottom chair and clumb up and got down the gun. I made sure it was loaded; and then I laid it across the turnip barrel, pointing towards Pap, and set down behind it to wait for him to stir.

Next thing I knew it was after sunup, and I had been sound asleep. Pap was standing over me looking sour—and sick, too. He says, "What you doin' with this gun?"

I judged he didn't know nothing about what he had been doing, so I says, "Somebody tried to get in, so I was laying for him."

"Why didn't you roust me out?"

"Well, I tried to, but I couldn't; I couldn't budge you."

"Well, all right. Don't stand there palavering all day, but out with you and see if there's a fish on the lines for breakfast. I'll be along in a minute."

He unlocked the door, and I cleared out up the riverbank. I noticed some pieces of limbs and things floating down; so I knowed the river had begun to rise. Over at the town the June rise used to be always luck for me; because as soon as that rise begins here comes cordwood floating down, and pieces of log rafts, so all you have to do is to catch them and sell them to the woodyards. I went along up the bank with one eye out for what the rise might fetch along, and all at once here comes a canoe; a beauty, too, about fourteen foot long, riding high like a duck. I shot head first off of the bank like a frog, clothes and all on, and struck out for it. It was a drift canoe sure enough, and I clumb in and paddled her ashore. Thinks I, The old man will be glad when he sees this—she's worth ten dollars. But when I got to shore Pap wasn't in sight yet, and I struck another idea: I judged I'd hide her, and then 'stead of taking to the woods when I run off, I'd go down the river fifty mile and camp in one place for good, and not have such a rough time tramping on foot.

I thought I heard the old man coming all the time; but I got her hid in a little creek all hung over with vines; and then I out and looked around a bunch of willows, and there was the old man down the path just drawing a bead on a bird with his gun. So he hadn't seen anything.

When he got along I was hard at it taking up a trotline. We got five catfish off the lines and went home.

While we laid off after breakfast to sleep up, both of us being about wore out, I got to thinking that if I could fix some way to keep Pap and the widow from trying to follow me, it would be a certainer thing than trusting to luck to get far enough off before they missed me. Well, I didn't see no way for a while, but by and by Pap raised up and says:

"Another time a man comes a-prowling round here you roust me out, you hear? That man warn't here for no good. I'd a shot him."

Then he dropped down and went to sleep again. What he had been saying give me the very idea I wanted. I says to myself, I can fix it now so nobody won't think of following me.

About twelve o'clock we turned out and went along up the bank. The river was coming up pretty fast, and lots of driftwood going by. By and by along comes part of a log raft—nine logs fast together. We towed it ashore with the skiff. Then we had dinner. Anybody but Pap would 'a' waited and seen the day through, so as to catch more stuff; but that warn't Pap's style. Nine logs was enough for one time; he must shove right over to town and sell. So he locked me in and took the skiff, and started off towing the raft about half past three. I judged he wouldn't come back that night. I waited till I reckoned he had got a good start; then I out with my saw, and went to work on that log again. Before he was t'other side of the river I was out of the hole; him and his raft was just a speck on the water away off yonder.

I took the sack of cornmeal to where the canoe was hid, and put it in; then I done the same with the side of bacon; then the whiskey jug. I took all the coffee and sugar there was, and all the ammunition; I took the bucket and a dipper and a tin cup, and my old saw and two blankets, and the skillet and the coffeepot. I took fishlines and matches and other things—everything that was worth a cent. I wanted an axe, but there was only the one at the woodpile, and I knowed why I was going to leave that. I fetched out the gun, and now I was done.

I had wore the ground a good deal crawling out of the hole and dragging out so many things. So I fixed that as good as I could from the outside by scattering dust; and then I fixed the piece of log back into its place. If you stood four or five foot away and didn't know it was sawed, you wouldn't never notice it; and besides, this was the back of the cabin.

It was all grass clear to the canoe, so I hadn't left a track. I stood on the bank and looked out over the river. All safe. So I took the gun and went a piece into the woods, and was hunting around for some birds when I see a wild pig. I shot him and took him into camp. Then I took the axe and smashed in the door. I fetched the pig in, and took him nearly to the table and hacked into his throat with the axe, and laid him down to bleed. Well, next I took an old sack and put a lot of big rocks in it, and I started it from the pig, and dragged it to the door and through the woods to the river and dumped it in. You could easy see that something had been dragged over the ground. I did wish Tom Sawyer was there; I knowed he would take an interest in this kind of business, and throw in the fancy touches. Nobody could spread himself like Tom Sawyer in such a thing as that.

Well, last I pulled out some of my hair, and blooded the axe good, and stuck it on the back side, and slung the axe in the corner. Then I took up the pig in my jacket (so he couldn't drip) till I got a good piece below the house and then dumped him into the river. Now I thought of something else. So I went and got the bag of meal out of the canoe, and fetched it to the house. I took the bag to where it used to stand and ripped a hole in the bottom of it. Then I carried the sack across the grass and through the willows east of the house, to a shallow lake that was five mile wide and full of rushes. There was a creek leading out of it on the other side that went miles away, I don't know where, but it didn't go to the river. The meal sifted out and made a little track all the way to the lake. I dropped Pap's whetstone there too, so as to look like it had been done by accident. Then I tied up the rip in the meal sack with a string, and took it to the canoe again.

It was about dark now; so I dropped the canoe down the river under some willows that hung over the bank, and waited for the moon to rise. I made fast to a willow; then I took a bite to eat, and by and by laid down in the canoe to smoke a pipe and lay out a plan. I says to myself, They'll follow the track of that sackful of rocks to the shore and then drag the river for me. And they'll follow that meal track to the lake and go browsing down the creek that leads out of it to find the robbers that killed me and took the things. They won't ever hunt the river for anything but my dead carcass. They'll soon get tired of that, and won't bother no more about me. All right; I can stop anywhere I want to. Jackson's Island is good enough for me; I know that island pretty well, and nobody ever comes there. And then I can paddle over to town nights, and slink around and pick up things I want. Jackson's Island's the place.

I was pretty tired, and the first thing I knowed I was asleep. When I woke up I didn't know where I was. I set up and looked around a little scared. Then I remembered. The river looked miles and miles across. The moon was so bright I could 'a' counted the drift logs that went a-slipping along, black and still, hundreds of yards out from shore. Everything was dead quiet, and it looked late, and *smelt late*. You know what I mean.

I took a good gap and a stretch, and was just going to unhitch and start when I heard a sound from oars working away over the water. I peeped out through the willow branches, and there it was—a skiff, away off. It kept a-coming, and I see there warn't but one man in it. Thinks I, Maybe it's Pap. By and by he came a-swinging up shore, and he went by so close I could 'a' reached out the gun and touched him. Well, it *was* Pap, sure enough—and sober, too, by the way he laid his oars.

I didn't lose no time. The next minute I was a-spinning downstream soft, but quick, in the shade of the bank. I made two mile and a half, and then struck out towards the middle of the river, because pretty soon I would be passing the ferry landing, and people might see me. I got out amongst the driftwood, and then laid down in the bottom of the canoe and let her float till I was away below the ferry. Then I rose up, and there was Jackson's

Island, about two mile downstream, heavy-timbered and standing up out of the middle of the river, big and dark and solid, like a steamboat without any lights.

It didn't take me long to get there. I shot past the head in the current, and then I got into the dead water and landed on the side towards the Illinois shore. I run the canoe into a deep dent in the bank that I knowed about; I had to part the willow branches to get in; and when I made fast nobody could 'a' seen the canoe from the outside.

There was a little gray in the sky now; so I stepped into the woods, and laid down for a nap before breakfast.

CHAPTER IV

THE SUN WAS UP SO HIGH when I waked that I judged it was after eight o'clock. I laid there in the cool shade thinking, and feeling rested and ruther satisfied. Mostly it was big trees all about, and there was freckled places on the ground where the light sifted down through the leaves. A couple of squirrels set on a limb and jabbered at me very friendly.

I was powerful lazy and comfortable, and was dozing off again, when I thinks I hears a deep sound of *boom!* away up the river. I rouses up and listens; pretty soon I hears it again. I hopped up and went and looked out at a hole in the leaves at the head of the island and I see a bunch of smoke laying on the water near the ferry. And there was the ferryboat full of people floating along down. I knowed what was the matter now. *Boom!* I see the white smoke squirt out of the ferryboat's side. You see, they was firing cannon over the water, trying to make my carcass come to the top.

I was pretty hungry, but it warn't going to do for me to start a fire, because they might see the smoke. So I set there and watched the cannon smoke and listened to the boom. The river was a mile wide there, and it always looks pretty on a summer morning—so I was having a good enough time seeing them hunt for my remainders.

The ferryboat was floating with the current, and I allowed I'd have a chance to see who was aboard when she come along, because she would come in close, the way the current did. When she'd got pretty well along towards me, I went and laid down behind a log on the bank. Where the log forked I could peep through.

By and by she come along, and she drifted in so close that they could 'a' run out a plank and walked ashore. Most everybody was on the boat. Pap, and Judge Thatcher, and Bessie Thatcher, and Joe Harper, and Tom Sawyer, and his old Aunt Polly, and his half brother Sid, and plenty more. Everybody was talking about the murder, but the captain broke in and says:

"Look sharp, now; the current sets in close here, and maybe he's washed ashore and got tangled amongst the brush at the water's edge. I hope so, anyway."

They all leaned over the rails, nearly in my face, watching with all their might. I could see them first-rate, but they couldn't see me. Then the captain sung out, "Stand away!" and the cannon let off such a blast right before me that it made me deef. If they'd 'a' had some bullets in, I reckon they'd 'a' got the corpse they was after. Well, I see I warn't hurt, thanks to goodness. The boat floated on and went out of sight. I could hear the booming now and then, further and further off, and then after an hour they turned around the foot of the island and started up the channel on the Missouri side, booming once in a while. I crossed over to that side and watched them. When they got abreast the head of the island they quit shooting and dropped over to the Missouri shore and went home to the town.

I knowed I was all right now. I got my traps out of the canoe and made a nice camp in the woods, and I catched a catfish, and towards sundown I started my campfire and had supper. When it was dark I set by my campfire smoking; but by and by it got sort of lonesome, and so I went and set on the bank and listened to the current swashing along, and counted the stars and drift logs, and then went to bed; there ain't no better way to put in time when you are lonesome; you can't stay so, you soon get over it.

And so for three days and nights. No difference—just the same

thing. But the next day I went exploring around down through the island. I was boss of it; it all belonged to me, so to say, and I wanted to know all about it. I found plenty strawberries, ripe and prime; and green summer grapes, and green razberries; and green blackberries was just beginning to show. They would all come handy by and by, I judged.

Well, I went fooling along in the deep woods till I judged I warn't far from the foot of the island. I clipped along, and all of a sudden I bounded right onto the ashes of a campfire that was all smoking.

My heart jumped up amongst my lungs. I never waited for to look further, but went sneaking back on my tiptoes as fast as ever I could. Every now and then I stopped a second amongst the thick leaves and listened, but my breath come so hard I couldn't hear nothing else.

When I got to camp I warn't feeling very brash, so I got all my traps into my canoe again, and I put out the fire and scattered the ashes around, and then I clumb a tree.

I reckon I was up in the tree two hours; but I didn't see nothing, didn't hear nothing—I only *thought* I heard and seen as much as a thousand things. Well, I couldn't stay up there forever; so at last I got down, but I kept in the thick woods and on the lookout all the time. All I could get to eat was berries and what was left over from breakfast.

When night come I reckoned I would sleep in the canoe. I didn't sleep much. I couldn't, somehow, for thinking. And every time I waked up I thought somebody had me by the neck. So the sleep didn't do me no good. By and by I says to myself, I can't live this way; I'm a-going to find out who it is that's here on the island with me. Well, I felt better right off.

So I took my paddle and slid out from shore, and then let the canoe drop along down amongst the shadows. When I was most down to the foot of the island I brung the canoe to shore. In a little while I see a pale streak over the treetops, and knowed the day was coming. Then I got my gun and slipped into the woods towards where I had run across the campfire. By and by, sure enough, I catched a glimpse of fire through the trees. I went for it cautious and slow, and there laid a man on the ground. It most give me the fantods. He had a blanket around his head, and his head was nearly in the fire. I set there behind a clump of bushes in about six foot of him, and kept my eyes on him steady. It was getting gray daylight now. Pretty soon he gapped and stretched himself and hove off the blanket, and it was Miss Watson's Jim! I bet I was glad to see him. I says, "Hello, Jim!" and skipped out.

He bounced up and stared at me wild. Then he drops down on his knees, and puts his hands together and says:

"Doan' hurt me—don't! I hain't ever done no harm to a ghos'. You go en git in de river ag'in, en doan' do nuffn to ole Jim, 'at 'uz alwuz yo' fren'."

Well, I warn't long making him understand I warn't dead. I was ever so glad to see Jim. I warn't lonesome now. I told him I warn't afraid of *him* telling the people where I was. Then I says, "It's daylight. Le's get breakfast. Make up your campfire good."

"What's de use er makin' up de campfire to cook strawbries en sich truck? But you got a gun, hain't you? Den we kin git sumfn better den strawbries."

"Strawberries and such truck," I says. "How long you been on the island, Jim?"

"I come heah de night arter you's killed."

"All that time? And ain't you had nothing but that kind of rubbage to eat?"

"No sah—nuffn else."

"Well, you must be most starved, ain't you?"

"I reck'n I could eat a hoss. How long you ben on de islan'?"

"Since the night I got killed."

"No! W'y, what has you lived on? Oh, you got a gun! Dat's good. Now you kill sumfn en I'll make up de fire."

While he built up the fire, I went over to the canoe, and fetched meal and bacon and coffee, and coffeepot and frying pan and cups. Jim was set back considerable, because he reckoned it was all done with witchcraft. I catched a good big catfish, too, and Jim cleaned him with his knife, and fried him. Then we lolled on the grass and eat breakfast smoking hot. When we had got pretty well stuffed, we laid off and lazied. By and by Jim says:

"But looky here, Huck, who wuz it dat 'uz killed in dat shanty ef it warn't you?"

Then I told him the whole thing, and he said it was smart. Then I says, "How do you come to be here, Jim, and how'd you get here?"

He looked pretty uneasy. "Maybe I better not tell," he says.

"Why, Jim?"

"Well, dey's reasons. But you wouldn' tell on me ef I 'uz to tell you, would you, Huck?"

"Blamed if I would, Jim."

"Well, I b'lieve you, Huck. I—I *run off.*"

"Jim!"

"But mind, you said you wouldn' tell, Huck."

"Well, I did. I said I wouldn't, and I'll stick to it. Honest *injun*, I will, even if people call me a lowdown Abolitionist. So, now, le's know all about it."

"Well, you see, it 'uz dis way. Ole missus—dat's Miss Watson—she pecks on me all de time, en treats me pooty rough, but she awluz said she wouldn' sell me down to Orleans. But I noticed dey wuz a nigger trader roun' de place lately, en I begin to git oneasy. Well, one night de do' warn't quite shet, en I hear old missus tell de widder she gwyne to sell me down to Orleans. She didn' want to, but she could git eight hund'd dollars for me, en she couldn' resis'. I never waited to hear de res'. I lit out quick, I tell you. I shin down de hill, en 'spec to steal a skift 'long de sho', but dey wuz people a-stirring yit, so I hid in de ole tumbledown cooper shop on de bank to wait for everybody to go 'way. Well, I wuz dah all night. Dey wuz somebody roun' all de time. 'Long 'bout six in de mawnin' skifts begin to go by, en every skift wuz talkin' 'bout how yo' pap say you's killed. I 'uz powerful sorry you's killed, Huck, but I ain't no mo' now.

"I laid dah under de shavin's all day. I knowed ole missus en widder wuz goin' to be gone to de camp meet'n', en so dey wouldn' miss me tell evenin'. When it come dark I tuck out up

de river road, to whah dey warn't no houses. I'd made up my mine
'bout what I's a-gwyne to do. I says, a raff is what I's arter, en
when I see a light a-comin' roun' de p'int bymeby, I wade' in en
shove' a log ahead o' me en swum to de stern uv de raff en tuck
a-holt. It 'uz pooty dark, so I clumb up en laid down on de planks.
De men 'uz all 'way yonder in de middle, whah de lantern wuz.
De river wuz a-risin', en dey wuz a good current; so I reck'n'd 'at
by fo' in de mawnin' I'd be twenty-five mile down de river, en
den I'd swim asho'.

"But I didn' have no luck. When we 'uz mos' down to de head
er de islan' a man begin to come aft wid de lantern. So I slid overboard en swum to de islan'. I went into de woods en jedged I
wouldn' fool wid raffs no mo', long as dey move de lantern roun'
so. I had my pipe en some matches in my cap, en dey warn't
wet, so I 'uz all right."

"And so you ain't had no meat nor bread all this time? Why
didn't you get mud turkles?"

"How you gwyne to git 'm in de night? I warn't gwyne to
show mysef on de bank in de daytime."

"Well, that's so. You've had to keep in the woods all the time,
of course. Did you hear 'em shooting the cannon?"

"Oh, yes. I knowed dey was arter you. I see um go by heah—
watched um thoo de bushes."

Some young birds come along, flying a yard or two at a time
and lighting. Jim said it was a sign it was going to rain. I was going
to catch some of them, but Jim wouldn't let me. He said it was
a sign of death. And he said you mustn't count the things you are
going to cook for dinner, because that would bring bad luck. The
same if you shook the tablecloth after sundown. Jim knowed all
kinds of signs. I said it looked to me like all the signs was about
bad luck, and so I asked him if there warn't any good-luck signs.
He says:

"Mighty few—an' *dey* ain't no use to a body. What you want to
know when good luck's a-comin' for? Want to keep it off?" And
he said, "Ef you's got hairy arms en a hairy breas', it's a sign dat
you's a-gwyne to be rich."

"Have you got hairy arms and a hairy breast, Jim?"

"Don't you see I has?"

"Well, are you rich?"

"No, but I ben rich wunst, and gwyne to be rich ag'in. Wunst I had foteen dollars, but I tuck to specalat'n', en got busted out."

"What did you speculate in, Jim?"

"Why, livestock—cattle, you know. I put de money in a cow. But de cow up 'n' died on my han's."

"Well, it's all right, Jim, long as you're going to be rich again some time or other."

"Yes; en I's rich now, come to look at it. I owns mysef, en I's wuth eight hund'd dollars. I wisht I had de money, I wouldn' want no mo'."

I WANTED TO GO AND LOOK at a place right about the middle of the island that I'd found when I was exploring; so we started and soon got to it. This place was a tolerable long, steep ridge about forty foot high. We clumb all over it, and by and by found a good big cavern in the rock, most up to the top on the side towards Illinois. Jim said if we had the canoe hid and had all the traps in the cavern, we could rush there if anybody was to come to the island, and they would never find us. And, besides, he said them little birds had said it was going to rain, and did I want the things to get wet?

So we went back and lugged all the traps up there. Then we hunted up a place close by to hide the canoe in, amongst thick willows. We took some fish off of the lines and set them again, and begun to get ready for dinner.

The door of the cavern was big enough to roll a hogshead in, and on one side of the door the floor was flat and a good place to build a fire on. So we built it and cooked dinner.

We spread the blankets inside for a carpet, and eat our dinner in there. Pretty soon it darkened up, and begun to thunder and lighten; so the birds was right about it. Directly it begun to rain, and it rained like all fury, too. It was one of these regular summer storms. It would get so dark that it looked all blue-black outside, and lovely; and the rain would thrash by so thick that the trees off a little ways looked dim and spiderwebby; and here would come a blast of wind that would bend the trees down; and next, when it was just about the bluest and blackest—*fst!* it was as bright as glory; dark as sin again in a second, and you'd hear the thunder let go with an awful crash.

"Jim, this is nice," I says. "I wouldn't want to be nowhere else but here. Pass me along another hunk of fish."

"Well, you wouldn' 'a' ben here 'f it hadn' 'a' ben for Jim. You'd 'a' ben down dah in de woods widout any dinner. Birds knows when it's gwyne to rain, chile."

The river went on raising and raising for ten or twelve days, till at last it was over the banks. The water was three or four foot deep on the island in the low places.

Daytimes we paddled all over the island in the canoe. We went winding in and out amongst the trees, and sometimes the vines hung so thick we had to back away and go some other way. On every old broken-down tree you could see rabbits and snakes and such things; and after a day or two they got so tame, on account of being hungry, that you could put your hand right on them. We could 'a' had pets enough if we'd wanted them.

One night we catched a little section of a lumber raft—nice pine planks. It was twelve foot wide and about fifteen foot long. We could see sawlogs go by in the daylight sometimes, but we let them go; we didn't show ourselves in daylight.

Another night when we was up at the head of the island, just before daylight, here comes a frame house down. She was a two-story house, and tilted over considerable. We paddled out and got aboard, but it was too dark to see yet, so we made the canoe fast and set in her to wait for daylight.

The light begun to come before we got to the foot of the island. Then we looked in at the upstairs window. We could make out a bed, and a table, and two old chairs, and something laying on the floor in the corner that looked like a man. So Jim says:

"Hello, you!"

But it didn't budge. Then Jim says, "De man ain't asleep—he's dead. I'll go en see."

He went and looked, and says, "It's a dead man. Yes, indeedy; naked, too. He's ben shot in de back. I reck'n he's ben dead two er three days. Come in, Huck, but doan' look at his face—it's too gashly."

Jim throwed some old rags over him, but he needn't done it. I didn't look at him at all. There was heaps of old greasy cards scattered around over the floor, and old whiskey bottles; and all over the walls was the ignorantest kind of words and pictures made with charcoal. There was two old calico dresses and a sun-bonnet hanging against the wall, and some men's clothing, too, and a boy's old speckled straw hat. We put the lot into the canoe—it might come good. The way things was scattered about we reckoned the people left in a hurry, and warn't fixed so as to carry off most of their stuff. Besides the clothes, we got an old tin lantern, and a bran-new Barlow knife, and a lot of candles, and a tin candlestick, and a cup, and a ratty old bedquilt, and a reticule with needles and pins and thread and such truck in it, and a hatchet and some nails, and a fishline with some hooks on it, and a roll of buckskin, and a dog collar, and a horseshoe.

And so, take it all around, we made a good haul.

When we was ready to shove off we was a quarter of a mile below the island, and it was pretty broad day; so I made Jim lay down in the canoe and cover up with the quilt, because if he set up people could tell he was a nigger a good ways off. I paddled back, and hadn't no accidents and didn't see nobody.

After breakfast I wanted to talk about the dead man and guess out how he come to be killed, but Jim didn't want to. He said it would fetch bad luck; and besides, he said, he might come and ha'nt us. That sounded pretty reasonable, so I didn't say no more, and we rummaged the clothes we'd got. We found eight dollars in silver sewed up in the lining of an old overcoat. Jim said he reckoned the people in that house stole the coat, because if they'd 'a' knowed the money was there they wouldn't 'a' left it. I said I reckoned they killed the dead man, too; but Jim didn't want to talk about that. I says:

"Now you think it's bad luck to talk about that man; but what did you say when I fetched in that snake skin I found yesterday? You said it was the worst bad luck in the world to touch a snake skin. Well, here's your bad luck! We've raked in all this truck and eight dollars besides. I wish we could have some bad luck like this every day, Jim."

"Don't you git too peart, honey. It's a-comin'."

It did come, too. It was Tuesday that we had that talk. Well, Friday night when we went to the cavern to sleep there was a rattlesnake in there. It was curled up on the foot of Jim's blanket, and when Jim flung himself down on the blanket while I was striking a light the snake bit him.

He jumped up yelling, and the first thing the light showed was the varmint curled up and ready for another spring. I laid him out with a stick, and Jim grabbed Pap's whiskey jug and begun to pour it down.

He was barefooted, and the snake bit him right on the heel. Jim told me to chop off the snake's head and throw it away, and then skin the body and roast a piece of it. I done it, and he eat it and said it would help cure him. He made me take off the rattles and tie them around his wrist, too. He said that would help. Then he sucked and sucked at the jug, and now and then he got out of his head and pitched around and yelled. His foot swelled up pretty big, and so did his leg; but by and by the drunk begun to come, and I judged he was all right; but I'd ruther been bit with a snake than Pap's whiskey.

Jim was laid up for four days and nights. Then the swelling was gone and he was around again. I made up my mind I wouldn't ever take a-holt of a snake skin again with my hands. Jim said he reckoned I would believe him next time. And he said that handling a snake skin was such awful bad luck that maybe we hadn't got to the end of it yet. He said he'd ruther see the new moon over his left shoulder as much as a thousand times than take up a snake skin in his hands.

Well, the days went along, and the river went down between its banks again. A day come when I said I was getting slow and dull, and I wanted to get a stirring-up someway. I said I reckoned I would slip over the river and find out what was going on. Jim liked that notion; but he said I must go in the dark and look sharp. Then he said, couldn't I put on some of them old things and dress up like a girl? That was a good notion. So we shortened up one of the calico gowns, and I turned my trouser legs to my knees and got into it, and it was a fair fit. I put on the sunbonnet and tied it under my chin, and then for a body to look in and see my face was like looking down a stovepipe. Jim said nobody would know me, even in the daytime, hardly. I practiced all day to get the hang of the things, and by and by I could do pretty well, only Jim said I didn't walk like a girl; and he said I must quit pulling up my gown to get at my britches pocket. I took notice, and done better.

I started up the Illinois shore in the canoe just after dark, crossed the river and fetched in at the bottom of the town. I tied up and started along the bank. There was a light burning in a little shanty that hadn't been lived in for a long time, and I slipped up and peeped in at the window. There was a woman about forty years old in there knitting by a candle that was on a pine table. I didn't know her face; she was a stranger, new to town. Now this was lucky, because I was weakening; I was getting afraid I had come; people might know my voice and find me out. But if this woman had been in such a little town two days she could tell me all I wanted to know; so I knocked at the door, and made up my mind I wouldn't forget I was a girl.

"Come in," says the woman, and I did. She says, "Take a cheer."

I done it. She looked me all over with her little shiny eyes, and says, "What might your name be?"

"Sarah Williams."

"Where'bouts do you live? In this neighborhood?"

"No'm. In Hookerville, seven miles below. I've walked all the way. My mother's down sick, and I come to tell my uncle Abner Moore. He lives at the upper end of the town, she says. Do you know him?"

"No; but I don't know everybody yet. I haven't lived here

quite two weeks. It's a ways to the upper end of the town. You better stay here all night. Take off your bonnet."

"No," I says; "I'll rest awhile, I reckon, and go on."

She said she wouldn't let me go by myself, but her husband would be in by and by, and she'd send him along with me. Then she got to talking about her husband, and about her relations up the river, and her relations down the river, and about how much better off they used to was, and so on and on, till I was afeard I had made a mistake coming to her; but by and by she dropped on to Pap and the murder, and then I was pretty willing to let her clatter right along. She told me about Tom Sawyer finding the twelve thousand dollars (only she got it twenty thousand) and all about Pap and what a hard lot he was, and what a hard lot I was, and at last she got down to where I was murdered. I says:

"Who done it? We've heard considerable in Hookerville, but we don't know who 'twas that killed Huck Finn."

"Well, there's a right smart chance of people *here* that'd like to know who killed him. At first most everybody thought old Finn done it himself. But before night they changed around and judged it was done by a runaway nigger named Jim."

"Why he—"

I stopped. I reckoned I better keep still. She run on, and never noticed I had put in at all:

"The nigger run off the very night Huck Finn was killed. So there's a reward out for him—three hundred dollars. And there's a reward out for old Finn, too—two hundred dollars. You see, he come to town the morning after the murder, and told about it. Before night they wanted to lynch him, but he was gone. Well, next day they found out the nigger was gone; so then they put the murder on him, you see; and while they was full of it, next day, back comes old Finn, and went boohooing to Judge Thatcher to get money to hunt for the nigger with. The judge gave him some, and that evening he got drunk, and was around with a couple of hard-looking strangers, and then went off with them. Well, he hain't come back sence, and they ain't looking for him back till this thing blows over, for people thinks now that he killed his boy and fixed things so he'd get Huck's money without having to bother with a lawsuit. He's sly, I reckon. If he don't come back for a year he'll be all right. You can't prove anything on him; everything will be quieted down then, and he'll walk off with Huck's money as easy as nothing."

"I reckon so, 'm. I don't see nothing in the way of it. Has everybody quit thinking the nigger done it?"

"No, not everybody. A good many think he done it. But they'll get the nigger pretty soon now, and maybe they can scare it out of him."

"Why, are they after him yet?"

"Well, does three hundred dollars lay around every day for people to pick up? Some folks think the nigger ain't far from here. I'm one of them—but I hain't talked it around. A day ago I was talking with an old couple that lives next door, and they happened to say hardly anybody ever goes to that island yonder that they call Jackson's Island. 'Don't anybody live there?' says I. 'No, nobody,' says they. I didn't say any more, but I was near certain I'd seen smoke over there a day or two ago, so I says to myself, Like as not that nigger's hiding over there; anyway, says I, it's worth the trouble to give the place a hunt. So my husband's going over to see—him and another man."

I had got so uneasy I couldn't set still. I had to do something with my hands, so I took up a needle off of the table and went to threading it. My hands shook, and I was making a bad job of it. When the woman stopped talking I looked up, and she was looking at me, smiling a little. I put down the needle and thread, and let on to be interested—and I was, too—and says:

"Three hundred dollars is a power of money. I wish my mother could get it. Is your husband going over there tonight?"

"Yes. He went up to town with the man I was telling you of, to get a boat. They'll go over after midnight."

"Couldn't they see better if they was to wait till daytime?"

"Yes. And couldn't the nigger see better, too? After midnight he'll likely be asleep, and they can slip around through the woods and hunt up his campfire, if he's got one."

"I didn't think of that."

The woman kept looking at me pretty curious. Pretty soon she says, "What did you say your name was, honey?"

"M—Mary Williams."

Somehow it didn't seem to me that I said it was Mary before, so I didn't look up—I felt sort of cornered, and was afeard maybe I was looking it, too. The longer the woman set still the uneasier I was. But now she says:

"Honey, I thought you said it was Sarah when you come in?"

"Oh, yes'm, I did. Sarah Mary Williams. Sarah's my first name. Some calls me Sarah, some calls me Mary."

"Oh, that's the way of it?"

"Yes'm."

Well, the woman fell to talking then about how hard times was, and how poor they had to live, and how the rats was as free as if they owned the place, and I got to feeling better again. She was right about the rats. You'd see one stick his nose out of a hole in the corner every little while. She said she had to have things handy to throw at them, or they wouldn't give her no peace. She showed me a bar of lead twisted up into a knot, and said she was a good shot with it generly, but she'd wrenched her arm a day or two ago, and would I try for the next one that come out. I wanted to be getting away before the old man got back, but of course I didn't let on. I got the thing, and the first rat that showed his nose I let drive, and if he'd 'a' stayed where he was he'd 'a' been a tolerable sick rat. She said that was first-rate, and she reckoned I would hive the next one. She went and got the lump of lead and fetched it back, and brought along a hank of yarn which she wanted me to help her with. I held up my two hands and she put the hank over them, and went on talking about her arm and her husband's matters.

Then she said, "Keep your eye on the rats. You better have the lead in your lap, handy." She dropped the lump into my lap just at that moment, and I clapped my legs together on it and she went on talking. But only about a minute. Then she took off the hank and looked me straight in the face, and very pleasant, and says:

47

"Come, now, what's your real name?"

"Wh-hat, mum?"

"Is it Bill, or Tom, or Bob? Or what?"

I shook like a leaf, but I says:

"Please to don't poke fun at a poor girl like me, mum. If I'm in the way here, I'll—"

"No, you won't. Set down and stay where you are. I ain't going to tell on you. You just tell me your secret, and trust me. I'll keep it; and, what's more, I'll help you. You see, you're a runaway 'prentice, that's all. There ain't no harm in it. You've been treated bad, and you made up your mind to cut. Bless you, child, I wouldn't tell on you. Tell me all about it now, that's a good boy."

So I said it wouldn't be no use to try to play it any longer, and I would just tell her everything, but she mustn't go back on her promise. Then I told her my father and mother was dead, and the law had bound me out to a mean old farmer in the country thirty mile from the river, and he treated me so bad I couldn't stand it no longer; he went away to be gone a couple of days, and so I stole some of his daughter's clothes and cleared out, and I had been three nights coming the thirty miles. I said I believed my uncle Abner Moore would take care of me, and so that was why I struck out for this town of Goshen.

"Goshen, child? This ain't Goshen. This is St. Petersburg. Goshen's ten mile further up the river. Who told you this was Goshen?"

"Why, a man I met at daybreak this morning. He told me when the roads forked I must take the right hand, and five mile would fetch me Goshen."

"He was drunk, I reckon. He told you just exactly wrong."

"Well, he did act like he was drunk, but it ain't no matter now. I got to be moving along. I'll fetch Goshen before daylight."

"Hold on a minute. I'll put you up a snack to eat. You might want it."

So she put me up a snack, and says:

"Say, when a cow's laying down, which end of her gets up first? Answer prompt, now."

"The hind end, mum."

"Well, then, a horse?"

"The for-rard end, mum."

"Well, I reckon you *have* lived in the country. I thought you was trying to hocus me again. What's your real name, now?"

"George Peters, mum."

"Well, try to remember it, George. Don't forget and tell me it's Elexander before you go. And don't go about women in that old calico. You do a girl tolerable poor, but you might fool men, maybe. Bless you, child, when you set out to thread a needle don't hold the thread still and fetch the needle up to it; hold the needle still and poke the thread at it. And when you throw at a rat or anything, hitch yourself up a-tiptoe and fetch your hand up over your head as awkward as you can; throw stiff-armed from the shoulder, not from the wrist and elbow, with your arm out to one side, like a boy. And, mind you, when a girl tries to catch anything in her lap she throws her knees apart; she don't clap them together, the way you did when you catched the lump of lead. Why, I spotted you for a boy when you was threading the needle; and I contrived the other things just to make certain. Now, trot along to your uncle, Sarah Mary Williams George Elexander Peters, and if you get into trouble you send word to Mrs. Judith Loftus, which is me, and I'll do what I can to get you out of it."

I went up the road about fifty yards, and then I doubled on my tracks and slipped back to where my canoe was. I jumped in and was off in a hurry. I took off the sunbonnet, for I didn't want no blinders on then. When I was about the middle of the river, I heard the clock begin to strike, so I stops and listens; the sound come faint over the water but clear—eleven. When I struck the head of the island I never waited to blow, but I shoved right into the timber where my old camp used to be, and started a good fire there on a high and dry spot. Then I jumped in the canoe and dug out for our place, a mile and a half below. I landed, and slopped through the dark up the ridge and into the cavern. There Jim laid, sound asleep. I roused him out and says:

"Git up and hump yourself, Jim! They're after us!"

Jim never said a word; but the way he worked for the next half hour showed about how he was scared. By that time everything we had in the world was on our raft—that section of lumber raft we'd got off the river during the flood—and she was ready to be shoved out from the willow cove where she was hid. I took the canoe out from the shore a little piece, and took a look; but if there was a boat around I couldn't see it in the starlight. Then we got out the raft and slipped along down in the shade, past the foot of the island dead still—never saying a word.

CHAPTER V

It must 'a' been close on to one o'clock when we got below the island at last, and the raft did seem to go mighty slow. If a boat was to come along we was going to take to the canoe and break for the Illinois shore; and it was well a boat didn't come, for we hadn't ever thought to put the gun in the canoe, or a fishing line, or anything to eat.

If the men went to the island I just expect they found the campfire I built, and watched it all night for Jim to come. Anyways, they stayed away from us, and if my building the fire never fooled them it warn't no fault of mine.

When the first streak of day began to show we tied up to a towhead in a big bend on the Illinois side. A towhead is a sandbar that has cottonwoods on it, as thick as harrow teeth. We hacked off cottonwood branches with the hatchet, and covered up the raft with them so she looked like there had been a cave-in in the bank there.

We had mountains on the Missouri shore and heavy timber on the Illinois side, and the channel was down the Missouri shore at that place, so we warn't afraid of anybody running across us. We laid there all day, and watched the rafts and steamboats spin down the Missouri shore, and I told Jim all about the time I had jabbering with that woman; Jim said she was a smart one.

When it was beginning to come on dark we poked our heads out of the cottonwood thicket, and looked up and down and across; nothing in sight; so Jim took up some of the top planks of the raft and built a snug wigwam to get under in blazing weather and rainy, and to keep the things dry. Jim made a floor for the wigwam, and raised it a foot or more above the level of the raft, so now the blankets and all the traps was out of reach of steamboat waves.

Right in the middle of the wigwam we made a layer of dirt about five or six inches deep with a frame around it; this was to build a fire on in sloppy weather or chilly; the wigwam would keep it from being seen. We made an extra steering oar, too, because one of the others might get broke; and we fixed up a forked stick to hang the old lantern on, because we must always light the lantern whenever we see a steamboat coming, to keep from getting run over.

This second night we run between seven and eight hours, with a current that was making over four mile an hour. We catched fish and talked, and we took a swim now and then to keep off sleepiness. It was kind of solemn, drifting down the big, still river, laying on our backs looking up at the stars, and we didn't ever feel like talking loud, and it warn't often that we laughed—only a little kind of low chuckle. We had mighty good weather as a general thing, and nothing ever happened to us at all—that night, nor the next, nor the next.

Every night we passed towns, some of them away up on black hillsides, nothing but just a shiny bed of lights. The fifth night we passed St. Louis, and it was like the whole world lit up. In St. Petersburg they used to say there was twenty or thirty thousand people in St. Louis, but I never believed it till I see that wonderful spread of lights at two o'clock that night. There warn't a sound there; everybody was asleep.

Every night now I used to slip ashore toward ten o'clock at some little village, and buy ten or fifteen cents' worth of meal or bacon or other stuff to eat; and sometimes I lifted a chicken that warn't roosting comfortable. Pap always said, take a chicken

when you get a chance, because if you don't want him yourself you can easy find somebody that does, and a good deed ain't ever forgot. I never see Pap when he didn't want the chicken himself, but that is what he used to say, anyway. Mornings before daylight I slipped into cornfields and borrowed a watermelon, or a punkin, or some new corn, or things of that kind. And we shot a waterfowl now and then that got up too early in the morning. Take it all round, we lived pretty high.

The fifth night below St. Louis we had a big storm after midnight, with a power of thunder and lightning, and the rain poured down in a solid sheet. We stayed in the wigwam and let the raft take care of itself. When the lightning glared out we could see a big straight river ahead, and high rocky bluffs on both sides. By and by says I, "Hel-*lo*, Jim, looky yonder!" It was a steamboat that had killed herself on a rock. We was drifting straight down for her. The lightning showed her very distinct. She was leaning over, with part of her upper deck above water, and you could see every little chimbly guy clean and clear, and a chair by the big bell, when the flashes come.

Well, it being away in the night and stormy, and all so mysterious-like, I felt just the way any other boy would 'a' felt when I seen that wreck. I wanted to get aboard of her. So I says, "Le's land on her, Jim."

But Jim was dead against it at first. "I doan' want to go fool'n' 'long er no wrack," he says. "Like as not dey's a watchman on it."

"Watchman your grandmother," I says. "There ain't nothing to watch but the texas and the pilothouse; and do you reckon anybody's going to resk his life for a texas and a pilothouse such a night as this, when it's likely to break up any minute? And besides," I says, "we might borrow something worth having out of the captain's stateroom. Seegars, *I* bet you. Stick a candle in your pocket, Jim. Do you reckon Tom Sawyer would ever go by this thing? Not for pie, he wouldn't. He'd call it an adventure—and wouldn't he throw style into it? I wish Tom Sawyer *was* here."

Jim he grumbled a little, but give in. The lightning showed us the wreck again, and we fetched the stabboard derrick, and made fast there. Then we went sneaking down the slope of the deck in the dark, feeling our way slow with our feet and hands. Pretty soon we struck the forward end of the skylight, and clumb onto it; and the next step fetched us in front of the captain's door, which was open, and by Jimminy, away down through the texas hall we see a light! And all in the same second we hear voices!

Jim whispered he was feeling powerful sick, and told me to come along. I was going to start for the raft; but just then I heard a voice wail out:

"Oh, please don't, boys; I swear I won't ever tell!"

Another voice said, pretty loud, "It's a lie, Jim Turner. You've acted this way before. You always want more'n your share of the truck, and got it, too, because you've swore 't if you didn't you'd tell. But this time you've said it jest one time too many."

By this time Jim was gone for the raft. I was just a-biling with curiosity; and I says to myself, Tom Sawyer wouldn't back out now, and so I won't either. So I dropped on my hands and knees in the little passage, and crept aft in the dark till there warn't but one stateroom betwixt me and the cross hall of the texas. Then in there I see a man stretched on the floor and tied hand and foot, and two men standing over him, and one of them had a dim lantern in his hand, and the other one had a pistol. This one kept pointing the pistol at the man's head. But the man with the lantern said, "Put *up* that pistol, Bill."

Bill says, "I don't want to, Jake Packard. I'm for killin' him. Didn't he kill old Hatfield jist the same way—and don't he deserve it?"

"But I don't *want* him killed, and I've got my reasons."

"Bless yo' heart for them words, Jake Packard!" says the man on the floor, sort of blubbering.

Packard didn't take no notice of that, but hung up his lantern on a nail and started towards where I was, there in the dark, and motioned Bill to come. I crawfished as fast as I could about two yards, and to keep from getting catched I crawled into a stateroom. The man came a-pawing along in the dark, and when Packard got to my stateroom, he says:

"Here—come in here."

And in he come, and Bill after him. But before they got in I was up in the upper berth, cornered, and sorry I come. Then they stood there and talked. I couldn't see them, but I could tell where they was by the whiskey they'd been having. They talked low and earnest.

Bill wanted to kill Turner. He says, "He's said he'll tell, and he will. Shore's you're born, he'll turn state's evidence. I'm for putting him out of his troubles."

"So'm I," says Packard, very quiet.

"Blame it, I'd sorter begun to think you wasn't. Well, let's go and do it."

"Hold on a minute; I hain't had my say. You listen to me. Shooting's good, but there's quieter ways if the thing's *got* to be done. Now I say it ain't a-goin' to be more'n two hours befo' this wrack breaks up and washes off down the river. See? He'll be drownded, and won't have nobody to blame for it but his own self. I reckon that's a considerable sight better 'n killin' of him. Ain't I right?"

"Yes, I reck'n you are. But s'pose she *don't* break up and wash off?"

"Well, we can wait the two hours anyway and see, can't we?"

"All right, then; come along."

So they started, and I lit out, all in a cold sweat, and scrambled forward. It was dark as pitch there; but I said, in a kind of whisper, "Jim!" and he answered up, right at my elbow, with a sort of a moan, and I says:

"Quick, Jim, it ain't no time for fooling around and moaning; there's a gang of murderers in yonder, and if we don't hunt up their boat and set her drifting down the river so these fellows can't get away from the wreck there's one of 'em going to be in a bad fix. But if we find their boat we can put *all* of 'em in a bad fix—for the sheriff 'll get 'em. Quick—hurry! I'll hunt the labboard side, you hunt the stabboard. You start at the raft, and—"

"Oh, my lordy! *Raf'?* Dey ain' no raf' no mo'; she done broke loose en gone—en here we is!"

WELL, I CATCHED MY BREATH and most fainted. Shut up on a wreck with such a gang as that! But it warn't no time to be sentimentering. We'd *got* to find that boat now—for ourselves. So we went a-quaking and shaking down the stabboard side, and slow work it was, too—and no sign of a boat. Then we struck for the stern of the texas, and scrabbled forwards on the skylight, hanging on from shutter to shutter. When we got pretty close to the cross-hall door there was the skiff, sure enough! I felt ever so thankful. In another second I would 'a' been aboard of her, but just then the door opened. One of the men stuck his head out only a couple of foot from me, and I thought I was gone; but he jerked it in again, and says:

"Heave that blame lantern out o' sight, Bill!"

He flung a bag of something into the boat, and then got in himself and set down. It was Packard. Then Bill *he* come out and got in. Packard says, in a low voice, "All ready—shove off!"

I couldn't hardly hang on to the shutters, I was so weak. But Bill says, "Hold on—'d you go through him?"

"No. Didn't you?"

"No. So he's got his share o' the cash yet."

"Well, then, come along; no use to leave money."

So they got out and went back in, and in a half second I was in the boat, and Jim come tumbling after me. I out with my knife and cut the rope, and away we went!

We didn't touch an oar, and we didn't hardly even breathe. We went gliding along, dead silent, past the tip of the paddle box, and past the stern; then in a second or two more we was a hundred yards below the wreck, and the darkness soaked her up, every last sign of her, and we was safe, and knowed it.

When we was three or four hundred yards downstream we see the lantern show like a little spark at the texas door for a second, and we knowed by that that the rascals had missed their boat, and was beginning to understand that they was in just as much trouble now as Jim Turner was.

Then Jim manned the oars, and we took out after our raft. Now was the first time that I begun to worry about the men—I reckon

I hadn't had time to before. I begun to think how dreadful it was, even for murderers, to be in such a fix. So says I to Jim:

"The first light we see we'll land below it, and you hide there, and then I'll go and fix up some kind of a yarn, and get somebody to go for that gang and get them out of their scrape, so they can be hung when their time comes."

But that idea was a failure; for pretty soon it begun to storm again. The rain poured down, and never a light showed; everybody in bed, I reckon. We boomed along down the river, watching for lights and watching for our raft. After a long time the rain let up, but the clouds stayed, and the lightning kept whimpering, and by and by a flash showed us a black thing ahead, floating, and we made for it. It was the raft, and mighty glad was we to get aboard of it again.

We seen a light now away down to the right, on shore. So I said I would go for it. The skiff was half full of plunder which that gang had stole there on the wreck. We hustled it onto the raft in a pile, and I told Jim to float along down, and show a light when he judged he had gone about two mile, and keep it burning till I come; then I manned my oars and shoved for the light on the shore. As I got down towards it three or four more showed—up on a hillside. It was a village. I closed in above the shore light, and laid on my oars and floated. As I went by I see it was a lantern hanging on the jack staff of a double-hull ferryboat. I skimmed around for the watchman, a-wondering whereabouts he slept; and by and by I found him roosting on the bitts forward, with his head between his knees. I gave his shoulder two or three shoves, and begun to cry. He stirred up and took a good gap and stretch. Then he says:

"Hello, what's up? Don't cry, bub. What's the trouble?"

I says, "Pap, and Mam, and Sis, and—"

Then I broke down. He says, "Oh, dang it now, *don't* take on so; we all has our troubles, and this 'n 'll come out all right. What's the matter with 'em?"

"They're—they're—are you the watchman of the boat?"

"Yes," he says, well-satisfied like. "I'm the captain and the owner and the mate and the pilot and watchman; and sometimes I'm the freight and passengers. I ain't as rich as old Jim Hornback, and I can't slam around money the way he does; but I've told him a many a time 't I wouldn't trade places with him, not for all his spondulicks and much more. Says I—"

I broke in and says, "They're in an awful peck of trouble, and—"

"Who is?"

"Why, Pap and Mam and Sis and Miss Hooker; and if you'd take your ferryboat and go up there—"

"Up where? Where are they?"

"On the wreck."

"What! You don't mean they're on the *Walter Scott?*"

"Yes."

"Good land! What are they doin' *there*, for gracious sakes? Why, great goodness, they better git off mighty quick! How in the nation did they ever git into such a scrape?"

"Easy. Miss Hooker was a-visiting up there to the town—"

"Yes, Booth's Landing—go on."

"She was a-visiting there at Booth's Landing, and just in the edge of the evening she started over with her nigger woman in the horse ferry—and they lost their steering oar, and swung around and went a-floating down, stern first, and saddlebaggsed on the wreck, and the ferryman and the nigger woman and the horses was all lost, but Miss Hooker she made a grab and got aboard the wreck. Well, about an hour after dark we come along down in our trading scow, and it was so dark *we* saddlebaggsed; but all of us was saved but Bill Whipple—and oh, he was the best cretur! I most wish 't it had been me, I do."

"My George! And *then* what did you all do?"

"Well, we hollered, but nobody heard, so Pap said somebody got to get ashore and get help. I was the only one that could swim, so I made a dash for it, and Miss Hooker she said if I didn't strike help sooner, come here and hunt up her uncle. I made the land about a mile below, and been fooling along ever since, trying to get people to do something, but they said, 'What, in such a night and such a current? There ain't no sense in it; go for the steam ferry.' Now if you'll go and—"

"By Jackson, I'd *like* to, but who in the dingnation's a-going to *pay* for it? Do you reckon your pap—"

"Why, *that's* all right. Miss Hooker she tole me, *particular*, that her uncle Hornback—"

"Great guns! Is *he* her uncle? Looky here, you break for that light over yonder-way, and you'll come to the tavern; tell 'em to dart you out to Jim Hornback's, and he'll foot the bill. And don't you fool around any, because he'll want to know the news. Tell him I'll have his niece all safe before he can get to town. Hump yourself, now; I'm a-going up around the corner to roust out my engineer."

I struck for the light, but as soon as he turned the corner I went back and got into my skiff and bailed her out, and then pulled up shore in the easy water, and tucked myself in among some wood-boats; for I couldn't rest easy till I see the ferryboat start. Take it all around, I was feeling ruther comfortable on accounts of taking all this trouble for that gang. But before long here comes the wreck, dim and dusky, sliding along down! A kind of cold shiver went through me, and then I struck out for her. She was very deep, and I see in a minute there warn't much chance for anybody being alive in her. I pulled all around her and hollered, but there wasn't any answer; all dead still.

Then here comes the ferryboat, so I shoved for the middle of the river, and when I judged I was out of eye-reach I laid on my oars, and looked back and see her go and smell around the wreck for Miss Hooker's remainders, because the captain would know her uncle Hornback would want them; and pretty soon the ferryboat give it up and went for the shore, and I laid into my work and went a-booming down the river.

It did seem a powerful time before Jim's light showed up; and when it did show it looked like it was a thousand mile off. By the time I got there the sky was getting gray in the east; so we struck for an island, and hid the raft, and sunk the skiff, and turned in and slept like dead people.

BY AND BY, WHEN WE GOT UP, we turned over the truck the gang had stole off of the wreck, and found boots, and blankets, and clothes, and a lot of books, and three boxes of seegars. We hadn't ever been this rich before in neither of our lives. The seegars was prime. We laid off all the afternoon in the woods talking, and me reading the books, and having a general good time. I told Jim all about what happened inside the wreck, and I said these kinds of things was adventures; but he said he didn't want no more adventures. He said that when I went in the texas and he crawled back and found the raft gone he nearly died, because he judged it was all up with *him* any way it could be fixed; for if he didn't get saved he would get drownded; and if he did get saved, whoever saved him would send him back home, and then Miss Watson would sell him South, sure. Well, he was right; he was most always right; he had an uncommon level head for a nigger.

I read considerable to Jim about kings and dukes and earls and such, and how gaudy they dressed, and how much style they put on, and called each other your majesty, and your grace, and so on; and Jim's eyes bugged out, and he was interested. He says:

"I didn't know dey was so many un um. I hain't hearn 'bout none un um, skasely, but ole King Sollermun. How much do a king git?"

"Get?" I says. "Why, they get a thousand dollars a month if they want it; they can have just as much as they want."

"*Ain'* dat gay? En what dey got to do, Huck?"

"*They* don't do nothing! Why, they just set around."

"No; is dat so?"

"Of course. They just set around—except, maybe, when there's a war; then they go to the war. But other times they just lazy around; or go hawking; or when things is dull, they fuss with the parlyment; and if everybody don't go just so he whacks their heads off. But mostly they hang around the harem."

"Roun' de which?"

"Harem."

"What's de harem?"

"The place where he keeps his wives. Don't you know about the harem? Solomon had one; he had about a million wives."

"Why, yes, dat's so; I—I'd done forgot it. A harem's a bo'd'n-house, I reck'n. Mos' likely dey has rackety times in de nussery. En I reck'n de wives quarrels considable; en dat 'crease de racket. Yit dey say Sollermun de wises' man dat ever live'. I doan' take no stock in dat. Would a wise man want to live in de mids' er sich a blim-blammin' all de time? No—'deed he wouldn't."

"Well, but he *was* the wisest man, anyway; because the widow she told me so, her own self."

"I doan' k'yer what de widder say, he *warn't* no wise man nuther. Doan' talk to me 'bout Sollermun, Huck, I knows him by de back."

I never see such a nigger. He was sure down on Solomon. So I went on talking about other kings, and let Solomon slide. I told about Louis Sixteenth that got his head cut off in France long time ago; and about his little boy the dolphin, that would 'a' been king, but they took and shut him up in jail, and some say he died there.

"Po' little chap."

"But some says he got away, and come to America."

"Dat's good! But he'll be pooty lonesome—dey ain' no kings here, is dey, Huck?"

"No."

"Den he cain't git no situation. What he gwyne to do?"

"Well, I don't know. Some of them gets on the police, and some of them learns people how to talk French."

"Why, Huck, doan' de French people talk de same way we does?"

"*No*, Jim; you couldn't understand a word they said—not a single word."

"Well, now, I be ding-busted! How do dat come?"

"*I* don't know; but it's so. I got some of their jabber out of a book. S'pose a man was to come to you and say Polly-voo-franzy—what would you think?"

"I wouldn' think nuffn; I'd take en bust him over de head—dat is, if he warn't white. I wouldn' 'low no nigger to call me dat."

"Shucks, it ain't calling you anything. It's only saying, do you know how to talk French?"

"Well, den, why couldn't he say it?"

"Why, he *is* a-saying it. That's a Frenchman's *way* of saying it."

"Well, it's a blame ridicklous way, en I doan' want to hear no mo' 'bout it. Dey ain' no sense in it."

"Looky here, Jim; does a cat talk like we do?"

"No, a cat don't."

"Well, does a cow?"

"No, a cow don't, nuther."

"Does a cat talk like a cow, or a cow talk like a cat?"

"No, dey don't."

"It's natural and right for 'em to talk different from each other, ain't it?"

"Course."

"And ain't it natural and right for a cat and a cow to talk different from *us*?"

"Why, mos' sholy it is."

"Well, then, why ain't it natural and right for a *Frenchman* to talk different from us? You answer me that."

"Is a cat a man, Huck?"

"No."

"Well, den, dey ain't no sense in a cat talkin' like a man. Is a cow a man? Er is a cow a cat?"

"No, she ain't either of them."

"Well, den, she ain't got no business to talk like either one er the yuther of 'em. Is a Frenchman a man?"

"Yes."

"*Well*, den! Dad blame it, why doan' he *talk* like a man? You answer me *dat*!"

I see it warn't no use wasting words—you can't learn a nigger to argue. So I quit.

WE JUDGED THAT THREE NIGHTS more would fetch us to Cairo, at the bottom of Illinois, where the Ohio River comes in, and that was what we was after. We would sell the raft and get on a steamboat and go up the Ohio amongst the free states, and then be out of trouble.

Well, the second night a fog begun to come on, and we made for a towhead to tie to; but when I paddled ahead in the canoe, with the line to make fast, there warn't anything but little saplings to tie to. I passed the line around one of them, but there was a stiff current, and the raft come booming down so lively she tore it out by the roots and away she went. I see the fog closing down, and it made me so sick and scared I couldn't budge for most a half a minute—and then there warn't no raft in sight; you couldn't see twenty yards. I jumped into the canoe and grabbed the paddle and took out after the raft, hot and heavy, right down the towhead. But the towhead warn't sixty yards long, and the minute I flew by the foot of it I shot into solid white fog, and hadn't no more idea which way I was going than a dead man.

Thinks I, It won't do to paddle; I'll run into the bank or a towhead or something; I got to set still and float. I whooped and listened. Away down there somewheres I hears a small whoop, and up comes my spirits. I went tearing after it. The next time it come I warn't heading for it, but heading away to the right of it. And the next time I was heading away to the left of it—and not gaining on it much either, for I was flying around, this way and that, but it was going straight ahead all the time. Well, I fought along, and directly I hears the whoop *behind* me. I was tangled good now. That was somebody else's whoop, or else I was turned around.

I throwed the paddle down. I heard the whoop again; it was behind me yet, but a different place; it kept coming, and I kept answering, till by and by it was in front of me again, and I knowed the current had swung the canoe's head downstream, and I was all right if that was Jim and not some other raftsman hollering. I couldn't tell nothing about voices in a fog, for nothing don't sound natural in a fog.

The whooping went on, and in about a minute I come a-booming down on a cutbank with smoky ghosts of big trees on it, and the current throwed me off to the left and shot by amongst a lot of snags that fairly roared, the current was tearing by them so swift.

Then in a second or two it was solid white and still again. I set listening to my heart thump, and I reckon I didn't draw a breath while it thumped a hundred.

I just give up then. I knowed what the matter was. That cutbank was an island. It had the big timber of a regular island; it might be five or six miles long, and Jim had gone down t'other side of it.

I kept quiet, with my ears cocked, about fifteen minutes. I was floating along, of course, four or five miles an hour; but you *feel* like you are laying dead still on the water; and if a little glimpse of a snag slips by you catch your breath and think, My! How that snag's tearing along.

Next, for about a half an hour, I whoops now and then; at last I hears the answer a long ways off, and tries to follow it, but I couldn't do it, for directly I got into a nest of towheads. Well, I warn't long losing the whoops amongst the towheads. By and by I seemed to be in the open river again, but I still couldn't hear no sign of a whoop nowheres. I reckoned Jim had fetched up on a snag, maybe, and it was all up with him. I was good and tired, so I laid down in the canoe and said I wouldn't bother no more. I didn't want to go to sleep, of course; but I was so sleepy I couldn't help it; so I thought I would take jest one little catnap.

But I reckon it was more than a catnap, for when I waked up the stars was shining bright, the fog was all gone, and I was spinning down a big bend stern first.

It was a monstrous big river here, and with the tallest kind of timber on both banks; just a solid wall, as well as I could see by the stars. I looked away downstream, and seen a black speck on the water. I took after it; but when I got to it it warn't nothing but a couple of sawlogs made fast together. Then I see another speck, and chased that; then another, and this time it was the raft.

When I got to it Jim was setting there with his head down between his knees, asleep. The steering oar was smashed off, and the raft was littered up with leaves and branches and dirt. So she'd had a rough time.

I made fast and laid down under Jim's nose on the raft, and

began to gap, and stretch, and I says, "Hello, Jim, have I been asleep? Why didn't you stir me up?"

"Goodness gracious, is dat you, Huck? En you ain' dead—you ain' drownded—you's back ag'in? It's too good for true, honey, it's too good for true!"

"What's the matter with you, Jim? You been a-drinking?"

"Drinkin'? Has I ben a-drinkin'?"

"Well, then, what makes you talk so wild? What makes you talk as if I been gone away?"

"Huck—Huck Finn, you look me in de eye. *Hain't* you ben gone away? Didn't you tote out de line in de canoe fer to make fas' to de towhead?"

"No, I didn't. What towhead? I hain't seen no towhead."

"You hain't seen no towhead? Looky here, didn't de line pull loose en de raf' go down de river, en leave you behine in de fog?"

"What fog?"

"Why, *de* fog! De fog dat's been aroun' all night!"

"Well, this is too many for me, Jim. I hain't seen no fog. I been setting here talking with you all night till you went to sleep about ten minutes ago, and I reckon I done the same."

"Dad fetch it, how is I gwyne to dream all dat in ten minutes?"

"Well, hang it all, you did dream it, because there didn't any of it happen."

Jim didn't say nothing for about five minutes, but set there studying over it. Then he says:

"Well, den, I reck'n I did dream it, Huck; but dog my cats ef it ain't de powerfulest dream I ever see. En I hain't ever had no dream b'fo' dat's tired me like dis one."

"Oh, well, a dream does tire a body sometimes. But tell me all about it, Jim."

So Jim went to work and told me the whole thing right through, just as it happened. Then he said he must start in and "'terpret'" it, because it was sent for a warning. He said the first towhead stood for a man that would try to do us some good, but the current was another man that would get us away from him. The whoops was warnings, and the other towheads was troubles we was going to get into with mean folks, but if we minded our business we would pull through and get out of the fog and into the big clear river, which was the free states, and wouldn't have no more trouble.

It had clouded up pretty dark just after I got onto the raft, but it was clearing up again now.

"Oh, well, that's all interpreted well enough as far as it goes, Jim," I says; "but what does *these* things stand for?"

It was the leaves and rubbish on the raft and the smashed oar. You could see them first-rate now.

Jim looked at the trash, and then at me, and back at the trash again. He had got the dream fixed so strong in his head that he couldn't seem to shake it loose. But when he did get the thing straightened around he looked at me steady without smiling, and says, "What do dey stan' for? I's gwyne to tell you. When I got all wore out wid work, en wid de callin' for you, en went to sleep, my heart wuz mos' broke bekase you wuz los', en when I wake up en fine you back ag'in, all safe en soun', de tears come, en I could 'a' got down on my knees en kiss yo' foot, I's so thankful. En all you wuz thinkin' 'bout wuz how you could make a fool uv ole Jim wid a lie. Dat truck is *trash;* en trash is what people is dat puts dirt on de head er dey fren's en makes 'em ashamed."

Then he got up slow and walked to the wigwam, and went in without saying anything but that. It made me feel so mean I could almost kissed *his* foot to get him to take it back.

It was fifteen minutes before I could work myself up to go and humble myself to him; but I done it, and I warn't ever sorry for it afterward. I didn't do him no more mean tricks, and I wouldn't done that one if I'd 'a' knowed it would make him feel that way.

WE SLEPT MOST ALL DAY, and started out at night, a little ways behind a monstrous long raft that was as long going by as a procession. She had four long sweeps at each end, so she carried as many as thirty men, likely. She had five big wigwams aboard, and an open campfire in the middle, and a tall flagpole at each end. There was a power of style about her. It *amounted* to something being a raftsman on such a craft as that.

We went drifting down into a big bend, and the night clouded up and got hot. The river was very wide, and was walled with solid timber on both sides; you couldn't see a break in it hardly ever, or a light. We talked about Cairo, and wondered whether we would know it when we got to it. I said I had heard say there warn't but a dozen houses there, and if they didn't have them lit up, how was we going to know we was passing a town? Jim said if the two big rivers joined together there, that would show. But I said maybe we might think we was just passing the foot of an island. That disturbed Jim—and me too. But there warn't nothing to do now but to look out sharp for the town, and not pass it without seeing it. Jim said he'd be mighty sure to see it, because he'd be a free man the minute he seen it, but if he missed it he'd be in a slave country again and no more show for freedom. Every little while he jumps up and says, "Dah she is!"

But it warn't. It was jack-o'-lanterns, or lightning bugs; so he sat down again. He said it made him all over trembly and feverish to be so close to freedom. Well, I can tell you it made me all over trembly and feverish, too, to hear him, because I begun to get it through my head that he *was* most free—and who was to blame for it? Why, *me*. I couldn't get that out of my conscience, no how nor no way. I tried to make out to myself that *I* warn't to blame, because *I* didn't run Jim off from his rightful owner; but it warn't no use, conscience up and says, every time, But you knowed he was running for his freedom, and you could 'a' paddled ashore and told somebody. That was so—I couldn't get around that. Conscience says to me, What had poor Miss Watson done to you that you could see her nigger go off right under your eyes and never say one single word? What did that poor old woman do to you that you could treat her so mean? Why, she tried to learn you your book, and your manners; she tried to be good to you every way she knowed how. *That's* what she done.

I got to feeling so mean and so miserable I most wished I was dead. I fidgeted up and down the raft, abusing myself to myself, and Jim was fidgeting up and down past me. He talked out loud all the time while I was talking to myself. He was saying how the first thing he would do when he got to a free state he would go to saving up money, and when he got enough he would buy his wife, which was owned on a farm close to where Miss Watson lived; and then they would both work to buy the two children, and if their master wouldn't sell them, they'd get an Ab'litionist to go and steal them.

It most froze me to hear such talk. Here was this nigger, which I had as good as helped to run away, coming right out flat-footed and saying he would steal his children—children that belonged to a man that hadn't ever done me no harm. My conscience got to stirring me up worse than ever, until at last I says to it, Let up on me—it ain't too late yet—I'll paddle ashore at the first light and tell. I felt easy and happy right off. All my troubles was gone and I went to looking out sharp for a light. By and by one showed. Jim sings out:

"We's safe, Huck, we's safe! Dat's Cairo at las'. I jis' knows it!"

I says, "I'll take the canoe and go and see, Jim. It mightn't be, you know."

He jumped and got the canoe ready, and as I shoved off, he says, "Pooty soon I'll be a-shout'n' for joy, en I'll say, it's all on accounts o' Huck; I's a free man, en Huck done it. Jim won't ever forget you, Huck; you's de bes' fren' Jim's ever had; en you's de *only* fren' ole Jim's got now."

I was paddling off, all in a sweat to tell on him; but when he says this, it seemed to kind of take the tuck all out of me. I went along slow then, and when I was fifty yards off, along comes a skiff with two men in it with guns. They stopped and I stopped. One of them says, "What's that yonder?"

"A piece of a raft," I says.

"Do you belong on it?"

"Yes, sir."

"Any men on it?"

"Only one, sir."

"Well, there's five niggers run off tonight up yonder, above the bend. Is your man white or black?"

I didn't answer up prompt. I tried to, but the words wouldn't come. I tried for a second or two to brace up and out with it, but I warn't man enough—hadn't the spunk of a rabbit; so I just give up trying, and says, "He's white."

"I reckon we'll go and see for ourselves."

"I wish you would," says I, "because it's Pap, and maybe you'd help me tow the raft ashore where the light is. He's sick—and so is Mam and Mary Ann."

"Oh, the devil! We're in a hurry, boy. But I s'pose we've got to. Come, let's get along."

We had made a stroke or two, when I says, "Pap 'll be much obleeged to you, I can tell you. Everybody goes away when I want them to help me tow the raft ashore, and I can't do it by myself."

"Well, that's odd. Say, boy, what's the matter with your father?"

"It's the—a—the—well, it ain't anything much."

They stopped pulling. It warn't but a little ways to the raft now. One says, "Boy, that's a lie. What *is* the matter with your pap? Answer up square."

"I will, sir, honest—but don't leave us, please. It's the— Gentlemen, if you'll only pull ahead, and let me heave you the headline, you won't have to come a-near the raft—please."

"Set her back, John!" says one. They backed water. "Keep away, boy, keep to looard. Confound it, I expect the wind has blowed it to us. Your pap's got the smallpox, and you know it. Why didn't you come out and say so?"

"Well," says I, a-blubbering, "I've told everybody before, and they just went away and left us."

"Poor devil, there's something in that. We are right down sorry for you, but we—well, hang it, we don't want the smallpox, you see. Look here, I'll tell you what to do. You float along down about twenty miles, and you'll come to a town on the left-hand side of the river. Tell them your folks are down with chills and fever. Don't be a fool again, and let people guess what is the matter. Say, I reckon your father's poor, and I'm bound to say he's in hard luck. Here, we'll each put a twenty-dollar gold piece on this board, and you get them when it floats by. I feel mighty mean to leave you; but my kingdom, it won't do to fool with smallpox! Good-by, boy; if you see any runaway niggers get help and nab them, and you can make some money by it."

They went off and I got aboard the raft, feeling bad and low, because I knowed I had done wrong, and I see it warn't no use for me to try to learn to do right; a body that don't get *started* right when he's little ain't got no show. Then I thought a minute, and says to myself, Hold on; s'pose you'd 'a' done right and give Jim up, would you felt better than what you do now? No, says I, I'd feel bad—I'd feel just the same way I do now. Well, then, says I, what's the use you learning to do right when it's troublesome to do right and ain't no trouble to do wrong, and the wages is just the same? I couldn't answer that. So I reckoned I wouldn't bother no more about it, but after this always do whichever come handiest at the time.

I went into the wigwam; Jim warn't there. I says, "Jim!"

"Here I is, Huck. Is dey out o' sight yit? Don't talk loud."

He was in the river under the stern oar, with just his nose out. I told him they were out of sight, so he come aboard. He says, "I was a-listenin' to de talk, en I was gwyne to shove off if dey come aboard. But lawsy, how you did fool 'em, Huck! Dat *wuz* de smartes' dodge! I tell you, chile, I 'spec it save' ole Jim—ole Jim ain't going to forgit you for dat, honey."

Then we talked about the money. It was a pretty good raise—twenty dollars apiece. Jim said we could take deck passage on a steamboat now, and the money would last us as far as we wanted to go in the free states.

Towards daybreak we tied up, hiding the raft good. Then Jim worked all day fixing things in bundles, and getting all ready to quit rafting.

That night about ten we hove in sight of the lights of a town down in a left-hand bend.

I went off in the canoe to ask about it. Pretty soon I found a man out in a skiff, setting a trotline, and I says, "Mister, is that town Cairo?"

"Cairo? No. You must be a blame' fool."

"What town is it, mister?"

"If you want to know, go find out. If you stay here botherin' me a minute longer you'll get something you won't want."

I paddled to the raft. Jim was awful disappointed, but I said never mind, Cairo would be the next place, I reckoned.

We passed another town before daylight, and I was going out again; but it was high ground, so I didn't go. No high ground about Cairo, Jim said. I had forgot it. We laid up for the day on a towhead. I begun to suspicion something. So did Jim. I says, "Maybe we went by Cairo in the fog that night."

He says, "Doan' le's talk about it, Huck. I alwuz 'spected dat rattlesnake skin warn't done wid its work."

When it was daylight, here was the clear Ohio water inshore, sure enough, and outside was the old regular Muddy! So it was all up with Cairo.

We talked it all over. We couldn't take the raft up the stream, of course; and it wouldn't do to take to the shore. There warn't no way but to wait for dark, and start back in the canoe. So we slept all day, so as to be fresh for the work, and when we went back to the raft about dark the canoe was gone!

We didn't say a word for a good while. We both knowed well enough it was some more work of the rattlesnake skin; so what was the use to talk about it? But by and by we talked about what we better do, and found there warn't no way but just to go along down with the raft till we got a chance to buy a canoe to go back in.

So we shoved out after dark on the raft.

Anybody that don't believe yet that it's foolishness to handle a snake skin, after all that that snake skin done for us, will believe it now if they read on and see what more it done.

The place to buy canoes is off of rafts laying up at shore. But we didn't see no rafts; so we went along three hours and more. Well, the night got gray and ruther thick, which is the next meanest thing to fog. It got to be very late and still, and then along comes a steamboat up the river. We lit the lantern, and judged she would see it. We could hear her pounding along, but we didn't see her good till she was close. She aimed right for us. Often they do that and try to see how close they can come without touching; and then the pilot sticks his head out and laughs, and thinks he's mighty smart. Well, here she comes, and we said she was going to try and shave us; but she didn't seem to be sheering off a bit. She was a high one, and she was coming in a hurry, too, looking like a black cloud with rows of glowworms around it; but all of a sudden she bulged out, big and scary, with her monstrous bows and guards hanging right over us. There was a yell at us, and a jingling of bells, a powwow of cussing and whistling of steam—and as Jim went overboard on one side and I on the other, she came smashing straight through the raft.

I dived—and I aimed to find the bottom, too, for a thirty-foot wheel had to go over me. I could always stay under water a minute; this time I reckon I stayed under a minute and a half. Then I bounced for the top in a hurry, popping out to my armpits and blowing the water out of my nose. Of course there was a booming current; and of course that boat started her engines again ten seconds after she stopped them, for they never cared much for raftsmen; so now she was churning along up the river, out of sight in the thick weather.

I sung out for Jim about a dozen times, but I didn't get any answer; so I grabbed a plank that touched me and struck out for shore, shoving it ahead of me. I was a good long time in getting there, but I made a safe landing. I couldn't see only a little ways, but I went poking along over rough ground for a quarter of a mile, and then I run across a big old-fashioned log house. I was going to rush by, but a lot of dogs jumped out and went to howling and barking at me, and I knowed better than to move another peg.

CHAPTER VII

IN ABOUT A MINUTE somebody spoke out of a window and says, "Be done, boys! Who's there?"

I says, "It's me."

"Who's me?"

"George Jackson, sir."

"What are you prowling around here for—hey?"

"I warn't prowling around, sir; I only want to go along by; I fell overboard off of the steamboat."

"Oh, you did, did you? Strike a light there, somebody. What did you say your name was?"

"George Jackson, sir. I'm only a boy."

"Look here, if you're telling the truth you needn't be afraid—nobody 'll hurt you. Is there anybody with you?"

"No, sir, nobody."

I heard people stirring around in the house now, and see a light. The man sung out, "Bob, if you and Tom are ready, take your places."

"All ready."

"Now, George Jackson, do you know the Shepherdsons?"

"No, sir. I never heard of them."

"Well, step forward, George Jackson. And mind, come mighty slow. If there's anybody with you, let him keep back—if he shows himself he'll be shot. Come along now; push the door open yourself—just enough to squeeze in, d'you hear?"

I took one slow step at a time and there warn't a sound, only I thought I could hear my heart. The dogs were as still as the humans, but they followed a little behind me. When I got to the three log doorsteps I heard them unlocking and unbolting. I put my hand on the door and pushed it till somebody said, "There, that's enough—put your head in." I done it, but I judged they would take it off.

A candle was on the floor, and there they all was, looking at me, and me at them. Three big men with guns pointed at me; the oldest, gray and about sixty, the other two thirty or more—all of them fine and handsome—and the sweetest old gray-headed lady, and back of her two young women. The old gentleman says:

"There; I reckon it's all right. Come in."

As soon as I was in the old gentleman he locked the door and bolted it. They took a good look at me, and all said, "Why, *he* ain't a Shepherdson—no, there ain't any Shepherdson about him."

Then the old man told me to make myself at home, and tell all about myself; but the old lady says:

"Why, bless you, Saul, the poor thing's as wet as he can be; and don't you reckon maybe he's hungry?"

"True for you, Rachel—I forgot."

So the old lady says, "Betsy," (this was a nigger woman) "you fly around and get him something to eat, poor thing; and one of you girls wake up Buck—oh, here he is himself. Buck, take this little stranger and get the wet clothes off from him and dress him up in some of yours that's dry."

Buck looked about as old as me—thirteen or fourteen. He hadn't on anything but a shirt, and he came in gaping and digging one fist into his eyes, and he was dragging a gun along with the other one. He says, "Ain't they no Shepherdsons around?"

They said, no, 'twas a false alarm.

"Well," he says, "if they'd 'a' ben some, I reckon I'd 'a' got one."

They all laughed, and Bob says, "Why, Buck, they might have scalped us all, you've been so slow in coming."

"Well, nobody come after me, and it ain't right. I'm always kept down; I don't get no show."

"Never mind, Buck, my boy," says the old man, "you'll have show enough, all in good time. Go 'long now, and do as your mother told you."

When we got upstairs to his room he got me a shirt and pants of his, and I put them on. While I was at it he asked what my name was, but before I could tell him he started to tell me about a blue jay he had catched day before yesterday, and he asked me where Moses was when the candle went out. I said I didn't know.

"Well, guess," he says.

"How'm I going to guess," says I, "when I never heard tell of it before?"

"But you can guess, can't you? It's just as easy."

"*Which* candle?" I says.

"Why, any candle," he says.

"I don't know where he was," says I. "Where was he?"

"Why, he was in the *dark!* That's where he was!"

"Well, if you knowed where he was, what did you ask me for?"

"Why, blame it, it's a riddle! Say, how long are you going to stay here? You got to stay always. We can just have booming times. Do you own a dog? I've got a dog—and he'll go in the river and bring out chips that you throw in. Do you like to comb up Sundays, and that kind of foolishness? I don't, but Ma she makes me. Confound these britches! I reckon I'd better put 'em on, but I'd ruther not, it's so warm. Are you all ready? All right. Come along, old hoss."

Cold corn pone, corn beef, butter and buttermilk—that is what they had for me down there, and there ain't nothing better that ever I've come across yet. While I eat they all asked me questions, and I told them how Pap and me and all the family was living on a little farm in Arkansaw, and my sister Mary Ann run off and got married and never was heard of no more, and Bill went to hunt them and he warn't heard of no more, and Tom and Mort died, and then there warn't nobody but me and Pap left, and he was just trimmed down to nothing, on account of his troubles; so when he died I took what there was left, and started up the river, deck passage, and fell overboard; and that was how I come to be here. So they said I could have a home there as long as I wanted it. Then everybody went to bed, and I went to bed with Buck, and when I waked up in the morning, drat it all, I had forgot what my name was. So I laid there trying to think, and when Buck waked up I says:

"Can you spell, Buck?"

"Yes," he says.

"I bet you can't spell my name," says I.

"I bet you what you dare I can," says he.

"All right," says I, "go ahead."

"G-e-o-r-g-e J-a-x-o-n—there now," he says.

"Well," says I, "you done it, but I didn't think you could."

I set it down, private, because somebody might want *me* to spell it next, and so I wanted to be handy with it.

It was a mighty nice family, and a mighty nice house, too. I hadn't seen no house out in the country before that was so nice and had so much style. It didn't have an iron latch on the front door, but a brass knob to turn, the same as houses in town. There was a big fireplace that was bricked on the bottom, with big brass dog irons that could hold up a sawlog. There was a clock on the middle of the mantelpiece, with a picture of a town painted on the bottom half of the glass front. It was beautiful to hear that clock tick; and sometimes when one of these peddlers had been along and scoured her up and got her in good shape, she would start in and strike a hundred and fifty before she got tuckered out. They wouldn't took any money for her.

Well, there was a big outlandish parrot on each side of the clock, made of something like chalk, and painted up gaudy. By one of the parrots was a cat made of crockery, and a crockery dog by the other; and when you pressed down on them they squeaked, but didn't open their mouth nor look different nor interested. They squeaked through underneath. On the table in the middle of the room was a kind of crockery basket that had apples and peaches and grapes piled up in it, which was much redder and yellower and prettier than real ones, but they warn't real because you could see where pieces had got chipped off and showed the white chalk, or whatever it was, underneath.

This table had a cover made out of beautiful oilcloth, with a red and blue spread eagle painted on it. There was some books, too, piled up exact, on each corner of the table. One was a big family Bible full of pictures. One was *Pilgrim's Progress*, about a man that left his family, it didn't say why. I read considerable in it now and then. There was a hymnbook, too, and a lot of other books. And there was nice split-bottom chairs, and perfectly sound, too—not bagged down in the middle and busted, like an old basket.

And they had pictures hung on the walls—mainly Washingtons and Lafayettes, and battles, and Highland Marys, and one called "Signing the Declaration." There was some that they called crayons, which one of the daughters which was dead made her own self when she was only fifteen years old. They was different from any pictures I ever see before—blacker, mostly, than is common. One was a woman in a slim black dress, belted small under the armpits, with bulges like a cabbage in the middle of the sleeves, and white slim ankles crossed about with black tape, and very wee black slippers, like a chisel, and she was leaning pensive on a tombstone on her elbow, under a weeping willow, and underneath the picture it said, "Shall I Never See Thee More Alas." Another one was a young lady with her hair all combed up straight to the top of her head, and she was crying into a handkerchief and had a dead bird lying on its back in her other hand with its heels up, and underneath the picture it said, "I Shall Never Hear Thy Sweet Chirrup More Alas." There was one where a young lady was at a window looking up at the moon, and tears running down her cheeks; and she had an open letter in one hand with black sealing wax on it, and she was mashing a locket against her mouth, and underneath the picture it said, "And Art Thou Gone Yes Thou Art Gone Alas."

These was all nice pictures, I reckon, but I didn't somehow take to them, because if ever I was down a little they always give me the fantods. Everybody was sorry she died, and a body could see by what she had done what they had lost. But I reckoned that with her disposition she was having a better time in the graveyard. She was at work on what they said was her greatest picture when she took sick, and every day and every night it was her prayer to be allowed to live till she got it done, but she never got the chance. It was a picture of a young woman, standing on the rail of a bridge all ready to jump off, with her hair all down her back, and looking up to the moon, with the tears running down her face, and she had two arms folded across her breast, and two arms stretched out in front, and two more reaching up toward the moon—and the idea was to see which pair would look best, and then scratch out all the other arms; but, as I was saying, she died before she got her mind made up, and now they kept this picture over her bed, and every time her birthday come they hung flowers on it. The young woman in the picture had a kind of a sweet face, but there was so many arms it made her look too spidery, seemed to me.

This young girl had kept a scrapbook, and used to paste obitu-

aries and accidents and cases of patient suffering in it, and write
poetry after them out of her own head. This is what she wrote
about a boy that fell down a well and was drownded:

ODE TO STEPHEN DOWLING BOTS, DEC'D

And did young Stephen sicken,
And did young Stephen die?
And did the sad hearts thicken,
And did the mourners cry?

No; such was not the fate of
Young Stephen Dowling Bots;
Though sad hearts round him thickened,
'Twas not from sickness' shots.

No whooping cough did rack his frame,
Nor measles drear with spots;
Not these impaired the sacred name
Of Stephen Dowling Bots.

O no. Then list with tearful eye,
Whilst I his fate do tell.
His soul did from this cold world fly
By falling down a well.

They got him out and emptied him;
Alas it was too late;
His spirit was gone for to sport aloft
In the realms of the good and great.

If Emmeline Grangerford could make poetry like that before
she was fourteen, there ain't no telling what she could 'a' done by
and by. Buck said she could rattle off poetry like nothing. She
didn't ever have to stop to think. Every time a man died, or a
woman, or a child, she would be on hand with her "tribute" before he was cold. The neighbors said it was the doctor first, then
Emmeline, then the undertaker. The undertaker never got in
ahead of Emmeline but once, and then she hung fire on a rhyme
for the dead person's name, which was Whistler. She warn't ever

the same after that; she never complained, but she kinder pined away and did not live long. They kept her room trim and nice, and all the things fixed in it just the way she liked to have them when she was alive. The old lady took care of the room herself, and she sewed there a good deal and read her Bible there mostly.

Well, as I was saying about the parlor, there was beautiful curtains on the windows: white, with pictures painted on them of castles with vines, and cattle coming down to drink. There was a little old piano too. The walls of all the rooms was plastered, and most had carpets on the floors, and the whole house was whitewashed on the outside. It was a cool, comfortable place. Nothing couldn't be better. And warn't the cooking good, and just bushels of it too!

Colonel Grangerford was a gentleman, you see. He was wellborn, as the saying is. He was very tall and very slim, and had a darkish-paly complexion; he was clean-shaved every morning all over his thin face, and he had the thinnest kind of lips, and a high nose, and the blackest kind of eyes, sunk so deep they seemed like they was looking out of caverns at you. His hair was gray and straight and hung to his shoulders. His hands was long and thin, and every day of his life he put on a clean shirt and a suit made out of white linen; and on Sundays he wore a blue tailcoat with brass buttons. There warn't no frivolishness about him, not a bit, and he warn't ever loud. He was as kind as he could be—you could feel that, you know, and so you had confidence. When him and the old lady come down in the morning all the family got out of their chairs and give them good-day, and didn't set down again till they had set down. Then Tom and Bob went to the sideboard and mixed a glass of bitters and handed it to him, and he held it and waited till Tom's and Bob's was mixed, and then they bowed and said, "Our duty to you, sir and madam," and *they* bowed and said thank you, and so they drank, all three, and Bob and Tom poured a spoonful of water on the sugar and the mite of whiskey in the bottom of their tumblers, and give it to me and Buck, and we drank to the old people too.

Bob was the oldest and Tom next—tall, beautiful men with

broad shoulders and long black hair and black eyes. They dressed in white linen, like the old gentleman, and wore broad Panama hats.

Then there was Miss Charlotte; she was twenty-five, and tall and proud and grand, but as good as she could be when she warn't stirred up. She was beautiful. So was her sister, Miss Sophia, but it was a different kind. She was gentle and sweet like a dove, and she was only twenty.

Each person had their own nigger to wait on them—Buck too. My nigger had a monstrous easy time, because I warn't used to having anybody do anything for me, but Buck's was on the jump most of the time.

This was all there was of the family now, but there used to be more—three sons, they got killed; and Emmeline that died.

The old gentleman owned a lot of farms and over a hundred niggers. Sometimes a stack of people would come there, horseback, from miles around, and stay five or six days, and have such junketings round about, dances and picnics daytimes and balls nights. These people was mostly kinfolks of the family. It was a handsome lot of quality, I tell you.

There was another clan of aristocracy around there—five or six families—mostly of the name of Shepherdson. They was as high-toned and rich as the Grangerfords. The Shepherdsons and Grangerfords used the same steamboat landing, two mile above our house; so sometimes when I went up there with our folks I used to see the Shepherdsons there on their fine horses.

One day Buck and me was in the woods hunting, and heard a horse coming. We was crossing the road. Buck says, "Quick! Jump for the woods!"

We done it, and then peeped down the woods through the leaves. Pretty soon a splendid young man came galloping down the road. He had his gun across his pommel. I had seen him before. It was young Harney Shepherdson. I heard Buck's gun go off at my ear, and Harney's hat tumbled off from his head. He grabbed his gun and rode straight to the place where we was hid. We didn't wait, but run. The woods warn't thick, so I looked over my shoulder to dodge the bullet, and twice I seen Harney cover Buck with his gun; and then he rode away the way he come—to get his hat, I reckon. We never stopped running till we got home. The old gentleman's eyes blazed a minute—'twas pleasure, mainly, I judged—and then he says, kind of gentle:

"I don't like that shooting from behind a bush. Why didn't you step into the road, my boy?"

"The Shepherdsons don't, Father. They always take advantage."

Miss Charlotte she held her head up like a queen, and her nostrils spread and her eyes snapped. The two young men looked dark, but never said nothing. Miss Sophia she turned pale, but the color come back when she found the man warn't hurt.

Soon as I got Buck by ourselves, I says, "Did you want to kill him, Buck?"

"Well, I bet I did."

"What did he do to you?"

"Him? He never done nothing to me."

"Well, then, what did you want to kill him for?"

"Why, nothing—only it's on account of the feud."

"What's a feud?"

"Why, where was you raised?" says Buck. "Don't you know what a feud is? A man has a quarrel with another man, and kills him; and then that other man's brother kills *him;* then the other brothers, on both sides, goes for one another; then the *cousins* chip in—and by and by everybody's killed, and there ain't no more feud. But it's kind of slow."

"Has this one been going on long, Buck?"

"Well, I *reckon!* It started thirty years ago, or som'ers along there. There was trouble 'bout something, and then a lawsuit to settle it; and the suit went agin one of the men, and so he up and shot the man that won the suit."

"Well, who done the shooting? Was it a Grangerford or a Shepherdson?"

"Laws, how do *I* know? It was so long ago."

"Don't anybody know?"

"Oh, yes, Pa knows, I reckon, and the other old people; but they don't know now what the row was about in the first place."

"Has there been many killed, Buck?"

"Yes; right smart chance of funerals."

"Has anybody been killed this year?"

"Yes; we got one and they got one. 'Bout three months ago my cousin Bud, fourteen year old, was riding through the woods and didn't have no weapon with him, and he hears a horse a-coming behind him, and sees old Baldy Shepherdson a-linkin' after him with his gun in his hand and his white hair a-flying; and 'stead of taking to the brush, Bud 'lowed he could outrun him; so they had it, nip and tuck, for five mile, the old man a-gaining all the time; so at last Bud stopped and faced around so as to have the bullet holes in front, you know, and the old man shot him down. But he didn't git much chance to enjoy his luck, for inside of a week our folks laid *him* out."

Next Sunday we all went to church, about three mile, everybody a-horseback. The men took their guns along, so did Buck, and kept them between their knees. The Shepherdsons done the same. It was pretty ornery preaching—all about brotherly love; but everybody said it was a good sermon, and they all talked it over going home, and had such a powerful lot to say about faith and grace and preforeordestination, that it did seem to me to be one of the roughest Sundays I had run across yet.

About an hour after dinner everybody was dozing around, and it got to be pretty dull. Buck and a dog was stretched out on the grass sound asleep. I went up to our room, and judged I would take a nap myself. I found that sweet Miss Sophia standing in her door, and she took me in her room and shut the door very soft; and she asked me if I would do something for her and not tell anybody, and I said I would. Then she said she'd forgot her Testament, and left it in the seat at church, and would I go fetch it, and not say nothing to nobody. I said I would. So I slid out and slipped off up the road to the church. Says I to myself, Something's up; it ain't natural for a girl to be in such a sweat about a Testament. So I give it a shake, and out drops a little piece of paper with *Half past two* wrote on it. I couldn't make anything out of that, so I put the paper in the book again, and when I got home and upstairs there was Miss Sophia in her door, waiting for me. She pulled me in and shut the door; then she looked in the Testament till she found the paper, and as soon as she read it her eyes lighted up, and she looked glad and grabbed me and give me a squeeze, and said I was the best boy in the world, and not to tell anybody.

I was a good deal astonished, but when I got my breath I asked her what the paper was about, and she asked me if I had read it, and I said no, and then she said the paper warn't anything but a bookmark, and I might go and play now.

I went off down to the river, studying over this thing, and pretty soon I noticed that my nigger was following. When we was out of sight of the house he comes a-running, and says:

"Mars Jawge, if you'll come into de swamp I'll show you a stack o' water moccasins."

Thinks I, That's mighty curious; he said that yesterday. He oughter know a body don't love water moccasins that much. What's he up to, anyway? But I says, "All right; trot ahead."

I followed a half a mile; then he struck out over the swamp till we come to a little flat piece of land which was dry and thick with trees and bushes. He says, "Right in dah, Mars Jawge; dah's whah I's seed 'm befo'; I don't k'yer to see 'em no mo'."

Then he slopped away, and I poked into the place a ways and pretty soon I come to a little open patch and found a man lying there asleep—and, by jings, it was my old Jim!

I waked him up, and I reckoned it was going to be a grand surprise to him to see me again, but it warn't. He nearly cried he was so glad, but he warn't surprised. Said he swum along behind me that night, and heard me yell every time, but dasn't answer, because he didn't want anybody to pick *him* up and take him into slavery again. Says he:

"I got hurt a little, so I wuz a considerable ways behine you towards de las'; when you landed I reck'ned I could ketch up wid you on de lan', but when I see dat house I go slow. I 'uz off too fur to hear what dey say to you—I wuz 'fraid o' de dogs; but when it 'uz all quiet ag'in I knowed you's in de house, so I struck out for de woods. Early in de mawnin' some er de niggers come along, en dey tuk me en showed me dis place, whah de dogs can't track me on account o' de water, en dey brings me truck to eat every night, en tells me how you's a-gittin' along."

"Why didn't you tell my Jack to fetch me here sooner, Jim?"

"'Twarn't no use to 'sturb you, Huck, tell we could do sumfn—but we's all right now. I ben a-buyin' pots en vittles, as I got a chanst, en a-patchin' up de raf'—"

"*What* raft, Jim?"

"Our ole raf'."

"You mean to say our old raft warn't smashed all to flinders?"

"No, she warn't. She was tore up a good deal—one en' of her was; but dey warn't no great harm done, on'y our traps was mos' all los'. Some er de niggers foun' her ketched on a snag along heah in de ben', en dey hid her in de willows, en dey wuz so much jawin' 'bout which un 'um she b'long to dat I heah 'bout it, so I ups en settles de trouble by tellin' 'um she b'long to you en me; en I ast 'm if dey gwyne to grab a young white genlman's propaty, en git a hid'n for it? Den I gin 'em ten cents apiece, en dey 'uz mighty satisfied, en wisht some mo' raf's 'ud come along en make 'm rich ag'in. Dey's mighty good to me, dese niggers, en whatever I wants 'm to do I doan' have to ast 'm twice, honey. Dat Jack's a good nigger, en pooty smart."

"Yes, he is. He ain't ever told me you was here; told me to come, and he'd show me a lot of water moccasins. If anything happens *he* ain't mixed up in it. He can say he never seen us together, and it'll be the truth."

I DON'T WANT TO TALK much about the next day. I reckon I'll cut it pretty short. I waked up about dawn, and was a-going to go to sleep again when I noticed how still it was. Next I noticed that Buck was up and gone. Well, I gets up, a-wondering, and goes downstairs—nobody around. Thinks I, What does it mean? Down by the woodpile I comes across my Jack, and says, "What's it all about?"

Says he, "Don't you know, Mars Jawge? Miss Sophia's run off! She run off in de night to get married to dat young Harney

Shepherdson. De fambly foun' it out 'bout half an hour ago—en' I *tell* you dey warn't no time los'. De womenfolks has gone for to stir up de relations, en ole Mars Saul en de boys tuck dey guns en rode up de river road for to try to ketch dat young man en kill him 'fo' he kin git acrost de river wid Miss Sophia. I reck'n dey's gwyne to be rough times."

"Buck went off 'thout waking me up."

"Well, I reck'n he *did!* Dey warn't gwyne to mix you up in it. Mars Buck he loaded up his gun en 'lowed he's gwyne to fetch home a Shepherdson or bust."

I took up the river road as hard as I could put. By and by I heard a gun a good ways off. When I come in sight of the log store and the woodpile where the steamboats lands I worked along under the trees and brush, and then I clumb up into a cottonwood, and watched. There was a wood-rank four foot high a little ways in front of the tree, and first I was going to hide behind that; but maybe it was luckier I didn't.

There was four or five men cavorting around on their horses in the open place before the store, cussing and yelling, and trying to get a couple of young chaps that was squatting behind the wood-rank alongside the steamboat landing. But they couldn't come it, so by and by the men stopped cavorting around and started riding towards the store. Then up gets one of the boys, draws a steady bead and drops one man out of his saddle. All the men jumped off of their horses and grabbed the hurt one to carry him to the store; and that minute the two boys started on the run. They got halfway to the tree I was in before the men noticed. Then the men see them, and jumped on their horses and took out after them. They gained on the boys, but it didn't do no good; the boys got to the woodpile that was in front of my tree, and slipped in behind it, and so they had the bulge on the men again. One of the boys was Buck, and the other was a slim young chap about nineteen years old.

The men ripped around awhile, and then rode away. As soon as they was out of sight I sung out to Buck. He didn't know what to make of my voice coming out of the tree at first. He was awful surprised. He told me to watch out sharp and let him know when the men come in sight again; said they must be up to some devilment or other. I wished I was out of that tree, but I dasn't come down. Buck begun to cry and rip, and 'lowed that him and his cousin Joe (that was the other young chap) would make up for this day yet. He said his father and his two brothers was killed, and two or three of the enemy. Said the Shepherdsons laid for them in ambush. I asked him what was become of young Harney and Miss Sophia. He said they'd got across the river and was safe. I was glad of that, but the way Buck did take on because he didn't manage to kill Harney that day he shot at him—I hain't ever heard anything like it.

All of a sudden, *bang! bang!* goes three or four guns—the men had slipped around through the woods and come in from behind without their horses! The boys jumped for the river—both of them hurt—and as they swum down the current the men run along the bank shooting at them and singing out, "Kill them, kill them!" It made me so sick I most fell out of the tree. I wished I hadn't ever come ashore that night to see such things. I ain't ever going to get shut of them—lots of times I dream about them.

I stayed in the tree till it begun to get dark, afraid to come down. Sometimes I heard guns away off, and I seen little gangs of men gallop past the log store; so I reckoned the trouble was still a-going on. I was mighty downhearted. I made up my mind I wouldn't ever go anear the house again, because I reckoned I was to blame, somehow. I judged that that piece of paper meant that Miss Sophia was to meet Harney somewheres at half past two and run off; and I judged I ought to told her father about that paper, and then maybe he would 'a' locked her up, and this awful mess wouldn't ever happened.

When I got down out of the tree I crept along down the riverbank a piece, and found the two bodies laying in the edge of the water. I covered up their faces, and got away as quick as I could. I cried when I was covering up Buck's face, for he was mighty good to me.

It was dark now. I never went near the house, but made for

the swamp. Jim warn't on his island, so I tramped off in a hurry for the crick, and crowded through the willows, red-hot to jump aboard the raft and get out of that awful country. I couldn't find it, and at last I raised a yell. A voice not twenty-five foot from me says, "Good lan'! Is dat you, honey? Doan' make no noise."

It was Jim's voice—nothing ever sounded so good before. I run along the bank and got aboard, and Jim he hugged me, he was so glad to see me. He says:

"Laws bless you, chile, I 'uz right down sho' you's dead ag'in. Jack's been heah; he says he reck'n you's ben shot, kase you didn' come home no mo'. Lawsy, I's glad to git you back ag'in, honey!"

I says, "All right—that's mighty good; they'll think I've been killed, and floated down the river—so don't you lose no time, Jim, but shove off fast as you can."

I never felt easy till the raft was two miles below there and in the middle of the Mississippi. Then we hung up our signal lantern, and judged that we was free and safe once more. I hadn't had a bite to eat since yesterday, so Jim he got out some corn dodgers and buttermilk, and whilst I eat my supper we talked and had a good time. I was powerful glad to get away from the feuds, and so was Jim to get away from the swamp. We said there warn't no home like a raft, after all. Other places do seem so cramped up and smothery, but a raft don't. You feel mighty free and easy and comfortable on a raft.

CHAPTER VIII

TWO OR THREE DAYS AND NIGHTS went by; I reckon I might say they swum by, they slid along so quiet and smooth and lovely. It was a monstrous big river down there—sometimes a mile and a half wide; we run nights, and laid up and hid daytimes. Soon as night was most gone we stopped navigating and tied up—nearly always in the dead water under a towhead; and then cut young cottonwoods, and hid the raft with them. Then we set out the lines. Next we slid into the river and had a swim; then we set down where the water was about knee-deep, and watched the daylight come. The first thing to see, looking away over the water, was a kind of dull line—that was the woods on t'other side; then a pale place in the sky; then more paleness spreading around; then the river softened up and warn't black anymore, but gray; and by and by the mist curls up off the water, and the east reddens up, and the river; then the nice breeze springs up, and comes fanning you, so cool and fresh and sweet to smell on account of the woods and the flowers; but sometimes not that way, because they've left dead fish laying around; and next you've got the full day, and everything smiling in the sun, and the songbirds just going it!

A little smoke couldn't be noticed now, so we would take some fish off of the lines and cook up a hot breakfast. And afterwards we would watch the lonesomeness of the river, and kind of lazy along, and by and by lazy off to sleep. Wake up by and by, and look, and maybe see a steamboat coughing along upstream, or a raft sliding by away off yonder. So we would put in the day, lazing around, listening to the stillness.

Soon as it was night out we shoved; when we got the raft out to about the middle of the river we let her alone, and let her float wherever the current wanted her to; then we lit the pipes, and dangled our legs in the water, and talked about all kinds of things we was always naked, day and night, whenever the mosquitos would let us—the new clothes Buck's folks made for me was too good to be comfortable, and besides I didn't go much on clothes, nohow.

Sometimes we'd have that whole river all to ourselves for the longest time. Yonder was the banks and the islands, across the water; and maybe a spark—which was a candle in a cabin window; and sometimes on the water you could see a spark or two—on a raft or a scow; and maybe you could hear a fiddle or a song coming from one of them crafts. It's lovely to live on a raft. We had the sky up there, all speckled with stars, and we used to lay on our backs and look up at them, and discuss about whether they was made or only just happened. Jim he allowed they was made, but I allowed they happened; I judged it would have took too long to *make* so many. Jim said the moon could 'a' *laid* them; well, that looked kind of reasonable, so I didn't say nothing against it, because I've seen a frog lay most as many, so of course it could be done.

After midnight the people on shore went to bed, and then for two or three hours the shores was black—no more sparks in the cabin windows. These sparks was our clock—the first one that showed again meant morning was coming, so we hunted a place to hide and tie up right away.

One morning about daybreak I found a canoe and crossed over to the main shore and paddled about a mile up a crick to see if I couldn't get some berries. Just as I was passing a place where a kind of cowpath crossed the crick, here comes a couple of men tearing up the path. They sung out and begged me to save their lives—said they hadn't been doing nothing, and was being chased for it—said there was men and dogs a-coming. They wanted to jump right in, but I says:

"Don't you do it. I don't hear the dogs yet; you've got time to crowd through the brush and get up the crick a little ways; then you take to the water and wade down to me—that'll throw the dogs off the scent."

They done it, and soon as they was aboard I lit out. In about five minutes we heard the dogs and the men away off, shouting. We heard them come along towards the crick, but couldn't see them; they seemed to stop and fool around awhile; then, as we got further away all the time, we couldn't hardly hear them at all; and when we struck the river, everything was quiet, and we paddled over to the towhead and hid in the cottonwoods and was safe.

One of these fellows was about seventy or upwards, and had a bald head and very gray whiskers. He had an old battered-up slouch hat on, and a greasy blue woolen shirt, and ragged blue jeans stuffed into his boot tops, and home-knit galluses—no, he only had one. The other fellow was about thirty, and dressed about as ornery. Both of them had big, fat, ratty-looking carpetbags.

After breakfast we laid off and talked, and the first thing that come out was that these chaps didn't know one another.

"What got you into trouble?" says the baldhead to t'other.

"Well, I'd been selling an article to take the tartar off the teeth—and it does take it off, too, and generly the enamel with it—but I stayed about one night longer than I ought to, and was just in the act of sliding out when I ran across you on the trail, and you told me they were coming, and begged me to help you to get off. So I told you I was expecting trouble myself, and would scatter out *with* you. That's the whole yarn—what's yourn?"

"Well, I'd been a-runnin' a little temperance revival thar 'bout a week, and was the pet of the womenfolks, big and little, for I was makin' it mighty warm for the rummies and takin' as much as five dollars a night—ten cents a head, children free—when somehow or another a little report got around last night that I was puttin' in my time with a private jug on the sly. A nigger rousted me out this mornin', and told me the people was getherin' on the quiet with their dogs and horses, and they'd be along pretty soon and give me 'bout half an hour's start, and then run me down; and if they got me they'd tar and feather me and ride me on a rail, sure. I didn't wait for no breakfast—I warn't hungry."

"Old man," said the young one, "I reckon we might double-team it together; what do you think?"

"I ain't undisposed. What's your line—mainly?"

"Printer by trade; do a little patent medicines; theater actor—tragedy, you know; sling a lecture sometimes—oh, I do lots of things, so it ain't work. What's your lay?"

"I've done considerable in the doctoring way in my time. Layin' on o' hands is my best holt—for cancer and paralysis, and sich things; and I k'n tell a fortune pretty good when I've got somebody along to find out the facts for me. Preachin's my line, too, and missionaryin' around."

Nobody never said anything for a while; then the young man hove a sigh and says, "Alas!"

"What 're you alassin' about?" says the baldhead.

"To think I should have lived to be leading such a life, and be degraded down in such company." And he begun to wipe the corner of his eye with a rag.

"Dern your skin, ain't the company good enough for you?" says the baldhead, pretty pert and uppish.

"Yes, it *is* good enough for me; it's as good as I deserve; for who fetched me so low when I was so high? *I* brought myself down. I don't blame *you*, gentlemen—far from it; I don't blame anybody. One thing I know—there's a grave somewhere for me. The world may go on just as it's always done, and take everything from me—loved ones, property, everything; but it can't take that. Someday I'll lie down in it and forget it all, and my poor broken heart will be at rest." He went on a-wiping.

"Drot your pore broken heart," says the baldhead. "Who brought you down from whar? An' whar was you brought down from?"

"Ah, you would not believe me; let it pass—'tis no matter. The secret of my birth—"

"The secret of your birth! Do you mean to say—"

"Gentlemen," says the young man, very solemn, "I will reveal it to you, for I feel I may have confidence in you. By rights I am a duke!"

Jim's eyes bugged out; and I reckon mine did, too. Then the baldhead says, "No! You can't mean it?"

"Yes. My great-grandfather, eldest son of the Duke of Bridgewater, fled to this country about the end of the last century, to breathe the pure air of freedom; married here, and died, leaving a son, his own father dying about the same time. The second son of the late duke seized the titles and estates—the infant real duke was ignored. I am the lineal descendant of that infant—I am the rightful Duke of Bridgewater; and here am I, forlorn, torn from my high estate, ragged, worn, heartbroken, and degraded to the companionship of felons on a raft!"

Jim pitied him ever so much and so did I. We tried to comfort him, but he said it warn't much use; said if we was a mind to acknowledge him, that would do him more good than most anything else; so we said we would, if he would tell us how. He said we ought to bow when we spoke to him, and say, "Your Grace," or "Your Lordship"—and he wouldn't mind it if we called him plain "Bridgewater," which, he said, was a title, and not a name; and one of us ought to wait on him at dinner, and do any little thing for him he wanted done.

Well, that was all easy, so we done it. All through dinner Jim stood around and waited on him, and says, "Will yo' Grace have some o' dis or some o' dat?" But the old man got pretty silent by and by—didn't look comfortable over all that petting that was going on around that duke. Along in the afternoon he says:

"Looky here, Bilgewater," he says, "I'm nation sorry for you, but you ain't the only person that's had troubles."

"No?"

"No, you ain't. You ain't the only person that's ben snaked down wrongfully out'n a high place. You ain't the only person that's had a secret of his birth." And by jinks, *he* begins to cry.

"Hold! What do you mean?"

"Bilgewater, kin I trust you?" says the old man, still sobbing.

"To the bitter death!" He took the old man by the hand. "That secret of your being: speak!"

"Bilgewater, I am the late Dauphin!"

You bet you, Jim and me stared this time. Then the duke says, "You are what?"

"Yes, my friend, it is true—your eyes is lookin' at this very moment on the pore disappeared Dauphin, Looy the Seventeen, son of Looy the Sixteen and Marry Antonette. Yes, gentlemen, you see before you, in blue jeans and misery, the wanderin', exiled, rightful King of France."

Well, he cried and took on so that me and Jim didn't know hardly what to do, we was so sorry. So we set in, like we done before with the duke, and tried to comfort *him*. But he said it warn't no use, nothing but to be dead and done with it all could do him any good; though he said it often made him feel better for a while if people treated him according to his rights, and got down on one knee to speak to him, and called him "Your Majesty," and waited on him first at meals, and didn't set down in his presence till he asked them. So Jim and me set to majestying him, and doing this and that for him, and standing up till he told us we might set down. This done him heaps of good, and so he got cheerful. But the duke kind of soured on him, and didn't look a bit satisfied with the way things was going, and he stayed huffy a good while, till by and by the king says:

"Like as not we got to be together a blamed long time on this h'yer raft, Bilgewater, and so what's the use o' your bein' sour? It ain't my fault I warn't born a duke, it ain't your fault you warn't born a king—so what's the use to worry? This ain't no bad thing that we've struck here—so come, give us your hand, Duke, and le's all be friends."

The duke done it, and Jim and me was glad to see it. It would 'a' been a miserable business to have any unfriendliness on the raft; for what you want, above all things, on a raft, is for everybody to be satisfied, and feel right and kind towards the others.

It didn't take me long to make up my mind that these liars warn't no kings nor dukes at all, but just low-down humbugs and frauds. But I never let on; kept it to myself; it's the best way; then you don't get into no trouble. If I never learned nothing else out of Pap, I learned that the best way to get along with his kind of people is to let them have their own way.

IN THE MEANTIME they asked us considerable many questions; wanted to know what we covered up the raft that way for, and laid by in the daytime—was Jim a runaway nigger? Says I, "Goodness sakes! Would a runaway nigger run *south*?"

No, they allowed he wouldn't. I had to account for things some ways, so I says:

"My folks was living in Pike County, Missouri, and they all died off but me and Pa and my brother Ike. Pa, he 'lowed he'd go live with Uncle Ben, who's got a little place on the river forty-four mile below Orleans. Pa was pretty poor; so when he'd squared up his debts there warn't nothing left but sixteen dollars and our nigger, Jim. That warn't enough to take us fourteen hundred mile, so Pa ketched this piece of a raft; and we reckoned we'd go to Orleans on it. But a steamboat run over the raft, and we all went overboard; Jim and me come up all right, but Pa was drunk, and

Ike was only four years old, so they never come up no more. Well, for the next day or two we had considerable trouble, because people was always trying to take Jim away from me, saying they believed he was a runaway nigger. We don't run daytimes no more now; nights they don't bother us."

The duke says, "Leave me alone to cipher out a way so we can run in the daytime. I'll invent a plan that'll fix it. We'll let it alone for today, because of course we don't want to go by that town yonder in daylight—it mightn't be healthy."

Towards night it begun to darken up and look like rain; the heat lightning was squirting around in the sky; but we got away anyway as soon as it was good and dark. The king told us to stand well out towards the middle of the river, and not show a light till we got below the town. We come in sight of the little bunch of lights by and by—that was the town—and slid by, all right. When we was three-quarters of a mile below we hoisted up our signal lantern; and about ten o'clock it come on to rain and blow and thunder like everything; so the king told us to both stay on watch till the weather got better; then him and the duke crawled into the wigwam and turned in for the night on Jim's and my tick beds. It was my watch below till twelve, but I wouldn't 'a' turned in anyway if I'd had a bed, because a body don't see such a storm as that every day in the week. My souls, how the wind did scream! And every second or two there'd come a glare that lit up the whitecaps for a half a mile around; then comes a *h-whack!—bum! bumble-umble-um-bum-bum-bum-bum*—and the thunder would go grumbling away, and quit—and then *rip* comes another flash and another sockdolager. The waves most washed me off the raft sometimes, but I hadn't any clothes on, and didn't mind.

I had the middle watch, you know, but I was pretty sleepy by that time, so Jim he said he would stand the first half of it for me; he was always mighty good that way, Jim was. I crawled into the wigwam, but the king and the duke had their legs sprawled around so there warn't no show for me; so I laid outside—I didn't mind the rain, because it was warm, and the waves warn't running so high now. About two I took the watch, and Jim he laid down and snored away; and by and by the storm let up; and the first cabin light that showed I rousted him out, and we slid the raft into hiding quarters for the day.

The king got out an old ratty deck of cards after breakfast, and him and the duke played seven-up awhile. Then they got tired of it, and allowed they would "lay out a campaign," as they called it. The duke went down into his carpetbag, and fetched up a lot of printed bills and read them out loud. One bill said, "The celebrated Dr. Armand de Montalban, of Paris," would "lecture on the Science of Phrenology," at such and such a place, on the blank day of blank, at ten cents admission, and "furnish charts of character at twenty-five cents apiece." The duke said that was *him*. In another bill he was the "world-renowned Shakespearian tragedian, Garrick the Younger, of Drury Lane, London." In other bills he had a lot of other names and done other wonderful things, like finding water and gold with a "divining rod," "dissipating witch spells," and so on. By and by he says, "But the histrionic muse is the darling. Have you ever trod the boards, Royalty?"

"No," says the king.

"You shall then, before you're three days older, Fallen Grandeur," says the duke. "The first good town we come to we'll hire a hall and do the sword fight in *Richard Third*, and the balcony scene in *Romeo and Juliet*. How does that strike you?"

"I'm in, up to the hub, for anything that will pay, Bilgewater; but, you see, I don't know nothing about playactin'. Do you reckon you can learn me?"

"Easy!"

"All right. Le's commence."

So the duke he told him all about who Romeo was and who Juliet was, and said he was used to being Romeo, so the king could be Juliet.

"But if Juliet's such a young gal, Duke, my peeled head and my white whiskers is goin' to look oncommon odd on her."

"No, don't you worry; these country jakes won't ever think of that. Besides, you'll be in costume, and that makes all the difference. Juliet's in a balcony, enjoying the moonlight before she goes to bed, and she's got on her nightgown and her ruffled nightcap. Here are the costumes." He got out two or three curtain-calico suits, which he said was meedyevil armor for Richard III and t'other chap, and a long white cotton nightshirt and a ruffled nightcap. The king was satisfied; so the duke got out his book and read the parts over in the most splendid spread-eagle way, prancing around to show how it had got to be done; then he gives the book to the king and told him to get his part by heart.

There was a little one-horse town about three miles down the bend, and after dinner the duke said he had ciphered out his idea about how to run in daylight without it being dangersome for Jim; so he allowed he would go down to the town and fix that thing. The king allowed he would go too. We was out of coffee, so Jim said I better go along with them in the canoe and get some.

When we got there, there warn't nobody stirring; streets empty and still, like Sunday. We found a sick nigger sunning himself, and he said everybody was gone to camp meeting, about two mile back in the woods. The king got the directions, and allowed he'd go and work that camp meeting, and I might go too.

The duke said what he was after was a printing office. We found it up over a carpenter shop—carpenters and printers all gone to the meeting, and no doors locked. It was a littered-up place, and had ink marks and handbills about runaway niggers all over the walls. The duke said he was all right now. So me and the king lit out for the camp meeting.

We got there fairly dripping, for it was an awful hot day. There was as much as a thousand people there from twenty mile around. The woods was full of teams and wagons, hitched everywhere, stomping to keep off the flies. There was sheds made out of poles and roofed with branches, where they had lemonade and ginger-bread to sell, and piles of watermelons and corn and suchlike truck. The preaching was going on in the same kinds of sheds, only they was bigger and held crowds of people.

The first shed we come to the preacher was lining out a hymn. He lined out two lines, and everybody sung it, and it was kind of grand to hear it; then he lined out two more for them to sing—and

97

so on. The people sung louder and louder; and towards the end some begun to groan, and some begun to shout. Then the preacher begun to preach, and went weaving first to one side of the platform and then the other, and then a-leaning down over the front of it, shouting with all his might; and every now and then he would hold up his Bible, crying, "Look upon it and live!" And the people would shout, "Glory—A-a-*men!*" And so he went on, and the people groaning and saying amen:

"Oh, come to the mourners' bench! (*Amen!*) Come, black with sin! (*Amen!*) Come, lame and halt and blind! (*Amen!*) Come, pore and needy, sunk in shame! (*A-a-men!*) Come, all that's worn and soiled and suffering! The door of heaven stands open—oh, enter and be at rest!" (*A-a-men! Glory, glory hallelujah!*)

And so on. You couldn't make out what the preacher said anymore, on account of the shouting and crying. Folks got up in the crowd, and worked their way to the mourners' bench with the tears running down their faces, and when they had got there they sung and shouted, just crazy and wild.

Well, the first I knowed the king got a-going and you could hear him over everybody; and next he went a-charging up onto the platform, and the preacher he begged him to speak to the people, and he done it. He told them he was a pirate—been a pirate for thirty years out in the Indian Ocean—and his crew was thinned out considerable last spring in a fight, and he was home now to take out some fresh men, and thanks to goodness he'd been robbed last night and put ashore off a steamboat without a cent, and he was glad of it; it was the blessedest thing that ever happened to him, because he was a changed man now, and happy for the first time in his life; and now he was going to work his way back to the Indian Ocean, and put in the rest of his life trying to turn the pirates into the true path; for he could do it better than anybody, being acquainted with all pirate crews in that ocean; and though it would take him a long time to get there without money, he would get there, and every time he convinced a pirate he would say to him, "Don't you thank me, don't you give me no credit; it all belongs to them dear people in Pokeville camp meeting, natural brothers and benefactors, and that dear preacher there, the truest friend a pirate ever had!"

And then he busted into tears, and so did everybody. Then somebody sings out, "Take up a collection for him!" Well, half a dozen made a jump to do it, but somebody sings out, "Let *him* pass the hat around!" Then everybody said it, the preacher too.

So the king went all through the crowd with his hat, swabbing his eyes and blessing the people; and every little while the prettiest girls, with the tears running down their cheeks, would up and ask to kiss him; and he always done it; and he was invited to stay a week; and everybody wanted him to live in their houses; but he said as this was the last day of the camp meeting he couldn't do no good, and besides he was in a sweat to get to the Indian Ocean right off and go to work on the pirates.

When we got back to the raft and the king come to count up he found he had collected eighty-seven dollars and seventy-five cents. And he said, take it all around, it laid over any day he'd ever put in in the missionarying line. He said it warn't no use talking, heathens don't amount to shucks alongside of pirates to work a camp meeting with.

The duke was thinking *he'd* been doing pretty well till the king come to show up, but after that he didn't think so so much. He had set up and printed off two little jobs for farmers in that printing office—and took the money, four dollars. And he had got in ten dollars' worth of advertisements for the paper, which he said he would put in for four dollars if they would pay in advance—so they done it. The price of the paper was two dollars a year, but he took in three subscriptions for half a dollar apiece on condition of them paying cash in advance. He set up a little piece of poetry, which he made himself, out of his own head—three verses—kind of sweet and saddish—the name of it was, "Yes, crush, cold world, this breaking heart"—and he left that all set up and ready to print in the paper, and didn't charge nothing for it. Well, he took in nine dollars and a half, and said he'd done a square day's work for it.

Then he showed us another little job he'd printed and hadn't charged for, because it was for us. It had a picture of a runaway nigger with a bundle on a stick over his shoulder, and " $200 reward" under it. The reading was all about Jim and described him to a dot. It said he run away from St. Jacques's plantation, forty mile below New Orleans, and likely went north, and whoever would catch him and send him back he could have the reward and expenses.

"Now," says the duke, "after tonight we can run in the daytime if we want to. Whenever we see anybody coming we can tie Jim with a rope, and show this handbill and say we captured him up the river and are going down to get the reward."

We all said the duke was pretty smart, and there couldn't be no trouble about running daytimes. We judged we could make miles enough that night to get out of the reach of the powwow we reckoned the duke's work in the printing office was going to make in that little town; then we could boom right along if we wanted to. We laid low and never shoved out till nearly ten o'clock; then we slid by, wide away from the town, and didn't hoist our lantern till we was clear out of sight of it.

When Jim called me to take the watch at four in the morning, he says, "Huck, does you reck'n we gwyne to run acrost any mo' kings on dis trip?"

"No," I says, "I reckon not."

"Well," says he, "dat's all right, den. I doan' mine one er two kings, but dat's enough. Dis one's powerful drunk, en de duke ain' much better."

I found Jim had been trying to get him to talk French, so he could hear what it was like; but he said he had been in this country so long, and had so much trouble, he'd forgot it.

CHAPTER IX

IT WAS AFTER SUNUP NOW, but we went right on and didn't tie up. The king and the duke turned out by and by looking pretty rusty; but after they'd jumped overboard and took a swim it chippered them up. After breakfast the king he rolled up his britches, and let his legs dangle in the water, so as to be comfortable, and went to getting his *Romeo and Juliet* by heart. When he had got it pretty good him and the duke begun to practice it together. The duke learned him how to say every speech; and he made him sigh, and put his hand on his heart, and after a while he said he done it pretty well.

"Only," the duke says, "you mustn't bellow out *Romeo!* that way, like a bull. You must say it soft and sick and languishy, so— R-o-o-meo! For Juliet's a dear sweet mere child, and she doesn't bray like a jackass."

Well, next they got out a couple of long swords that the duke made out of laths, and begun to practice the sword fight. The duke called himself Richard III; and the way they laid on and pranced around the raft was grand to see. But by and by the king tripped and fell overboard, and after that they took a rest. Then after dinner the duke says:

"Well, King, we'll want to make this a first-class show, you know, so I guess we'll add a little more to it. We want a little something to answer encores with, anyway."

"What's onkores, Bilgewater?"

The duke told him, and then says, "I'll answer by doing the Highland fling, and you—well, let me see—oh, I've got it—you can do Hamlet's soliloquy."

"Hamlet's which?"

"Hamlet's soliloquy, you know; the most celebrated thing in Shakespeare. Ah, it's sublime, sublime! I haven't got it in the book—but I reckon I can piece it out from memory. I'll just walk up and down a minute, and see if I can call it back from recollection's vaults."

So he went to marching up and down, thinking, and frowning horrible every now and then; then he would squeeze his hand on his forehead and stagger and kind of moan; next he would sigh, and drop a tear. It was beautiful to see him. By and by he got it. He told us to give attention. Then he strikes a most noble attitude, with one leg shoved forwards, and his arms stretched up, and his head tilted back, looking up at the sky; and then he begins to rip

and rave. This is the speech—I learned it, easy, while he was
learning it to the king:

> To be, or not to be; that is the bare bodkin
> That makes calamity of so long life;
> For who would fardels bear, till Birnam Wood do
>   come to Dunsinane,
> But that the fear of something after death
> Murders the innocent sleep,
> And makes us rather sling the arrows of outrageous
>   fortune
> Than fly to others that we know not of.
> There's the respect must give us pause:
> Wake Duncan with thy knocking! I would thou couldst;
> For who would bear the whips and scorns of time,
> The oppressor's wrong, the proud man's contumely,
> In the dead waste and middle of the night,
> But that the undiscovered country from whose bourne no
>   traveler returns,
> Breathes forth contagion on the world,
> And thus the native hue of resolution, like the poor
>   cat i' the adage,
> Is sicklied o'er with care,
> And loses the name of action.
> But soft, the fair Ophelia:
> Ope not thy ponderous and marble jaws,
> But get thee to a nunnery—go!

Well, the old man he liked that speech, and he mighty soon got it
so he could do it first-rate. It was lovely the way he would rip and
tear and rair up behind when he was getting it off.

The first chance we got the duke he had some showbills printed;
and after that, for two or three days, the raft was a most uncommon
lively place, for there warn't nothing but rehearsing going on all
the time.

One morning, when we was pretty well down the state of Arkansaw, we come in sight of a little one-horse town in a big bend,
so we tied up about a mile above it, in the mouth of a crick

which was shut in like a tunnel by the cypress trees, and all of us but Jim took the canoe and went down there to see if there was any chance in that place for our show.

We struck it lucky; there was going to be a circus there that afternoon, and the country people was already beginning to come in, in all kinds of shackly wagons, and on horses. The circus would leave before night, so our show would have a pretty good chance. The duke he hired the courthouse, and we went around and stuck up our bills. They read like this:

SHAKESPEREAN REVIVAL!!!!

☞ For One Night Only! ☜

THE WORLD RENOWNED TRAGEDIANS,

David Garrick the Younger,
OF DRURY LANE THEATRE, LONDON,

◄◄◄ AND ►►►

Edmund Kean the Elder,
of the Royal Haymarket Theatre, Whitechapel, Pudding Lane, Piccadilly, London,

<u>*in their sublime*</u> SHAKESPEREAN SPECTACLE

"THE BALCONY SCENE" IN

ROMEO and JULIET!!!!

Romeo .... Mr. Garrick
Juliet .... Mr. Kean

◄◄◄ ALSO ►►►

The thrilling, masterly, and
bloodcurdling BROADSWORD conflict

IN RICHARD III !!!!

Richard III .... Mr. Garrick
Richmond .... Mr. Kean

ALSO: (*by Special Request*)

HAMLET'S IMMORTAL SOLILOQUY!!

By the Illustrious KEAN!

Done by him 300 consecutive nights in PARIS!
ADMISSION 25 cents; children and servants, 10 cents.

———◆·◆———

Then we went loafing around town. The stores and houses was
most all old, shackly frame concerns that hadn't ever been painted;
they was set up three or four foot above ground on stilts, so as to
be out of reach of the water when the river was overflowed. The
houses had little gardens around them, but they didn't seem to
raise hardly anything in them but jimpsonweeds, and ash piles, and
old curled-up shoes. The fences was made of different kinds of
boards, nailed on at different times; and they leaned every which
way. There was generly hogs in the garden, and people driving
them out.

All the stores was along one street. They had awnings in front,
and the country people hitched their horses to the awning posts.
There was empty dry-goods boxes under the awnings, and loafers
roosting on them all day long, whittling with their Barlow knives;
and chawing tobacco, and gaping and yawning and stretching—a
mighty ornery lot. There was as many as one loafer leaning up
against every awning post, and he most always had his hands in
his britches pockets, except when he fetched them out to scratch.
What a body was hearing amongst them all the time was:

"Gimme a chaw 'v tobacker, Hank."

"Cain't; I hain't got but one chaw left. Ask Bill."

All the streets and lanes was just mud; they warn't nothing else
but mud—mud nigh about a foot deep in some places. The hogs
loafed and grunted around everywheres. You'd see a muddy sow
and a litter of pigs come lazying along the street and whollop herself right down in the way, and she'd stretch out and shut her eyes
and wave her ears whilst the pigs was milking her, and look as
happy as if she was on salary. And pretty soon you'd hear a loafer

sing out, "Hi! *So* boy! Sick him, Tige!" And away the sow would go, squealing most horrible, with a dog or two swinging to each ear, and three or four dozen more a-coming; and then you would see all the loafers get up and watch the thing out of sight, and laugh and look grateful for the noise. Then they'd settle back again till there was a dogfight. There couldn't anything wake them up all over, and make them happy all over, like a dogfight.

The nearer it got to noon that day the thicker and thicker was the wagons and horses in the streets, and more coming all the time. Families fetched their dinners with them from the country, and eat them in the wagons. At last it was time for the circus. I went, and loafed around the back side till the watchman went by, and then dived in under the tent. I ain't opposed to spending money on circuses when there ain't no other way, but there ain't no use in *wasting* it on them.

It was a real bully circus. All through it they done the most astonishing things; and all the time there was a clown that carried on in the funniest way so it most killed the people. But the splendidest sight ever was when they all came riding in on horses, two and two, gentleman and lady, side by side, the men just in their drawers and undershirts, and no shoes nor stirrups, and resting their hands on their thighs easy and comfortable—there must 'a' been twenty of them—and every lady perfectly beautiful, and looking just like a gang of queens, and dressed in clothes that cost millions of dollars, and just littered with diamonds. And then one by one they got up and stood, and went a-weaving around the ring so gentle and wavy and graceful, the men looking ever so tall and airy and straight.

And faster and faster they went, all of them dancing, first one foot out in the air and then the other, the horses leaning more and more, and the ringmaster going round and round the center pole, cracking his whip and shouting, "Hi! Hi!" and the clown cracking jokes behind him; and by and by all hands dropped the reins, and every lady put her knuckles on her hips and every gentleman folded his arms, and then how the horses did lean over and hump themselves! And so one after the other they all skipped off into the ring, and made the sweetest bow I ever see, and then scampered out, and everybody clapped their hands and went just about wild.

I don't know; there may be bullier circuses than what that one was, but I never struck them yet. Anyways, it was plenty good enough for *me*.

Well, that night we had *our* show; but there warn't only about twelve people there. And they laughed all the time, and that made the duke mad; and everybody left before the show was over, but one boy which was asleep. So the duke said these Arkansaw lunkheads couldn't come up to Shakespeare; what they wanted was low comedy—and maybe something worse. So next morning he got some big sheets of wrapping paper and some black paint, and drawed off some handbills, and stuck them up all over the village. The bills said:

At The court house for 3 nights only!
The world-renowned tragedians
DAVID GARRICK THE YOUNGER!
and
EDMUND KEAN THE ELDER!
In their THRILLING Tragedy of
THE KINGS CAMELEOPARD
OR
The ROYAL NONESUCH !!
Admission 50¢

Then at the bottom was the biggest line of all, which said:

LADies ANd CHILDREN NOT AdMITTed

"There," says he, "if that line don't fetch them, I don't know Arkansaw!"

Well, all day him and the king was hard at it, rigging up a stage and a curtain, and candles for footlights; and that night the house was jam full of men in no time. When the place couldn't hold no more, the duke he quit tending the door and come and stood up before the curtain and made a little speech, and praised up this tragedy, and said it was the most thrillingest one that ever was; and at last when he'd got everybody's expectations up high, he rolled up the curtain, and the next minute the king come a-prancing out on all fours, naked; and he was painted all over, ring-streaked-and-striped, all sorts of colors, as splendid as a rainbow. And—but never mind the rest of his outfit; it was just wild, but it was awful funny. The people most killed themselves laughing; and when the king got done capering and capered off, they roared and clapped and haw-hawed till he come back and done it over again, and after that they made him do it another time. Well, it would make a cow laugh to see the shines that old idiot cut.

Then the duke he lets the curtain down, and bows to the people, and says the great tragedy will be performed only two nights more, on account of pressing London engagements; and then he makes them another bow, and says if he has succeeded in pleasing them, he will be deeply obleeged if they will mention it to their friends.

Twenty people sings out, "What, is it over? Is that *all?*"

The duke says yes. Then there was a fine time. Everybody sings out, "Sold!" and rose up mad, and was a-going for that stage and them tragedians. But a big, fine-looking man jumps up on a bench and shouts:

"Hold on! Just a word, gentlemen." They stopped to listen. "We are sold—mighty badly. But we don't want to be the laughing-stock of this whole town, I reckon. *No.* What we want is to go out of here quiet, and talk this show up, and sell the *rest* of the town! Then we'll all be in the same boat. Ain't that sensible?" ("You bet it is!" "The jedge is right!" everybody sings out.) "All right, then, go along home, and advise everybody to come and see the tragedy."

Next day you couldn't hear nothing around that town but how splendid that show was. House was jammed again that night, and we sold this crowd the same way. When me and the king and the duke got home to the raft we all had supper; and by and by they made Jim and me back the raft out and float her down the river, and hide her about two mile below town.

The third night the house was crammed again—and they warn't

newcomers this time, but people that was at the show the other two nights. I stood by the duke at the door, and I see that every man that went in had his pockets bulging, or something muffled up under his coat—and it warn't no perfumery, neither. I smelt sickly eggs by the barrel, and rotten cabbages; and if I know the signs of a dead cat being around there was sixty-four of them went in. Well, when the place couldn't hold no more people the duke he give a fellow a quarter and told him to tend door for him a minute, and then he started for the stage door, I after him; but the minute we turned the corner and was in the dark he says:

"Walk fast now till you get away from the houses, and then shin for the raft like the dickens was after you!"

I done it, and he done the same. We struck the raft at the same time, and in less than two seconds we was gliding downstream, all dark and still. I reckoned the poor king was in for a gaudy time of it with the audience, but nothing of the sort; soon he crawls out from the wigwam. He hadn't been up to town at all.

We never showed a light till we was about ten mile below the village. Then we lit up and had a supper. Them rapscallions had took in four hundred and sixty-five dollars in that three nights, and the king and the duke fairly laughed their bones loose over the way they'd served them people.

By and by, when they was asleep and snoring, Jim says:

"Don't it s'prise you de way dem kings carries on, Huck?"

"No," I says, "it don't."

"Why don't it, Huck?"

"Well, it don't, because it's in the breed. I reckon they're all alike; all kings is mostly rapscallions, as fur as I can make out. You read about them, you'll see. Look at Henry the Eight; this 'n' 's a Sunday-school superintendent to *him*. And look at Charles Second, and Louis Fourteen, and Louis Fifteen, and Richard Third, and forty more. My, you ought to seen old Henry the Eight when he was in bloom. He *was* a blossom. He used to marry a new wife every day, and chop off her head next morning. He would do it just as indifferent as if he was ordering up eggs. You don't know kings, Jim, but I know them; and this old rip of ourn is one of the cleanest I've struck in history. Kings is kings, and you got to make allowances. It's the way they're raised."

"But dis one do *smell* so, Huck."

"Well, they all do, Jim."

"Now de duke, he's a tolerble likely man in some ways."

"Yes, a duke's different. But not very. This one's a middling hard lot for a duke. When he's drunk there ain't no nearsighted man could tell him from a king."

"Well, anyways, I doan' hanker for no mo' un um, Huck. Dese is all I kin stan'."

"It's the way I feel, too, Jim. Sometimes I wish we could hear of a country that's out of kings."

What was the use to tell Jim these warn't real kings and dukes? It wouldn't 'a' done no good; and, besides, it was just as I said: you couldn't tell them from the real kind.

I went to sleep, and Jim didn't call me when it was my turn. He often done that. When I waked up just at daybreak he was sitting there with his head down, moaning and mourning to himself. I knowed he was thinking about his wife and his children, away up yonder, and he was low and homesick; and I do believe he cared just as much for his people as white folks does for their'n. He was often mourning that way nights, when he judged I was asleep, and saying, "Po' little 'Lizabeth! Po' little Johnny. I spec' I ain't ever gwyne to see you no mo'!" But this time I somehow got to talking to him about his wife and young ones; and by and by he says:

"What makes me feel so bad dis time 'uz bekase I 'uz thinkin' er de time I treat my little 'Lizabeth so ornery. She warn't on'y 'bout fo' year ole, en she tuck de sk'yarlet fever; but she got well, en one day she was a-stannin' aroun', en I says to her, I says, 'Shet de do'.'

"She never done it; jis stood dah, kiner smilin' up at me. It make me mad; en I says ag'in, mighty loud, 'Doan' you hear me? Shet de do'!' She jis stood de same way, kiner smilin' up. I was a-bilin'! I says, 'I lay I *make* you mine!' En wid dat I fetch' her a slap side de head dat sont her a-sprawlin'. Den I went into de yuther room; en when I come back dah was dat do' a-stannin' open *yit*, en dat chile stannin' mos' right in it, a-lookin' down and mournin', en de tears runnin' down. My, but I *wuz* mad. I was a-gwyne for de chile, but jis' den, 'long come de wind en slam dat do' to, behine de chile, ker-*blam!* En my lan', de chile never move'! My breff mos' hop outer me; en I feel so—so—I doan' know *how* I feel. I crope out, all a-tremblin', en crope aroun' en open de do' easy en slow, en poke my head in behine de chile, en all uv a sudden I says *pow!* jis' as loud as I could. *She never budge!* Oh, Huck, I bust out a-cryin' en grab her up in my arms, en say, 'Oh, de po' little thing! De Lord God fogive ole Jim, kaze he never gwyne to fogive hisself as long's he live!' Oh, she was plumb deef en dumb from the fever, Huck, deef en dumb—en I'd ben a-treat'n her so!"

CHAPTER X

NEXT DAY, TOWARDS NIGHT, we laid up under a little willow towhead out in the middle, where there was a village on each side of the river, and the duke and the king begun to lay out a plan for working them towns. Jim he spoke to the duke, and said he hoped it wouldn't take but a few hours, because it got mighty tiresome to him to lay all day in the wigwam tied with the rope. You see, when we left him alone we had to tie him, because if anybody happened on to him not tied it wouldn't look much like he was a runaway nigger. So the duke said he'd cipher out some way to get around it, and he soon struck it. He dressed Jim up in King Lear's outfit—it was a long calico gown, and a white wig and whiskers; and then he took his theater paint and painted Jim's face and hands and ears and neck all over a dead, dull solid blue, like a man that's been drownded nine days. Then the duke wrote a sign on a shingle:

Sick Arab—but harmless when not out of his head.

He nailed that shingle to a lath, and stood the lath up in front of the wigwam. And he told Jim if anybody come meddling around, he must hop out of the wigwam, and carry on a little, and fetch a howl or two, and he reckoned they would light out and leave him alone. Which was sound enough; but you take the average man, he wouldn't wait for him to howl. Why, Jim didn't only look like he was dead, he looked considerable more than that.

Then the duke said he reckoned he'd see if he couldn't put up something on the Arkansaw village; and the king he allowed he would drop over to t'other village. We had all bought store clothes where we stopped last; and now the king put his'n on, and he told me to put mine on. I done it, of course. The king's duds was all black. I never knowed how clothes could change a body before; he looked that grand and pious that you'd say he had walked right out of the ark. Jim cleaned up the canoe, and I got my paddle ready. There was a big steamboat lying at the shore, about three mile above the town, taking on freight. Says the king:

"Seein' how I'm dressed, I reckon I better arrive from St. Louis or Cincinnati, or some other big place. Go for the steamboat, Huckleberry; we'll come down to the village on her."

I fetched the shore a half a mile above the village, and then went scooting along the bank in the easy water. Pretty soon we come to a nice innocent-looking young country jake setting on a log swabbing the sweat off of his face; and he had a couple of big carpetbags by him.

"Run inshore," says the king. I done it. "Wher' you bound for, young man?"

"For the steamboat; going to Orleans."

"Git aboard," says the king. "My servant 'll he'p you with them bags. He'p the gentleman, Adolphus," meaning me, I see.

I done so, and then we all three started on again. The young chap was mighty thankful. He asked the king where he was going, and the king told him he'd landed at the other village this morning, and now he was going up a few mile to see an old friend. The young fellow says, "When I first see you I says to myself, 'It's Mr. Wilks, sure, and he come mighty near getting here in time.' But you *ain't* him, are you?"

"No, my name's Blodgett—Reverend Elexander Blodgett. I'm one o' the Lord's poor servants. But I'm sorry for Mr. Wilks for not arriving in time, if he's missed anything by it."

"Well, he don't miss any property by it; he'll get that all right; but he's missed seeing his brother Peter die. Peter never talked about nothing else all these three weeks; hadn't seen Harvey since they was boys together—and hadn't ever seen his brother William at all—that's the deef and dumb one—William ain't more than thirty-five. Peter and George were the only ones that come out here; George was the married brother; him and his wife both died last year. Harvey and William's the only ones that's left now; and, as I was saying, they haven't got here in time."

"Did anybody send 'em word?"

"Oh, yes; a month or two ago, when Peter was first took. You see, he was pretty old, and he most desperately wanted to see Harvey—and William, too, for that matter—because he was one of them kind that can't bear to make a will. He left a letter behind for Harvey, and said he'd told in it where his money was hid, and how he wanted the property divided up so George's g'yirls would be all right. That letter was all they could get him to put a pen to."

"Why do you reckon Harvey don't come? Wher' does he live?"

"Oh, he lives in England—Sheffield—preaches there. He hasn't had any too much time to get here."

"Too bad, poor soul. You going to Orleans, you say!"

"Yes, but that ain't only a part. I'm going in a ship, Wednesday, for Ryo Janeero, where my uncle lives."

"It's a long journey. But it'll be lovely; I wisht I was a-going. How old is the girls?"

"Mary Jane the redheaded one's nineteen, Susan's fifteen, and Joanna's about fourteen—that's the one that has a harelip."

"Poor things, to be left alone in the cold world so!"

"Well, they could be worse off. Peter had friends who ain't going to let them come to no harm. There's Hobson, the Babtis' preacher; and Deacon Hovey, and Abner Shackleford, and Levi Bell, the lawyer; and Dr. Robinson."

Well, the old man went on asking questions till he just fairly emptied that young fellow. Blamed if he didn't inquire about Peter's business—which was a tanner; and about Harvey's—which was a dissentering minister; and how much property Peter left;

and so on and so on. And finally he asks, "When did you say he died?"

"I didn't say, but it was last night."

"Well, it's all terrible sad; but we've all got to go, sometime. So what we want to do is to be prepared."

"Yes, sir. Ma used to always say that."

When we struck the boat she was about done loading, and pretty soon she got off. The king never said nothing more about going aboard. When the boat was gone the king made me paddle up to a lonesome place, and then he got ashore and says, "Now hustle back and fetch the duke up here, and the new carpetbags. Shove along, now."

I see what *he* was up to; but I never said nothing, of course. When I got back with the duke they set down on a log, and the king told him everything, just like the young fellow had said it. And all the time he was a-doing it he tried to talk like an Englishman; and he done it pretty well, too. I can't imitate him, and so I ain't a-going to try. Then he says:

"How are you on the deef and dumb, Bilgewater?"

The duke said he had played a deef and dumb person on the histrionic boards. So we hid the canoe, and then they waited for a steamboat. At last about the middle of the afternoon there was a big one, and they hailed her. She sent out her yawl, and we went aboard, and she was from Cincinnati; and when they found we only wanted to go four or five mile they was booming mad. But the king offered to pay a dollar a mile apiece for us, so they softened down and said it was all right; and when we got to the village they yawled us ashore. About two dozen men flocked down when they see the yawl a-coming, and when the king says, "Kin any of you gentlemen tell me wher' Mr. Peter Wilks lives?" they give a glance at one another. Then one of them says, kind of gentle:

"I'm sorry, sir, but the best we can do is to tell you where he *did* live yesterday evening."

Sudden as winking the ornery old cretur went all to smash, and fell up against the man, and put his chin on his shoulder, and cried down his back, and says:

"Alas, alas, our brother—gone! Oh, it's *too* hard!"

Then he turns around, blubbering, and makes a lot of idiotic signs to the duke on his hands, and blamed if *he* didn't drop a carpetbag and bust out a-crying. If they warn't the beatenest lot, them two frauds, that ever I struck! It was enough to make a body ashamed of the human race.

The news was all over town in two minutes, and you could see the people tearing down on the run from every which way. When we got to the house the street in front of it was packed, and the three girls was standing in the door. Mary Jane *was* redheaded and she was most awful beautiful, and her eyes was all lit up like glory, she was so glad her uncles was come. The king he spread his arms, and Mary Jane she jumped for them, and the harelip jumped for the duke. Everybody most, leastways women, cried for joy to see them meet at last.

Then the king he hunched the duke private—I see him do it— and then he looked around and see the coffin, over in the corner on two chairs; so then him and the duke, with a hand across each other's shoulder, and t'other hand to their eyes, walked over there, everybody dropping back to give them room. And when they got there they looked in the coffin, and then they bust out a-crying so you could 'a' heard them to Orleans, most; and then for three minutes, or maybe four, I never see two men leak the way they done. Then they kneeled down and rested their foreheads on the coffin, and let on to pray all to themselves. Well, when it come to that it worked the crowd like anything, and everybody went to sobbing right out loud.

Well, by and by the king he gets up and slobbers out a speech, all full of tears and flapdoodle, about its being a sore trial for him and his poor brother to lose the diseased, but it's a trial that's sweetened and sanctified by this dear sympathy and these holy tears, and all that kind of rot and slush, till it was just sickening. Then he says how him and his nieces would be glad if a few of the main principal friends of the family would take supper here with them this evening, and help set up with the diseased; and says if his poor brother laying yonder could speak he knows who he

would name; and so he will name the same, to wit, as follows, viz.: Rev. Mr. Hobson, and Deacon Hovey, and Abner Shackleford, and Levi Bell, and Dr. Robinson.

Rev. Hobson and Dr. Robinson was down to the end of the town with a sick man. Lawyer Bell was up to Louisville on business. But the others was on hand, and so they come and thanked the king; and then they shook hands with the duke whilst he made all sorts of signs with his hands and said "Goo-goo-goo-goo-goo" all the time, like a baby.

Then Mary Jane she fetched the letter her father left, and the king he read it out loud. It give the dwelling house and three thousand dollars in gold to the girls; and it give the tanyard along with some other houses and land (worth about seven thousand), and three thousand dollars in gold to Harvey and William, and told where the six thousand cash was hid down cellar. So these two frauds said they'd go and fetch it, and told me to come with a candle. We shut the cellar door behind us, and when they found the bag they spilt it out on the floor, and it was a lovely sight, all them yaller boys. My, the way the king's eyes did shine! He slaps the duke on the shoulder and says, "Oh, ain't *this* bully! Why, Biljy, it beats the Nonesuch, *don't* it?"

The duke allowed it did. They pawed the yaller boys and let them jingle down on the floor. "Say," says the duke, "I got an idea. Le's go upstairs and count this money, and then *give it to the girls.*"

"Good land, Duke, lemme hug you! Oh, this is the boss dodge! This 'll lay 'em out."

When we got upstairs the king he counted the money and stacked it up in elegant little piles on the table, and everybody looked hungry at it. Then they raked it into the bag again, and the king says, "Friends, my poor brother that lays yonder has done generous by them that's left behind in the vale of sorrers. He has done generous by these pore little lambs that he loved. Yes, and we that knowed him knows that he would 'a' done *more* generous by 'em if he hadn't ben afeard o' woundin' his dear William and me. Now, *wouldn't* he? Well, then, what kind o' brothers would it be that 'd stand in his way at sech a time? And what kind o' uncles would it be that 'd rob—yes, *rob*—sech poor sweet lambs as these at sech a time?" Then the king says, "Here, Mary Jane, Susan, Joanner, William 'n' I want you to take the money—take it *all*. It's the gift of him that lays yonder, cold but joyful."

Mary Jane she went for him, Susan and the harelip went for the duke, and then such another hugging and kissing I never see yet. And everybody crowded up and most shook the hands off of them frauds, saying all the time, "You *dear* good souls! How *lovely!* How *could* you!"

Well, then, pretty soon all hands got to talking about the diseased again; and before long a big iron-jawed man worked himself in from outside, and stood a-listening, not saying anything. The king was saying—in the middle of something he'd started in on—

"—they bein' partikler friends o' the diseased who's invited here this evenin'; but tomorrow we want *all* to come—everybody; for he respected everybody, he liked everybody, and so it's fitten that his funeral orgies sh'd be public."

And so he went a-mooning on, and every little while he fetched in his funeral orgies again, till the duke he couldn't stand it; so he writes on a scrap of paper, "*Obsequies*, you old fool," and folds it up, and goes to goo-gooing and reaching it over people's heads to him. The king he reads it, and says:

"Poor William, his *heart's* aluz right. Asks me to invite everybody to the funeral. But he needn't 'a' worried." Then he weaves along again, perfectly ca'm, and goes to dropping in his funeral orgies again, and then he says, "I says orgies, not because it's the common term, because it ain't—obsequies bein' the common term—but because orgies is the right term. Obsequies ain't used in England no more—we say orgies now in England. Orgies is a word that's made up out'n the Greek *orgo*, outside, open; and the Hebrew *jeesum*, to plant, cover up; hence in*ter*. So, you see, funeral orgies is an open er public funeral."

He was the *worst* I ever struck. Well, the iron-jawed man he laughed right in his face. Everybody was shocked. Everybody says, "Why, *Doctor!*" and Abner Shackleford says, "Why, Robinson, hain't you heard the news? This is Harvey Wilks."

The king he smiled eager, and shoved out his flapper, and says, "*Is* it my brother's dear friend and physician? I—"

"Keep your hands off me!" says the doctor. "*You* talk like an Englishman, *don't* you? It's the worst imitation I ever heard. You're a fraud, that's what you are!"

Well, how they all took on! They crowded around the doctor and tried to quiet him down, and tried to explain to him how Harvey's showed in forty ways that he *was* Harvey. But it warn't no use. All of a sudden the doctor turns on the girls, and he says:

"I was your father's friend, and I'm your friend; and I warn you, *as* one that wants to protect you, to turn your backs on that scoundrel. He has come here with a lot of empty names and facts which he picked up somewheres; and you take them for *proofs*. Mary Jane Wilks, you know me for your friend. Listen to me; turn this rascal out—I *beg* you. Will you?"

Mary Jane straightened up, and my, but she was handsome! She says, "*Here* is my answer." She hove up the bag of money and put it in the king's hands, and says, "Take this six thousand dollars, and invest it for me and my sisters, and don't give us no receipt."

Then everybody clapped their hands and stomped like a perfect storm. The doctor says, "All right; I wash *my* hands of the matter. But I warn you all, a time's coming when you're going to feel sick when you think of this day."

"All right, Doctor," says the king, kinder mocking him; "we'll try and get 'em to send for you"; which made them all laugh, and they said it was a prime good hit.

CHAPTER XI

WELL, WHEN THEY WAS ALL GONE the king he asks Mary Jane how they was off for spare rooms, and she said she had one spare room, which would do for Uncle William, and she'd give her own room to Uncle Harvey, and turn into the room with her sisters; and up garret was a little cubby, with a pallet in it. The king said the cubby would do for his valley—meaning me. So Mary Jane took us up, and she showed them their rooms, which was plain but nice. She said she'd have her frocks took out of her room if they was in Uncle Harvey's way, but he said they warn't. The frocks was behind a calico curtain that hung down to the floor. The duke's room was pretty small, but plenty good enough, and so was my cubby.

That night they had a big supper, and all them men and women was there, and I stood behind the king and the duke's chairs and waited on them, and the niggers waited on the rest.

When it was all done me and the harelip had supper in the kitchen, and the harelip she got to pumping me about England. She says, "Did you ever see the king?"

"Who? William Fourth? Well, I bet I have—he goes to our church."

"What—regular?"

"Yes—regular. His pew's right over opposite ourn."

"I thought he lived in London?"

"Well, he does. Where *would* he live?"

"But I thought *you* lived in Sheffield."

I see I was up a stump. I had to let on to get choked with a chicken bone, so as to get time to think. Then I says, "I mean he goes to our church regular when he's in Sheffield. That's only in the summertime, when he comes there to take the sea baths."

"Why, how you talk—Sheffield ain't on the sea."

"Well, who said it was?"

"Why, you did."

"I *didn't*, nuther. I said he come to take the sea *baths*. He don't have to go to the sea to get a sea bath."

"How does he get it, then?"

"Gets it in barrels. In the palace at Sheffield they've got furnaces, and he wants his water hot. They can't bile that amount of water away off there at the sea. They haven't got no conveniences for it."

"Oh, I see. You might 'a' said that in the first place and saved time."

When she said that I see I was out of the woods again, and so I was glad. Next, she says, "Do you go to church, too?"

"Yes—regular."

"Where do you set?"

"Why, in our pew—your Uncle Harvey's."

"His'n? What does *he* want with a pew?"

"Wants it to set in. What did you *reckon* he wanted with it?"

"Why, I thought he'd be in the pulpit."

Rot him, I forgot he was a preacher. I see I was up a stump again, so I played another chicken bone. Then I says, "Blame it, do you suppose there ain't but one preacher to a church?"

"Why, what do they want with more?"

"What—to preach before a king? I never did see such a girl as you. They don't have no less than seventeen."

"Seventeen! My land! Why, I'd *never* set out such a string as that. It must take 'em a week."

"Shucks, they don't *all* of 'em preach the same day—only *one*."

"Well, then, what does the rest of 'em do?"

"Oh, loll around, pass the plate—one thing or another. But mainly they don't do nothing."

"Well, then, what are they *for?*"

"Why, they're for *style*."

I see she still warn't satisfied. She says, "Honest injun, hain't you been telling me a lot of lies?"

"Honest injun," says I, "not a lie in it."

"Lay your hand on this book and say it."

It warn't nothing but a dictionary, so I laid my hand on it and said it. So then she says, "Well, then, I'll believe some of it; but I hope to gracious if I'll believe the rest."

"What is it you won't believe, Jo?" says Mary Jane, stepping in. "It ain't right nor kind for you to talk so to him, and him a stranger and so far from his people."

"I hain't done nothing to him, Maim. He's told some stretchers, I reckon, and I said I wouldn't swallow it all; but I reckon he can stand a little thing like that, can't he?"

"I don't care whether 'twas little or whether 'twas big; he's here in our house and a stranger. It don't make no difference what he said. The thing is for you to treat him *kind*."

I says to myself, *This* is a girl that I'm letting that old reptile rob her of her money!

Then Susan *she* waltzed in; and if you'll believe me, she too give Harelip hark from the tomb!

Says I to myself, And this is *another* one that I'm letting him rob her of her money!

When they both got done there warn't hardly anything left o' poor Harelip. So she hollered.

"All right," says the other girls, "you just ask his pardon."

She done it, too; and she done it beautiful. She done it so beautiful I wished I could tell her a thousand lies, so she could do it again. I says to myself, This is *another* one that I'm letting him rob her of her money. And I felt so ornery and mean that I says to myself, My mind's made up; I'll hive that money for them or bust.

So then I lit out—for bed, I said. When I got by myself I went to thinking the thing over. I says to myself, Shall I go to that doctor, private, and blow on these frauds? No, he might tell who told him; then the king and the duke would make it warm for me. Shall I go private, and tell Mary Jane? No, her face would give them a hint, sure; they've got the money, and they'd slide right out and get away with it. No; there ain't no good way but one. I got to steal that money, somehow, and hide it; and by and by, when I'm away down the river, I'll write and tell Mary Jane where it's hid.

So, thinks I, I'll go and search them rooms. Upstairs the hall was dark, but I found the king's room, and begun to paw around there. But I see I couldn't do nothing without a candle, and I dasn't light one. So I judged I'd lay for them and eavesdrop. About that time I hears their footsteps coming, and was going to skip under the bed when I touched the curtain that hid Mary Jane's frocks, so I jumped in behind that and snuggled in amongst the gowns, and stood there perfectly still. They come in and shut the door; and the first thing the duke done was to look under the bed. Then they sets down, and the king says:

"Well, what is it? Cut it short, because it's better for us to be down there a-whoopin' up the mournin' than up here givin' 'em a chance to talk us over."

"Well, this is it, King. That doctor lays on my mind. I've got a notion that we better glide out of this before morning, and clip it down the river with what we've got."

The king rips out and says, "What! And not sell out the rest o' the property?"

The duke he grumbled; said the bag of gold was enough, and he didn't want to rob a lot of orphans of *everything* they had.

"Why, how you talk!" says the king. "We shan't rob 'em of nothing but jest this money. The people that *buys* the property is the suff'rers; because as soon 's it's found out 'at we didn't own it—after we've slid—the sale won't be valid. These yer orphans 'll get their house back ag'in."

Well, at last the duke said all right, and they got ready to go downstairs again. The duke says, "I don't think we put that money in a good place."

That cheered me up. I'd begun to think I warn't going to get a hint of no kind of help. The king says, "Why?"

"Because Mary Jane 'll be in mourning; and first you know the nigger that does up the rooms will get an order to box these duds up; and do you reckon a nigger can run across money and not borrow some of it?"

"Your head's level ag'in, Duke," says the king; and he comes a-fumbling under the curtain two or three foot from where I was. I kept mighty still, though quivery; and I wondered what them fellows would say if they catched me. But the king he got the bag before I could think more than half a thought, and he never suspicioned I was around. They shoved the bag through a rip in the straw tick that was under the featherbed, and said it warn't in no danger of getting stole now.

But I knowed better. I had it out of there before they was halfway downstairs. I groped along up to my cubby, and hid it there till I could get a chance to do better. I judged I better hide it outside of the house somewheres, because if they missed it they would give the house a good ransacking; I knowed that very well. Then

I turned in, with my clothes all on; but I couldn't 'a' gone to sleep if I'd 'a' wanted to.

By and by I heard the king and the duke come up. Still I held on till all sounds had quit; and then I rolled off my pallet and slipped down the ladder and downstairs.

There warn't a sound anywheres. I peeped through the dining-room door, and see the men that was watching the corpse all sound asleep on their chairs. The door was open into the parlor, where the corpse was laying, and there was a candle in both rooms. I see there warn't anybody in the parlor but the remainders of Peter; so I shoved on by; but the front door was locked, and the key wasn't there. Just then I heard somebody coming down the stairs behind me. I run in the parlor and took a swift look, and the only place I see to hide the bag was in the coffin. The lid was shoved along about a foot, showing the dead man's face. I tucked the moneybag in under the lid, just down beyond where his hands was crossed, which made me creep, they was so cold, and then I run back across the room and in behind the door.

The person coming was Mary Jane. She went to the coffin, very soft, and kneeled down and looked in; then she put up her hand-kerchief and begun to cry. Her back was to me so I slid out. Then I slipped up to bed, feeling ruther blue, on accounts of the thing playing out that way after I had took so much trouble about it. Says I, If it could stay where it is, all right; because when we get down the river I could write back to Mary Jane, and she could dig him up again and get it; but that ain't the thing that's going to happen; the money'll be found when they come to screw on the lid, and the king 'll get it again. Of course I *wanted* to slide down and get it out of there, but I dasn't try it. Every minute it was getting earlier now, and I might get catched—catched with six thousand dollars that nobody hadn't hired me to take care of. I didn't wish to be mixed up in no such business as that.

When I got downstairs in the morning the parlor was shut up, and the watchers was gone. There warn't nobody around but the family and our tribe. I watched their faces to see if anything had been happening, but I couldn't tell.

Towards the middle of the day the undertaker come with his man, and they set the coffin in the middle of the room, and then set all our chairs in rows, and borrowed more from the neighbors till the hall and the parlor was full. I see the coffin lid was the way it was before, but I dasn't go look under it.

Then people begun to flock in, and for a half an hour they filed around slow, and looked down at the dead man's face, and some dropped in a tear, and it was all very still and solemn, only the girls sobbing a little into their handkerchiefs.

When the place was packed full the undertaker he slid around in his black gloves with his softy soothering ways, getting people seated, and making no more sound than a cat. He was the softest, glidingest, stealthiest man I ever see; and there warn't no more smile to him than there is to a ham.

They had borrowed a melodeum—a sick one; and when everything was ready a young woman set down and worked it, and it was pretty skreeky and colicky, but everybody joined in and sung. Then the Reverend Hobson opened up, slow and solemn, and begun to talk; and straight off the most outrageous row busted out in the cellar a body ever heard; it was only one dog, but he made a most powerful racket; the parson he had to stand there, over the coffin, and wait—you couldn't hear yourself think, and nobody didn't seem to know what to do. But pretty soon that long-legged undertaker made a sign to the preacher as much as to say, "Don't you worry—just depend on me." Then he stooped down and begun to glide along the wall, just his shoulders showing over the people's heads. So he glided along, and the powwow and racket getting more and more outrageous all the time; and at last, when he had gone around two sides of the room, he disappears down the cellar. Then in about two seconds we heard a whack, and the dog he finished up with a most amazing howl or two, and then everything was dead still, and the parson begun his solemn talk where he left off. In a minute or two here comes this undertaker's back and shoulders gliding along the wall again; and so he glided and glided around three sides of the room, and then rose up, and shaded his mouth with his hands, and stretched his neck out towards the preacher, over the people's heads, and says, in a kind of coarse whisper, *"He had a rat!"* Then he dropped down and glided along the wall again to his place. You could see it was a great satisfaction to the people, because naturally they wanted to know. A little thing like that don't cost nothing, and it's just the little things that makes a man to be looked up to and liked. There warn't no more popular man in town than what that undertaker was.

Well, the funeral sermon was good, though pison long; but at last the job was through, and the undertaker sneaked up on the coffin with his screwdriver. I was in a sweat then; but he just slid the lid along and screwed it down. So there I was! I didn't know whether the money was in there or not. Says I, S'pose somebody has hogged that bag on the sly? Now how do *I* know whether to write to Mary Jane? S'pose she dug him up and didn't find nothing? Blame it, I says, maybe I'd better not write at all; the thing's awful mixed now; and I wish I'd just let it alone, dad fetch the whole business!

They buried him, and we come back home. After that the king he visited around and made himself friendly to everybody; and he give out the idea that his congregation over in England would be in a sweat about him, so he must hurry and settle up the estate and leave for home. And he said of course him and William would take the girls home with them; and that pleased everybody; because then the girls would be well fixed and amongst their own relations; and it pleased the girls, too—tickled them so they told him to sell out as quick as he wanted to.

Well, blamed if the king didn't bill the house and the niggers and all the property for auction straight off—sale two days after the funeral; but anybody could buy private beforehand if they wanted to.

So the next day after the funeral, along about noontime, the girls' joy got the first jolt. A couple of nigger-traders come along, and the king sold them the niggers reasonable, and away they went, the two sons up the river to Memphis, and their mother down the river to Orleans. I thought them poor girls and them niggers would break their hearts for grief; they cried so it most made me sick to see it. The girls said they hadn't ever dreamed of seeing the family separated or sold away from the town; and I reckon I couldn't 'a' stood seeing them cry if I hadn't knowed the sale warn't no account and the niggers would be back home in a week or two.

Next day was auction day. In the morning the king and the duke come up in the garret and woke me up, and I see by their look that there was trouble. The king says, "Was you in my room night before last?"

"No, your majesty"—which was the way I always called him when nobody warn't around—"I hain't been a-near your room since Mary Jane showed it to you."

The duke says, "Have you seen anybody else go in there?"

I studied awhile and see my chance; then I says, "Well, I see the niggers go in there several times."

Both of them gave a little jump, and looked like they hadn't expected it, and then like they *had*. The duke says, "What, *all* of them?"

"No—leastways, not all at once—that is, I don't think I ever see them all come *out* at once but just one time."

"Hello! When was that?"

"The day we had the funeral. In the morning. It warn't early, because I overslept, and I was just starting down the ladder, and I see them."

"Well, go on, *go* on! What did they do? How'd they act?"

"They didn't do nothing. They tiptoed away; so I seen, easy enough, that they'd shoved in there to do up your majesty's room, or something, and found you warn't up, and so they was hoping to slide out without waking you."

"Great guns, *this* is a go!" says the king; and both of them looked pretty silly. Then the duke he bust into a little raspy chuckle, and says:

"It does beat all how neat the niggers played their hand. They let on to be *sorry* they was going out of this region!"

Says I, kind of timid-like, "Is something gone wrong?"

The king whirls on me. "None o' your business! Keep your

head shet, and mind y'r own affairs." Then he says to the duke, "We got to jest swaller it and say noth'n': mum's the word."

So they went off down the ladder; and I felt dreadful glad I worked it all off onto the niggers, and yet hadn't done the niggers no harm by it.

By AND BY IT WAS GETTING-UP TIME, so I started for downstairs; but as I come to the girls' room the door was open, and I see Mary Jane setting by her trunk, crying. I felt awful bad to see it; and I went in and says:

"Miss Mary Jane, you can't a-bear to see people in trouble, and *I* can't—most always. Tell me about it."

So she done it. And it was the niggers—I just expected it. She said the beautiful trip to England was about spoiled for her; and then she busted out bitterer than ever, "Oh, dear, dear, to think that that mother and her children ain't *ever* going to see each other any more!"

"But they *will*—and inside two weeks—I *know* it!" says I.

Laws, it was out before I could think! And she throws her arms around my neck and told me to say it *again*, say it *again!* I see I had said too much, and was in a close place. I asked her to let me think a minute, and she set there, very impatient and excited and handsome. So I went to studying it out. I says to myself, I reckon a body that ups and tells the truth when he is in a tight place is taking considerable many resks; but here's a case where I'm blest if it don't look to me like the truth is better and actuly *safer* than a lie. So I says to myself at last, I'm a-going to chance it; and then I says:

"Miss Mary Jane, is there any place out of town a little ways where you could go and stay three or four days?"

"Yes; Mr. Lothrop's. Why?"

"Never mind why yet. If I'll tell you how I know the niggers will see each other again—will you go to Mr. Lothrop's and stay four days?"

"Four days!" she says. "I'll stay a year!"

"All right," I says, "I don't want nothing more than just your word—I'd ruther have it than another man's kiss-the-Bible." She smiled and reddened up very sweet, and I says, "If you don't mind it, I'll shut the door—and bolt it."

Then I come back and set down again, and says, "Don't you holler now. Just set still. I got to tell the truth, and you want to brace up, Miss Mary, because it's going to be hard to take. These uncles of yourn ain't no uncles at all; they're a couple of frauds— regular deadbeats. There, now we're over the worst of it; you can stand the rest middling easy."

It jolted her up like anything, of course; but I was over the shoal water now, so I went right along, and told her every blame thing clear through—and then up she jumps, with her face afire like sunset, and says:

"The brutes! Come, don't waste a *second*—we'll have them tarred and feathered, and flung in the river!"

Says I, "Cert'nly. But do you mean *before* you go to Mr. Lothrop's, or—"

"Oh," she says, "what am I *thinking* about!" she says, and sets down again. "I never thought, I was so stirred up," she says, laying her hand on mine. "Now go on, and I won't do so any more; just you tell me what to do."

"Well," I says, "it's a rough gang, them two frauds, and I got to travel with them a while longer—I'd ruther not tell you why; and if you was to blow on them *I'd* be all right; but there'd be another person that you don't know about who'd be in big trouble. Well, we got to save *him*."

Saying them words put an idea in my head. I see how maybe I could get me and Jim rid of the frauds; get them jailed here, and then leave. But I didn't want to run the raft in the daytime; so I didn't want the plan to begin working till late tonight. I says, "Miss Mary Jane, I'll tell you what we'll do, and you won't have to stay at Mr. Lothrop's so long, nuther. How fur is it?"

"Four miles—right out in the country, back here."

"Well, now you go along out there, and lay low till nine tonight, and then get them to fetch you home again. If you get here before eleven put a candle in this window, and if I don't turn up wait *till* eleven, and *then* if I don't turn up it means I'm gone, and safe.

Then you come out and spread the news around, and get these beats jailed."

"Good," she says, "I'll do it."

"And if it happens that I don't get away, but get took up along with them, you must up and say I told you the whole thing beforehand, and stand by me all you can."

"Stand by you! Indeed I will!" she says, and I see her eyes snap when she said it.

"If I get away I shan't be here," I says, "to prove these rapscallions ain't your uncles, and I couldn't do it if I *was* here. I could swear they was beats and bummers, that's all. Well, there's others can do that better than what I can. I'll tell you how to find them. Gimme a pencil and a piece of paper. There—'Royal Nonesuch, Bricksville.' Put it away and don't lose it. When the court wants to find out something about these two, let them send up to Bricksville and say they've got the men that played the 'Royal Nonesuch,' and ask for some witnesses—why, you'll have that entire town down here before you can hardly wink, Miss Mary. They'll come a-biling, too."

I judged we had got everything fixed now. So I says, "Just let the auction go along, and don't worry. Nobody don't have to pay for the things they buy till a whole day after the auction on accounts of the short notice, and them two frauds ain't going out of this till they get that money. And the way we've fixed it the sale ain't going to count; it's just like the way it was with the niggers—it warn't no sale, and the niggers will be back before long."

"Well," she says, "I'll run down to breakfast now, and then I'll start straight for Mr. Lothrop's."

"'Deed, *that* ain't the ticket, Miss Mary Jane," I says, "by no manner of means. Go *before* breakfast."

"Why?"

"What did you reckon I wanted you to go at all for, Miss Mary? It's because there ain't no better book than what your face is. A body can set down and read it off like coarse print. Do you reckon you can go and face your uncles when they come to kiss you good-morning, and never—"

"There, there, don't! Yes, I'll go before breakfast. And leave my sisters with them?"

"Yes; never mind about them. They've got to stand it yet awhile. They might suspicion something if all of you was to go. No, you go right along, Miss Mary Jane, and I'll fix it with them and say you've went away for a few hours." Then I says, "There's one more thing—the bag of money."

"Well, they've got that; and it makes me feel pretty silly to think *how* they got it."

"No, you're out, there. They hain't got it, because I stole it from them! I stole it to give to you; and I know where I hid it, but I'm afraid it ain't there no more. I'm just as sorry as I can be, Miss Mary Jane, but I done the best I could; I did honest. And I'd ruther not *tell* you where I put it; but I'll write it for you on a piece of paper, and you can read it along the road to Mr. Lothrop's. Do you reckon that'll do?"

"Oh, yes."

So I wrote: "I put it in the coffin. It was in there when you was crying there, way in the night. I was behind the door, and I was mighty sorry for you, Miss Mary Jane."

It made my eyes water to remember her crying there; and when I folded it up and give it to her I see the water come into her eyes, too; and she shook my hand, hard, and says:

"*Good*-by. I'm going to do everything just as you've told me; and if I don't ever see you again, I shan't ever forget you, and I'll *pray* for you, too!" And she was gone.

Pray for me! I reckoned if she knowed me she'd take a job that was more nearer her size. But I bet she done it, just the same—she was just that kind. In my opinion she had more sand in her than any girl I ever see. I hain't ever seen her since that time that I see her go out of that door; but I reckon I've thought of her a million times, and of her saying she would pray for me; and if ever I'd 'a' thought it would do any good for me to pray for *her*, blamed if I wouldn't 'a' done it or bust.

Well, Mary Jane she lit out the back way, I reckon; because nobody see her go. When I struck Susan and the harelip, I says,

"What's the name of them people on t'other side of the river that you all goes to see sometimes?"

They says, "There's several; but it's the Proctors, mainly."

"That's the name," I says. "Well, Miss Mary Jane she told me to tell you she's gone over there in a dreadful hurry—one of them's sick."

"Sakes alive, I hope it ain't *Hanner?*"

"I'm sorry to say it," I says, "but Hanner's the very one. They set up with her all night, Miss Mary Jane said."

"Only think of that, now! What's the matter with her?"

I couldn't think of anything reasonable, right off, so I says, "Mumps."

"Mumps, your granny! They don't set up with people that's got mumps."

"These mumps is different. It's a new kind, Miss Mary Jane said, because it's all mixed up with measles, and whooping cough, and consumption, and janders, and brain fever, and I don't know what all."

"Well, what in the nation do they call it the *mumps* for?"

"Why, because it *is* the mumps. That's what it starts with."

"Well, ther' ain't no sense in it," says the harelip. "A body might stump his toe, and take pison, and fall down the well, and break his neck, and bust his brains out, and somebody come along and ask what killed him, and some numskull up and say, 'Why, he stumped his *toe.*' Would ther' be any sense in that? *No.* And ther' ain't no sense in *this,* nuther. It's awful, *I* think. I'll go to Uncle Harvey and—"

"Oh, yes," I says. "Of *course.* I wouldn't lose no time."

"Well, why wouldn't you?" says Susan.

"Just look a minute. Hain't your uncles obleeged to get along home to England as fast as they can? And do you reckon they'd be mean enough to go off and leave you to go all that journey by yourselves? *You* know they'll wait for you. So fur, so good. Your Uncle Harvey's a preacher, ain't he? Very well, then; is a *preacher* going to deceive a *steamboat clerk* so as to get them to let Miss Mary Jane go aboard? *You* know he ain't. What *will* he do, then? Why, he'll say, 'It's a great pity, but my church matters has got to get along the best way they can; for my niece has been exposed to the dreadful pluribus-unum mumps, and so it's my bounden duty to set here and wait the three months it takes to show on her if she's got it.' But never mind, if you think it's best to tell your Uncle Harvey—"

"Shucks, and stay fooling around here when we could all be having good times in England? Why, you talk like a muggins. Ther' ain't no way but just to not tell anybody at all."

"Well, maybe you're right—yes, I judge you are right."

"But I reckon we ought to tell Uncle Harvey she's gone out awhile, anyway, so he won't be uneasy about her?"

"Yes, Miss Mary Jane she wanted you to do that. She says, 'Tell them to give Uncle Harvey and William my love, and say I've run over to see Mr—Mr.—what is the name of that rich family over the river?"

"Why, you must mean the Apthorps, ain't it?"

"Of course. Yes, she said, say she has run over for to ask the Apthorps to be sure and come to the auction and buy this house; and she's going to stick to them till they say they'll come, and then, if she ain't too tired, she's coming home; and if she is, she'll be home in the morning."

"All right," they said, and cleared out to lay for their uncles and tell them the message.

Everything was all right now. The girls wouldn't say nothing because they wanted to go to England; and the king and the duke would ruther Mary Jane was off working for the auction than around in reach of Doctor Robinson. I felt good; I judged I had done it pretty neat—I reckoned Tom Sawyer couldn't 'a' done it no neater himself.

Well, they held the auction in the public square in the afternoon, and the old man he was up there longside of the auctioneer, and chipping in a little Scripture now and then, and the duke was around goo-gooing and just spreading himself generly. By and by everything was sold—everything but a little old lot in the grave-yard. So they was working that off when a steamboat landed, and in about two minutes up comes a crowd a-whooping and laughing, and singing out:

"*Here's* your opposition line! Here's two sets o' heirs to old Peter Wilks—you pays your money and you takes your choice!"

THEY WAS FETCHING A NICE-LOOKING old gentleman along, and a nice-looking younger one, with his right arm in a sling. I reckoned the duke and the king'd at least turn pale. But no. The duke he never let on he suspicioned what was up, but just went on a goo-gooing around; and as for the king, he just gazed and gazed down sorrowful on them newcomers like it give him the stomach ache in his very heart to think there could be such frauds and rascals in the world. As for that old gentleman that had just come, he looked all puzzled to death. Pretty soon he begun to speak, and I see straight off he pronounced *like* an Englishman. I can't give his words nor imitate him; but he turned to the crowd, and says, about like this:

"This is a surprise to me, and I'll acknowledge, candid, I ain't well fixed to meet it; for my brother and me has had misfortunes; he's broke his arm and our baggage got put off at a town above here by mistake. I am Peter Wilks's brother Harvey, and this is his brother William, which can't hear nor speak—and can't even make signs to amount to much, now't he's only got one hand to work with. We are who we say we are; and in a day or two, when I get the baggage, I can prove it. But up till then I won't say no more, but go to the hotel and wait."

So him and the new dummy started off; and the king he laughs, and blethers out, "Broke his arm—*very* convenient, *ain't* it, for a fraud that's got to make signs! Lost their baggage! That's *mighty* ingenious—under the *circumstances!*"

So he laughed again; and so did everybody else, except maybe half a dozen. One of these was that doctor; another one was a sharp-looking gentleman that had just come off the steamboat—it was Levi Bell, the lawyer that was gone up to Louisville; and another one was a big rough husky. When the king got done this husky up and says:

"Say, looky here; if you are Harvey Wilks, when'd you come to this town?"

"The day before the funeral, friend, in the afternoon," says the king.

"How'd you come?"

"I come down on the *Susan Powell* from Cincinnati."

"Well, then, how'd you come to be up at the Pint in the *mornin'*—in a canoe?"

"I warn't up at the Pint in the mornin'."

"It's a lie."

Several of them jumped for him and begged him not to talk that way to an old man and a preacher.

"Preacher be hanged, he's a fraud. He was up at the Pint that mornin'. I live up there, don't I? Well, I *see* him there. He comes in a canoe, along with Tim Collins and a boy."

The doctor he says, "Would you know the boy again, Hines?"

"I reckon I would. Why, yonder he is, now!"

It was me he pointed at. The doctor says:

"Neighbors, I don't know whether the new couple is frauds or not, but if *these* two ain't frauds, I am an idiot. I think it's our duty to see that they don't get away from here till we've looked into this thing. Come along, Hines; come along, the rest of you. We'll take these fellows to the tavern and affront them with t'other couple, and I reckon we'll find out *something* before we get through."

It was nuts for the crowd, so we all started. It was about sundown. The doctor he led me by the hand, and was plenty kind enough, but he never *let go* my hand.

We all got in a big room in the hotel, and lit up some candles, and fetched in the new couple.

Then they sailed in on a general investigation. It *was* the worst mixed-up thing you ever see. They made the king tell his yarn, and they made the old gentleman tell his'n; and by and by they had me up to tell what I knowed. The king he give me a left-handed look, out of the corner of his eye, and so I knowed enough to talk on the right side.

I begun to tell about Sheffield and how we lived there, and all about the English Wilkses, and so on; but I didn't get fur till the doctor began to laugh; and Levi Bell, the lawyer, says:

"Set down, my boy. I reckon you ain't used to lying; what you want is practice. You do it pretty awkward."

I didn't care nothing for the compliment, but I was glad to be let off, anyway.

Well, what do you think? That mule-headed old fool the king wouldn't give in *then!* He went warbling right along till he was actuly beginning to believe what he was saying *himself;* but pretty soon the new gentleman broke in, and says:

"I've thought of something. Is there anybody here that helped to lay out my br—helped to lay out the late Peter Wilks for burying?"

"Yes," says somebody, "me and Ab Turner done it. We're both here."

Then the old man turns towards the king, and says, "Perhaps this gentleman can tell me what was tattooed on his breast?"

It took the king sudden, and it was mighty still in there, and everybody bending fowards and gazing at him. Says I to myself, *Now* he'll throw up the sponge. Well, did he? A body can't hardly believe it, but he didn't. He begun to smile, and says, "Mf! It's a *very* tough question, *ain't* it! *Yes,* sir, I k'n tell you what's tattooed on his breast. It's jest a small, thin, blue arrow; and if you don't look clost, you can't see it. *Now* what do you say—hey?"

Well, *I* never see anything like that old blister for clean out-and-out cheek.

The new old gentleman turns brisk towards Ab Turner and his pard, and his eye lights up like he judged he'd got the king *this* time, and says, "There—you've heard what he said! Was there any such mark on Peter Wilks's breast?"

Both of them says, "We didn't see no such mark."

"Good!" says the old gentleman. "Now, what you *did* see on his breast was a small dim P, and a w, and a dash between. Ain't that what you saw?"

Both of them spoke again, and says, "No, we *didn't.* We never seen any marks at all."

Well, everybody *was* in a state of mind now, and they sings out: "The whole *bilin'* of 'm 's frauds! Le's duck 'em! Le's ride 'em on a rail!" And everybody was whooping at once. But the lawyer he jumps up and yells, "Gentlemen—PLEASE! There's one way yet— let's go dig up the corpse and look."

That took them. "Hooray!" they all shouted. "And if we don't find them marks we'll lynch the whole gang!"

I *was* scared now, I tell you. But there warn't no getting away. They gripped us all, me and the four men, and marched us right along for the graveyard, a mile and a half down the river, and the whole town at our heels, for we made noise enough. It was now about nine in the evening. As we went by our house I wished I hadn't sent Mary Jane out of town; because now if I could tip her the wink she'd save me.

Well, we swarmed along down the river road; and to make it more scary the sky was darking up, and the lightning beginning to wink and flitter. This was the most awful trouble I ever was in; and I was kinder stunned; everything was going so different from what I had allowed for; stead of being fixed so I could have Mary Jane to save me when the close fit come, here was nothing in the world betwixt me and sudden death but just them tattoo marks. If they didn't find them—

I couldn't bear to think about it; and yet, somehow, I couldn't think about nothing else. It got darker and darker, and it was a beautiful time to give the crowd the slip; but that big husky had me by the wrist—Hines—and a body might as well try to give Goliar the slip.

When they got there they swarmed into the graveyard and washed over it like an overflow. And when they got to the grave they found they had about a hundred shovels, but nobody hadn't thought to fetch a lantern. But they sailed into digging anyway by the flicker of the lightning, and sent a man to the nearest house, a half a mile off, to borrow one.

So they dug and dug like everything; and it got awful dark, and the rain started, and the wind swished and swushed, and the lightning come brisker and brisker; but them people never took no

notice of it. At last they got out the coffin and begun to unscrew the lid, and then such another crowding and shoving as there was, to scrouge in and get a sight; and in the dark, that way, it was awful. Hines he hurt my wrist dreadful pulling and tugging. Then all of a sudden the lightning let go a perfect sluice of white glare, and somebody sings out:

"By the living jingo, here's the bag of gold on his breast!"

Hines let out a whoop, like everybody else, and dropped my wrist to bust in and get a look, and the way I lit out and shinned for the road in the dark there ain't nobody can tell.

I had the road all to myself in the storm, and I fairly flew. When I struck the town I see there warn't nobody out, so I never hunted for no back streets, but humped in straight through the main one; and when I begun to get towards our house I aimed my eye at it. No light there; but at last, just as I was sailing by, *flash* comes the light in Mary Jane's window! My heart swelled up sudden, like to bust. She *was* the best girl I ever see, and had the most sand.

The minute I was above the town I begun to look for a boat to borrow, and the first time the lightning showed me one that wasn't chained I snatched it and shoved. It was a canoe and warn't fastened with nothing but a rope. The towhead was a rattling big distance off, but I didn't lose no time. When I struck the raft at last I sprung aboard and sung out:

"Set her loose, Jim! Glory be to goodness, we're shut of them!"

Jim was a-coming for me with both arms spread, he was so full of joy; but when I glimpsed him in the lightning my heart shot up in my mouth and I went overboard backwards; for I forgot he was old King Lear and a drownded A-rab all in one; and it most scared the livers and lights out of me. But Jim fished me out, and was going to hug me and bless me, and so on, he was so glad I was back and we was shut of the king and the duke, but I says:

"Not now; have it for breakfast! Cut loose!"

So in two seconds away we went a-sliding down the river, and it *did* seem so good to be free again and all by ourselves. I had to skip around and jump up and crack my heels a few times—but about the third crack I noticed a sound, and held my breath and waited; and sure enough, when the next flash busted out, here they come—a-laying to their oars and making their skiff hum! It was the king and the duke.

So I wilted right down onto the planks then, and give up; and it was all I could do to keep from crying.

CHAPTER XII

When they got aboard the king shook me by the collar, and says, "Tryin' to give us the slip, was ye, you pup!"

I says, "No, your majesty, we warn't—*please* don't, your majesty!"

"Quick, then, and tell us what *was* your idea, or I'll shake the insides out o' you."

"Honest, I'll tell you everything just as it happened, your majesty. The man that had a-holt of me was very good to me, and kept saying he had a boy as big as me that died, and he was sorry to see a boy in such a fix; and when they was all took by surprise by finding the gold, he lets go of me and whispers, 'Heel it now, or they'll hang ye, sure!' and I lit out. It didn't seem no good for *me* to stay—so I never stopped running till I found the canoe; and when I got here I told Jim to hurry, or they'd hang me yet, and said I was afeard you and the duke wasn't alive now, and I was awful sorry, and so was Jim; you may ask Jim if I warn't."

So the king let go of me, and begun to cuss that town. But the duke says:

"You better a blame' sight give *yourself* a good cussing. You hain't done a thing from the start that had any sense in it, except coming out so cool and cheeky with that imaginary blue-arrow mark. That *was* bright; that trick took 'em to the graveyard, and the gold done us a still bigger kindness; for if the excited fools hadn't let go all holts and made that rush to get a look we'd 'a' slept in our cravats tonight—cravats warranted to *wear*, too."

They was still a minute—thinking; then the king says, kind of absentminded-like, "Mf! And we reckoned the *niggers* stole it!"

That made me squirm!

"Yes," says the duke, kinder slow and sarcastic, "*we* did."

After about a half a minute the king drawls out, "Leastways, *I* did."

The duke says, the same way, "On the contrary, *I* did."

The king kind of ruffles up and says, "Looky here, Bilgewater, what'r you referrin' to?"

The duke bristles up now, and says, "Oh, let *up* on this nonsense; do you take me for a blame' fool? Don't you reckon *I* know who hid that money in that coffin?"

"*Yes*, sir! I know you do, because you done it yourself!"

"It's a lie!"—and the duke went for him. The king sings out, "Take y'r hands off—leggo my throat!"

The duke says, "Well, you just own up, first, that you *did* hide that money there, intending to give me the slip one of these days, and come back and dig it up."

"Wait, jest a minute, Duke—answer me this one question, honest and fair; if you didn't put the money there, say it, and I'll b'lieve you, and take back everything I said."

"You old scoundrel, I didn't, and you know I didn't."

"Well, then, I b'lieve you. But as for me, I never done it either, Duke! I won't say I warn't *goin'* to do it, because I *was;* but you— I mean somebody—got in ahead o' me."

"It's a lie! You done it, and you got to *say* you done it, or—"

The king began to gurgle, and then he gasps out, "'Nough! *I own up!*"

I was very glad to hear him say that; it made me feel much more easier. So the duke took his hands off and says, "If you ever deny it again I'll drown you. And now dry up! I don't want to hear no more *out* of you!"

The king, still a-snuffling, sneaked into the wigwam and took to his bottle for comfort. Before long the duke tackled *his* bottle, too; and so in about a half an hour they was as thick as thieves again. They both got powerful mellow, and the tighter they got the lovinger they got, and went off a-snoring in each other's arms. Then Jim and I had a long gabble, and I told him everything.

WE DASN'T STOP AGAIN AT ANY TOWN for days and days; kept right along down the river. We was down South in the warm weather now, and we begun to come to trees with Spanish moss on them. So now the frauds reckoned they was out of danger, and they begun to work the villages again.

First they done a lecture on temperance; but they didn't make enough for them both to get drunk on. They tackled missionary-ing, and doctoring, and telling fortunes; but they couldn't seem to have no luck. So at last they got just about dead broke, and laid around the raft as she floated along, thinking and thinking, by the half a day at a time, and dreadful blue and desperate.

At last they took a change and begun to lay their heads together in the wigwam and talk low and confidential. Jim and me got uneasy; we judged they was studying up some kind of worse devil-try than ever, and was going to break into somebody's house or store, or was going into the counterfeit-money business, or some-thing. So then we was pretty scared, and made up an agreement that if we ever got the least chance we would give them the cold shake and clear out and leave them behind.

Well, early one morning we hid the raft in a good, safe place about two mile below a little shabby village named Pikesville, and the king he told us all to stay hid whilst he went up to town and smelt around to see if anybody had got any wind of the "Royal Nonesuch" there yet. (House to rob, you *mean*, says I to myself.) And he said if he warn't back by midday the duke and me would know it was all right, and we was to come along.

So we stayed where we was. The duke he fretted and sweated, and was in a mighty sour way. Something was a-brewing, sure. I was glad when midday come and no king; we could have a change, anyway—and maybe a chance for *the* chance. So me and the duke went up to the village, and hunted around for the king, and by and by we found him in a little low doggery, very tight, and a lot of loafers bullyragging him for sport. The duke he begun to abuse him for an old fool, and the king begun to sass back, and the minute they was fairly at it I lit out and spun down the river road like a deer, for I see our chance; and I made up my mind that it would be a long day before they ever see me and Jim again. I got there all out of breath but loaded up with joy, and sung out:

"Set her loose, Jim; we're all right now!"

But there warn't no answer, and nobody come out of the wigwam. Jim was gone! I run this way and that in the woods, whooping and screeching; but it warn't no use—old Jim was gone. Then I set down and cried; I couldn't help it. But I couldn't set still long. Pretty soon I went out on the road and I run across a boy walking, and asked him if he'd seen a strange nigger dressed so and so, and he says, "Yes."

"Whereabouts?" says I.

"Down to Phelps's place, two mile below here. He's a runaway nigger, and they've got him. Was you looking for him?"

"You bet I ain't! I run across him in the woods an hour or two ago, and he said if I hollered he'd cut my livers out—and told me to stay where I was. Been there ever since; afeard to come out."

"Well," he says, "they've got him. He run off f'm down South, som'ers. There's two hundred dollars' reward on him. I see the handbill. It tells all about him, to a dot, and tells the plantation he's frum, below Newrleans."

"And I could 'a' had it if I'd been big enough! Who nailed him?"

"It was an old fellow—a stranger—and he sold out his chance in him for forty dollars, becuz he's got to go up the river and can't wait. Think o' that, now! You bet I'd wait. Say, gimme a chaw tobacker, won't ye?"

I didn't have none, so he left. I went to the raft, and set down to think. I thought till I wore my head sore, but I couldn't see no way out of the trouble. After all this long journey, and after all we'd done for them scoundrels, here it was all come to nothing, everything all busted up and ruined, because they could have the heart to serve Jim such a trick as that, and make him a slave again all his life, for forty dirty dollars.

Once I said to myself it would be a thousand times better for Jim to be a slave at home where his family was as long as he'd *got* to be a slave, and so I'd better write a letter to tell Miss Watson where he was. But I soon give up that notion for two things: she'd be mad and disgusted at his ungratefulness for leaving her, and so she'd sell him straight down the river again; and if she didn't, everybody naturally despises an ungrateful nigger, and they'd make Jim feel it all the time. And then think of *me!* It would get all around that Huck Finn helped a nigger to get his freedom; and if I was ever to see anybody from that town again I'd be ready to lick his boots for shame.

That's just the way: a person does a low-down thing, and thinks as long as he can hide, it ain't no disgrace. That was my fix exactly. The more I studied about this the more my conscience went to grinding me, and the more wicked and low-down I got to feeling.

At last it hit me all of a sudden that here was the plain hand of Providence slapping me in the face and letting me know my wickedness in stealing a poor old woman's nigger that hadn't ever done me no harm, and letting me know I was being watched all the time from up there in heaven. Then I most dropped in my tracks, I was so scared. I thought about the everlasting fire, and it made me shiver, and I about made up my mind to pray, and see if I couldn't try to quit being the kind of a boy I was and be better. So I kneeled down. But the words wouldn't come. Why wouldn't they? It warn't no use to try and hide it from Him. Nor from *me*, neither. I knowed very well why they wouldn't come. It was because my heart warn't right; it was because I was playing double. I was letting *on* to give up sin, but away inside of me I was holding on to the biggest one of all. I was trying to make my mouth *say* I would go and write to that nigger's owner and tell where he was; but deep down in me I knowed it was a lie, and He knowed it. You can't pray a lie—I found that out.

So I was full of trouble, full as I could be. At last I had an idea; and I says, I'll go and write the letter—and *then* see if I can pray. Why, it was astonishing, the way I felt as light as a feather right off. So I got a piece of paper and a pencil, and set down and wrote:

Miss Watson, your runaway nigger Jim is down here two mile below Pikesville, and Mr. Phelps has got him.

Huck Finn

I felt good and all washed clean of sin for the first time in my life, and I knowed I could pray now. But I didn't do it straight off, but laid the paper down and set there thinking—thinking how good it was all this happened so, and how near I come to being lost and going to hell. And went on thinking. And got to thinking over our trip down the river; and I see Jim before me all the time: in the day and in the nighttime, sometimes moonlight, sometimes storms, and we a-floating along, talking and singing and laughing. But somehow I couldn't seem to strike no places to harden me against him, but only the other kind. I'd see him standing my watch on top of his'n, so I could go on sleeping; and see him how glad he was when I come back out of the fog; and suchlike times; and how he would always call me honey, and do everything he could think of for me; and at last I struck the time I saved him by telling the men we had smallpox aboard, and he said I was the best friend old Jim ever had in the world, and the *only* one he's got now; and then I happened to look around and see that paper.

I took it up in my hand. It was a close place. I was a-trembling, because I'd got to decide, forever, betwixt two things, and I knowed it. I sort of held my breath, and then says to myself, All right, then, I'll *go* to hell—and tore it up.

It was awful thoughts and awful words, but they was said. And I let them stay said. I shoved the whole thing out of my mind, and thought I would take up wickedness again, which was in my line, being brung up to it, and the other warn't. And for a starter I would go to work and steal Jim out of slavery again.

Then I set to thinking over how to get at it, and at last fixed up a plan that suited me. As soon as it was fairly dark I crept out with my raft and went for a woody island that was down the river a piece, and hid the raft there, and then turned in. I slept the night through, and got up before it was light, and put on some clothes, and tied up the others in a bundle, and took the canoe and cleared for shore. I landed below where I judged was Phelps's place, and hid my bundle in the woods, and then filled up the canoe with rocks and sunk her where I could find her again, about a

quarter of a mile below a little steam sawmill that was on the bank.

Then I struck up the road, and when I passed the mill I see a sign on it, PHELPS'S SAWMILL, and I see some farmhouses, two or three hundred yards further along. I didn't want to see nobody there just yet, so I just took a look and shoved along for town. Well, the very first man I see when I got there was the duke—sticking up a bill for the "Royal Nonesuch" three-night performance. They had the cheek, them frauds! I was right on him before I could shirk. He looked astonished, and says:

"Hel-*lo!* Where'd *you* come from?" Then he says, kind of eager, "Where's the raft—got her in a good place?"

I says, "Why, that's just what I was going to ask your grace."

Then he didn't look so joyful, and says, "What was your idea for asking *me?*"

"Well," I says, "when I see the king in that doggery yesterday I says to myself, We can't get him home for hours; so I went a-loafing around town to put in the time. A man up and offered me ten cents to help him pull a skiff over the river to fetch a sheep, and so I went along; but when we was dragging the sheep to the boat it got loose and run. We didn't have no dog, and so we had to chase him all over, and we never got him till dark; then we fetched him over, and I started for the raft. When I got there and see it was gone, I says to myself, They've got into trouble and had to leave; and they've took my nigger, and now I'm in a strange country, and ain't got no property no more, nor nothing; so I set down and cried. I slept in the woods all night. But what *did* become of the raft, then? And Jim—poor Jim!"

"Blamed if I *know*—that is, what's become of the raft. That old fool had made a trade and got forty dollars, and when we found him in the doggery the loafers had matched half-dollars with him and got every cent but what he'd spent on whiskey; and when I got him home late last night and found the raft gone, we said, 'That little rascal has stole our raft and shook us, and run off down the river.'"

"I wouldn't shake my *nigger*, would I—the only nigger I had in the world, and the only property?"

"We never thought of that. Fact is, I reckon we'd come to consider him *our* nigger; yes, we did consider him so—goodness knows we had trouble enough for him. And now that old fool the king has sold him, and never divided with me, and the money's gone."

"*Sold* him?" I says, and begun to cry. "Why, he was *my* nigger! Where is he? I want my nigger!"

"Well, you can't *get* your nigger, that's all—so dry up your blubbering. Looky here—" He stopped, and I never see the duke look so ugly out of his eyes before. "Blamed if I think I trust you. Do you think *you'd* venture to blow on us? Why, if you *was* to blow on us—"

I went on a-whimpering, and says, "I don't want to blow on nobody; and I ain't got no time to blow, nohow; I got to turn out and find my nigger."

He looked kinder bothered, and stood there thinking. At last he says, "I'll tell you something. We got to be here three days. If you'll promise you won't blow, and won't let the nigger blow, I'll tell you where to find him."

So I promised, and he says, "A farmer by the name of Silas Ph—" and then he stopped. You see, he started to tell me the truth; but when he stopped I reckoned he was changing his mind. And so he was. Soon he says, "The man that bought him is named Foster—Abram G. Foster—and he lives forty mile back in the country, on the road to Lafayette."

"All right," I says, "I can walk it in three days. And I'll start this very afternoon."

"No you won't, you'll start *now;* and don't you do any gabbling by the way. Just move right along, and then you won't get into trouble with *us,* d'ye hear?"

That was the order I wanted.

"So clear out," he says; "and maybe you can get Mr. Foster to believe that Jim *is* your nigger—some idiots don't require documents. Tell him anything you want to; but mind you don't work your jaw any *between* here and there."

So I left, and struck for the back country. After a mile I stopped; then I doubled back through the woods towards Phelps's. I reckoned I better start in on my plan straight off without fooling around, because I wanted to stop Jim's mouth till these fellows could get away. I'd seen all I wanted to of them, and wanted to get entirely shut of them.

WHEN I GOT TO PHELPS's it was still and Sunday-like, and hot and sunshiny; the hands was gone to the fields; and there was them kind of faint dronings of flies in the air that makes it seem so lonesome and like everybody's dead and gone. It was one of these little one-horse cotton plantations, and they all look alike. A rail fence round a two-acre yard, with a stile; some sickly grass patches in the big yard, but mostly it was bare and smooth, like an old hat with the nap rubbed off; big loghouse for the white folks—hewed logs with the chinks stopped up with mud or mortar, and these mud stripes whitewashed; log kitchen, with a roofed passage joining it to the house; log smokehouse back of the kitchen; three little log nigger cabins t'other side of the smokehouse; outbuildings down a piece; hounds asleep round about in the sun; three shade trees away off in a corner; outside of the fence a garden and a watermelon patch; then the cotton fields begins, and after the fields the woods.

I clumb over the stile and started for the kitchen, not fixing up any particular plan, but just trusting to Providence to put the right words in my mouth when the time come.

When I got halfway, first one hound and then another got up and went for me, and of course I stopped and faced them. Such a powwow as they made! In a quarter of a minute I was a kind of hub of a wheel—spokes made out of dogs—circle of fifteen of them packed together around me a-barking and howling; and more a-coming; you could see them sailing over fences and around corners from everywheres.

A nigger woman come tearing out of the kitchen with a rolling pin in her hand, singing out, "Begone! *You* Tige! Spot! Begone!" And she fetched first one and then another of them a clip and sent them howling, and then the rest followed. Behind the woman comes a little nigger girl and two little nigger boys, and they hung on to their mother's gown, and peeped out, bashful. And here comes the white woman running from the house, about forty-five or fifty year old; and behind her comes her little white children, acting the same way as the little niggers. She was smiling all over so she could hardly stand—and says:

"It's *you* at last—*ain't* it?"

I out with a "Yes'm" before I thought.

She grabbed me and hugged me tight; and the tears come in her eyes; and she kept saying, "You don't look as much like your mother as I reckoned you would; but law sakes, I don't care, I'm *so* glad to see you! Children, it's your cousin Tom! Tell him howdy. And Lize, hurry up and get him a hot breakfast—or did you get breakfast on the boat?"

I said I had got it on the boat. So then she started for the house, leading me by the hand, and the children tagging after. When we got there she set me down in a chair, and says, "Now I can have a *good* look at you! We been expecting you a couple of days. What kep' you—boat get aground?"

"Yes'm—she—"

"Don't say yes'm—say Aunt Sally. Where'd she get aground?"

I didn't rightly know what to say, because I didn't know whether the boat would be coming up the river or down. I see I'd got to invent a bar or forget the name of one we got aground on—or— Now I struck an idea.

"It warn't the grounding. We blowed out a cylinder head."

"Good gracious! Anybody hurt?"

"No'm."

"Well, it's lucky; because sometimes people do get hurt. Two years ago your Uncle Silas was coming up from Newrleans on the old *Lally Rook*, and she blowed out a cylinder head and crippled a man. And I think he died afterwards. He was a Baptist. Your uncle's been up to the town every day to fetch you. And he's gone again, not more'n an hour ago. You must 'a' met him on the road, didn't you? Oldish man, with a—"

"No, I didn't see nobody, Aunt Sally. The boat landed just at daylight, and I left my baggage on the wharf boat and went looking around, to put in the time and not get here too soon, and so I come down the back way."

"How'd you get your breakfast so early on the boat?"

It was kinder thin ice, but I says, "The captain see me standing around, and told me I better have something to eat before I went ashore; so he took me in to the officers' lunch, and give me all I wanted."

I was getting so uneasy I couldn't listen good. I had my mind on the children; I wanted to get them to one side and pump them to find out who I was. But I couldn't get no show, and pretty soon Mrs. Phelps made the cold chills streak all down my back, because she says:

"But here we're a-running on this way, and you hain't told me a word about Sis, nor any of them. Now just tell me *everything*— how they are, and what they're doing, and every last thing you can think of."

Well, I see I was up a stump now—up it good. So I says to myself, Here's another place where I got to resk the truth. I opened my mouth to begin; but she grabbed me and hustled me in behind the bed, and says:

"Here he comes! Stick your head down; don't let on you're here. I'll play a joke on him. Children, don't say a word."

I see I was in a fix now. But there warn't nothing to do but just hold still, and try and be ready when the lightning struck.

I had just one little glimpse of the old gentleman when he come in; then the bed hid him. Mrs. Phelps she jumps for him, and says, "Has he come?"

"No," says her husband.

"Good-*ness* gracious!" she says. "What in the world *can* have become of him?"

"I can't imagine," says the old gentleman, "and I must say it makes me dreadful uneasy."

"Uneasy!" she says. "I'm ready to go distracted! He *must* 'a' come; and you've missed him along the road."

"Why, Sally, I *couldn't* miss him along the road—*you* know that. I don't know what in the world to make of it, and I don't mind acknowledging 't I'm right down scared. Sally, something's happened to the boat, sure!"

"Why, Silas! Look! Up the road! Ain't that somebody coming?"

He sprung to the window, and at that Mrs. Phelps stooped down quick at the foot of the bed and give me a pull, and out I come; and when he turned back from the window there she stood, a-beaming and a-smiling, and I standing meek and sweaty alongside. The old gentleman stared, and says:

"Why, who's that?"

"Who do you reckon 'tis?"

"I hain't no idea. Who *is* it?"

"It's *Tom Sawyer!*"

By jings, I most slumped through the floor! The old man grabbed me by the hand and shook; and the woman danced around and laughed and cried; and then how they both did fire off questions about Sid, and Aunt Polly, and the rest of the tribe! But if they was joyful, it warn't nothing to what I was; for it was like being born again, I was so glad to find out who I was.

Well, they froze to me for two hours; and at last I had told them more about the Sawyer family than ever happened to any six Sawyer families. Now I was feeling pretty comfortable all down one side and pretty uncomfortable all up the other; because by and by I hear a steamboat coughing along down the river; and then I says to myself, S'pose Tom Sawyer comes down on that boat? And s'pose he steps on in here and sings out my name before I can throw him a wink to keep quiet?

Well, I couldn't *have* it that way. I must go up the road and waylay him. So I told the folks I reckoned I would go to the town and fetch my baggage. The old gentleman was for going along with me, but I said no, I could drive the horse, and I'd ruther he wouldn't take no trouble.

So I started for town in the wagon, and when I was halfway I see a wagon coming, and sure enough it was Tom Sawyer. I says, "Hold on!" and he stopped alongside, and his mouth opened up like a trunk, and stayed so; and he swallowed two or three times like a person that's got a dry throat, and then says:

"I hain't ever done you no harm. You know that. So, then, what you want to come back and ha'nt *me* for?"

I says, "I hain't come back—I hain't been *gone*."

When he heard my voice it righted him up some, but he warn't quite satisfied yet. He says, "Honest injun, you ain't a ghost?"

"Honest injun, I ain't," I says.

"Well—I—I— Looky here, warn't you ever murdered?"

"No. I warn't ever murdered—I played it on them. Come here and feel of me if you don't believe me."

So he done it; and it satisfied him; and he was that glad to see me again he didn't know what to do. And he wanted to know all about it right off, because it was a grand adventure, and mysterious. But I said, leave it alone till by and by; and I told his driver to wait, and we drove off a little piece, and I told him the kind of a fix I was in, and what did he reckon we better do? He thought and thought, and pretty soon he says:

"It's all right; I've got it. Take my trunk in your wagon, and let on it's yourn; and you turn back and fool along slow, so as to get to the house about the time you ought to; and I'll go towards town a piece, and take a fresh start, and get there a quarter or a half an hour after you; and you needn't let on to know me at first."

"All right; but wait a minute," I says. "There's one more thing—a thing that *nobody* don't know but me. And that is, there's a nigger here that I'm a-trying to steal, and his name is *Jim*—old Miss Watson's Jim."

He says, "What! Why, Jim is—" Then he stopped and went to studying.

I says, "*I* know what you'll say. You'll say it's dirty, low-down business; but what if it is? *I*'m low-down, and I'm a-going to steal him, and I want you to keep mum and not let on. Will you?"

His eye lit up, and he says, "I'll *help* you steal him!"

Well, I let go all holts then, like I was shot. It was the most astonishing speech I ever heard. I couldn't believe it. Tom Sawyer a *nigger-stealer!*

"Oh, shucks!" I says. "You're joking."

"I ain't joking, either."

"Well, then," I says, "joking or no joking, if you hear anything said about a runaway nigger, don't forget to remember that you and I don't know nothing about him."

Then he put his trunk in my wagon, and he drove off his way and I drove mine. I got home, and then in about half an hour Tom's wagon drove up to the front stile. Aunt Sally she see it through the window, and says:

"Why, there's somebody come! I do believe it's a stranger. Jimmy," (that's one of the children) "run and tell Lize to put on another plate for dinner."

Everybody made a rush for the front door, because, of course, a stranger don't come *every* year. Tom was starting for the house; the wagon was spinning up the road for the village, and we was all bunched in the front door. Tom had his store clothes on, and an audience—and that was always nuts for Tom Sawyer. In them circumstances it warn't no trouble to him to throw in an amount of style that was suitable. He warn't a boy to meeky along up that yard like a sheep; no, he come ça'm and important, like the ram. When he got a-front of us he lifts his hat ever so gracious and dainty, like it was the lid of a box that had butterflies asleep in it and he didn't want to disturb them, and says:

"Mr. Archibald Nichols, I presume?"

"No, my boy," said the old gentleman, "I'm sorry to say 't your driver has deceived you; Nichols's place is down a matter of three mile more. Come in, come in."

Tom he took a look back over his shoulder, and says, "Too late—he's out of sight."

"Yes, he's gone, my son, and you must come in and eat dinner with us; and then we'll hitch up and take you to Nichols's."

"Oh, I *can't* make so much trouble. I'll walk."

"But we won't *let* you walk—it wouldn't be Southern hospitality to do it. Come right in and make yourself at home."

So Tom he thanked them very hearty and handsome and come in; and he said he was from Hicksville, Ohio, and his name was William Thompson—and he made another bow.

Well, he run on, and on, making up stuff about Hicksville and everybody in it, and I getting nervous, and wondering how this was going to help me out of my scrape; and at last, still talking, he reached over and kissed Aunt Sally right on the mouth, and then settled back again in his chair and was going on talking; but she jumped up and wiped it off with her hand, and says:

"You owdacious puppy!"

He looked hurt, and says, "I'm surprised at you, m'am."

"You're s'rp— Why, what do you reckon *I* am? Say, what do you mean by kissing me?"

He looked kind of humble, and says, "I didn't mean nothing, ma'am. I—I—thought you'd like it. They—they—told me you would."

"*They* told you I would! Who's *they?*"

"Why, everybody. They all said so, m'am."

It was all she could do to hold in; her eyes snapped, and her fingers worked like she wanted to scratch him; and she says, "Who's 'everybody'? Out with their names!"

He got up and looked distressed, and fumbled his hat, and says, "They all said, kiss her and she'd like it. But I'm sorry, m'am, and I won't do it no more—till you ask me."

"Till I *ask* you! I lay you'll be the Methusalem-numskull of creation before ever *I* ask you!"

"Well," he says, "it does surprise me. But—" He stopped and looked around slow, and fetched up on me, and says, "Tom, didn't *you* think Aunt Sally 'd like me to kiss her, and open out her arms and say, 'Sid Sawyer—'"

"My land!" she says, jumping for him. "You impudent young rascal, to fool a body so—" and was going to hug him, but he fended her off, and says, "No, not till you've asked me first."

So she didn't lose no time, but asked him; and hugged him and kissed him over and over again, and then turned him over to the old man, and he took what was left. And after they got a little quiet again she says, "Why, dear me, I never see such a surprise. We warn't looking for *you* at all, but only Tom."

"It warn't *intended* for any of us to come but Tom," he says; "but I begged and begged, and at the last minute Aunt Polly let me come, too; so, coming down the river, me and Tom thought it would be a first-rate surprise for him to come here first, and for me to let on to be a stranger. But it was a mistake, Aunt Sally. This ain't no healthy place for a stranger."

"No—not impudent whelps, Sid. You ought to had your jaws boxed. But I'd be willing to stand a thousand such jokes to have you here."

We had dinner then, and there was things enough on that table for seven families. Uncle Silas he asked a pretty long blessing over it, but it was worth it.

There was considerable talk all the afternoon, and me and Tom was on the lookout all the time; but it warn't no use, they didn't happen to say nothing about any runaway nigger, and we was afraid to try to work up to it. But at supper one of the little boys says:

"Pa, mayn't Tom and Sid and me go to the show?"

"No," says the old man, "I reckon there ain't going to be any; and you couldn't go if there was, because the runaway nigger told Burton and me all about that scandalous show, and Burton said he would tell the people; so I reckon they've drove the owdacious loafers out of town before this time."

So there it was! Tom and me was to sleep in the same room; so, being tired, we bid good-night and went up to bed right after supper, and clumb out of the window and down the lightning rod, and shoved for the town; for I didn't believe anybody was going to give the king and the duke a hint, and so if I didn't hurry and give them one they'd get into trouble sure.

On the road Tom he told me all about how it was reckoned I was murdered, and how Pap disappeared, and what a stir there was when Jim run away; and I told Tom all about our "Royal Nonesuch" rapscallions, and as much of the raft voyage as I had time to; and as we struck into the town here comes a raging rush of people with torches, and an awful whooping and yelling and banging tin pans; and we jumped to one side to let them go by; and as they went by I see they had the king and the duke astraddle of a rail—that is, I knowed it was the king and the duke, though they was all over tar and feathers. Well, it made me sick to see it; and I was sorry for them poor pitiful rascals. Human beings *can* be awful cruel to one another.

We see we was too late. We asked some stragglers about it, and they said everybody went to the show looking very innocent; and laid low and kept dark till the poor old king was on the stage; then the house rose up and went for them.

So we poked along back home, and I warn't feeling so brash as I was before, but kind of ornery, and humble, and to blame, somehow—though *I* hadn't done nothing. But that's always the way; a person's conscience ain't got no sense, and just goes for him *anyway*. If I had a yeller dog that didn't know no more than a person's conscience does I would pison him. Tom he says the same.

By and by Tom says, "Looky here, Huck, what fools we are to not think of it before! I bet I know where Jim is."

"No! Where?"

"In that hut down by the ash hopper. Why, looky. When we was at dinner, didn't you see a nigger go in there with some vittles?"

"Yes."

"What did you think the vittles was for?"

"For a dog."

"So 'd I. Well, it wasn't for a dog."

"Why?"

"Because part of it was watermelon."

"So it was. I never thought about that. It shows how a body can see and don't see at the same time."

"Well, the nigger unlocked the padlock when he went in, and locked it again when he come out, and he fetched Uncle a key about the time we got up from the table. Watermelon shows man, lock shows prisoner; and it ain't likely there's two prisoners on such a little plantation, so Jim's the prisoner. All right—I'm glad we found it out detective fashion. Now you work your mind, and study out a plan to steal Jim, and I'll study out one, too; and we'll take the one we like the best."

What a head! If I had Tom Sawyer's head I wouldn't trade it off to be a duke, nor mate of a steamboat, nor clown in a circus. I went on thinking out a plan, but only just to be doing something; I knowed very well where the right plan was going to come from. Pretty soon Tom says, "Ready?"

"Yes," I says. "My plan is this. Tomorrow we fetch my raft from the island. Then the first dark night we steal the key out of the old man's britches after he goes to bed, and shove off down the river on the raft with Jim. Wouldn't that work?"

"*Work?* Why, cert'nly it would work, like rats a-fighting. But it's too blame' simple. What's the good of a plan that ain't no more trouble than that? It's as mild as goose milk."

I never said nothing, because I warn't expecting nothing different; but I knowed mighty well that whenever he got *his* plan ready it wouldn't have none of them objections to it.

And it didn't. He told me what it was, and I see in a minute it was worth fifteen of mine for style, and would make Jim just as free a man as mine would, and maybe get us all killed besides. So I was satisfied, and said we would waltz in on it. I needn't tell what it was here, because I knowed it wouldn't stay the way it was; he would be changing it around every which way as we went along. And that is what he done.

Well, one thing was dead sure, and that was that Tom Sawyer was in earnest, and was actually going to help steal that nigger out of slavery. That was the thing that was too many for me. Here was a boy that was respectable and well brung up; and had a character to lose. I *couldn't* understand it no way at all. It was outrageous, and I knowed I ought to just up and tell him so; and so be his true friend. And I *did* start to tell him; but he shut me up, and says:

"Don't you reckon I know what I'm about?"

"Yes."

"Didn't I *say* I was going to help steal the nigger?"

"Yes."

"*Well,* then."

That's what he said, so I let it go, and never bothered no more about it.

When we got home the house was all dark and still; so we went on down to the hut by the ash hopper for to examine it. We went through the yard so as to see what the hounds would do. They knowed us, and didn't make no noise. When we got to the cabin we took a look at the front and the two sides; and on one side I warn't acquainted with—which was the north side—we found a square window hole, up high, with just one board nailed across it. I says:

"Here's the ticket. This hole's big enough for Jim to get through if we wrench off the board."

Tom says, "It's too simple. I should *hope* we can find a way that's a little more complicated than *that*, Huck Finn."

"Well, then," I says, "how'll it do to saw him out?"

"That's more *like*," he says. "It's mysterious and troublesome. But I bet we can find a way that's twice as long. Let's keep looking around."

Betwixt the hut and the fence, on the back side, was a lean-to that joined the hut at the eaves, and was made out of plank. The door to it was at the south end, and was padlocked. Tom he went to the soap kettle and searched around, and fetched back the iron thing they lift the lid with; so he took it and prized out one of the staples. The chain fell down, and we opened the door and went in and struck a match, and see the shed was only built against the cabin and hadn't no connection with it; and there warn't no floor to the shed, nor nothing in it but some old rusty hoes and spades and picks. The match went out, and so did we, and shoved in the staple again, and the door was locked as good as ever. Tom was joyful. He says:

"Now we're all right. We'll *dig* him out. It'll take about a week!"

Then we started for the house, and I went in the back door— you only have to pull a buckskin latchstring, they don't fasten the doors—but that warn't romantical enough for Tom; no way would do him but he must climb up the lightning rod. He got up halfway about three times, and the last time most busted his brains out; but he allowed he would give her one more turn for luck, and this time he made the trip.

In the morning we was up at break of day, and down to the nigger cabins to make friends with the nigger that fed Jim—if it *was* Jim that was being fed. The niggers was just starting for the fields; and Jim's nigger was piling up a tin pan with bread and things; and whilst the others was leaving, the key come from the house.

This nigger had a good-natured, chuckleheaded face, and his wool was all tied up in little bunches to keep witches off. He said the witches was pestering him awful these nights, and he got so worked up, and got to running on so about his troubles, he forgot all about what he'd been a-going to do. So Tom says, "What's the vittles for? Going to feed the dogs?"

The nigger kind of smiled graduly and he says, "Yes, Mars Sid, *a* dog. Cur'us dog, too. Does you want to look at 'im?"

"Yes."

I hunched Tom, and whispers, "You going, right here in the daybreak? *That* warn't the plan."

"No, it warn't; but it's the plan *now*."

So, drat him, we went along. When we got in we couldn't hardly see, it was so dark; but Jim was there, sure enough, and could see us; and he sings out, "Why, *Huck!* En good *lan*'; ain' dat Misto Tom?"

I just knowed how it would be; and the other nigger busted in and says, "Why, de gracious sakes! Do he know you genlmen?"

We could see pretty well now. Tom he looked at the nigger, steady and kind of wondering, and says, "Does *who* know us?"

"Why, dis-yer runaway nigger."

"I don't reckon he does; but what put that into your head?"

"What *put* it dar? Didn' he jus' dis minute sing out like he knowed you?"

Tom says, in a puzzled-up kind of way, "Well, that's mighty curious." And turns to me and says, "Did *you* hear anybody sing out?"

And of course I says, "No; *I* ain't heard nobody say nothing."

Then he turns to Jim, and looks him over like he never see him before, and says, "Did *you* sing out?"

"No, sah," says Jim; "*I* hain't said nothing, sah."

"Did you ever see us before?"

"No, sah; not as *I* knows on."

So Tom turns to the nigger, who was looking wild and distressed, and says, kind of severe, "What do you reckon's the matter with you, anyway?"

"Oh, it's de dad-blame witches, sah, en I wisht I was dead! Dey do mos' kill me. Please don't tell nobody 'bout it, sah, or ole Mars Silas he'll scole me; he say dey *ain't* no witches—but I jis' wish to goodness he was heah now!"

Tom give him a dime, and said we wouldn't tell nobody; and told him to buy some more thread to tie up his hair with. And whilst the nigger stepped to the door to look at the dime, he whispers to Jim, "Don't let on to know us. And if you hear any digging going on nights, it's us; we're going to set you free."

Jim only had time to grab us by the hand and squeeze; then the nigger come back, and we said we'd come again sometime if the nigger wanted us to; and he said he would, more particular if it was dark, because the witches went for him mostly in the dark, and it was good to have folks around then.

CHAPTER XIII

It would be most an hour yet till breakfast, so we left and struck down into the woods; because Tom said we got to have *some* light to dig by, and a lantern makes too much; what we must have was a lot of them rotten chunks that's called fox fire, and just makes a kind of glow when you lay them in a dark place. We fetched an armful and hid it in the weeds; and set down to rest, and Tom says, kind of dissatisfied:

"Blame it, this whole thing is just as easy and awkward as it can be. And so it makes it rotten difficult to get up a difficult plan. There ain't no watchman to be drugged—now there *ought* to be a watchman. There ain't even a dog to give a sleeping mixture to. And there's Jim chained by one leg, with a ten-foot chain, to the leg of his bed; why, all you got to do is to lift up the bedstead and slip off the chain. Drat it, Huck, it's the stupidest arrangement

I ever see. You got to invent *all* the difficulties. Look at just that one thing of the lantern. When you come down to the cold facts, we simply got to *let on* that a lantern's resky. Why, we could work with a torchlight procession if we wanted to, *I* believe. Now, whilst I think of it, we got to hunt up something to make a saw out of the first chance we get."

"What do we want of a saw?"

"What do we *want* of a saw? Hain't we got to saw the leg of Jim's bed off, so as to get the chain loose?"

"Why, you just said a body could lift up the bedstead and slip the chain off."

"Well, if that ain't just like you, Huck Finn. You *can* get up the infant-schooliest ways of going at a thing. Why, hain't you ever read any books at all? Baron Trenck, nor Casanova, nor Benvenuto Chelleeny? Who ever heard of getting a prisoner loose in such an old-maidy way as that? No; the way all the best authorities does is to saw the bed leg in two, and leave it just so, and swallow the sawdust, so it can't be found. Then the night you're ready, fetch the leg a kick, down she goes; slip off your chain, and there you are. Nothing to do but hitch your rope ladder to the battlements and shin down it to the moat. It's gaudy, Huck. I wish there was a moat to this cabin. If we get time, the night of the escape, we'll dig one."

I says, "What do we want of a moat when we're going to snake him out from under the cabin?"

But he never heard me. He had forgot me. He had his chin in his hands, thinking. Pretty soon he says, "Anyway, he can have a rope ladder; we can tear up some sheets and make him a rope ladder easy enough. And we can send it to him in a pie; it's mostly done that way."

"Why, Tom Sawyer," I says, "Jim ain't got no use for a rope ladder."

"He *has* got use for it. He's *got* to have a rope ladder; they all do."

"What in the nation can he *do* with it?"

"*Do* with it? He can hide it in his bed, can't he? That's what they all do; and *he's* got to, too."

"Well," I says, "if it's in the regulations, and he's got to have it, all right; I don't wish to go back on no regulations; but there's one thing, Tom Sawyer—if we go to tearing up our sheets to make Jim a rope ladder, we're sure going to get into trouble with Aunt Sally. Now, the way I look at it, a hickry-bark ladder don't cost nothing, and don't waste nothing, and is just as good to load up a pie with—"

"Oh, shucks, Huck Finn, who ever heard of a state prisoner escaping by a hickry-bark ladder? Why, it's perfectly ridiculous."

"Well, all right, fix it your way; but if you'll take my advice, you'll let me borrow a sheet off the clothesline."

He said that would do. And that gave him another idea, and he says, "Borrow a shirt, too."

"What do we want of a shirt, Tom?"

"Want it for Jim to keep a journal on."

"Journal your granny—*Jim* can't write."

"S'pose he *can't* write—he can make marks on the shirt, can't he, if we make him a pen out of an old pewter spoon or a piece of an old iron barrel hoop?"

"Why, Tom, we can pull a feather out of a goose and make him a better one; and quicker, too."

"*Prisoners* don't have geese running around the donjon-keep to pull pens out of, you muggins. They wouldn't *use* a goose quill if they had it. It ain't regular."

"Well, then, what'll we make him the ink out of?"

"Many makes it out of iron rust and tears; but the best authorities uses their own blood. Jim can do that; and when he wants to send any little common message to let the world know where he's captivated, he can write it on the bottom of a tin plate with a fork and throw it out of the window. The Iron Mask always done that—"

He broke off there, because we heard the breakfast horn blowing. So we cleared out for the house.

Along during the morning I borrowed a sheet and a white shirt off of the clothesline; and I found an old sack and put them in it, and we went and got the fox fire, and put that in too. I called it borrowing, because that was what Pap always called it; but Tom said it warn't borrowing, it was stealing. But he said we was representing prisoners; and it ain't no crime in a prisoner to steal the thing he needs to get away with, Tom said; it's his right; and so long as we was representing a prisoner, we had a perfect right to steal anything we had the least use for to get ourselves out of prison with.

Well, as I was saying, we waited that morning till everybody was settled down to business, and nobody in sight around the yard; then Tom he carried the sack into the lean-to whilst I stood off to keep watch. By and by he come out, and we set down on the woodpile to talk. He says, "Everything's all right now except tools; and that's easy fixed."

"Tools for what?" I says.

"Why, to dig with. We ain't a-going to *gnaw* him out, are we?"

"Ain't them old picks and things in there good enough to dig with?" I says.

He turns on me, looking pitying, and says, "Huck Finn, did you *ever* hear of a prisoner having picks and shovels to dig himself out with? Why, they wouldn't furnish 'em to a king."

"Well, then," I says, "if we don't want the picks and shovels, what do we want?"

"A couple of case knives."

"To dig the foundations out from under that cabin with?"

"Yes."

"Confound it, it's foolish, Tom."

"It don't make no difference how foolish it is, it's the *right* way—and it's the regular way. They always dig out with a case knife—and not through dirt, mind you; generly through solid rock. And it takes them forever and ever. Why, one of them prisoners in the bottom dungeon of the Castle Deef in Marseilles dug himself out that way; he was at it *thirty-seven year*—and he come out in China. *That's* the kind. I wish the bottom of *this* fortress was solid rock."

"*Jim* don't know nobody in China."

"What's *that* got to do with it? You're always a-wandering off on a side issue. Why can't you stick to the main point?"

"All right—*I* don't care where he comes out, so he *comes* out;

165

and Jim don't either, I reckon. But there's one thing—Jim's too old to be dug out with a case knife. He won't last."

"Yes, he will *last*, too. You don't reckon it's going to take thirty-seven years to dig through a *dirt* foundation, do you?"

"How long will it take, Tom?"

"Well, we can't resk being as long as we ought to, because it mayn't take very long for Uncle Silas to hear from down there by New Orleans. Then his next move will be to advertise Jim, or something like that. So, things being so uncertain, what I recommend is this: that we really dig right in, quick; and after that, we can *let on*, to ourselves, that we was at it thirty-seven years. Then we can snatch him out the first time there's an alarm."

"Now, there's *sense* in that," I says. "Letting on don't cost nothing. It wouldn't strain me none to let on we was at it a hundred and fifty years. So I'll mosey along now, and smouch a couple of case knives."

"Smouch three," he says. "We want one to make a saw out of."

"Tom, if it ain't unregular to sejest it," I says, "there's an old saw blade sticking under the boarding behind the smokehouse."

He looked kind of weary, and says:

"It ain't no use to try to learn you nothing, Huck. Run along and smouch the knives—three of them." So I done it.

As soon as we reckoned everybody was asleep that night we went down the lightning rod, and shut ourselves up in the lean-to, and got out our pile of fox fire, and went to work. We cleared everything out of the way along the middle of the bottom log. Tom said we was right behind Jim's bed now, and we'd dig in under it, and when we got through there couldn't nobody in the cabin ever know there was any hole there, because Jim's counterpane hung down to the ground. So we dug and dug with the case knives till most midnight; and then we was dog-tired, and our hands was blistered, and yet you couldn't see we'd done anything hardly. At last I says:

"This ain't no thirty-seven-year job; this is a thirty-eight-year job, Tom Sawyer."

He never said nothing. But he sighed, and pretty soon he stopped digging. Then he says:

"It ain't no use, Huck, it ain't a-going to work. If we was prisoners it would, because then we'd have as many years as we wanted, and no hurry; and so our hands wouldn't get blistered, and we could keep it up year in and year out, and do it right. But *we* can't fool along; we got to rush; we ain't got no time to spare. If we was to put in another night this way we'd have to knock off for a week to let our hands get well—couldn't touch a case knife with them sooner."

"Well, then, what we going to do, Tom?"

"I'll tell you. It ain't right, and it ain't moral; but we got to dig him out with the picks, and *let on* it's case knives."

"*Now you're talking!*" I says. "Your head gets leveler and leveler all the time, Tom Sawyer. Picks is the thing, moral or no moral; and as for me, I don't care shucks for the morality of it, nohow. When I start in to steal a nigger, or a watermelon, what I want is the nigger, or what I want is the watermelon; and if a pick's the handiest thing, that's the thing I'm a-going to dig that nigger or that watermelon out with; and I don't give a dead rat what the authorities thinks about it nuther."

"Well," he says, "it might answer for *you* to dig Jim out with a pick, *without* any letting on, because you don't know no better; but it wouldn't do for me, because I do know better. Gimme a case knife."

He had his own by him, but I handed him mine. He flung it down, and says, "Gimme a *case knife.*"

I didn't know just what to do—but then I thought. I got a pickaxe and give it to him, and he took it and went to work, and never said a word.

He was always just that particular. Full of principle.

So then I got a shovel, and then we picked and shoveled, turn about. We stuck to it about a half an hour, which was as long as we could stand up; but we had a good deal of a hole to show for it. When I got upstairs I looked out at the window and see Tom doing his level best with the lightning rod, but he couldn't come it, his hands was so sore. At last he says, "It ain't no use. What you reckon I better do? Can't you think of no way?"

"Yes," I says, "but I reckon it ain't regular. Come up the stairs, and let on it's a lightning rod."

So he done it.

NEXT DAY TOM STOLE a pewter spoon and a brass candlestick in the house, for to make some pens for Jim out of, and six tallow candles; and I hung around the nigger cabins and stole three tin plates for Jim to write messages on. Then Tom says, "Now, the thing is, how to get the things to Jim?"

"Take them in through the hole," I says, "when we get it done."

He just looked scornful, and said something about nobody ever heard of such an idiotic idea.

That night we went down the lightning rod a little after ten, and took one of the candles along, and listened under the window hole and heard Jim snoring. Then we whirled in with the pick and shovel, and in about two hours and a half the job was done. We crept in under Jim's bed, and took the candle and lit it, and then we woke Jim up gentle. He was so glad to see us he most cried; and he was for having us hunt up a cold chisel to cut the chain off his leg with right away, and clearing out. But Tom he showed him how unregular it would be, and told him all about our plans, and how we could alter them in a minute any time there was an alarm; and not to be the least afraid, because we would see he got away, *sure*. So Jim he said it was all right, and we set there and talked over old times awhile. Then Tom asked a lot of questions, and when Jim told him Uncle Silas come in every day to pray with him, and Aunt Sally come in to see if he was comfortable, Tom says:

"*Now* I know how to fix it. We'll send you some things by them."

He told Jim how we'd have to smuggle in the rope-ladder pie and other large things by Nat, the nigger that fed him, and he must be on the lookout, and not be surprised, and not let Nat see him open them; and we would put small things in Uncle's coat pockets and he must steal them out; and we would put things in

Aunt's apron pocket; and we told him what they would be and what they was for. And told him how to keep a journal on the shirt with his blood, and all that. Jim he couldn't see no sense in the most of it; but he said he would do it all just as Tom said.

Jim had plenty corncob pipes and tobacco; so we had a right down good sociable time; then we crawled out through the hole, and so home to bed.

In the morning we went out to the woodpile and chopped up the brass candlestick into handy sizes. Then we went to the nigger cabins, and while I got Nat's notice off, Tom shoved a piece of candlestick into the middle of a corn pone that was in Jim's pan, and we went along with Nat to see how it would work, and it just worked noble; when Jim bit into it it most mashed all his teeth out. Jim he never let on but what it was only just a piece of rock or something like that that gets into bread, you know; but after that he never bit into nothing but what he jabbed his fork into it three or four places first.

And whilst we was a-standing there in the dimmish light, here comes a couple of the hounds bulging in from under Jim's bed; and they kept on piling in till there was eleven of them. By jings, we forgot to fasten that lean-to door! The nigger Nat he just hollered "Witches" once, and he keeled over onto the floor amongst the dogs.

Tom jerked the door open and flung out a slab of Jim's meat, and the dogs went for it, and in two seconds he was out himself and back again and shut the door, and I knowed he'd fixed the other door too. Then he went to work on the nigger, coaxing him and asking him if he'd been imagining he saw something again. He raised up, and blinked his eyes around, and says:

"Mars Sid, you'll say I's a fool, but I see most a million dogs, er devils, er some'n. I did, mos' sholy! Mars Sid, I *felt* um—I *felt* um, sah! Dad fetch it, I jis' wisht dem witches 'd lemme 'lone!"

Tom says, "Well, I tell you what *I* think. What makes them come here just at this runaway nigger's breakfast-time? It's because they're hungry. You make them a witch pie; that's the thing for *you* to do."

"But my lan', Mars Sid, how's I gwyne to make 'em a witch pie? I doan' know how to make it."

"Well, then, I'll have to make it myself."

"Will you do it, honey—will you?"

"All right, seeing it's you, and you've been good to us. But you got to be mighty careful. When we come around, you turn your back; and then whatever we've put in the pan, don't you let on you see it at all. And don't you look when Jim unloads the pan—something might happen, I don't know what. And above all, don't you *handle* the witch things."

"*Hannel* 'm, Mars Sid? I wouldn' lay my finger on um, f'r ten hund'd thous'n billion dollars!"

So that was all fixed. Then we went away and went to the rubbage pile in the backyard and scratched around and found an old tin washpan to bake the pie in, and took it down cellar and stole it full of flour, and found a couple of shingle nails that Tom said would be handy for a prisoner to scrabble his name on the dungeon walls with, and dropped one of them in Aunt Sally's apron pocket which was hanging on a chair, and t'other we stuck in the band of Uncle Silas's hat, which was on the bureau, and then went to breakfast, and Tom dropped the pewter spoon in Uncle Silas's coat pocket, and Aunt Sally wasn't come yet, so we had to wait a little while.

And when she come she was hot and red and cross, and couldn't hardly wait for the blessing; and then she went to sluicing out coffee, and says:

"I've hunted high and I've hunted low, and it does beat all what *has* become of your other shirt."

My heart fell down amongst my lungs and livers and things, and a hard piece of corn crust started down my throat after it and got met on the road with a cough, and was shot across the table, and took one of the children in the eye and curled him up like a fishing worm, and let a cry out of him the size of a war whoop, and Tom he turned kinder blue around the gills, and it all amounted to a considerable state of things for about a quarter of a minute or as much as that, and I would 'a' sold out for half price if there was a bidder. But after that we was all right again—it was the sudden surprise of it that knocked us so kind of cold. Uncle Silas he says:

"It's most uncommon curious, I can't understand it. I know perfectly well I took it *off*, because—"

"Because you hain't got but one *on*. Just *listen!* I know you took it off. It was on the clo'sline yesterday—but it's gone now, and you'll just have to change to a red flann'l one till I can get time to make a new one. And the shirt ain't all that's gone, nuther. Ther's a spoon gone; and *that* ain't all. There was ten, and now ther's only nine. The calf got the shirt, I reckon, but the calf never took the spoon, *that's* certain."

"Why, what else is gone, Sally?"

"Ther's six *candles* gone—that's what. The rats could 'a' got the candles, and I reckon they did; I wonder they don't walk off with the whole place, the way you're always going to stop their holes and don't do it; but you can't lay the *spoon* on the rats, and that I *know*."

"Well, Sally, I'm in fault, and I acknowledge it; but I won't let tomorrow go by without stopping up them holes."

"Oh, I wouldn't hurry; next year 'll do. Matilda Angelina *Phelps!*"

Whack comes her thimble, and the child snatches her claws out of the sugar bowl. Just then the nigger woman steps onto the passage, and says, "Missus, dey's a sheet gone."

"A *sheet* gone! Well, for the land's sake!"

"I'll stop up them holes today," says Uncle Silas.

"Oh, *do* shet up! S'pose the rats took the *sheet?* Where's it gone? I *never* see the beat of it in all my born days. A shirt gone, and a sheet, and a spoon, and six can—"

"Missus," comes a young yaller wench, "dey's a brass candlestick miss'n."

"Cler out from here, you hussy, er I'll take a skillet to ye!"

Well, she was just a-biling. She kept a-raging right along, running her insurrection all by herself, and everybody else mighty meek and quiet; and at last Uncle Silas, looking kind of foolish, fishes up that spoon out of his pocket. She stopped, with her mouth open; but not long, because she says:

"It's *just* as I expected. So you had it in your pocket all the time. How'd it get there?"

"I reely don't know, Sally," he says, kind of apologizing, "I was a-studying over my text in Acts Seventeen before breakfast, and I reckon I put it in there, not noticing, meaning to put my Testament in—"

"Oh, for the land's sake! Give a body a rest! Go 'long now, the whole kit and biling of ye; and don't come nigh me again till I've got back my peace of mind."

As we was passing through the setting room the old man he took up his hat, and the shingle nail fell out on the floor, and he just merely picked it up and laid it on the mantelshelf and never said nothing, and went out. Tom see him do it, and remembered about the spoon, and says:

"Well, it ain't no use to send things by *him* no more, he ain't reliable." Then he says, "But he done us a good turn with the spoon anyway, without knowing it, and so we'll go and do him one without *him* knowing it—stop up his rat holes."

There was a noble good lot of them down cellar, and it took us a whole hour, but we done the job tight and good. Then we heard steps on the stairs, and blowed out our light and hid; and here comes the old man with a candle in one hand, looking as absentminded as year before last. He went a-mooning around, first to one rat hole and then another, till he'd been to them all. Then he stood about five minutes, picking tallow drips off his candle and thinking. Then he turns off slow and dreamy towards the stairs, saying, "Well, for the life of me I can't remember when I done it. I could show her—but never mind—let it go." And so he went on a-mumbling upstairs, and then we left. He was a mighty nice old man.

Tom was a good deal bothered about what to do for a spoon, but he said we'd got to have it; so he took a think. When he had ciphered it out he told me how we was to do; then we went and waited around the spoon basket till we see Aunt Sally coming, and then Tom went to counting the spoons, and I slid one of them up my sleeve, and Tom says:

"Why, Aunt Sally, there ain't but nine spoons *yet*."

She says, "Go 'long, don't bother me. I know better, I counted 'm myself."

"Well, I've counted them twice, Aunty, and *I* can't make but nine."

She looked out of all patience, but of course she come to count—anybody would. "I declare ther' *ain't* but nine!" she says. "Why, what in the world—plague *take* the things, I'll count 'm again."

So I slipped back the one I had, and when she got done counting, she says, "Hang the troublesome rubbage, ther's *ten* now!" and she looked huffy and bothered both. But Tom says:

"Why, Aunty, *I* don't think there's ten."

"You numskull, didn't you see me *count* 'm?"

"I know, but—"

"Well, I'll count 'm again."

So I smouched one, and they come out nine, same as the other time. Well, she *was* in a tearing way—just a-trembling all over, she was so mad. But she counted and counted, and three times they come out right, and three times they come out wrong. Then she grabbed up the basket and slammed it across the house and knocked the cat galley-west; and she said cler out and let her have some peace, and if we come bothering around her again betwixt that and dinner she'd skin us. So we had the odd spoon, and dropped it in her apron pocket whilst she was a-giving us our sailing orders, and Jim got it all right, along with her shingle nail, before noon.

We put the sheet back on the line that night, and stole one out of her closet; and kept on putting it back and stealing it again for a couple of days till she didn't know how many sheets she had anymore, either, and she didn't *care*, and warn't a-going to count them again not to save her life; she'd ruther die first. So we was all right now, as to the shirt and the sheet and the spoon and the candles, by the help of the calf and rats and the mixed-up counting; and as to the candlestick, it warn't no consequence, it would blow over by and by.

But that pie was a job; we had no end of trouble with that pie. We fixed it up away down in the woods, and cooked it there; and we got it done at last; but not all in one day; and we had to use up three washpans full of flour before we got through. We tore up the sheet all in little strings and twisted them together, and so we had a lovely rope that you could 'a' hung a person with. But it wouldn't go into the pie. Being made of a whole sheet, that way, there was rope enough for forty pies if we'd 'a' wanted them, and all we needed was just enough for the pie; so we throwed the rest away.

We didn't cook none of the pies in the washpan—afraid the solder would melt; but Uncle Silas he had a noble brass warming pan which he thought considerable of; it was hid away up garret with a lot of other old things that was valuable, and we snaked her out, private, and took her down to the woods. She failed on the first pies, because we didn't know how, but she come up smiling on the last one. We took and lined her with dough, and set her in the coals and loaded her up with rag rope, and put on a dough roof, and shut down the lid, and put hot embers on top, and stood off five foot, with the long handle, cool and comfortable, and in fifteen minutes she turned out a pie that was a satisfaction to look at.

Nat didn't look when we put the witch pie in Jim's pan; and we put the three tin plates in the bottom of the pan under the vittles; and so Jim got everything all right, and as soon as he was by himself he busted into the pie and hid the rope ladder inside of his straw tick, and scratched some marks on a tin plate and throwed it out of the window hole.

MAKING THEM PENS WAS a distressid tough job, and so was the saw; and Jim allowed the inscription was going to be the toughest of all. That's the one which the prisoner had to scribble on the wall. But he had to have it; Tom said he'd *got* to; there warn't no case of a state prisoner not scrabbling his inscription to leave behind. So whilst me and Jim filed away at the pens on a brick-bat apiece, Jim a-making his'n out of the brass and I making mine out of the spoon, Tom set to work to think out the inscription. He made up a lot, and wrote them out on a paper, and read them off, so:

"1. Here a captive heart busted.
2. Here a poor prisoner, forsook by the world and friends, fretted his sorrowful life.
3. Here a lonely heart broke, and a worn spirit went to its rest, after thirty-seven years of solitary captivity.
4. Here, homeless and friendless, after thirty-seven years of bitter captivity, perished a noble stranger, natural son of Louis XIV."

Tom's voice trembled whilst he was reading them, and he most broke down. When he got done he couldn't no way make up his mind which one for Jim to scrabble onto the wall, they was all so good; but at last he allowed he would let him scrabble them all on. Jim said it would take him a year to scrabble such a lot of truck onto the logs with a nail, and he didn't know how to make letters, besides; but Tom said he would block them out for him. Then he says:

"Come to think, the logs ain't a-going to do; they don't have log walls in a dungeon: we got to dig the inscriptions into a rock. We'll fetch a rock."

Jim said the rock was worse than the logs; he said it would take him a pison long time to dig them into a rock. But Tom said he would let me help him do it. Then he took a look to see how me and Jim was getting along with the pens. It was most pesky tedious hard work and slow, and we didn't seem to make no headway, hardly; so Tom says:

"I know how to fix it. We got to have a rock for the inscriptions, and we can kill two birds with that same rock. There's a big grindstone down at the mill, and we'll smouch it, and carve the things on it, and file out the pens and the saw on it, too."

It warn't no slouch of an idea; and we allowed we'd tackle it. It warn't quite midnight yet, so we cleared out for the mill, leaving

Jim at work. We smouched the grindstone, and set out to roll her home, but it was a most nation tough job. Sometimes we couldn't keep her from falling over, and she come mighty near mashing us every time. We got her halfway; and then we was plumb played out, and most drownded with sweat. We see it warn't no use; we got to fetch Jim. So he raised up his bed and slid the chain off of the bed leg, and wrapt it round his neck, and we crawled out through our hole and down there, and Jim and me laid into that grindstone and walked her along like nothing, and got her through our hole.

Then Tom marked out them things on it with the nail, and set Jim to work on them, with the nail for a chisel and an iron bolt for a hammer. Tom told him to work till the rest of his candle quit on him, and then he could go to bed, and hide the grindstone under his straw tick and sleep on it. We helped him fix his chain back on the bed leg, and was ready for bed ourselves. But Tom thought of something, and says:

"You got any spiders in here, Jim?"

"No, sah, thanks to goodness I hain't, Mars Tom."

"All right, we'll get you some."

"Bless you, honey, I doan' *want* none. I's afeard un um. I jis' 's soon have rattlesnakes aroun'."

Tom thought a minute or two, and says, "It's a good idea. Yes, it's a prime good idea. Where could you keep it?"

"Keep what, Mars Tom?"

"Why, a rattlesnake."

"De goodness gracious alive, Mars Tom! Why, if dey was a rattlesnake to come in heah I'd bust right out thoo dat log wall, I would, wid my head."

"Why, Jim, you wouldn't be afraid of it after a little. You could tame it."

"*Tame* it!"

"Yes—easy enough. Every animal is grateful for kindness and petting, and they wouldn't *think* of hurting a person that pets them. Any book will tell you that. You try—just try for two or three days. Why, you can get him so that he'll love you; and sleep with you; and let you wrap him round your neck and put his head in your mouth."

"*Please*, Mars Tom—*doan'* talk so! I can't *stan'* it! I doan' *want* him to sleep wid me or shove his head in my mouf."

"Jim, blame it, can't you *try?* I only *want* you to try—you needn't keep it up if it don't work."

"But de trouble all *done* ef de snake bite me while I's a-tryin' him. Mars Tom, I's willin' to tackle mos' anything 'at ain't onreasonable, but ef you en Huck fetches a rattlesnake in heah for me to tame, I's gwyne to *leave*, dat's *shore*."

"Well, then, let it go, if you're so bullheaded about it. We can get you some garter snakes, and some rats, instead."

"Why, Mars Tom, I doan' want no rats either!"

"But, Jim, they all have 'em! Prisoners ain't ever without rats. They train them, and learn them tricks, and they get to be as sociable as flies. But you got to play music to them. You got anything to play music on?"

"I ain' got nuffn but a coase comb en a piece o' paper, en a juice harp; but I reck'n dey wouldn't take no stock in a juice harp."

"Yes, they would. *They* don't care what kind of music 'tis. A jew's harp's plenty good enough for a rat. All animals like music—in a prison they dote on it. Specially, painful music; and you can't get no other kind out of a jew's harp. Yes, you're fixed very well. You want to set on your bed nights before you go to sleep, and play your jew's harp; play 'The Last Link is Broken'; and when you've played about two minutes you'll see all the rats, and the snakes, and spiders and things begin to feel worried about you, and come. And they'll just fairly swarm over you, and have a noble good time."

"Yes, *dey* will, I reck'n, Mars Tom, but what kine er time is Jim havin'? Blest if I kin see de pint. But I'll do it ef I got to. I reck'n I better keep de animals satisfied, en not have no trouble in de house."

Tom waited to think it over, and see if there wasn't nothing else; and pretty soon he says, "Oh, there's one thing I forgot. Could you raise a flower here, do you reckon?"

"I doan' know; maybe I could, Mars Tom; but it's tolable dark in heah."

"Well, you try it, anyway. Some other prisoners has done it. You want to water it with your tears."

"She'll die on my han's, Mars Tom; kase I doan' skasely ever cry."

So Tom was stumped. But he studied it over, and then said Jim would have to worry along the best he could with an onion. He promised he would drop one, private, in Jim's coffeepot, in the morning. Jim said he would "jis' 's soon have tobacker in his coffee"; and found so much fault with it, and with the work and bother of jew's-harping the rats, and petting and flattering up the snakes and spiders, on top of all the other work he had to do on pens, and inscriptions, and journals, and things, which made it more trouble and worry to be a prisoner than anything he ever undertook, that Tom most lost all patience with him; and said he was loadened down with more chances than a prisoner ever had in the world to make a name for himself, and yet he didn't know enough to appreciate them, and they was just about wasted on him. So Jim he was sorry, and said he wouldn't behave so no more, and then me and Tom shoved for bed.

IN THE MORNING WE WENT up to the village and bought a wire rat trap and fetched it down, and unstopped the best rat hole, and in about an hour we had fifteen of the bulliest kind of ones; and then we took it and put it in a safe place under Aunt Sally's bed. But while we was gone for spiders little Thomas Franklin Benjamin Phelps found it there, and opened the door of it to see if the rats would come out, and they did; and Aunt Sally she come in, and when we got back she was a-standing on top of the bed raising Cain, and the rats was doing what they could to keep off the dull times for her. So she took and dusted us both with the hickry, and we was as much as two hours catching another fifteen or sixteen, drat that meddlesome cub, and they warn't the likeliest, nuther, because the first haul was the pick of the flock. I never see a likelier lot of rats than what that first haul was.

We got a splendid stock of sorted spiders, and bugs, and frogs, and caterpillars, and one thing or another; and then we went for the snakes, and grabbed a couple of dozen garters and house snakes, and put them in a bag, and put it in our room, and by that time it was suppertime, and a rattling good day's work; and hungry? Oh, no, I reckon not! And there warn't a blessed snake up there when we went back—they worked out of that sack somehow, and left. But it didn't matter much, because they was still on the premises somewheres. So we judged we could get some of them again. No, there warn't no real scarcity of snakes about the house for a considerable spell. You'd see them dripping from the rafters and places every now and then; and they generly landed in your plate, or down the back of your neck, and most of the time where you didn't want them. Well, they was handsome and striped, and there warn't no harm in a million of them; but Aunt Sally couldn't stand them no way you could fix it; and every time one of them flopped down on her, it didn't make no difference what she was doing, she would just lay that work down and light out. I never see such a woman. And you could hear her whoop to Jericho. Why, after every last snake had been gone clear out of the house for a week Aunt Sally warn't over it yet; when she was setting thinking about something you could touch her on the back of her neck with a feather and she would jump right out of her stockings. It was very curious. But Tom said all women was just so. He said they was made that way for some reason or other.

We got a licking every time one of our snakes come in her way, and she allowed these lickings warn't nothing to what she would do if we ever loaded up the place again with them. I didn't mind the lickings; but I minded the trouble we had to lay in another lot. But we got them laid in, and all the other things; and you never see a cabin as blithesome as Jim's was when they'd all swarm out for music and go for him. Jim didn't like the spiders, and the spiders didn't like Jim; and so they'd lay for him. And he said that between the rats and the snakes and the grindstone there warn't no room in bed for him, skasely; and when there was, a body couldn't sleep, it was so lively, because *they* never all slept at one time, but took turn about, so when the snakes was asleep the rats was on deck, and when the rats turned in the snakes come on watch, so he always had one gang under him, in his way, and t'other gang having a circus over him, and if he got up to hunt a new place the spiders would take a chance at him as he crossed over. He said if he ever got out of this he wouldn't ever be a prisoner again, not for a salary.

Well, by the end of three weeks everything was in pretty good shape. The shirt was sent in early, in a pie, and every time a rat bit Jim he would get up and write a line in his journal whilst the ink was fresh; the pens was made, the inscriptions and so on was all carved on the grindstone; the bed leg was sawed in two, and we had et up the sawdust, and it give us a most amazing stomach ache. It was the most undigestible sawdust I ever see; and Tom said the same.

But, as I was saying, we'd got all the work done now, at last; and we was all pretty much fagged out, too, but mainly Jim. The old man had wrote a couple of times to the plantation below Orleans to come and get the runaway nigger, but hadn't got no answer; so he allowed he would advertise Jim in the St. Louis and New Orleans papers; and when he mentioned the St. Louis ones it give me the cold shivers. We hadn't no time to lose. So Tom said, now for the nonnamous letters.

"What's them?" I says.

"Warnings to the people that something is up. Sometimes it's done one way, sometimes another. But there's always somebody spying around that gives notice to the governor of the castle. When Louis Sixteen was going to light out of the Tooleries a servant girl done it. It's a very good way, and so is the nonnamous letters. We'll use them both. And it's usual for the prisoner's mother to change clothes with him, and she stays in, and he slides out in her clothes. We'll do that, too."

"But looky here, Tom, what do we want to *warn* anybody for that something's up? Let them find it out for themselves—it's their lookout."

"Yes, I know; but you can't depend on them. They're so confiding and mullet-headed, if we don't *give* them notice there won't be nobody or nothing to interfere with us, and so after all our hard work and trouble this escape 'll go off perfectly flat."

"Well, as for me, Tom, that's the way I'd like."

"Shucks!" he says, and looked disgusted. So I says:

"But I ain't going to complain. Any way that suits you suits me. What you going to do about the servant girl?"

"You'll be her. You slide in, in the middle of the night, and hook that yaller girl's frock."

"Why, Tom, that 'll make trouble next morning; because, of course, she prob'bly hain't got any but that one."

"I know; but you don't want it but fifteen minutes, to carry the nonnamous letter and shove it under the front door."

"All right, I'll do it; but I could carry it just as handy in my own togs."

"You wouldn't look like a servant girl *then*, would you?"

"All right, I'm the servant girl. Who's Jim's mother?"

"I'm his mother. I'll hook a gown from Aunt Sally."

"Well, then, you'll have to stay in the cabin when me and Jim leaves."

"Not much. I'll stuff Jim's clothes full of straw and lay it on his bed to represent his mother in disguise, and Jim 'll take the gown off of me and wear it, and we'll all evade together. When a prisoner of style escapes it's called an evasion. It's always called so when a king escapes, f'rinstance. And the same with a king's son."

So Tom he wrote the nonnamous letter, and I smouched the yaller wench's frock that night, and put it on, and shoved it under the front door, the way Tom told me to. It said:

Beware. Trouble is brewing. Keep a sharp lookout.
                                                        Unknown Friend

Next night we stuck a picture, which Tom drawed in blood, of a skull and crossbones on the front door; and next night another one of a coffin on the back door. I never see a family in such a sweat. They couldn't 'a' been worse scared if the place had 'a' been full of ghosts laying for them. If a door banged, Aunt

Sally she jumped and said "Ouch!" If anything fell, she jumped and said "Ouch!" She was afraid to go to bed, but she dasn't set up. So the thing was working very well, Tom said; he said it showed it was done right.

So he said, now for the grand bulge! So the very next morning at dawn we got another letter ready, and was wondering what we better do with it, because we heard them say at supper they was going to have a nigger on watch at both doors all night. Tom he went down the lightning rod to spy around; and the nigger at the back door was asleep, and he stuck it in the back of his neck and come back. This letter said:

Don't betray me, I wish to be your friend. There is a desprate gang of cutthroats from over in the Indian Territory going to steal your runaway nigger tonight, and they have been trying to scare you so as you will stay in the house and not bother them. I am one of the gang, but have got relligion and wish to betray the helish design. They will sneak down from northards, along the fence, at midnight, with a false key, and go in the nigger's cabin to get him. I am to be off a piece and blow a tin horn if I see any danger; but stead of that I will *ba* like a sheep soon as they get in; then whilst they are getting his chains loose, you slip there and lock them in, and can kill them at your leisure. Don't do anything but just the way I am telling you; if you do they will suspicion something and raise whoop-jamboreehoo. I do not wish any reward but to know I have done the right thing.

Unknown Friend

CHAPTER XIV

We was feeling good after breakfast, and took my canoe and went a-fishing, with a lunch, and took a look at the raft and found her all right, and got home to supper, and found them in such a sweat they didn't know which end they was standing on, and made us go right off to bed the minute we was done supper, and wouldn't tell us what the trouble was. As soon as we was half upstairs and her back was turned we slid for the cellar cupboard and loaded up a good lunch and took it up to our room and went to bed, and got up about half past eleven, and Tom put on Aunt Sally's dress that he stole and was going to start with the lunch, but says, "Where's the butter?"

"I laid out a hunk," I says, "on a piece of corn pone."

"Well, you *left* it laid out, then—it ain't here. Just you slide down cellar and fetch it. And then mosey down the lightning rod and come along. I'll go and stuff the straw into Jim's clothes to represent his mother in disguise, and be ready to *ba* like a sheep and shove soon as you get there."

So out he went, and down cellar went I. The hunk of butter, big as a person's fist, was where I had left it, so I took up the slab of corn pone with it on, and blowed out my light, and started upstairs very stealthy, and got up to the main floor all right, but here comes Aunt Sally with a candle, and I clapped the truck in my hat, and clapped my hat on my head, and the next second she see me; and she says, "You been down cellar?"

"Yes'm."

"What you been doing down there?"

"Noth'n."

"*Noth'n!*"

"No'm. I haint been doing a single thing, Aunt Sally, I hope to gracious if I have."

I reckoned she'd let me go now, and as a generl thing she would; but I s'pose there was so many strange things going on she was in a sweat; so she says, very decided, "You just march into that setting room and stay there till I come. You been up to something, and I lay I'll find out what it is before *I'm* done with you."

So she went away as I opened the door and walked into the setting room. My, but there was a crowd there! Fifteen farmers, and every one of them had a gun. I was most powerful sick, and slunk to a chair and set down. I did wish Aunt Sally would come, and get done with me, and lick me, and let me get away and tell Tom how we'd overdone this thing, so we could stop fooling around, and clear out with Jim before these rips got out of patience and come for us. Then at last she come and begun to ask me questions, but I *couldn't* answer them straight; because these men was in such a fidget now that some was wanting to start right *now* and lay for them desperadoes; and others was trying to get them to hold on and wait for the sheep signal; and here was Aunty pegging away at the questions, and me a-shaking all over I was that scared; and the place getting hotter and hotter, and the butter beginning to melt and run down my neck; and pretty soon, when one of them says, "*I'm* for going and getting in the cabin *first* and right *now*, and catching them when they come," I most dropped, and a streak of butter come a-trickling down my forehead, and Aunt Sally she see it, and turns white as a sheet, and says:

"For the land's sake, what *is* the matter with the child? He's got the brain fever fer shore, and they're oozing out!"

And everybody runs to see, and she snatches off my hat, and out comes the bread and what was left of the butter, and she grabbed me, and hugged me, and says:

"Oh, what a turn you did give me! And how glad and grateful I am it ain't no worse; for when I see that truck I thought we'd lost you, for I knowed by the color and all it was just like your brains would be if— Dear, dear, whydn't you *tell* me that was what you'd been down there for? Now cler out to bed, and don't lemme see no more of you till morning!"

I was upstairs in a second, and down the lightning rod in another one, and shinning through the dark for the lean-to. I told Tom as quick as I could we must jump for it—the house full of men, yonder, with guns!

His eyes just blazed; and he says:

"No! Is that so? *Ain't* it bully!"

"Hurry! *Hurry!*" I says. "Where's Jim?"

"Right at your elbow. He's dressed, and everything's ready. Now we'll slide out and give the sheep signal."

But then we heard the tramp of men coming to the door, and heard them begin to fumble with the padlock, and heard a man say, "I *told* you we'd be too soon; they haven't come—the door is locked. Here, I'll lock some of you into the cabin, and you lay for 'em in the dark and kill 'em when they come; and the rest scatter around a piece."

So in they come, but couldn't see us in the dark, and most trod on us whilst we was hustling to get under the bed. But we got under all right, and out through the hole, swift but soft—Jim first, me next, and Tom last, which was according to Tom's orders. Now we was in the lean-to, and heard trampings close outside. So we crept to the door, and Tom put his eye to the crack, but couldn't make out nothing, it was so dark; then we slid out anyway, not breathing, and slipped stealthy towards the fence in Injun file, and got to it all right, and me and Jim over it; but Tom's britches catched fast on a splinter on the top rail, and then he hear the steps coming, so he had to pull loose, which snapped the splinter and made a noise; and as he dropped in our tracks somebody sings out:

"Who's that? Answer, or I'll shoot!"

But we didn't answer; we just unfurled our heels and shoved. Then there was a rush, and a *bang, bang, bang!* and the bullets fairly whizzed around us! We heard them sing out:

"They've broke for the river! After 'em, boys, and turn loose the dogs!"

So here they come, full tilt. We could hear them because they wore boots and yelled. We was in the path to the mill; and when they got pretty close onto us we dodged into the bush and let them go by, and then dropped in behind them. They'd had all the dogs shut up, so they wouldn't scare off the robbers; but by this time somebody had let them loose, and here they come, making pow-wow enough for a million; but they was our dogs; so we stopped till they catched up; and when they see it warn't nobody but us, they just said howdy, and tore right ahead towards the shouting; and then we struck upstream again, through the bush to my canoe, and hopped in and pulled for dear life towards the middle of the river. Then we struck out, easy and comfortable, for the island where my raft was; and we could hear them yelling and barking at each other all up and down the bank, till we was so far away the sounds got dim and died out. And when we stepped onto the raft

I says, "*Now*, old Jim, you're a free man *again*, and I bet you won't ever be a slave no more."

"En a mighty good job it wuz, too, Huck. It 'uz planned beautiful, en *done* beautiful; dey ain't *nobody* kin git up a plan dat's mo' mixed up en splendid den what dat one wuz."

We was all glad as we could be, but Tom was the gladdest of all because he had a bullet in the calf of his leg.

When me and Jim heard that we didn't feel as brash as we did before. It was hurting him considerable, and bleeding; so we laid him in the wigwam and tore up a shirt for to bandage him, but he says:

"Gimme the rags; I can do it myself. Don't stop now, and the evasion booming along so handsome; man the sweeps, and set her loose! Boys, we done it elegant—'deed we did! Slick as nothing at all. Man the sweeps—man the sweeps!"

But me and Jim was consulting—and thinking. And after we'd thought a minute, I says, "Say it, Jim."

So he says, "Well, den, dis is de way it look to me, Huck. Ef it wuz *him* dat 'uz bein' sot free, en one er de boys wuz to git shot, would he say, 'Go on en save me, nemmine 'bout a doctor f'r to save dis one'? You *bet* he wouldn't! *Well*, den, is *Jim* gwyne to say it? No, sah—I doan' budge a step out'n dis place 'dout a *doctor;* not if it's forty year!"

I reckoned he'd say what he did say—so it was all right now, and I told Tom I was a-going for a doctor. He raised considerable row about it, but me and Jim stuck to it and wouldn't budge. So I left in the canoe, and Jim was to hide in the woods when he see the doctor coming till he was gone again.

THE DOCTOR WAS AN OLD MAN, a very nice, kind-looking old man. When I got him up I told him me and my brother was over on Spanish Island hunting yesterday, and camped on a piece of a raft we found, and about midnight he must 'a' kicked his gun in his dreams, for it went off and shot him in the leg, and we wanted him to fix it and not say nothing about it, because we wanted to come home this evening and surprise the folks.

"Who is your folks?" he says.

"The Phelpses, down yonder."

"Oh," he says. And after a minute he says, "How'd you say he got shot?"

"He had a dream," I says, "and it shot him."

"Singular dream," he says.

So he got his saddlebags, and we started. But when he see the canoe he didn't like the look of her—said she didn't look safe for two. I says, "You needn't be afeard, sir, she carried the three of us easy."

"What three?"

"Why, me and Sid, and—and—and *the guns*."

"Oh," he says.

But he put his foot on the gunnel and rocked her, and shook his head, and said he'd look around for a bigger one. But they was all chained; so he took my canoe, and said for me to wait till he come back, or maybe I better go home and get them ready for the surprise. I told him just how to find the raft, and then he started.

So then I crept into a lumber pile to get some sleep; and next time I waked up the sun was away up! I shot out and went for the doctor's house, but they told me he warn't back yet. Well, thinks I, that looks bad for Tom, and I'll dig out for the island right off. So away I shoved, and turned the corner, and nearly rammed my head into Uncle Silas's stomach! He says, "Why, *Tom!* Where you been all this time, you rascal?"

"*I* hain't been nowheres," I says, "only just hunting for the runaway nigger—me and Sid."

"Why, where ever did you go?" he says. "Your aunt's been mighty uneasy."

"She needn't," I says. "We was all right. We followed the men and the dogs, but they outrun us; and we thought we heard them on the water, so we got a canoe, but couldn't find nothing of them; so we cruised along till we got kind of tired; and tied up and went to sleep; then we paddled over here to hear the news, and Sid's at the post office to see what he can hear."

So we went to the post office to get "Sid"; but just as I sus-picioned, he warn't there; so the old man he got a letter out of the office, and we waited awhile; then the old man said, come along, let Sid foot it home, when he got done fooling around.

When we got home Aunt Sally was that glad to see me she laughed and cried both. And the place was plum full of farmers and farmers' wives, to dinner; and such clack a body never heard. Old Mrs. Hotchkiss was the worst. She says:

"Well, Sister Phelps, I've ransacked that-air cabin over, an' I b'lieve the nigger was crazy. I says to Sister Damrell—didn't I, Sister Damrell?—s'I, he's crazy, s'I; everything shows it, s'I. Look at that-air grindstone, s'I; want to tell *me* any cretur 't's in his right mind 's a-goin' to scrabble all them crazy things onto a grindstone? Here sich 'n' sich a person busted his heart; 'n' here so 'n' so pegged along for thirty-seven year! He's plumb crazy, s'I; it's what I says in the fust place, it's what I says in the middle, 'n' it's what I says last 'n' all the time—the nigger's crazy—crazy 's Nebokoodneezer, s'I."

"An' look at that-air ladder made out'n rags, Sister Hotchkiss," says old Mrs. Damrell. "What in the name o' goodness *could* he ever want of—"

"The very words I was a-saying no longer ago th'n this minute to Sister Utterback. 'N' how in the nation'd they ever *git* that grindstone *in* there, *any*way? 'N' who dug that-air *hole*? 'N' who—"

"My very *words*, Brer Penrod! I was a-sayin'—pass that-air sasser o' m'lasses, won't ye?—I was a-sayin' to Sister Dunlap, how *did* they git that grindstone in there? Without *help*, mind you. Don't tell *me*, s'I; there *wuz* help, s'I; ther's ben a *dozen* a-helpin' that nigger; 'n' moreover, s'I—"

"A *dozen* says you! *Forty* couldn't 'a' done everything that's been done. Look at them case-knife saws and things, how tedious they've been made; look at that bed leg sawed off with 'm; look at that nigger made out'n straw on the bed! Why, dog my cats, they must 'a' ben a houseful o' niggers in there every night for four weeks to 'a' done all that work, Sister Phelps. Look at that shirt—every last inch of it kivered over with secret African writ'n done with blood!"

"People to *help* him, Brother Marples! Well, I reckon you'd *think* so if you'd 'a' been in this house for a while back. Why, they've stole everything they could lay their hands on. They stole that shirt right off o' the line! And as for that sheet they made the rag ladder out of, ther' ain't no telling how many times they *didn't* steal that; and flour, and candles, and candlesticks, and spoons, and the old warming pan; and me and Silas and my Sid and Tom on the constant watch day *and* night. Why, *sperits* couldn't 'a' done better. And I reckon they must 'a' *been* sperits—because, *you* know our dogs; ther' ain't no better; well, them dogs never even got on the *track* of 'm once! You explain *that* to me if you can—*any* of you!"

"Well, it does beat—"

"Laws alive, I never—"

"*House* thieves as well as—"

"Goodnessgraciousakes, I'd ben afeard to *live* in sich a—"

"'Fraid to *live!* Why, I was that scared I dasn't hardly go to bed; why, goodness sakes, if I warn't afraid they'd steal some o' the family! I says to myself, There's my two poor boys asleep, 'way upstairs in that lonesome room, and I declare I was that uneasy 't I crep' up there and locked 'em in! I *did*." And Aunt Sally stopped, looking kind of wondering, and then she turned around slow, and when her eye lit on me—I got up and took a walk.

Says I to myself, I can explain better how we come to not be in that room this morning if I go out to one side and study over it a little. So I done it. And when it was late in the day the people all went, and then I come in and told her the noise and shooting waked up me and "Sid," and the door was locked, and we wanted to see the fun, so we went down the lightning rod. And then I went on and told her all what I told Uncle Silas before; and then she said she'd forgive us; and so, as long as no harm hadn't come of it, she judged she better put in her time being grateful we was alive and well, stead of fretting over what was past and done. So then she kissed me, and dropped into a kind of a brown study; and pretty soon jumps up, and says:

"Why, lawsamercy, it's most night, and Sid not come yet! What *has* become of that boy?"

I see my chance; so I says, "I'll run right up to town and get him," I says.

"No you won't," she says. "You'll stay right wher' you are; *one's* enough to be lost at a time. If he ain't here to supper your uncle 'll go."

Well, he warn't there to supper; so right after supper Uncle went.

He come back about ten a bit uneasy; hadn't run across Tom's track. Aunt Sally was a good *deal* uneasy; but Uncle Silas he said there warn't no occasion to be—boys will be boys, he said, and you'll see this one turn up in the morning. But she said she'd set up awhile anyway, and keep a light burning so he could see it.

And then when I went up to bed she come up with me and tucked me in, and mothered me so good I felt mean; and she set down on the bed and talked with me a long time, and said what a splendid boy Sid was, and didn't seem to want to ever stop talking about him. And when she was going away she looked down in my eyes so steady and gentle, and says:

"The door ain't going to be locked, Tom, and there's the window and the rod; but you'll be good, *won't* you? And you won't go? For *my* sake."

Laws knows I *wanted* to go bad enough to see about Tom; but after that I wouldn't 'a' went, not for kingdoms. But Tom was on my mind, so I slept very restless. And twice I went down the rod in the night, and slipped around front, and see her setting there by the candle in the window with her eyes towards the road and the tears in them; and I wished I could do something for her, but I couldn't. And the third time I waked up at dawn, and slid down, and she was there yet, and her old gray head was resting on her hand, and she was asleep.

CHAPTER XV

THE OLD MAN WAS UP TO TOWN again before breakfast, but couldn't get no track of Tom; and both of them set at the table thinking, and not saying nothing, and their coffee getting cold. And by and by the old man says to Aunt Sally, "Did I give you the letter?"

"What letter?"

"The one I got yesterday out of the post office."

"No, you didn't give me no letter."

"Well, I must 'a' forgot it."

So he went off somewheres, and fetched the letter, and give it to her. She says, "Why, it's from St. Petersburg—it's from Sis."

I allowed another walk would do me good. But before she could break it open she dropped it and run—for she see something. And so did I. It was Tom Sawyer on a mattress; and that old doctor; and Jim, in *her* calico dress, with his hands tied behind him; and a lot of people. I hid the letter behind the first thing that come handy, and rushed. She flung herself at Tom, crying, and says, "Oh, he's dead, he's dead, I know he's dead!"

And Tom turned his head a little, and muttered something or other, which showed he warn't in his right mind; then she flung up her hands, and says, "He's alive, thank God! And that's enough!" and she snatched a kiss of him, and flew for the house to get the bed ready.

I followed the men to see what they was going to do with Jim; and the old doctor and Uncle Silas followed after Tom into the house. The men was very huffy, and some of them wanted to hang Jim for an example to all the other niggers around there. But the others said, don't do it; he ain't our nigger, and his owner would turn up and make us pay for him, sure. So that cooled them down a little.

They cussed Jim considerable, though, and give him a cuff or two side the head once in a while, but Jim never said nothing, and he never let on to know me, and they took him to the same cabin, and put his own clothes on him, and chained him again, and not to no bed leg this time, but to a big staple drove into the bottom log, and chained his hands, too, and both legs. Then the old doctor comes and takes a look, and says:

"Don't be no rougher on him than you're obleeged to, because he ain't a bad nigger. When I got to where I found the boy I see I couldn't cut the bullet out without some help, and he warn't in no condition for me to leave to go and get help; and he got worse and worse, and after a time he went out of his head, and wouldn't let me come a-nigh him any more; so I says, I got to have *help* somehow; and the minute I says it out crawls this nigger from somewheres and says he'll help, and he done it, too, and done it very well. Of course I judged he must be a runaway nigger, and there I *was!* So I had to stick plumb until daylight this morning; but I never see a nigger that was a better nuss or faithfuler, and yet he was risking his freedom to do it. I liked the nigger for that! I tell you, gentlemen, a nigger like that is worth a thousand dollars—and kind treatment, too. I had everything I needed, and the boy was doing as well there as he would 'a' done at home; but there I *was*, with both of 'm on my hands, and there I had to stick till dawn this morning; then some men in a skiff come by, and as luck would have it the nigger was setting by the pallet asleep; so I motioned them in quiet, and they grabbed him and tied him before he knowed what he was about. He ain't no bad nigger, gentlemen; that's what I think."

Somebody says, "Well, it sounds very good, Doctor, I'm obleeged to say"; and then the others softened up a little, too, and they all agreed that Jim had acted very well.

Then they come out and locked Jim up. I hoped they was going to say he could have the chains took off; but they didn't think of it, and I reckoned it warn't best for me to mix in, but I judged I'd get the doctor's yarn to Aunt Sally somehow as soon as I'd got through the breakers that was laying just ahead of me—explanations, I mean, of how I forgot to mention about Sid being shot. But I had plenty time. Aunt Sally she stuck to the sickroom, and every time I see Uncle Silas mooning around I dodged him.

Next morning I heard Tom was a deal better, and they said Aunt Sally was gone to get a nap. So I slips to the sickroom, and if I found him awake I reckoned we could put up a yarn for the family that would wash. But he was sleeping, and sleeping very peaceful, too; and pale. So I set down and laid for him to wake. In about half an hour Aunt Sally comes in, and there I was, up a stump again! She motioned me to be still, and set down by me, and begun to whisper, and said we could all be joyful now, because all the symptoms was first-rate, and he'd been sleeping like that for ever so long, and ten to one he'd wake up in his right mind. So we set there watching, and by and by he stirs a bit, and opens his eyes, and says:

"Hello! Why, I'm at *home!* How's that? Where's the raft?"

"It's all right," I says.

"And *Jim?*"

"The same," I says, but couldn't say it pretty brash. But he never noticed, but says, "Good! Splendid! *Now* we're all right and safe! Did you tell Aunty?"

I was going to say yes; but she chipped in and says, "About what, Sid?"

"Why, about the way the whole thing was done. About how we set the runaway nigger free—me and Tom."

"Good land! What *is* the child talking about! Dear, dear, out of his head again!"

"*No*, I ain't out of my HEAD; I know all what I'm talking about. We *did* set him free—me and Tom. We laid out to do it, and we *done* it. And we done it elegant, too." He'd got a start, and she just set and stared and stared, and let him clip along, and I see it warn't no use for *me* to put in. "Why, Aunty, it cost us a power of work—weeks of it—every night, whilst you was all asleep. And we had to steal candles, and the sheet, and the shirt, and your dress, and no end of things, and you can't think what work it was to make the saws, and pens, and inscriptions, and you can't think *half* the fun it was. And we had to make up the pictures of coffins and things, and get up and down the lightning rod, and dig the hole into the cabin—"

"Mercy sakes!"

"—and load up the cabin with rats and so on, for company for Jim; and then you kept Tom here so long with the butter in his hat that you come near spiling the whole business, because the men come before we was out of the cabin, and we had to rush, and they heard us and let drive at us, and I got my share, and then the dogs come, and we got our canoe, and made for the raft, and was all safe, and Jim was a free man, and we done it all by ourselves, and *wasn't* it bully, Aunty!"

"Well, I never heard the likes of it in all my born days! So it was *you*, you little rapscallions, that's been making all this trouble! To think—why, *you* just get well once, you young scamp, and I'll tan the Old Harry out o' both o' ye!"

But Tom, he *was* so proud and joyful, he just *couldn't* hold in, and his tongue just *went* it—she a-chipping in, and spitting fire all along, and both of them going it at once, like a cat convention; and she says, "*Well*, you get all the enjoyment you can out of it *now*, for mind I tell you if I catch you meddling with him again—"

"Meddling with *who?*" Tom says, dropping his smile.

"With *who?* Why, the runaway nigger, of course!"

Tom looks at me, and says, "Tom, didn't you tell me he was all right? Hasn't he got away?"

"*Him?*" says Aunt Sally. "The runaway nigger? 'Deed he hasn't. They've got him back, and he's in that cabin again, and loaded down with chains, till he's claimed or sold!"

Tom rose up in bed, with his eye hot, and sings out to me, "They hain't no *right* to shut him up! *Shove!* And don't you lose a minute. Turn him loose! He ain't no slave; he's as free as any cretur that walks this earth!"

"What *does* the child mean?"

"I mean every word I *say*, Aunt Sally. I've knowed him all his life, and so has Tom, there. Old Miss Watson died two months ago, and she was ashamed she ever was going to sell him down the river, and *said* so; and she set him free in her will."

"Then what on earth did *you* want to set him free for, seeing he was already free?"

"Well, that *is* a question, I must say; and *just* like women! Why, I wanted the *adventure* of it; and I'd 'a' waded neck-deep in blood to—goodness alive, AUNT POLLY!"

If she warn't standing right there, just inside the door, looking as sweet and contented as an angel half full of pie, I wish I may never!

Aunt Sally jumped for her, and most hugged the head off of her, and cried over her, and I found a good enough place for me under the bed, for it was getting pretty sultry for *us*, seemed to me. And

I peeped out, and in a little while Tom's Aunt Polly shook herself loose and stood looking across at Tom over her spectacles. And then she says:

"Yes, you *better* turn away—I would if I was you, Tom."

"Oh, deary me!" says Aunt Sally. "*Is* he changed so? Why, that ain't *Tom*, it's Sid; Tom's—why, where is Tom? He was here a minute ago."

"You mean where's Huck *Finn!* I reckon I hain't raised such a scamp as my Tom all these years not to know him when I *see* him. That *would* be a pretty howdy-do. Come out from under that bed, Huck Finn."

So I done it. But not feeling brash.

Aunt Sally she was one of the mixed-upest-looking persons I ever see—except one, and that was Uncle Silas, when he come in and they told it all to him. Tom's Aunt Polly, she told all about who I was, and what; and I had to up and tell how I was in such a tight place that when Mrs. Phelps took me for Tom Sawyer I had to stand it—there warn't no other way, and I knowed Tom wouldn't mind, because it would be nuts for him, being a mystery, and he'd make an adventure out of it. And so it turned out, and he let on to be Sid, and made things as soft as he could for me.

And his Aunt Polly she said Tom was right about old Miss Watson setting Jim free in her will; and so, sure enough, Tom Sawyer had gone and took all that trouble to set a free nigger free! And I couldn't ever understand before, until that minute, how he *could* help a body set a nigger free with his bringing-up.

Well, Aunt Polly she said that when Aunt Sally wrote to her that Tom and *Sid* had come all right, she says to herself:

"Look at that, now! I might have expected it, letting him go off that way without anybody to watch him. So now I got to go and trapse all the way down the river, eleven hundred mile, and find out what the creetur's up to *this* time, as long as I couldn't seem to get any answer out of you about it."

"Why, I never heard nothing from you," says Aunt Sally.

"Well, I wonder! Why, I wrote you twice to ask you what you could mean by Sid being here."

"Well, I never got 'em, Sis."

Aunt Polly she turns around slow and severe, and says:

"You, Tom!"

"Well—*what?*" he says, kind of pettish.

"Don't you what *me*—hand out them letters."

"What letters?"

"*Them* letters. I be bound, if I have to take a-holt of you—"

"They're in the trunk. There, now. I hain't touched them. But I knowed they'd make trouble, and I thought I'd—"

"Well, you *do* need skinning. And I wrote another one to tell you I was coming; and I s'pose he—"

"No, it come yesterday," Aunt Sally said. "I hain't read it yet, but *it's* all right, I've got that one."

I wanted to offer to bet two dollars she hadn't, but I reckoned maybe it was just as safe to not to. So I never said nothing.

THE FIRST TIME I CATCHED Tom private I asked him what was his idea, time of the evasion—what it was he'd planned to do if the evasion worked all right and he managed to set a nigger free that was already free before? And he said, what he had planned in his head from the start, if we got Jim out all safe, was for us to run him down the river on the raft, and have adventures plumb to the mouth of the river, and then tell him about his being free, and take him back up home on a steamboat, in style, and pay him for his lost time, and write ahead and get out all the niggers, and have them waltz him into town with a brass band, and then he would be a hero, and so would we. But I reckoned it was about as well the way it was.

We had Jim out of the chains in no time, and when Aunt Polly and Uncle Silas and Aunt Sally found out how good he helped the doctor nurse Tom, they made a heap of fuss over him. And we had him up to the sickroom, and had a high talk; and Tom give Jim forty dollars for being prisoner for us so patient, and Jim was pleased most to death, and busted out, and says:

"*Dah*, now, Huck, what I tell you up dah on Jackson Islan'? I *tole* you I got a hairy breas'; en I *tole* you I ben rich wunst, en gwineter be rich *ag'in;* en it's come true! Dah, now, doan' talk to *me*—signs is *signs*, mine I tell you!"

And then Tom he says, le's all three slide out of here one of these nights and get an outfit, and go for howling adventures amongst the Injuns, over in the territory, for a couple of weeks or two; and I says, all right, that suits me, but I ain't got no money for to buy the outfit, and I reckon I couldn't get none from home, because it's likely Pap's been back before now, and got it all away from Judge Thatcher.

"No, he hain't," Tom says. "It's all there yet—six thousand dollars and more; and your pap hain't ever been back since. Hadn't when I come away, anyhow."

Jim says, kind of solemn, "He ain't a-comin' back, Huck."

I says, "Why, Jim?"

"Nemmine why, Huck—but he ain't comin' back no mo'."

But I kept at him; so at last he says, "Doan' you 'member de house dat was float'n down de river, en dey wuz a man in dah, en I went in en didn' let you come in? Well, den, you kin git yo' money when you wants it, kase dat wuz him."

Tom's most well now, and got his bullet around his neck on a watch guard for a watch, and is always seeing what time it is, and so there ain't nothing more to write about, and I am rotten glad of it, because if I'd 'a' knowed what a trouble it was to make a book I wouldn't 'a' tackled it, and ain't a-going to no more. But I reckon I got to light out for the territory ahead of the rest, because Aunt Sally she's going to adopt me and sivilize me, and I can't stand it. I been there before.

THE SEA
AROUND US

The
Sea Around Us

A condensation of the book by
Rachel L. Carson

Paintings by Merle Shore

THE SEA is the last frontier of Earth, and Rachel Carson's exploration of its secrets has been enthralling readers ever since it was first published in 1951. Here, expressed with a poet's imagery, is the accumulated lore of oceanography: what man has been able to learn of the winds and waves, the restless tides and turbulent currents, the awesome undersea mountains and canyons, the incredibly profuse and beautiful creatures of the marine world.

The Sea Around Us brought its author many honors, including the National Book Award; it became a worldwide best seller. But long before its publication Rachel Carson's eminence as a scientist and skill as a writer had been established. A native of Pennsylvania, she graduated from Pennsylvania College for Women and did advanced study at Johns Hopkins University as well as at the Marine Biological Laboratory in Woods Hole, Massachusetts. For some years she was editor in chief of the United States Fish and Wildlife Service. Her first book, *Under the Sea-Wind,* appeared in 1941.

The gifted and courageous Miss Carson died at her home in Silver Spring, Maryland, in 1964. Just two years previously she had stirred national debate with *Silent Spring,* a biologist's protest against the indiscriminate use of insecticides and chemical sprays which were, she believed, upsetting the balance of nature. But *The Sea Around Us* remains her most memorable achievement. "It is a work of science," said the New York *Herald Tribune;* "it is stamped with authority. It is a work of art; it is saturated with the excitement of mystery. It is literature."

CHAPTER I: *The Gray Beginnings*

BEGINNINGS ARE APT TO BE shadowy, and so it is with the beginnings of that great mother of life, the sea. Many people have debated how and when the earth got its ocean, and it is not surprising that their explanations do not always agree. For the plain and inescapable truth is that no one was there to see, and the story of how the young planet Earth acquired an ocean must be pieced together from many sources and contain whole chapters the details of which we can only imagine. The story is founded on the testimony of the earth's most ancient rocks, which were young when the earth was young; on other evidence written on the face of the earth's satellite, the moon; and on hints contained in the history of the sun and the whole universe of star-filled space. For although no man was there to witness this cosmic birth, the stars and the moon and the rocks were there and, indeed, had much to do with the fact that there is an ocean.

The tempestuous and violent events of which I write must have occurred somewhat more than four billion years ago. As nearly as science can tell, that is the approximate age of the oldest rocks found anywhere on earth, and the ocean must be very nearly as old. But this is only a minimum estimate. Our ideas about the age of the earth are constantly undergoing revision as older and older rocks are discovered and as methods of study are refined. Geologists are generally of the opinion that present concepts of geologic time will be considerably lengthened in the future.

The new earth, freshly torn from its parent sun, was a ball of whirling gases, intensely hot, rushing through the black spaces of the universe on a path and at a speed controlled by immense forces. Gradually the ball of flaming gases cooled. The gases began to liquefy, and Earth became a molten mass. The materials of this mass eventually became sorted out in a definite pattern: the heaviest forming the earth's iron core, the less heavy becoming the basalt layer surrounding it, and the least heavy forming the granite outer rim. This pattern persists today.

The outer shell of the young earth must have been a good many millions of years changing from the liquid to the solid state, and it is believed that, before this change was completed, an event of the greatest importance took place—the formation of the moon. Next time you stand on a beach at night, watching the moon's bright path across the water and conscious of the moon-drawn tides, remember that the moon itself may have been born of a great tidal wave of earthly substance, torn off into space.

There were tides in the new earth long before there was an ocean. In response to the pull of the sun the molten liquids of the earth's whole surface rose in tides that rolled unhindered around the globe. Those who believe that the moon is a child of Earth say that during an early stage of the earth's development something happened that caused this rolling, viscid tide to gather speed and momentum and to rise to unimaginable heights. Every sun tide was given increased momentum by the push of the earth's oscillation, and each of the twice-daily tides was larger than the one before it. Physicists have calculated that, after five hundred years of such monstrous, steadily increasing tides, those on the side toward the sun became too high for stability, and a great wave was torn away and hurled into space. But immediately, of course, the newly created satellite which we call the moon became subject to physical laws that sent it spinning into orbit about the earth.

This probably took place after the earth's crust had cooled somewhat and become slightly hardened. There is to this day a great scar on the surface of the globe. This scar or depression holds the Pacific Ocean. Some geophysicists say the floor of the Pacific is composed of basalt, the substance of the earth's middle layer, while all other oceans are floored with a thin layer of granite, which makes up most of the earth's outer layer. What became of the Pacific's granite covering? The most convenient assumption is that it was torn away when the moon was formed.

The birth of the moon probably helped shape other regions of the world ocean besides the Pacific. When part of the crust was torn away, strains must have been set up in the remaining granite envelope. Perhaps the granite mass cracked open on the side opposite the moon scar. Perhaps, as the earth spun on its axis and rushed on its orbit through space, the masses of granite began to drift apart. Gradually the tarry, slowly hardening basalt layer became solid and the wandering continents came to rest, frozen into place with oceans between them.

But this is to anticipate the story, for when the moon was born there was no ocean. The gradually cooling earth was enveloped in heavy layers of cloud, which contained much of the water of the new planet. For a long time its surface was so hot that no moisture could fall without immediately being reconverted to steam, which perpetually renewed the dense cloud covering—so thick that no sunlight could penetrate it.

As soon as the earth's crust cooled enough, the rains began to fall. They fell continuously, day and night, days passing into months, into years, into centuries. They poured into the waiting ocean basins or, falling upon the continental masses, drained away to become sea.

That primeval ocean must have been only faintly salt. But the ever-falling rains were the symbol of the dissolution of the continents. It is an endless, inexorable process that has never stopped— the dissolving of the rocks, the leaching out of their contained minerals, the carrying of the rock fragments and dissolved minerals to the ocean. And over the eons of time the sea has grown ever more bitter with the salt of the continents.

In what manner the sea produced the mysterious and wonderful living stuff called protoplasm no one is yet wise enough to be sure. It seems probable that, within the warm, dimly lit saltiness of the primeval sea, certain organic substances were fashioned from carbon dioxide, sulfur, nitrogen, phosphorus, potassium and calcium. Perhaps these were transition steps from which the complex molecules of protoplasm arose—molecules that somehow acquired the ability to reproduce themselves and begin the endless stream of life.

Those first living things may have resembled bacteria—mysterious borderline forms that were not quite plants, not quite animals, barely over the intangible line that separates the nonliving from the living. Probably the sea's first children lived on the organic substances then present in the ocean waters, or lived directly on inorganic food.

All the while the cloud cover was thinning, and finally the sun for the first time shone through upon the sea. By this time some of the living things that floated in the sea must have developed the magic green substance chlorophyll, with which plants in sunlight are able to transform lifeless chemicals into the living stuff of their tissues. So the first true plants came into being. Another group of organisms, lacking the chlorophyll but needing organic food, found they could make a way of life for themselves by devouring the plants. So the first animals arose.

As the years passed, and the centuries, and the millions of years, the stream of life grew more and more complex. From simple, one-celled creatures others arose, with specialized cells and with organs for feeding, digesting, breathing, reproducing. Sponges grew on the rocky bottom of the sea's edge and coral animals built their habitations in warm, clear waters. Jellyfish swam and drifted in the sea. Worms evolved, and starfish, and hard-shelled creatures with many-jointed legs, the arthropods. The plants, too, progressed, from microscopic algae to branched and fruiting seaweeds that were plucked from the coastal rocks by the surf and cast adrift.

During all this time the continents had no life. There was little to induce living things to come ashore. The lands must have been bleak and hostile beyond the power of words to describe. Imagine a whole continent of naked rock across which no covering mantle of green had been drawn, a silent land, except for the sound of the rains and winds that swept across it.

Meanwhile, the gradual cooling of the planet was progressing into its deeper layers; and as the interior slowly cooled and contracted it drew away from the outer shell. This shell, accommodating itself to the shrinking sphere within it, fell into folds and wrinkles—the earth's first mountain ranges. The epochs of mountain building only served to speed up the processes of erosion by which the continents were worn down and their crumbling rock and contained minerals returned to the sea. And in the sea, life continued to evolve.

The earliest forms were probably soft-bodied and have left no fossils by which we can identify them. For the past five hundred million years, however, the rocks have preserved the fossil record. By the dawn of the Cambrian period, when the history of living things was first inscribed on rock pages, life in the sea had progressed so far that all the main groups of backboneless or invertebrate animals had been developed. But there were no animals with backbones, no insects, and still no plant or animal had been evolved that was capable of venturing onto the forbidding land. Meanwhile, with violent tremblings of the earth and with the fire and smoke of roaring volcanoes, more mountains rose and wore away, glaciers moved to and fro over the earth, and the sea crept over the continents and again receded.

It was not until Silurian time, only some three hundred and fifty million years ago, that the first pioneer of land life crept out on the shore. It was an arthropod, one of the great tribe that later produced crabs and lobsters and insects. It lived a strange life, half terrestrial, half aquatic, something like that of the ghost crabs that speed along the beaches today, now and then dashing into the surf to moisten their gills.

It is doubtful that the animals alone would have succeeded in colonizing the land. Only the plants had the power to make soil of the crumbling rocks, to hold it back from the rains that would have swept it away, and little by little to soften and subdue the bare rock and lifeless desert. The first land plants must have been closely related to some of the larger seaweeds that had learned to live in the coastal shallows, developing strengthened stems and grasping, rootlike holdfasts to resist the drag and pull of the waves. Perhaps in some coastal lowlands, periodically drained and flooded, some such plants found it possible to survive, though separated from the sea. This also seems to have taken place in the Silurian period. The lakes, the river shores and the coastal swamps of those days were testing grounds in which plants and animals either became adapted to new conditions or perished.

As the lands rose and the seas receded, a strange fishlike creature emerged on the land, and over the thousands of years its fins became legs, and instead of gills it developed lungs. In the Devonian sandstone this first amphibian left its footprint.

On land and sea the stream of life poured on. New forms evolved; some old ones declined and disappeared. On land the mosses and the ferns and the seed plants developed. The reptiles for a time dominated the earth, gigantic, grotesque and terrifying. Birds learned to live and move in the ocean of air. The first small mammals lurked inconspicuously in hidden crannies of the earth as though in fear of the reptiles.

Animals that took up a land life carried with them a part of the sea in their bodies, a heritage passed on to their children which even today links each land animal with the ancient sea. Fish, amphibian and reptile, warm-blooded bird and mammal—each of us carries in our veins a salty stream in which the elements sodium, potassium and calcium are combined in almost the same proportions as in seawater. This is our inheritance from the day, untold millions of years ago, when a remote ancestor, having progressed from the one-celled to the many-celled stage, first developed a circulatory system in which the fluid was merely the water of the sea. And as life itself began in the sea, so each of us begins his individual life in a miniature ocean within his mother's womb, and in the stages of his embryonic development repeats the steps by which his race evolved, from gill-breathing inhabitants of a water world to creatures able to live on land.

Some of the land reptiles later returned to the ocean. These huge and formidable creatures disappeared millions of years ago, but we remember them when we come upon a large sea turtle swimming many miles at sea. Much later, perhaps no more than fifty million years ago, some of the mammals, too, abandoned a land life for the ocean. Their descendants are the sea lions, seals, sea elephants and whales of today.

Among the land mammals there was a race of creatures that took to an arboreal existence. Their hands underwent remarkable development, becoming skilled in manipulating and examining objects, and along with this skill came a superior brainpower that compensated for what these comparatively small mammals lacked in strength. At last, perhaps somewhere in the vast interior of Asia, they descended from the trees and became again terrestrial. The past million years have seen their transformation into beings with the body and brain and spirit of man.

Eventually man, too, found his way back to the sea. Standing on its shores, he must have looked out upon it with wonder and curiosity, compounded with an unconscious recognition of his lineage. He could not physically reenter the ocean as the seals and whales had done. But over the centuries, with all the skill and ingenuity and reasoning powers of his mind, he has sought to explore and investigate even its most remote parts. He built boats to venture out on its surface. Later he found ways to descend to its floor, carrying with him the air he needed to breathe. He learned ways to probe its depths, he let down nets to capture its life, he invented mechanical eyes and ears that could re-create for his senses a world long lost, but never wholly forgotten.

And yet man has returned to his mother sea only on her own terms. He cannot control or change the ocean as, in his brief tenancy of earth, he has subdued and plundered the continents. In the artificial world of his cities and towns, he often forgets the true nature of his planet and the long vistas of its history, in which the existence of the race of men has occupied a mere moment of time. The sense of all these things comes to him most clearly in the course of a long ocean voyage, when he watches day after day the receding rim of the horizon, ridged and furrowed by waves; when at night he becomes aware of the earth's rotation as the stars pass overhead; or when, alone in this world of water and sky, he feels the loneliness of his earth in space. Then he knows the truth that his world is a water world, a planet dominated by its covering mantle of ocean, in which the continents are but transient intrusions of land above the surface of the all-encircling sea.

CHAPTER II: *The Pattern of the Surface*

NOWHERE IN ALL THE SEA does life exist in such bewildering abundance as in the surface waters. From the deck of a vessel you may look down, hour after hour, on the shimmering disks of jellyfish, their gently pulsating bells dotting the surface as far as you can see. Or again, you may glimpse not only the abundance but something of the fierce uncompromisingness of sea life as you look over the rail and down, down into the clear, deep green water. Suddenly there passes a silver shower of finger-long fishlets. The sun strikes a metallic gleam from their flanks as they streak by with the desperate speed of the hunted. Perhaps then you see the gulls hovering, with eager, mewing cries, waiting for the little fish to be driven to the surface.

Or you may sail for days seeing only empty water and empty sky, apparently barren of life. But if you towed a fine-meshed net through the seemingly lifeless water and examined the washings of the net, you would find life scattered through the surface waters like a fine dust. A cupful of water may contain millions upon millions of diatoms, tiny plant cells, each far too small to be seen by the human eye; or it may swarm with an infinitude of animal creatures, none larger than a dust mote.

With these surface waters, through a series of delicately adjusted, interlocking relationships, the life of all parts of the sea is linked. What happens to a diatom in the upper, sunlit strata of the sea may well determine what happens to a cod lying on a ledge of some rocky canyon a hundred fathoms below, or to a bed of multicolored, gorgeously plumed sea worms carpeting an underlying shoal, or to a prawn creeping over the soft oozes of the sea floor in the blackness of mile-deep water.

Feeding directly on such microscopic vegetables of the sea as the diatoms are the marine protozoa, many crustaceans, the young of crabs, barnacles, sea worms and fishes. Hordes of small carnivores, the first link in the chain of flesh eaters, move among these peaceful grazers: half-inch long, sharp-jawed arrowworms; gooseberrylike comb jellies, armed with grasping tentacles. Since they drift where the currents carry them, this strange community of creatures and the marine plants that sustain them are called plankton, a word derived from the Greek, meaning "wandering."

From the plankton the food chains lead on to the schools of plankton-feeding fishes like the herring, menhaden and mackerel; to the fish-eating bluefish, tuna and sharks; to the great whales who live on fishes, shrimps or some of the smallest plankton.

Unmarked and trackless though it may seem to us, the surface of the ocean is divided into definite zones, and the pattern of the surface water controls the distribution of its life. Fishes and plankton, whales and squid, birds and sea turtles, all are linked by unbreakable ties to certain kinds of water—warm or cold, clear or turbid, rich in phosphates or in silicates. They are bound to water where their food is plentiful, and the food is there because the water conditions are right.

To the human senses, the most obvious patterning of the surface waters is indicated by color. The deep blue water of the open sea is the color of barrenness; the green water of the coastal areas, with all its varying hues, is the color of life. The sea far from land is blue because in the journey of the light rays into deep water all the red rays and most of the yellow of the spectrum have been absorbed, so when the light returns to our eyes it is chiefly the cool blue rays that we see. The coastal water, rich in plankton, loses the transparency that permits deep penetration of light rays. The yellow and brown and green hues are derived from the minute algae and other microorganisms so abundant there. Seasonal abundance of certain forms containing reddish or brown pigments may cause the "red water" so common in some enclosed seas that they owe their names to it—the Red Sea is an example.

The colors of the sea are only the indirect signs of the presence or absence of conditions needed to support the surface life; other zones, invisible to the eye, are the ones that largely determine where marine creatures may live. For the sea is by no means a uniform solution of water; parts of it are more salty than others, and parts are warmer or colder.

The saltiest ocean water in the world is that of the Red Sea, where the burning sun and fierce heat produce such rapid evaporation that the salt content is forty parts per thousand, compared to about thirty-three for the waters off Cape Cod. The Sargasso Sea, receiving no inflow of river water or melting ice because of its remoteness from land, is the saltiest part of the Atlantic, which is the saltiest of the oceans. The polar seas are the least salty, because they are constantly being diluted by rain, snow and melting ice.

Ocean temperatures vary from about 28° Fahrenheit in polar seas to 96° in the Persian Gulf, which contains the hottest ocean water in the world. To creatures of the sea, which with few exceptions must match in their own bodies the temperature of the surrounding water, this range is tremendous, and change of temperature is probably the most important single condition that controls the distribution of marine animals. The beautiful reef corals are a perfect example. If you took a map of the world and drew a line thirty degrees north of the equator and another thirty degrees south of it, you would have outlined in general the waters where reef corals may be found, for the calcareous structure of the coral reef can be fashioned only in water at least as warm as 70° F.

In the tropics, sea life is intense, vivid and infinitely varied. The warm temperatures speed up the processes of reproduction and growth, so that many generations are produced in the time required to bring one to maturity in cold seas. There is more opportunity for genetic mutations; hence the bewildering variety of tropical life. Yet in any species there are far fewer individuals than in the colder zones. In cold seas life proceeds at a pace slowed by the icy water. But the mineral richness of these waters makes possible the enormous abundance of whatever forms inhabit them. Swarms of surface plankton, the copepods and swimming snails fill the surface waters of cold seas and lure the herring and the mackerel, the flocks of seabirds, the whales and the seals.

The mid-ocean regions, bounded by the currents that sweep around the ocean basins, are in general the deserts of the sea. There are few birds and few surface-feeding fishes; indeed there is little surface plankton to attract them. The life of these regions is largely confined to deep water.

The Sargasso Sea, a place forgotten by the winds, undisturbed by the strong flow of waters that girdle it, is an exception. It is so different from any other central ocean basin, or, indeed, any other place on earth, that it may well be considered a definite geographic region. It lies all about Bermuda and extends more than halfway across the Atlantic, its entire area being roughly as large as the United States. The Sargasso, with all its legendary terrors for sailing ships, is a creation of the great currents of the North Atlantic that encircle it and bring into it millions of tons of floating sargasso weeds. These are brown algae that live attached to reefs or rocky outcroppings off the coasts of the West Indies and Florida. Plants are torn away by storms, especially during the hurricane season. They are picked up by that great and rapidly flowing river-in-the-sea, the Gulf Stream, and drift northward. With them go, as involuntary passengers, many small fishes, crabs, shrimps, and innumerable larvae of assorted species of marine creatures.

Curious things happen to the animals that have ridden for months on the sargasso weed into a new home. Once they lived near the sea's edge, a few feet or a few fathoms below the surface, but never far above a firm bottom. They could leave the shelter of the weeds at will and creep or swim about over the bottom in search of food. Now, in the middle of the ocean, the bottom lies two or three miles below them. For poor swimmers the weed to which they cling now represents a life raft. Over the ages since their ancestors came here some species have developed special organs of attachment, either for themselves or for their eggs, so that they may not sink into the cold, dark water far below.

There has long been controversy about the origin of the drifting weeds of the Sargasso. Some hold that the supply is maintained by weeds recently torn away from coastal beds; others that the rather limited sargasso fields of the West Indies and Florida cannot possibly supply the immense area of the Sargasso. They believe that we find here a self-perpetuating community of plants that have become adapted to life in the open sea, needing no roots or holdfasts for attachment and able to propagate vegetatively by a process of fragmentation. Probably there is truth in both ideas.

It takes about half a year for plants torn from West Indian shores to reach the northern border of the Sargasso, perhaps several years for them to be carried into the inner parts of this area. Meanwhile, some have been swept away by storms, others killed by cold where the Gulf Stream comes into contact with waters from the Arctic. For the plants that reach the calm of the Sargasso there is virtual immortality. Some may live for decades, others for centuries, according to their species. Some of the very weeds you would see if you visited the place today may have been seen by Columbus and his men. Apparently almost the only plants that die are those that drift into unfavorable conditions around the edges of the Sargasso or are picked up by outward-moving currents.

It must have taken eons to accumulate the present enormous quantities of weed, estimated at about ten million tons. But this is distributed over so large an area that most of the Sargasso is open water. The dense fields of weeds waiting to entrap a vessel never existed except in the imaginations of sailors, and the gloomy hulks of vessels doomed to endless drifting in the clinging weed are only the ghosts of things that never were.

CHAPTER III: *The Changing Year*

FOR THE SEA AS A WHOLE, the alternation of day and night, the passage of the seasons, the procession of the years are lost in its vastness, obliterated in its own changeless eternity. But the surface waters are different. The face of the sea, sparkling in the sun, mysterious in the twilight, is always changing. The surface waters move with the tides, stir to the breath of the winds, and rise and fall to the endless, hurrying forms of the waves. Most of all, they change with the advance of the seasons.

In the sea, as on land, spring is a time for renewal of life. During the long months of winter in the temperate zones the surface waters have been absorbing the cold. Now the heavy water begins to sink, displacing the warmer layers below. Rich stores of minerals have been accumulating on the floor of the continental shelf—some freighted down the rivers from the lands; some derived from sea creatures that have died and whose remains have drifted to the bottom. Nothing is wasted in the sea; every particle of material is used over and over again, first by one creature, then by another. In spring, the warm bottom water brings to the surface a rich supply of minerals, ready for use by new forms of life.

Just as land plants depend on minerals in the soil for their growth, every marine plant, even the smallest diatom, is dependent upon the nutrient salts or minerals in the seawater. Some of these elements are in short supply in winter. The microplant population must tide itself over this season as best it can, existing in a dormant state, like seeds of wheat in a field under snow and ice.

These, then, are the elements of the vernal blooming of the sea: the "seeds" of the dormant plants, the fertilizing chemicals, the warmth of the spring sun.

In a sudden awakening, incredible in its swiftness, the simplest plants of the sea begin to multiply. In the fierce intensity of their growth they cover vast areas of ocean with a living blanket of cells. Mile after mile of water may appear red or brown or green, the whole surface taking on the color of the plant cells.

Plants have undisputed sway in the sea for only a short time. Almost at once their own burst of multiplication is matched by a similar increase in the small animals of the plankton and in larger creatures. Now in the spring it is spawning time; the surface waters become a vast nursery. From far below, from the scattered shoals and banks, the eggs or young of many of the bottom animals rise to the surface. Even those which, in their maturity, will sink down to a sedentary life on the bottom spend the first weeks of life as freely swimming hunters of the plankton. As spring progresses new batches of larvae rise into the surface each day, the young of fishes and crabs and mussels and tube worms, mingling for a time with the regular members of the plankton. For a time each spring the waters may become blotched with brown, jellylike masses, and the fishermen's nets come up dripping a brown slime and containing no fish, for the herring have turned away from these waters as though in loathing of the viscid, foul-smelling algae. But in less time than passes between the full moon and the new, the spring flowering is past and the waters have cleared again.

In the spring the sea is filled with migrating fishes, some of them bound for the mouths of great rivers, which they will ascend to deposit their spawn. Chinook from the deep Pacific breast the rolling flood of the Columbia; shad move in to the Chesapeake, the Hudson and the Connecticut; salmon feel their way to the Penobscot and the Kennebec. For months or years these fish have known only the vast spaces of the ocean. Now spring and the maturing of their own bodies lead them back to the rivers of their birth.

Other mysterious comings and goings are linked with the advance of the year. Birds whose winter feeding territory may have encompassed the whole Atlantic or the whole Pacific converge upon some small island, the entire breeding population arriving within a few days. Whales appear off the slopes of the coastal banks, having come from no one knows where, by no one knows what route.

With the subsiding of the diatoms' orgy of cell division and the completed spawning of many of the plankton animals and most of the fish, life in the surface waters slackens to the slower pace of midsummer. Along the meeting places of the currents the pale moon jelly *Aurelia* gathers in thousands, forming sinuous lines or windrows across miles of sea. By midsummer the large red jellyfish, grown from the size of a thimble to that of an umbrella, moves through the sea with rhythmic pulsations, trailing long tentacles and as likely as not shepherding a little group of young cod or haddock, which find shelter under its bell and travel with it.

A hard, brilliant, coruscating phosphorescence often illuminates the summer sea. In waters where the protozoa *Noctiluca* is abundant it is the chief source of this luminescence which causes fishes, squid or dolphins to fill the water with racing flames and to clothe themselves in a ghostly radiance. Out over the plankton meadows of the North Atlantic the dry twitter of the phalaropes, small brown birds, wheeling and turning, dipping and rising, is heard for the first time since early spring. The phalaropes have nested on the arctic tundras, reared their young and now are returning to the sea. Most of them will continue south over the open water, crossing the equator into the South Atlantic, following the great whales, for where the whales are there also are the swarms of plankton on which these strange little birds grow fat.

Now come other movements that betoken the end of summer. Down through the treacherous passes between the islands of the Aleutian chain and southward into the open Pacific the herds of fur seals are moving. Left behind are two small islands, treeless bits of volcanic soil thrust up into the fog-covered waters of the Bering Sea. The islands are silent now, but for the several months of summer they resounded with the roar of millions of seals come ashore to bear and rear their young—all the fur seals of the eastern Pacific crowded into a few square miles of bare rock and crumbling soil. Now once more the seals turn south, to roam down along the sheer underwater cliffs of the continent's edge, where the rocky foundations fall away steeply into the deep sea. In a blackness more absolute than that of arctic winter the seals will find rich feeding as they swim down to prey on the fishes of this dark region.

Autumn comes to the sea with a fresh blaze of phosphorescence, eerie and unearthly, when every wave crest is aflame. Here and there the whole surface may glow with sheets of cold fire, while below schools of fish pour through the water like molten metal. Often the autumnal phosphorescence is caused by a fall flowering of the dinoflagellates, multiplying furiously in a short-lived repetition of their vernal blooming.

Like the blazing colors of the autumn leaves before they wither and fall, the autumnal phosphorescence betokens the approach of winter. After their brief renewal of life the flagellates and other minute algae dwindle away to a scattered few; so do the shrimps and the copepods, the arrowworms and the comb jellies. The larvae of the bottom fauna have long since drifted away. Even the roving fish schools have migrated into warmer latitudes or found equivalent warmth in the deep, quiet waters along the edge of the continental shelf. There the torpor of semihibernation descends upon them and will possess them during the months of winter.

The surface waters now become the plaything of the winter gales. As the winds build up the giant storm waves and roar along their crests, it seems that life must forever have deserted this place. Read Joseph Conrad's description of the winter sea:

> The grayness of the whole immense surface, the wind furrows upon the faces of the waves, the great masses of foam, tossed about and waving like matted white locks, give to the sea in a gale an appearance of hoary age, lustreless, dull, without gleams, as though it had been created before light itself.

On land we know that the apparent lifelessness of winter is an illusion. Look closely at the leaf buds spaced along the bare branches of a tree. There is all spring's magic of swelling green concealed and preserved under the insulating, overlapping layers. Pick a piece of bark off of the trunk; there you will find hibernating insects. Dig down through the snow into the earth. There are the eggs of next summer's grasshoppers; there are the dormant seeds from which will come the grass, the herb, the oak tree.

So, too, the lifelessness of the winter sea is an illusion. Everywhere is the promise of a new spring and new life—even in the very iciness of the winter seawater, which must, in time, become so heavy that it will plunge downward, precipitating the overturn that is the first act in the drama of spring. There is promise in the small, almost formless polyps from which a new generation of jellyfish will bud off; in the sluggish forms of the copepods hibernating on the bottom, safe from surface storms; the glassy globules of eggs already rising into the surface waters to begin the swift divisions by which a granule of protoplasm becomes a living fishlet.

Most of all, perhaps, there is assurance in the fine dust of life that remains in the surface waters, the invisible spores of the diatoms, needing only the touch of warming sun and fertilizing chemicals to repeat the magic of spring.

CHAPTER IV: *The Sunless Sea*

THE WHOLE WORLD OCEAN extends over about three fourths of the surface of the globe. If we subtract the shallow areas of the continental shelves, where at least the pale ghost of sunlight moves over the underlying bottom, there still remains about half the earth that is covered by miles-deep, lightless water.

This region, dark since the world began, has withheld its secrets more obstinately than any other. Man, with all his ingenuity, has been able only recently to venture, step by step, across its threshold. Wearing a diving helmet, he can walk on the ocean floor about ten fathoms down. He can descend to an extreme limit of about five hundred feet in a complete diving suit, carrying with him a constant supply of oxygen. The first two men in all history to descend, alive, beyond the range of visible light, were William Beebe and Otis Barton. In the bathysphere they reached a depth of 3028 feet in the open ocean off Bermuda, in the year 1934.

But man's dream of exploring the deepest recesses of the sea was not realized until the Swiss physicist, Professor Auguste Piccard, proposed a depth-exploring vehicle which, instead of being suspended at the end of a cable like the bathysphere, would move freely, independent of control from the surface. In such a bathyscaphe (depth boat) observers ride in a pressure-resisting ball suspended from a metal envelope containing high-octane gasoline, an extremely light, almost incompressible fluid. Silos loaded with iron pellets provide ballast; the pellets are held by electromagnets, to be released by the touch of a button when the divers are ready to surface.

In September 1953 Professor Piccard and his son, Jacques,

descended in a bathyscaphe to a depth of 10,330 feet in the Mediterranean. In 1958 the bathyscaphe *Trieste* was purchased from the Piccards by the United States Office of Naval Research and taken to Guam, in the vicinity of which lies the great Marianas Trench. Echo soundings there have revealed the deepest hole now known in any part of the ocean. On January 23, 1960, manned by Jacques Piccard and Don Walsh, the *Trieste* descended to the bottom of this trench, 35,800 feet (or nearly seven miles) beneath the surface.

Unlike the surface waters, which are sensitive to every gust of wind, which know day and night, respond to the pull of sun and moon, and change as the seasons change, the deep sea is a place where change comes slowly, if at all. For most of its creatures, groping their way endlessly through its black waters, it must be a place of hunger, where food is scarce, where there is no sanctuary from ever-present enemies, where one can only move on and on, from birth to death.

They used to say that nothing could live in this eerie, forbidding region. Without proof to the contrary, how could anyone conceive of life in such a place? Then Sir John Ross, during his exploration of the arctic seas in 1818, brought up from a depth of one thousand fathoms mud in which there were living worms, "thus proving there was animal life in the bed of the ocean notwithstanding the darkness, stillness, silence, and immense pressure."

In 1860, from the surveying ship *Bulldog*, examining a proposed cable route near Labrador, came another report. The *Bulldog*'s sounding line, which at one place had been allowed to lie for some time on the bottom at a depth of twelve hundred and sixty fathoms, came up with thirteen starfish clinging to it.

Then in 1872 the *Challenger*, the first ship ever equipped for oceanographic exploration, set out from England and traced a course around the globe. From bottoms lying under miles of water, from silent deeps carpeted with red clay ooze, and from all the lightless intermediate depths, net-haul after net-haul of fantastic creatures came up and were spilled out on the decks. Poring over the weird beings thus brought up for the first time into the light of day, beings no man had ever seen before, the *Challenger* scientists realized that life existed even on the deepest floor of the abyss.

During the first quarter of the twentieth century, echo sounding was developed to allow ships to record the depth of the bottom while under way. Operators of the new instruments soon discovered that the sound waves, directed downward from the ship like a beam of light, were reflected back from any solid object they met: from schools of fish, whales or submarines. After World War II the United States Navy reported that several scientists, working with sonic equipment aboard the U.S.S. *Jasper* in deep water off the California coast, had discovered a widespread "layer" of some sort which gave back an answering echo to the sound waves. This reflecting layer, seemingly suspended between the surface and the floor of the Pacific, was found over a three-hundred-mile area and lay from a thousand to fifteen hundred feet below the surface. Then in 1945 Martin W. Johnson, marine biologist of the Scripps Institution of Oceanography, made the exciting discovery which gave the first clue to the nature of this mysterious phenomenon. Whatever sent back the echoes moved upward and downward in rhythmic fashion, being found near the surface at night, in deep water during the day, showing that the layer is composed of living creatures capable of controlled movement.

Further discoveries soon revealed that the sea's "phantom bottom" occurs almost universally in the deep-ocean basins. Despite attempts to sample it or photograph it, however, no one is sure what the layer is. There are three principal theories. According to the first, the sea's phantom bottom may consist of small planktonic shrimps, which are known to rise toward the surface at night and sink down below the zone of light penetration very early in the morning. A second theory is that fish are the reflectors of the sound waves. The vertical migrations of the layer might suggest that the fish are feeding on planktonic shrimps and are following their food. Proponents of this theory believe that the air bladder of a fish is, of all structures concerned, most likely from its construction to return a strong echo. The most startling theory (and the one with the fewest supporters) is that the layer consists of concentrations of squid, "hovering below the illuminated zone of the sea and awaiting the arrival of darkness in which to resume their raids into the plankton-rich surface waters." When some persistent technical difficulties of deep-water photography are solved it may give us the solution of the mystery.

Shadowy and indefinite though they be, these recent indications of an abundant life at mid depths agree with what William Beebe actually observed from his bathysphere. More than a quarter of a mile down, he found aggregations of living things "as thick as I have ever seen them." At half a mile—his deepest descent—he recalled that "there was no instant when a mist of plankton . . . was not swirling in the path of the beam."

The existence of plentiful deep-sea fauna was discovered, probably millions of years ago, by certain whales. The ancestors of all whales, we know by fossil remains, were predatory land mammals. Perhaps in their foragings about the deltas of great rivers or around the edges of shallow seas they discovered the abundance of fish and, over the centuries, formed the habit of following them farther and farther into the sea. Little by little their bodies took on a form more suitable for aquatic life.

Eventually the immense, square-headed, formidably toothed whale known as the sperm whale discovered long ago what men have known for only a short time—that hundreds of fathoms below the almost untenanted surface waters of the tropics and of the open ocean basins there is abundant animal life. His quarry is the deep-water population of squid, including the giant squid which lives in open water at depths of fifteen hundred feet or more. The head of the sperm whale is often marked with long circular scars made by the suckers of the squid. We can imagine the battles that go on, in the darkness of the deep water, between these two huge creatures—the sperm whale with its seventy-ton bulk, the squid with a body as long as thirty feet, and writhing, grasping arms extending the total length of the animal to perhaps fifty feet.

It appears from fish bones found in their stomachs that seals also have discovered the hidden food reserves of the deep ocean. But how either whales or seals endure the tremendous pressure changes involved in dives of several hundred fathoms is not definitely known. They are warm-blooded mammals like ourselves. Rapid accumulation of nitrogen bubbles in the blood from the sudden release of pressure kills human divers if they are brought up rapidly from depths of two hundred feet or so. Yet, according to whalers, a baleen whale, when harpooned, can dive straight down to a depth of half a mile and return almost immediately to the surface unharmed. The most plausible explanation is that, unlike the human diver, who has air pumped to him while he is underwater, the whale has in its body only the limited supply it carries down, and does not have enough nitrogen in its blood to do serious harm.

At first thought it seems a paradox that creatures of such great fragility as the glass sponge and the jellyfish can live under the conditions of immense pressure that prevail in deep water. For creatures at home in the deep sea, however, the saving fact is that the pressure inside their tissues is the same as that without and, as long as this balance is preserved, they are no more inconvenienced by a pressure of a ton or so than we are by ordinary atmospheric pressure. And as most abyssal creatures live out their whole lives in a comparatively restricted zone, they are never required to adjust themselves to extreme changes of pressure.

The real miracle of sea life in relation to great pressure is not the animal that lives its whole life on the bottom, bearing a pressure of perhaps five or six tons, but those that regularly move up and down through hundreds or thousands of feet of vertical change. The small shrimps and other planktonic creatures are examples. Fish that possess air bladders, on the other hand, are vitally affected by abrupt changes of pressure. In their pursuit of food they may sometimes wander out of the zone to which they are adjusted and find themselves unable to return. In the lessened pressure of these upper waters the gas enclosed within the air bladder expands. The fish becomes lighter and more buoyant. Perhaps he tries to fight his way down again, opposing the upward lift with all the power of his muscles. If he does not succeed, he "falls" to the surface, injured and dying, for the sudden release of pressure from without causes distension and rupture of the tissues.

Immense pressure, then, is one of the governing conditions of life in the deep sea; darkness is another. It is a blackness so divorced from the world of the sunlight that probably only the few men who have seen it with their own eyes can visualize it. Light fades out rapidly with descent below the surface. The red rays are gone at the end of the first two or three hundred feet, and with them all the orange and yellow warmth of the sun. Then the greens fade out, and at one thousand feet only a deep, dark, brilliant blue is left. In very clear waters the violet rays of the spectrum may penetrate another thousand feet. Beyond this is only blackness.

The colors of marine animals tend to be related to the zone in which they live. Fishes of the surface waters, like the mackerel and herring, often are blue or green. Down below the diatom meadows, where the water becomes ever more deeply, brilliantly blue, many creatures are crystal clear. The ghostly, transparent forms of the arrowworms, the comb jellies, and the larvae of many fishes blend with their surroundings and make it easier for them to elude the ever-present, ever-hungry enemy. At a thousand feet silvery fishes are common, and many others are red, drab brown or black. Arrowworms are here a deep red, jellyfish (medusae) a deep brown. Below fifteen hundred feet all the fishes are black, deep violet or brown, but the prawns wear amazing hues of red, scarlet and purple. Why? No one knows, since their raiment can only look black to their neighbors.

The deep sea has its stars, and an eerie and transient equivalent of moonlight, for the mysterious phenomenon of luminescence is often displayed by creatures that live in darkened waters. Many fishes carry luminous torches that can be turned on or off at will, presumably helping them find or pursue their prey. Others have rows of lights over their bodies, in patterns that may be a sort of recognition mark for friend or enemy. The deep-sea squid ejects a spurt of fluid that becomes a luminous cloud, the counterpart of the "ink" of his shallow-water relative.

Down beyond the reach of even the longest and strongest of the sun's rays the eyes of fishes become enlarged, as though to make the most of any chance illumination of whatever sort, or they may become telescopic, large of lens, and protruding. Some deep-sea creatures have become blind, compensating for the lack of eyes with marvelously developed feelers and long, slender fins with which they grope their way, like so many blind men with canes, their whole knowledge of friends, enemies or food coming to them through the sense of touch.

No plants can live below about six hundred feet and, below two hundred feet, few find enough sunlight for their food-manufacturing activities. Since no animal can make its own food, the creatures of the deeper waters prey relentlessly upon each other. Yet they are ultimately dependent upon the slow rain of descending food particles from above. The components of this never-ending rain are dead and dying plants and animals from the surface, or from one of the intermediate layers. For each of the communities of the sea that lie in tier after tier between the surface and the sea bottom, the food supply is different and poorer than for the layer above. There is a hint of the fierce and uncompromising competition for food in the saber-toothed jaws of some of the small, dragonlike fishes of the deeper waters, in the immense mouths and in the elastic and distensible bodies that enable a fish to swallow another several times its size, enjoying swift repletion after a long fast.

Only a few years ago we should have added silence to pressure and darkness as the conditions of life in the deep sea. But wide experience with hydrophones and other listening devices for the detection of submarines has now proved that the sea is far from silent. Around shorelines there is an extraordinary uproar produced by fishes, shrimps, porpoises, and probably other forms not yet identified. There has been little investigation as yet of sound in the deep offshore areas, but when the crew of the *Atlantis* lowered a hydrophone into deep water off Bermuda they recorded strange mewing sounds, shrieks and ghostly moans, the sources of which have not been traced.

During World War II the hydrophone network set up by the United States Navy to protect the entrance to Chesapeake Bay was temporarily made useless when, in the spring of 1942, the speakers at the surface began to give forth, every evening, a sound like "a pneumatic drill tearing up pavement," which completely masked the sounds of ships. Eventually it was discovered that the sounds were voices of fish known as croakers, which in the spring move into Chesapeake Bay from their offshore wintering grounds. It was then possible to screen them out with an electric filter, so that once more only the sounds of ships came through the speakers.

One of the most extraordinarily widespread sounds of the undersea is the crackling, sizzling sound, like dry twigs burning or fat frying, heard near beds of the snapping shrimp. This small, round shrimp, about half an inch in diameter, is forever clicking the two joints of the claw which it uses to stun its prey. No one had any idea these little shrimps were so abundant or so widely distributed until hydrophones began to pick up their signals.

Biologists listening through a hydrophone in an estuary of the St. Lawrence River heard "high-pitched resonant whistles and squeals, varied with the ticking and clucking sounds slightly reminiscent of a string orchestra tuning up." This remarkable medley was heard only while schools of white porpoise were seen passing up or down the river and so was assumed to be produced by them.

There has been much speculation as to the function served by sound production on the part of marine species. We know that the bat finds its way about in lightless caves by means of a physiological equivalent of radar, emitting a stream of high-frequency sound which echoes from any obstructions in its path. Could the sounds of sea creatures serve a similar purpose, aiding inhabitants of deep waters to swim in darkness and to find prey? Actual evidence of marine echo ranging came only recently with some ingenious experiments on captive porpoises by W. N. Kellogg of Florida State University. Dr. Kellogg found that porpoises emit streams of underwater sound pulses by which they are able to swim accurately through a field of obstructions without collision, in water too turbid for vision, or in darkness. When food fish were introduced into the tank under such circumstances, the porpoises located them by sound signals, turning their heads to right and left as the returning echoes allowed them to fix the location of their targets.

The mysteriousness, the eeriness, the ancient unchangingness of the great depths have led many people to suppose that some very old forms of life—some "living fossils"—may be lurking there undiscovered. Some such hope may have been in the minds of the *Challenger* scientists. The weird forms they brought up in their nets had never before been seen by man. But basically they were found to be types that have developed in rather recent geologic time: fishes, squid and shrimps, grotesquely modified, to be sure, for life in the difficult deep-sea world.

In December 1938 hope was revived that the deep sea may, after all, conceal strange links with the past. Off the southeast tip of Africa an amazing fish was caught alive in a trawl—a fish that, according to fossil records, was supposed to have been extinct for at least sixty million years! The fishermen who brought it up from a depth of only forty fathoms realized that this five-foot, bright blue fish, with its large head and strangely shaped scales, fins and tail, was different from anything they had ever caught before, and on their return to port they took it to the nearest museum. It was eventually identified as a coelacanth, one of an incredibly ancient group of fishes that first appeared in the seas some three hundred million years ago. The reappearance of a coelacanth as a live fish was at first considered too extraordinary to be repeated; but since then more specimens have been obtained.

Possibly there are other such anachronisms lurking down in these regions of which we know so little, but they are likely to be few and scattered. The terms of existence in these deep waters are far too uncompromising to support life unless that life is constantly molding itself to the harsh conditions, seizing every advantage that makes possible the survival of living protoplasm in a world only a little less hostile than the black reaches of interplanetary space.

CHAPTER V: *Hidden Lands*

THE FIRST EUROPEAN EVER to sail across the wide Pacific was curious about the hidden worlds beneath his ship. Between two coral islands in the Tuamotu Archipelago, Magellan ordered his sounding line to be lowered. It was no more than two hundred fathoms long, and it did not touch bottom. But the occasion was none the less historic. It was the first time a navigator had attempted to sound the depths of the open ocean.

Taking soundings in the deep ocean long remained a laborious and time-consuming task, and knowledge of undersea topography lagged considerably behind our acquaintance with the landscape of the near side of the moon. By 1854 only a hundred and eighty deep soundings were available from the Atlantic, and by the time modern echo sounding was developed the total that had been taken from all the ocean basins of the world was only about fifteen thousand. This is roughly one sounding for each area of six thousand square miles.

Now hundreds of vessels equipped with sonic sounding instruments capable of sounding the maximum depths of the sea are accumulating echo soundings faster than they can be plotted on the charts. Little by little the hidden contours of the ocean are emerging, but it will still be years before an accurate and detailed relief map of the ocean basins can be constructed.

The general bottom topography is, however, well established. Of the three great geographic provinces of ocean—the continental shelves, the continental slopes and the floor of the deep sea—the continental shelf is most like the land. Sunlight penetrates to all but its deepest parts. Plants drift in the waters above it; seaweeds cling to its rocks and sway to the passage of the waves. Familiar fishes— unlike the weird monsters of the abyss—move over its plains like herds of cattle. Its submerged valleys and hills have been carved by glaciers, and the terrain is strewn with rocks and gravel deposited by the moving ice sheets. Indeed many parts (or perhaps all) of the shelf have been dry land in the geologic past. The Grand Banks of Newfoundland rose above the ancient seas and were submerged again. The Dogger Bank of the North Sea shelf was once a forested land inhabited by prehistoric beasts. Of all parts of the sea, the continental shelves are most directly important to man. The world's great fisheries are confined to these relatively shallow waters, and no one knows how much oil may lie, as yet unexploited, under these bordering lands of the sea.

The shelves, which extend seaward as gently sloping plains until they descend abruptly toward abyssal depths, vary greatly in width. Off the Pacific coast of the United States the continental shelf is seldom more than twenty miles wide—a narrowness characteristic of coasts bordered by young mountains perhaps still in the process of formation. On the American east coast, however, the shelf is as much as a hundred and fifty miles wide. But at Cape Hatteras and off southern Florida it is merely the narrowest of thresholds, due to the press of the rapidly flowing Gulf Stream, which at these places swings close inshore. The widest shelves in all the world are those bordering the Arctic. The Barents Sea shelf is seven hundred and fifty miles across. It is also relatively deep, lying one to two hundred fathoms below the surface, as though its floor had sagged under the load of glacial ice.

Once beyond the edge of the shelf, as we visualize the steeper declivities of the continental slope, we begin to feel the mystery and the alien quality of the deep sea—the gathering darkness, the growing pressure, the starkness of a seascape in which all plant life has been left behind. Biologically, the world of the continental slopes, like the abyss, is a world of animals which prey upon one another. Geographically, the slopes are the walls of the deep-sea basins, the farthermost bounds of the continents. They are the longest and highest escarpments found anywhere on earth; their average height is twelve thousand feet, but in some places they reach the immense height of thirty thousand feet.

The slopes are also the site of one of the most mysterious features of the sea—the submarine canyons whose steep cliffs and winding valleys cut back into the walls of the continents. Were the canyons not so deeply hidden in the darkness of the sea (many extend a mile or more below present sea level) they would be classed with the world's most spectacular scenery. The comparison with the Grand Canyon of the Colorado River is irresistible.

Like river-cut land canyons, sea canyons are deep and winding valleys, V-shaped in cross section. The location of many of the largest ones suggests a past connection with some of the great rivers of the earth of our time. There are large canyons off the

Hudson River, the Congo, the Indus, the Ganges, the Columbia, the São Francisco and the Mississippi. But geologists disagree hotly as to how and by what they were carved.

The floor of the deep-ocean basins is probably as old as the sea itself. Never, as far as we can learn, since the formation of the abyss, have these depressions been drained of their cover of miles-deep water. But the contours of the abyss have not remained unchanged. The floor of the sea, like the stuff of the continents, is a thin crust, thrusting up into folds and wrinkles or falling away into deep trenches as the earth's interior cools and shrinks away from its covering layer. Or, again, it pushes up into cone-shaped undersea mountains as volcanoes boil upward from fissures in the crust.

Until recent years, geographers and oceanographers spoke of the floor of the deep sea as a vast and comparatively level plain. Certain topographic variations were recognized but were considered exceptional. But in the summer of 1947 scientists of the Swedish Deep-Sea Expedition, which sailed from Göteborg aboard the *Albatross* and spent fifteen months exploring the bed of the ocean, destroyed this idea. Rarely did their fathometers reveal more than a few consecutive miles of level plain. Instead the bottom profile rose and fell in curious steps constructed on a gargantuan scale half a mile to several miles wide. In the Pacific, the uneven bottom contours made it difficult to use many oceanographic instruments. More than one coring tube was left behind, probably lodged in some undersea crevasse.

In the Indian Ocean, southeast of Ceylon, however, the *Albatross* did run for several hundred miles across a level plain. Attempts to take bottom samples from this plain had little success, for the corers were broken repeatedly, suggesting that the bottom was hardened lava and that the whole vast plateau might have been formed by the outpourings of submarine volcanoes on a stupendous scale.

Surprisingly, the deepest depressions on the floor of the sea occur not in the centers of the oceanic basins but near the continents. The Mindanao Trench, lying east of the Philippines, is an awesome six and a half miles deep. The Tuscarora Trench east of Japan, nearly as deep, is one of the long, narrow trenches that border Pacific island chains such as the Marianas. The greatest deeps of the Atlantic lie adjacent to the islands of the West Indies, and also below Cape Horn, where other curving chains of islands go out like stepping-stones into the Southern Ocean. And again in the Indian Ocean the curving island arcs of the East Indies have their accompanying deeps. This invariable association of island arcs and deep trenches always occurs in areas of volcanic unrest. The pattern, it is now agreed, is associated with mountain making and the sharp adjustments of the sea floor that accompany it.

For years the least-known region of the ocean floor lay under the Arctic Sea. The physical difficulties of sounding here were enormous. A permanent sheet of ice, as much as fifteen feet thick, covers the whole central basin and is impenetrable to ships, so that even as late as the middle 1940s, most of the top of the world was still an unsounded sea whose contours could only be guessed.

The revolutionary development that made it possible to chart the Arctic basin was the use of American nuclear-powered submarines to pass beneath the ice cover and directly explore the depths of this ocean. In 1957 the United States Navy's *Nautilus* first penetrated beneath Arctic ice in a preliminary exploration, collecting a vast amount of data. Then in 1958 the *Nautilus* crossed the entire Arctic basin from Point Barrow in Alaska to the North Pole and thence to the Atlantic. In this historic voyage it made the first continuously recorded echo-sounder profile across the center of the Arctic basin. Other nuclear submarines have subsequently contributed to our Arctic knowledge. The greatest depth so far discovered is somewhat more than three miles. And it is now clear the Arctic Ocean's bottom topography is that of a normal oceanic basin, with flat abyssal plains, rugged mountains and seamounts.

Seamounts were never shown on maps of undersea relief before the 1940s. It happened that a Princeton University geologist, H. H. Hess, commanded the U.S.S. *Cape Johnson* during two years of wartime cruising in the Pacific. He was struck by the number of undersea mounts that appeared on the fathograms of the vessel.

Time after time, as the moving pen of the fathometer traced the depth contours it would abruptly begin to rise in an outline of a steep-sided mount, standing solitarily on the bed of the sea. Unlike a typical volcanic cone, all the mounts have broad, flat tops, as though the peaks had been cut off and planed down by waves. But their summits are from half a mile to a mile or more below the surface. How they acquired their flat-topped contours is a mystery perhaps as great as that of the submarine canyons.

Unlike the scattered seamounts, the long ranges of undersea mountains have been marked on the charts for many years. The Atlantic Ridge was discovered about a century ago. Surveys for the transatlantic cable route gave first hints of the existence of this long range of undersea mountains. The German oceanographic vessel *Meteor*, which crossed and recrossed the Atlantic during the 1920s, established the contours of much of the ridge. The *Atlantis* of the Woods Hole Oceanographic Institution spent several summers in an exhaustive study of the ridge in the general vicinity of the Azores.

Now we can trace the hidden peaks and valleys of the ridge as it runs south midway between the continents, crosses the equator into the South Atlantic and continues to about fifty degrees south latitude, where it turns sharply eastward under the tip of Africa and runs toward the Indian Ocean. From its western foothills across to its eastern slopes the range is about twice as wide as the Andes and several times the width of the Appalachians. Near the equator a deep gash cuts across it from east to west, and among its higher peaks there are other, lesser mountain passes.

The greater part of the ridge is, of course, submerged. Its central backbone rises some five to ten thousand feet above the sea floor, but another mile of water lies above most of its summits. Yet here and there a peak thrusts itself up out of the deep and pushes above the surface to become the islands of the mid Atlantic. The highest, Pico Island of the Azores, rises twenty-seven thousand feet above the ocean floor, with only its upper seven to eight thousand feet emergent. The sharpest peaks of the ridge are the half dozen islets known as the Rocks of Saint Paul, near the equator. Their rocky slopes drop off at so sheer an angle that water more than half a mile deep lies only a few feet offshore. The sultry volcanic bulk of Ascension is another Atlantic Ridge peak.

Though most of the ridge lies forever hidden from human eyes, some details of its landscape have been photographed with deep-sea cameras. With this aid our imaginations can picture the grandeur of undersea mountains, with their sheer cliffs and rocky terraces. We can only compare them to terrestrial mountains far above the timber line, with their silent snow-filled valleys and their naked rocks swept by the winds. For the sea has an inverted timber line, or "plant line," below which no vegetation can grow. The bare, rocky slopes of the undersea mountains are far beyond the reach of the sun's rays and there, in the valleys, are deep drifts of sediments that have been silently piling up through millions upon millions of years.

Neither the Pacific Ocean nor the Indian Ocean has any submerged mountains that compare in length with the ten-thousand-mile Atlantic Ridge, but they have their smaller ranges. The Hawaiian Islands are the peaks of a mountain range, as are the Gilbert and Marshall islands. In the Indian Ocean a long, broad ridge runs from India to Antarctica, for most of its length broader and deeper than the Atlantic Ridge.

Mountains that have been thrust up on the continents, to the accompaniment of volcanic outpourings and violent tremblings of the earth, crumble and wear away under the attacks of rain and frost and flood. What of the sea's mountains? There are indications that the earth's crust is no more stable undersea than on land. A fair proportion of earthquakes are traced through seismographs to sources under the oceans, and there are probably as many active volcanoes underwater as on land. Yet the submarine mountains are earth's nearest approach to the "eternal hills" of the poets. A mountain of the deep sea is beyond the reach of ordinary erosive forces. Here in the twilight of the sea, in the calm of deep water, below the push and pull and drag of even the heaviest storm waves, the mountain is likely to remain almost unchanged, perhaps throughout the life of the earth.

Because of this virtual immortality, the oldest oceanic mountains must be infinitely older than any of the ranges left on land. The Pacific seamounts must have been of substantial age when the Appalachians were thrust up, two hundred million years ago; they stood almost unchanged while the Appalachians wore down to mere wrinkles on the earth's face. The seamounts were old sixty million years ago, when the Alps, the Himalayas, the Rockies and the Andes rose to their majestic heights. Yet it is probable that they will be standing unchanged in the deep sea when these, too, shall have crumbled away to dust.

Can the undersea mountains be linked with the famed "lost continents"? Shadowy and insubstantial accounts of such legendary lands persistently recur like some deeply rooted racial memory in the folklore of many parts of the world.

Best known is Atlantis, which according to Plato's account was a large island or continent beyond the Pillars of Hercules. Atlantis was the home of a warlike people ruled by powerful kings who made frequent attacks upon the mainlands of Africa and Europe. However, "with great earthquakes and inundations, in a single day and one fatal night, all were swallowed up. The Island of Atlantis disappeared beneath the sea."

The Atlantis legend has lived on through the centuries. Various Atlantic Ridge islands, especially the lonely wave-washed Rocks of Saint Paul, have been identified as the remains of Atlantis. Unfortunately for these picturesque imaginings, if any sizable area of the ridge was ever exposed, it must have been long before there were men to populate such an Atlantis. Some of the cores taken from the ridge show a continuous series of sediments typical of open oceans, far from land, running back to a period some sixty million years ago. And man, even the most primitive type, has appeared only within the past million years or so.

Like other legends deeply rooted in folklore, however, the Atlantis story may have in it an element of truth. In the shadowy beginnings of human life on earth, primitive men here and there must have had knowledge of the gradual sinking of an island or a peninsula. Witnesses of such a happening would have described it to their neighbors and children, and so the legend of a sinking continent might have been born.

Such a lost land is the Dogger Bank, which lies today beneath the waters of the North Sea. During the Pleistocene era, when immense quantities of water were withdrawn from the ocean and locked up in the glaciers, the floor of the North Sea emerged and became land. It was a low, wet land, covered with peat bogs; then little by little the forests from the neighboring highlands must have moved in. Animals moved down from the mainland: bears and wolves and hyenas, the wild ox, the bison. Primitive men carrying crude stone instruments stalked deer and other game and with their flints grubbed up roots. Then as the glaciers retreated and floods from the melting ice poured into the sea and raised its level, this land became an island. Probably the men escaped to the mainland before the intervening channel had become too wide, leaving their stone implements behind. Finally the sea covered the island. And perhaps the story of the men who escaped passed down through the ages until it became fixed in the memory of the race.

None of these facts were part of recorded history until, a generation ago, European fishermen began to trawl on the Dogger. They soon made out the contours of an irregular plateau nearly as large as Denmark, lying about sixty feet underwater, but sloping off abruptly at its edges into much deeper water. Their trawls began to bring up loose masses of peat, bones of large land mammals, fragments of trees and crude stone implements. In this strange debris of the fishing nets scientists recognized a whole Pleistocene fauna and flora, and the artifacts of Stone Age man; and they reconstructed the story of the lost island.

CHAPTER VI: *The Long Snowfall*

WHEN I THINK OF THE FLOOR of the deep sea, I see always the steady, unremitting, downward drift of materials from above, flake upon flake, layer upon layer—a drift that has continued for hundreds of millions of years, that will go on as long as there are seas and continents. For this accumulation of sediments comprises the most stupendous "snowfall" the earth has ever seen. It began when the first rains fell on the barren rocks and set in motion the forces of erosion. It was accelerated when living creatures developed in the surface waters. So little in a year, or in a human lifetime, but so enormous an amount in the life of earth and sea.

In addition to the silt load of every river that finds its way to the sea there are other sediments: volcanic dust, blown perhaps halfway around the earth in the upper atmosphere, comes eventually to rest on the ocean, and sinks; sands from coastal deserts are carried seaward on offshore winds; gravel, pebbles, small boulders and shells carried by icebergs and drift ice are released when the ice melts; fragments of iron, nickel and other meteoric debris that enter the earth's atmosphere over the sea become flakes of the great snowfall. But most widely distributed of all are the billions upon billions of tiny shells and skeletons of minute creatures that once lived in the upper waters. The sediments are a sort of epic poem of the earth. Someday perhaps we can read in their successive layers all that has happened in the waters above them and on the surrounding lands.

The book of the sediments has been opened only within relatively recent years. Early oceanographers could scrape up surface layers of sediment from the sea bottom with dredges. But what was needed was an instrument, operating on the principle of an apple corer, that could be driven vertically into the bottom to remove a long sample, or "core," in which the order of the different layers was undisturbed. In 1935 Dr. C. S. Piggot invented such an instrument. With the aid of this "gun" he obtained a series of ten-foot-long cores across the deep Atlantic. A piston core sampler developed by the Swedish oceanographer B. Kullenberg now takes undisturbed cores seventy feet long, a sample representing millions of years of geologic history.

Another ingenious method is used to measure the thickness of the carpeting layer of sediments that overlies the rock of the ocean floor. Depth charges are exploded and their echoes recorded; one echo is received from the top of the sediment layer (the apparent bottom of the sea), another from the "bottom below the bottom," or the true rock floor.

Before these techniques were developed, we could only guess at the thickness of the sediment blanket over the floor of the sea. We might have expected the amount to be vast, if we thought back through the ages of gentle, unending fall—one sand grain at a time, one fragile shell after another, here a shark's tooth, there a meteorite fragment—but the whole continuing persistently, relentlessly. A similar process built up the layers of rock that help to make our mountains: they, too, were once soft sediments under the invading shallow seas. The sediments eventually became consolidated and cemented and, as the seas retreated again, gave the continents their thick, covering layers of sedimentary rocks— layers which we can see uplifted, tilted, compressed and broken by the vast earth movements. We know that in places they are many thousands of feet thick. Yet most people felt a shock of surprise and wonder when Hans Pettersson, leader of the Swedish Deep-Sea Expedition, announced that measurements taken in the open Atlantic basin showed sediment layers as much as twelve thousand feet thick.

The sediments, however, have been unevenly distributed both in place and time. The Swedish oceanographers never found sediments thicker than one thousand feet in the Pacific or in the Indian Ocean. And interesting variations in the thickness of the sediment layer of the Atlantic Ridge were reported by Professor W. Maurice Ewing of the Woods Hole Oceanographic Institution. Mammoth drifts piled up against the slopes of the hills. But along the backbone of the ridge, on the peaks and pinnacles, bare rock emerged.

Reflecting on this, our minds return to the simile of the long snowfall. On an Arctic tundra there are days of storm, when driving snow fills the air; then a lull comes, and the snowfall is light. In the abyssal snowfall of the sediments, also, there is an alternation of light and heavy falls. The heavy falls correspond with periods of mountain building on the continents, when the lands are lifted high and rain rushes down their slopes, carrying mud and rock fragments to the sea; the light falls mark the lulls between mountain-building periods, when the continents are flat and erosion is slowed. And again, on the tundra, winds blow the snow into deep drifts, filling in the valleys but scouring the ridges clear. In the drifting sediments on the ocean floor we see the work of "winds," which may be deep ocean currents, distributing the sediments according to laws not yet grasped by human minds.

We have known the general pattern of the sediment carpet, however, for a good many years. In the deep waters bordering the continental slopes are the muds of terrestrial origin. There are muds of many colors—blue, green, red, black and white—varying with the dominant soils and rocks of the lands of their origin. Farther at sea are the oozes of predominantly marine origin.

In temperate oceans the sea floor is largely covered with the remains of unicellular creatures of which the most abundant genus is *Globigerina*, a simple microscopic animal living in an intricately sculptured shell of carbonate of lime. After the fashion of unicellular beings, the individual globigerina normally did not die, but by division of its substance became two. At each division the old shell was abandoned and two new ones were formed. In warm, lime-rich seas these tiny creatures multiply prodigiously, and so, although each is minute, their shells blanket millions of square miles of ocean bottom to a depth of thousands of feet.

The immense pressures and the high carbon-dioxide content of very deep water dissolve much of the globigerina shell's lime long before it reaches the bottom and return it to the great chemical reservoir of the sea. Silica is more resistant to solution. It is one of the curious paradoxes of the ocean that the bulk of the organic remains that reach the great depths intact belong to unicellular creatures seemingly of the most delicate construction. These are the radiolarians, and they remind us irresistibly of snowflakes, as lacy and as infinitely varied in pattern. Yet because their shells are fashioned of silica they can descend unchanged into the abyssal depths. So there are broad bands of radiolarian ooze in the deep waters of the North Pacific, underlying the surface zones where the living radiolarians occur most numerously.

Two other kinds of organic sediments are named for the creatures whose remains compose them. Diatoms flourish most abundantly in cold waters. There is a broad belt of diatom ooze on the floor of the Antarctic Ocean and another across the North Pacific, from Alaska to Japan. Both are zones where nutrient-laden water wells up from the depths, sustaining a rich growth of plants. The diatoms, like the radiolarians, are encased in siliceous coverings—small, boxlike cases of varied shape and meticulously etched design.

In relatively shallow parts of the open Atlantic there are patches of ooze composed of transparent shells of great beauty, the remains of delicate swimming snails, called pteropods. Pteropod ooze is the characteristic bottom deposit in the vicinity of Bermuda, and a large patch occurs in the South Atlantic.

Mysterious and eerie are the immense areas, especially in the depths of the North Pacific, carpeted with a soft red sediment in which there are no organic remains except sharks' teeth and the ear bones of whales. Perhaps all the materials of the other sediments are dissolved before they can reach this zone of immense pressures and glacial cold.

The reading of the story contained in the sediments has only begun. Even now the flakes of a new snowstorm are falling, falling, one by one, out there on the ocean floor, writing their unequivocal record of this, our present world. Who will read their record ten thousand years from now?

CHAPTER VII: *The Birth of an Island*

MILLIONS OF YEARS AGO a volcano built a mountain on the floor of the Atlantic. In eruption after eruption it pushed up a great pile of volcanic rock, a hundred miles across at its base. Finally its cone emerged as an island with an area of about two hundred square miles. Many thousands of years passed, during which the waves of the Atlantic cut down the cone until only a small fragment remained above water. This fragment we know as Bermuda.

With variations, the life story of Bermuda has been repeated by almost every one of the islands that interrupt the watery expanses of the oceans far from land. For these isolated islands, unlike the continents, are ephemeral, created today, destroyed tomorrow. With few exceptions they are the result of the violent, earth-shaking eruptions of submarine volcanoes. It is one of the paradoxes in the ways of earth and sea that a process seemingly so destructive, so catastrophic in nature, can result in an act of creation.

The birth of a volcanic island is marked by prolonged travail: the forces of the earth striving to create, and the forces of the sea opposing. In the sea floor are deep cracks and fissures, the results of unequal cooling and shrinkage in past ages. Along such lines of weakness the molten lava from the earth's interior presses up and finally bursts forth into the sea. But a submarine volcano is different from a terrestrial eruption, where the lava, molten rocks and gases are hurled into the air through an open crater. Here on the bottom of the ocean the volcano has resisting it all the weight of the ocean water above it. Despite the immense pressure of, it may be, two or three miles of seawater, the new volcanic cone builds upward toward the surface in flow after flow of lava. Eventually the cone is pushed up into the air and a rampart against the attacks of the waves is built of hardened lava.

Among the undersea mountains marked on navigators' charts may be the islands of tomorrow, which at this moment are growing upward toward the surface. For submarine eruptions still occur fairly commonly. Ships in volcanic zones may suddenly find themselves in violently disturbed water. There are heavy discharges of steam. The sea appears to boil furiously. Fountains spring from its surface. Floating up from deep, hidden places come the bodies of fishes and quantities of ash and pumice.

One of the youngest of the large volcanic islands is Ascension, in the South Atlantic, a forbidding mass of cinders in which the vents of no less than forty extinct volcanoes can be counted. It has not always been so barren, for its slopes have yielded the fossil remains of trees. But today it has no natural greenness except on its highest peak, known as Green Mountain.

In modern times we have never seen the birth of an island as large as Ascension, though now and then there is a report of a little stillborn island, doomed to only a brief emergence. Waves, wind and rain soon attack it. Its substance is rapidly eaten away and it again sinks beneath the sea. Falcon Island, nearly two thousand miles east of Australia, completely disappeared in 1913. Fourteen years later, after violent eruptions in the vicinity, it rose again above the surface and remained as a physical bit of the British Empire until 1949. Then it was reported by the Colonial undersecretary to be missing again.

Almost from the moment of its creation a volcanic island has in itself the seeds of its own dissolution, for new explosions—or landslides—may violently accelerate its disintegration. The greatest explosion in history was the literal evisceration of the island of Krakatoa, in the Netherlands Indies. In the spring of 1883, smoke and steam began to ascend from fissures in the volcanic cone. The ground became noticeably warm, and warning rumblings and hissings were heard. Then, on August 27, Krakatoa exploded. In an appalling series of eruptions that lasted three days the whole northern half of the cone was carried away. The sound of the explosions was heard in the Philippines, in Australia, and on the island of Madagascar nearly three thousand miles away. When the inferno of white-hot lava, molten rock, steam and smoke finally subsided, the island that had stood 2620 feet above the sea had become a cavity a thousand feet below sea level.

The eruption gave rise to a hundred-foot wave that wiped out villages on neighboring islands and killed people by tens of thousands; rounding Cape Horn into the Atlantic, it sped northward and retained its identity even as far as the English Channel. Clouds of volcanic dust, the pulverized rock that had been torn from the heart of Krakatoa, ascended into the stratosphere and were carried around the globe to give rise to a series of spectacular sunsets in every country of the world for nearly a year.

Subterranean fires and deep unrest disturb the whole area occupied by the Aleutians. The islands themselves are the peaks of a thousand-mile chain of undersea mountains. On many of the islands volcanoes are now active, or only temporarily quiescent. In the short history of modern navigation in this region, it has often happened that a new island has been reported but perhaps only the following year could not be found.

One of the few exceptions to the rule that oceanic islands have a volcanic origin seems to be that remarkable group of islets known as the Rocks of Saint Paul. Lying in the open Atlantic between Brazil and Africa, Saint Paul's Rocks are thrust up from the ocean's floor into the racing Equatorial Current, a mass against which the seas, which have rolled a thousand miles unhindered, break in sudden violence. The entire cluster of rocks covers not more than a quarter of a mile. The highest is no more than sixty feet above the sea; spray wets it to the summit. Abruptly the rocks dip underwater and slope steeply into great depths.

Geologists since the time of Darwin have puzzled over the origin of these black wave-washed islets. Most agree they are composed of material like that of the sea floor itself. In some remote period, inconceivable stresses in the earth's crust must have pushed a solid rock mass upward more than two miles.

So bare and desolate that not even a lichen grows on them, Saint Paul's Rocks would seem one of the most unpromising places in the world to look for a spider, spinning its web in hope of snaring passing insects. Yet Darwin found spiders when he visited the Rocks in 1832. A few insects are there, too, some as parasites on the seabirds, three species of which nest on the Rocks. And grotesque crabs swarm over the islets, living chiefly on the flying fish brought by the birds to their young.

The natural inhabitants of oceanic islands are amazingly different from those of the continents. Aside from forms recently introduced by man, islands remote from the continents are never inhabited by any land mammals, except sometimes the one mammal that has learned to fly—the bat. There are never any frogs, salamanders or other amphibians. Of reptiles, there may be a few snakes, lizards and turtles.

The plants and animals we find on oceanic islands are those that could have come by wind or water. So we must suppose that the stocking of these islands has been accomplished by a strange and selective migration—a migration that began long before man ap-

peared on earth and is still continuing. Certainly in its original state an oceanic island is bare, harsh and repelling. No living thing moves over the slopes of its volcanic hills; no plants cover its naked lava fields. But little by little, riding on the winds, drifting on the currents or rafting in on logs, floating brush or trees, plants and animals arrive from the distant continents.

So deliberate, so unhurried, so inexorable are the ways of nature that the stocking of an island may require thousands or millions of years. It may be that no more than half a dozen times in all these eons does a particular form, such as a tortoise, make a successful landing upon its shores. Yet we have occasional glimpses of the method. Natural rafts of uprooted trees and matted vegetation have frequently been seen adrift at sea more than a thousand miles off the mouths of such great tropical rivers as the Congo, the Ganges, the Amazon and the Orinoco. Such rafts could easily carry an assortment of insect, reptile or mollusk passengers.

And thousands of feet above the earth, the air is crowded with living creatures, drifting, flying, gliding, ballooning or involuntarily swirling along on the high winds. With special nets and traps, scientists have now collected from the upper atmosphere many of the forms that inhabit oceanic islands. Spiders, whose almost invariable presence on these islands is a fascinating problem, have been captured nearly three miles above the earth's surface. Airmen have passed through great numbers of the white silken filaments of spiders' "parachutes" at heights of two to three miles. At such altitudes and on strong winds, they might well have been carried hundreds of miles. Seeds, too, have been collected at altitudes up to five thousand feet, especially the so-called thistledown typical of oceanic islands.

The wide-ranging birds that visit islands of the ocean in migration may also have a lot to do with the distribution of plants, and perhaps even of some insects and minute land shells. From a ball of mud taken from a bird's plumage Charles Darwin raised eighty-two separate plants, belonging to five distinct species! Many plant seeds have hooks or prickles, ideal for attachment to feathers. Such birds as the Pacific golden plover, which annually flies from Alaska to the Hawaiian Islands and even beyond, probably figure in many riddles of plant distribution.

Isolated from the great mass of life on the continents, with no opportunity for the crossbreeding that tends to preserve the average and to eliminate the unusual, island life has developed in a remarkable manner. On these remote bits of earth, nature has excelled in the creation of strange and wonderful forms. Almost every island has developed species that are duplicated nowhere else.

It was from the pages of Earth's history written on the lava fields of the Galápagos that young Charles Darwin got his first inkling of the great truths of the origin of species. Observing the strange plants and animals—giant tortoises, amazing black lizards that hunted their food in the surf, sea lions, birds in extraordinary variety—Darwin was struck by their vague similarity to mainland species of South and Central America, yet was haunted by the differences. Years later he was to write in reminiscence:

Both in space and time, we seem to be brought somewhat near to that great fact—that mystery of mysteries—the first appearance of new beings on earth.

Of the "new beings" evolved on islands, some of the most striking examples have been birds. In some remote age before there were men, a small, pigeonlike bird found its way to the island of Mauritius, in the Indian Ocean. By processes of change at which we can only guess, this bird lost the power of flight, developed short, stout legs and grew larger until it reached the size of a modern turkey. Such was the origin of the fabulous dodo, which did not long survive the advent of man on Mauritius.

One of the most engaging characteristics of island species is their tameness—a lack of sophistication in dealings with the human race which even the bitter teachings of experience do not quickly alter. When Robert Cushman Murphy visited Trinidad in 1913 with a party from the brig *Daisy*, terns alighted on the heads of the men in the whaleboat and peered inquiringly into their faces.

Albatrosses on Laysan allowed naturalists to walk among their colonies and responded with grave bows to similar polite greetings from the visitors.

But man, unhappily, has written one of his blackest records as a destroyer on the oceanic islands. He has destroyed environments by cutting, clearing and burning; he has brought with him as a chance associate the nefarious rat; and he has turned loose upon the islands a whole Noah's ark of goats, hogs, cattle, dogs, cats and other nonnative animals as well as plants. Upon species after species of island life the black night of extinction has fallen. For in all the world of living things, it is doubtful whether there is a more delicately balanced relationship than that of island life to its environment. When this gentle pattern is abruptly changed, the island creatures have little ability to make the adjustments necessary for survival.

The Hawaiian Islands are a classic example of the results of interfering with natural balances. When man brought in cattle and goats, the resulting damage to forests and other vegetation was enormous. Many plant introductions were as bad. Lantana, brought in as an ornamental species, now covers thousands of acres with a thorny, scrambling growth—despite large sums of money spent to import parasitic insects to control it.

Most of the original birdlife has been wiped out. Today you see, instead of the exquisite native birds that greeted Captain Cook, mynas from India, cardinals from the United States or Brazil, doves from Asia, weavers from Australia, skylarks from Europe, and titmice from Japan.

The tragedy of the oceanic islands lies in the uniqueness, the irreplaceability of the species they have developed by the slow processes of the ages. In a reasonable world men would have treated these islands as precious possessions, as natural museums filled with beautiful and curious works of creation, valuable beyond price because nowhere in the world are they duplicated. W. H. Hudson's lament for the birds of the Argentine pampas might even more truly have been spoken of the islands: "The beautiful has vanished and returns not."

WE LIVE IN AN AGE of rising seas. Along all the coasts of the United States a continuing rise of sea level has been perceptible on the tide gauges of the Coast and Geodetic Survey since 1930. For the Atlantic and Gulf coasts the rise amounted to about a third of a foot between 1930 and 1948. The water is also rising (but more slowly) along the Pacific shores.

What is happening is nothing new. Over the long span of geologic time the boundary between sea and land has been the most fleeting and transitory feature of the earth. The sea is forever repeating its encroachments upon the continents. It rises and falls like a great tide, sometimes engulfing half a continent in its flood, reluctant in its ebb, moving in a rhythm mysterious and infinitely deliberate.

Now once again the ocean is overfull. It is spilling over the rims of its basins, filling the shallow seas that border the continents, like the Barents, Bering and China seas. Here and there it has advanced into the interior and lies in such inland seas as Hudson Bay, the Saint Lawrence embayment, the Baltic. On the Atlantic coast of the United States the mouths of many rivers, like the Hudson and the Susquehanna, have been drowned by the advancing flood; the old, submerged channels are hidden under bays like the Chesapeake and the Delaware.

This advance may be part of a long rise that began thousands of years ago—perhaps when the glaciers of the latest ice age began to melt. But it is only within recent decades that there have been instruments to measure it. Where and when the present advance will halt no one can say. If the rise over the continent of North America should amount to a hundred feet (and there is more than enough water now frozen in land ice to provide such a rise) most of the Atlantic seaboard, with its cities and towns, would be submerged. The surf would break against the foothills of the Appalachians. The coastal plain of the Gulf of Mexico and the lower part of the Mississippi Valley would be submerged.

All of this would seem to us extraordinary and catastrophic, but most of the continents have known far more extensive invasions by the sea than the one we have just imagined. Probably the greatest submergence in the history of the earth took place in the Cretaceous period, about a hundred million years ago. Then the ocean waters advanced upon North America from the north, south and east, finally forming an inland sea that extended from the Arctic to the Gulf of Mexico. They covered most of the British Isles and much of southern Europe. The ocean moved into Africa and laid down deposits of sandstone which, with later weathering, would provide the desert sands of the Sahara. Parts of India were submerged, and of Australia, Japan and Siberia. On the South American continent, the area where later the Andes were to rise was covered by sea.

With variations of extent and detail, events of this Cretaceous flood have been repeated again and again. The very ancient Ordovician seas, some four hundred million years ago, submerged more than half of North America. The marine transgressions of Devonian and Silurian times were almost as extensive. But each time the pattern of invasion was a little different, and it is doubtful that there is any part of the continent that at some time has not lain at the bottom of one of these shallow seas.

On a mountaintop in Pennsylvania, I have sat on rocks of whitened limestone, fashioned of the shells of billions upon billions of minute sea creatures. Once they had lived and died in an arm of the ocean that overlay this place, and their limy remains had settled to the bottom. There, after many eons, they had become compacted into rock and the sea had receded; after yet more eons the rock had been uplifted by bucklings of the earth's crust, and now it formed the backbone of a long mountain range.

Outcroppings of marine limestone in the Himalayas, now at an elevation of twenty thousand feet, are reminders of a warm, clear sea that lay over southern Europe and northern Africa and extended into southwestern Asia some fifty million years ago. Large protozoans known as nummulites swarmed in this sea and each, in death, contributed to the building of a thick layer of nummulitic limestone. Eons later, the ancient Egyptians were to carve their Sphinx from a mass of this rock. The famous white cliffs of Dover are composed of chalk deposited by the seas during that great inundation of the Cretaceous period. The chalk consists of shells of minute sea creatures cemented together with a fine-textured deposit of calcium carbonate.

Many of the natural wonders of the earth owe their existence to the sea's invasions of the land. In Kentucky's Mammoth Cave, for example, miles of underground passages and rooms with two-hundred-fifty-foot ceilings were dissolved by groundwater out of an immense thickness of limestone deposited by a Paleozoic sea. Niagara Falls goes back to Silurian time, when a vast embayment of the Arctic Sea crept southward over the continent and deposited large beds of the hard rock called dolomite in a long escarpment near the present border between Canada and the United States. Millions of years later, floods of water released from melting glaciers poured over this cliff, cutting away the soft shales that underlay the dolomite, causing masses of the undercut rock to break away. In this fashion Niagara Falls and its gorge were created.

What brings the ocean out of its deep basins, where it has been contained for eons, to invade the lands? The infinitely slow warping upward or downward of the earth's crust is one cause. Crustal movements may require millions of years for completion. Each downward movement of the continental crust is accompanied by a slow flooding of the land, each upward buckling by the retreat of the water. Another important cause is the displacement of ocean water by land sediments. Every grain of sand or silt carried out by the rivers and deposited at sea displaces a corresponding amount of water. Since this seaward freighting of the land's substance has gone on without interruption from the beginning of geologic time, it might be thought that the sea level would have been rising continuously.

But the matter is not so simple. As they lose substance the continents tend to rise higher, like a ship relieved of part of its cargo. The ocean floor, to which the sediments are transferred, sags under its load. The exact combination of all these conditions

that will result in a rising ocean level is a very complex matter, not easily recognized or predicted.

Then there is the growth of the great submarine volcanoes, which some geologists believe may have an important effect on changing sea levels. The bulk of some of these is impressive. Bermuda is one of the smallest, but its submerged volume is about twenty-five hundred cubic statute miles. The Hawaiian chain of volcanic islands extends for nearly two thousand miles across the Pacific and contains several islands of great size; its total displacement of water must be tremendous. Perhaps it is more than coincidence that this chain arose in Cretaceous time, when the greatest flood the world has ever seen advanced upon the continents.

For the past million years, all other causes of marine transgressions have been dwarfed by the glaciers. Four times the ice caps formed and grew, pressing southward into the valleys and over the plains. And four times the ice melted and shrank and withdrew from the lands it had covered. We live now in the last stages of this fourth withdrawal. About half the ice formed in the last Pleistocene glaciation remains in the ice caps of Greenland and Antarctica and the scattered glaciers of certain mountains.

Each time the ice sheet thickened and expanded with the unmelted snows of winter after winter, its growth meant a corresponding withdrawal of moisture from the reservoir of the sea. So little by little the level of the sea dropped, and at the climax of each major glaciation oceans all over the world stood at very low levels.

During this half of the cycle, waters of every river were speeded in their course to the ocean and given new strength for the deepening and cutting of their channels. Following the downward-moving shorelines, the rivers extended their courses over the drying sands and muds of what only recently had been the sloping sea bottom. During one or more of the Pleistocene lowerings of sea level, the floor of the North Sea was drained of its water and for a time became dry land. The rivers of northern Europe and of the British Isles followed the retreating waters seaward. Eventually the Rhine captured the whole drainage system of the

Thames. The Seine rolled through what is now the English Channel and cut itself a trough out across the continental shelf.

The greatest of all Pleistocene glaciations came rather late in the period—probably only about two hundred thousand years ago, and well within the time of man. The tremendous lowering of sea level must have affected the life of Paleolithic man. Certainly he was able, at more than one period, to walk across a wide bridge at Bering Strait, which became dry land when the level of the ocean dropped below this shallow shelf. There were other land bridges, such as "Adam's Bridge" connecting the island of Ceylon to the coast of India. Many of the settlements of Paleolithic man must have been located on the seacoast or near the great deltas of the rivers, and relics of his civilization may lie in caves long since covered by the rising ocean.

Some of our Stone Age ancestors must have known the rigors of life near the glaciers. While men as well as plants and animals moved southward before the ice, some must have remained within sight and sound of the great frozen wall. To these the world was a place of storm and blizzard, with bitter winds roaring down out of the blue mountain of ice that dominated the horizon, while the roaring tumult of the advancing glacier filled the air with the thunder of moving tons of ice breaking away and plunging into the sea. But those who lived on some sunny coast of the Indian Ocean, and walked and hunted on dry land over which the sea had once rolled deeply, knew nothing of the distant glaciers.

In any imaginative reconstruction of the world of the Ice Age, we are plagued by one tantalizing uncertainty: how low did the ocean level fall during the period of greatest spread of the glaciers, when unknown quantities of water were frozen in the ice? Most geologists say that the greatest lowering of the sea level could not have amounted to more than four hundred feet, a change paralleled many times in geologic history. Others, who argue that the drawing down was two thousand, even three thousand feet, base their reasoning upon the submarine canyons, those deep gorges cut in the continental slopes a mile or more below the present level of the sea. They maintain that at least the upper parts of the canyons were stream-cut and that the sea level must have fallen enough to permit this during the Pleistocene glaciation.

It is not surprising that there should be disagreement among geologists on this question. It has been little more than a century since Louis Agassiz gave the world its first understanding of the moving mountains of ice and their dominating effect on the Pleistocene world. Since then, scientists have been patiently accumulating the facts and reconstructing the events of those four successive advances and retreats of the ice. Only the present generation has understood that the ocean lowers with each glacial advance, and rises with each retreat of the melting ice.

Meanwhile, the sea ebbs and flows in these grander tides of earth, whose stages are measurable not in hours but in millennia. The ultimate cause of these vast tides, should it ever be discovered, may be found deep within the fiery center of the earth or somewhere in the dark spaces of the universe.

CHAPTER IX: *Wind and Water*

AS THE WAVES ROLL IN toward Land's End on the westernmost tip of England they bring the feel of the distant places of the Atlantic. They roll up over the continental shelf in confused ripplings and turbulence, and sweep landward over the shoaling bottom. As they approach Land's End they pass over a strange instrument lying on the sea bottom. By the fluctuating pressure of their rise and fall they tell this instrument many things.

If you visited this place, the meteorologist in charge could tell you the histories of the waves that are rolling in hour after hour, bringing messages of far-off places. He could tell you where the waves were created, the strength of the winds that produced them, how fast the storm is moving, and how soon, if at all, storm warnings should be raised along the English coast.

Over millions of years waves, running ahead of storms, have been crying a warning, but only now are we learning to read their language scientifically. There is a basis in folklore for the modern achievements in wave research. To generations of Pacific Island natives, a certain kind of swell has signaled the approach of a typhoon. And centuries ago, when peasants on the lonely shores of Ireland saw the long swells that herald a storm rolling in upon their coasts, they shuddered and talked of death waves.

Now our study of waves has come of age, and on all sides we find modern man turning to the waves of the sea for practical purposes. At Long Branch, New Jersey, a wave-recording instrument silently and continuously takes note of the arrival of waves from the open Atlantic. These records are carefully studied by the Army Corps of Engineers, which is concerned about the rate of erosion along the New Jersey coast.

Off the coast of Africa, high-flying planes took a series of overlapping photographs of the surf and the areas immediately offshore. From these photographs trained men determined the speed of the waves moving in toward shore. Then they applied a mathematical formula that relates the behavior of waves advancing into shallow water to the depths beneath them. This information provided the British government with usable surveys of the depths off the coast of an almost inaccessible part of its empire, which could have been sounded in the ordinary way only at great expense and with endless difficulty. Like much of our new knowledge of waves, this practical method was born of wartime necessity. Forecasts of the state of the sea and particularly the height of the surf became regular preliminaries to beach invasion in World War II.

As long as there has been an earth, the moving masses of air that we call winds have swept back and forth across its surface. And as long as there has been an ocean, its waters have stirred to the passage of the winds. Most waves are the result of the action of wind on water. It is a confused pattern that the waves make in the open sea—intermingling, overtaking, passing, or sometimes engulfing one another; each group differing from the others in origin, speed, direction; some doomed never to reach any shore, others destined to roll across half an ocean before they dissolve in thunder on a distant beach.

While there is still much to be learned, there is a solid basis of fact on which to reconstruct the life history of a wave, predict its behavior, and foretell its effect on human affairs.

A wave has height, from trough to crest. It has length, the distance from its crest to that of the following wave. The period of the wave refers to the time required for succeeding crests to pass a fixed point. None of these dimensions is static; all bear definite relations to the wind, the depth of the water and many other matters. Furthermore, the water that composes a wave does not advance with it across the sea; each water particle describes a circular or elliptical orbit with the passage of the wave form, but returns very nearly to its original position. This is fortunate, for if the huge masses of water that comprise a wave actually moved across the sea, navigation would be impossible.

A picturesque expression—the "length of fetch"—is used to denote the distance that a wave has run, under the drive of a wind blowing in a constant direction, without obstruction. The greater the fetch, the higher the waves. Really large waves cannot be generated within the confined space of a bay. A fetch of perhaps six to eight hundred miles, with winds of gale velocity, is required to get up the largest waves.

Suppose that, after a period of calm, a storm develops far out in the Atlantic. Its winds blow shoreward, though irregularly, with sudden gusts. The sheet of water under the winds responds to the changing pressures. It is no longer a level surface, but furrowed with alternating troughs and ridges. As the storm continues toward the coast, the waves receive energy from the wind and increase in height until they begin to topple in foaming whitecaps, forming a confused, irregular pattern known as a "sea." As the waves gradually pass out of the storm area their height diminishes, the distance between successive crests increases, and the "sea" becomes a "swell," moving at an average speed of about fifteen miles an hour. But as the swell enters shallow coastal water and feels the drag of shoaling bottom, its speed slackens. Crests of following waves crowd in toward it. Abruptly its height increases and the wave form steepens, falls down into its trough, and dissolves in a seething confusion of foam.

Sitting on a beach, you can guess whether the surf spilling out onto the sand before you has been produced by an offshore gale or a distant storm. Young waves, recently shaped by the wind, have a steep, peaked shape even well out at sea. Far out on the horizon, they form whitecaps, bits of foam spill down their fronts, and their final breaking is a prolonged and deliberate process. But if a wave, on coming into the surf zone, rears high as though gathering all its strength for the final act of its life, if the crest forms all along its advancing front and then begins to curl forward, if the whole mass of water plunges with a booming roar into its trough, it has traveled from some very distant part of the ocean before its dissolution at your feet.

How long a wave will live, how far it will travel, to what manner of end it will come are all determined, in large measure, by the conditions it meets in its progression. For the one essential quality of a wave is that it moves; anything that retards or stops its motion dooms it to death.

Forces within the sea itself may affect a wave most profoundly. Some of the most terrible furies of the ocean are unleashed when tidal currents cross the path of the waves or move in direct opposition to them. This is the cause of the famous "roosts" of Scotland, like the one off the southernmost tip of the Shetland Islands, or those at opposite ends of the Pentland Firth, which separates the Orkney Islands from the northern tip of Scotland. "Before entering the Pentland Firth," warns the *North Sea Pilot*, "all vessels should be prepared to batten down, and the hatches of small vessels ought to be secured even in the finest weather, as . . . the transition from smooth water to a broken sea is so sudden that no time is given for making arrangements. A sea is raised which cannot be imagined by those who have never experienced it."

Out in the open sea, a train of waves encountering a hostile wind may be rapidly destroyed, for the power that created a wave may also destroy it. So a fresh trade wind in the Atlantic has often flattened out the swells as they rolled down from Iceland toward Africa. Rocky ledges, shoals and coastal islands all play their part in the fate of advancing waves. The long swells that roll from the open ocean toward the shores of northern New England spend their energy passing over that great submerged highland known as Georges Bank. Ice, snow, rain—all are enemies of the waves and may knock down a sea or cushion the force of surf on a beach. Within loose pack ice a vessel may count on smooth seas even if a gale is raging and surf is breaking heavily about the edges of the pack. A hailstorm will knock down a rough sea, and even a sudden downpour of rain may often turn the surface of the ocean to oiled-silk smoothness, rippling to the passage of the swells.

The divers of ancient times who carried oil in their mouths to release beneath the surface when rough water made their work difficult were applying what every seaman today knows—that oil appears to have a calming effect on the free waves of the open ocean. Instructions for the use of oil in emergencies at sea are carried by most official sailing directions of maritime nations. Oil has little effect on surf, however, once the dissolution of the wave form has begun.

Waves higher than twenty-five feet from trough to crest are rare in all oceans. Storm waves may grow twice as high, and if a full gale blows long enough in one direction to have a fetch of six to eight hundred miles, the resulting waves may be even higher. The greatest possible height of storm waves at sea is a much debated question, with most textbooks citing a conservative sixty feet, and mariners stubbornly describing much higher waves. Yet there is one record of a giant wave which seems to be accepted as reliable.

In February 1933 the U.S.S. *Ramapo*, proceeding from Manila to San Diego, encountered seven days of stormy weather, part of a disturbance that extended all the way from Kamchatka to New York and permitted the winds an unbroken fetch of thousands of miles. When the gale reached its fiercest intensity, winds of sixty-eight knots came in gusts and squalls, and the seas reached mountainous height. Standing watch on the bridge, one of the officers saw a great wave rising astern to a level above an iron strap on the crow's nest of the mainmast. Since the *Ramapo* was on even keel and her stern in the trough of the sea, he had an exact line of sight from the bridge to the crest of the wave. The dimensions of the ship gave the height of the wave. It was one hundred and twelve feet.

Waves have taken their toll of shipping and of human life on the open sea, but it is around the shorelines of the world that they are most violent and destructive. Some coasts have never known the sea in its milder moods. "There is not in the world a coast more terrible than this!" exclaimed Lord Bryce of Tierra del Fuego, where the breakers' roar, according to report, can be heard twenty miles inland on a still night. "The sight of such a coast," Darwin wrote in his diary, "is enough to make a landsman dream for a week about death, peril, and shipwreck."

Whatever the height of storm waves at sea, there is abundant evidence that breaking surf and the upward-leaping water masses from thundering breakers may engulf lighthouses, shatter buildings, and hurl stones through lighthouse windows anywhere from one to three hundred feet above the sea. The first man who ever measured the force of an ocean wave was Thomas Stevenson, father of Robert Louis. Stevenson developed the instrument known as a wave dynamometer and with it studied the waves that battered the coast of his native Scotland. He found that in winter gales the force of a wave might be as great as six thousand pounds to the square foot. Before the power of such surf, piers and breakwaters and other shore installations are fragile as a child's toys.

A list of the perverse and freakish doings of the sea can easily be compiled from the records of the keepers of lights on lonely ledges at sea, or on rocky headlands exposed to the full strength of storm surf. The ninety-seven-foot tower on Minots Ledge in Massachusetts is often completely enveloped by masses of water from breaking surf, and an earlier light on this ledge was swept away in 1851. At Unst, the most northern of the Shetland Islands, a door in the lighthouse was broken open a hundred and ninety-five feet above the sea. At the Bishop Rock Light, on the English Channel, a bell was torn away from its attachment a hundred feet above high water during a winter gale. Once, in 1840, the entrance door of the Eddystone Light tower was made fast by strong bolts, as usual. During a night of heavy seas the door was broken open *from within*, and all its iron bolts and hinges were torn loose. Engineers explain it was a result of pneumatic action—the sudden back draft created by the recession of a heavy wave combined with an abrupt release of pressure on the outside of the door.

Along a rocky coast, the waves of a severe storm may be armed with stones and rock fragments. Once a rock weighing a hundred and thirty-five pounds was hurled high above the lightkeeper's house on Tillamook Rock on the Oregon coast, a hundred feet above sea level. In falling, it tore a twenty-foot hole through the roof. At the Dunnet Head lighthouse, which stands on the summit of a three-hundred-foot cliff at the southwestern entrance to Pentland Firth, windows have often been broken by stones swept from the cliff and tossed aloft by waves.

Thus the sea's waves batter the coastlines of the world with erosive effect, here cutting back a cliff, there stripping away tons of sand from a beach, and yet again, in a reversal of their destructiveness, building up a bar or a small island. And the work of the waves, unlike slow geologic changes, is attuned to the brief span of human life, and so the sculpturing of the continent's edge is something each of us can see.

The high clay cliff of Cape Cod is wearing back so fast that half of the ten acres which the Government acquired as a site for the Highland Light has disappeared, and the cliffs are said to be receding about three feet a year. At this rate of erosion, the outer cape will cease to exist in another four or five thousand years.

The sea's method on a rocky coast is to wear it down by grinding, to chisel out and wrench away fragments of rock, each of which becomes a tool to wear away the cliff. This grinding and polishing of rocks and fragments of rocks goes on incessantly and audibly, for the breakers on such a coast have a different sound from those that have only sand to work with—a deep-toned mutter and rumble not easily forgotten by those who have heard it.

Great Britain, an island, has always been conscious of that "powerful marine gnawing" by which her coasts are eaten away. Old records show astonishing annual rates of cliff erosion—up to nineteen feet between Cromer and Mundesley, and fifteen to forty-five feet at Southwold. An old map dated 1786 gives a long list of towns and villages on the Holderness Coast marked "washed away by the sea." And yet we owe some of the most beautiful and interesting shoreline scenery to the sculpturing effect of moving water. Sea caves are almost literally blasted out of the cliffs by waves, which pour into crevices in the rocks and force them apart by hydraulic pressure. Or, on a narrow promontory, what began as a cave may be cut through from side to side, so that a natural bridge is formed. Later, after years of erosion, the arch may fall, leaving the seaward mass of rock to stand alone—one of the strange, chimneylike formations known as a stack.

The sea waves that have fixed themselves most firmly in the human imagination are the so-called tidal waves. The term is popularly applied to two very different kinds of waves, neither of which has any relation to the tide. One is a *seismic* sea wave produced by undersea earthquakes; the other is a *storm* wave—an immense mass of water driven by winds of hurricane force far above the normal high-water line.

One of the earliest seismic sea waves of record rose along the eastern shores of the Mediterranean in A.D. 358, passing over islands and low-lying shores, leaving boats on the housetops of Alexandria, and drowning thousands of people. In 1868, soon after a three-thousand-mile stretch of the western coast of South America was shaken by earthquakes, the sea receded from the shore, leaving ships that had been anchored in forty feet of water stranded in mud; then the water returned in a great wave, and boats were carried a quarter of a mile inland.

This ominous withdrawal of the sea is often the first warning of the approach of seismic sea waves. Natives on the beaches of Hawaii on April 1, 1946, were alarmed when the accustomed voice of the breakers was suddenly stilled, leaving a strange quiet. They could not know that this recession of the waves from the reefs and the shallow coastal waters was the sea's response to an undersea earthquake off the island of Unimak in the Aleutian chain, more than two thousand miles away; or that in a matter of moments the ocean waters would return at twenty-five feet or more above the normal levels of the tide. The subsequent outflow of these waters was turbulent, sweeping people and houses out to sea. In the open ocean the waves produced by the Aleutian quake were only about a foot or two high, but their length was enormous. It took the waves less than five hours to reach the Hawaiian chain, so they must have moved at an average speed of about four hundred and seventy miles per hour.

After this disaster, seismologists and specialists on waves established a seismic sea-wave warning system to protect the Hawaiian Islands. A network of stations equipped with special instruments is scattered over the Pacific from Kodiak to Pago Pago and from Balboa to Palau. When seismologists in Honolulu are notified that an undersea earthquake has occurred and its waves have been recorded at certain stations, they can calculate when the waves will arrive at any point between the epicenter of the quake and the Hawaiian Islands. They can then issue warnings for the evacuation of beaches and waterfront areas.

From the time of its establishment up to 1960, the warning system issued eight alerts warning residents of the Hawaiian Islands of the approach of seismic sea waves. On three of these occasions, waves of major proportions did in fact strike the islands; the largest and most destructive followed the violent earthquakes on the coast of Chile on May 23, 1960. Without such warning the loss of life would almost certainly have been enormous.

The storm waves generated by tropical hurricanes belong in the class of wind waves, but unlike the waves of ordinary winds and storms, they are accompanied by a rise of the general water level, called a storm tide. Such waves claim about three fourths of the lives lost by hurricanes. The most notable disasters from storm waves in the United States have been those at Galveston, Texas, on September 8, 1900, and on the lower Florida Keys on September 2 and 3, 1935. The most fearful destruction by hurricane waves within historic time occurred in the Bay of Bengal on October 7, 1737, when twenty thousand boats were destroyed and three hundred thousand people drowned.

The flood that overwhelmed the coast of the Netherlands on

February 1, 1953, deserves a place in the history of great storm waves. A winter gale that formed west of Iceland swept across the Atlantic and into the North Sea, to bring to bear all its force on the first land mass obstructing its course—the southwestern corner of Holland. Storm-driven waves and tides battered against the dikes so violently that these ancient defenses were breached in a hundred places. The storm struck on Saturday, January 31, and by midday of Sunday one eighth of Holland was under seawater. The toll included about half a million acres of Holland's best agricultural land—ravaged by water and permeated with salt—thousands of buildings, hundreds of thousands of livestock, and an estimated seventeen hundred people. In all the long history of Holland's struggle against the sea, there has been no comparable disaster.

There are other great waves, usually called "rollers," that periodically rise on certain coasts and batter them for days with damaging surf. These, too, are wind waves, but they are related to changes in barometric pressure over the ocean, perhaps several thousand miles away. Low-pressure areas—like the one south of Iceland—are notorious storm breeders, their winds lashing the sea into great waves. After the waves leave the storm area they tend to become lower and longer until they become transformed into the undulations known as a ground swell. These swells are so regular and so low that often they are unnoticed as they pass through the short, choppy, new-formed waves of other areas. But when a swell approaches a coast, it begins to "peak up." Within the surf zone a crest forms, breaks, and a great mass of water plunges downward.

Winter swell on the west coast of North America is the product of storms that travel south of the Aleutians into the Gulf of Alaska. Swell reaching this coast during the summer has been traced back to its origin in the belt of the "roaring forties," several thousand miles south of the equator. Because of the direction of the prevailing winds, the American east coast and the Gulf of Mexico do not receive the swell from far-distant storms.

The largest and most awe-inspiring waves of the ocean are invisible; they move ponderously and unceasingly through the hidden depths of the sea. Though mystery still surrounds the causes of

these waves, their oceanwide occurrence is well established. Down in deep water they toss submarines about, just as their surface counterparts set ships to rolling. They seem to break against the Gulf Stream and other strong currents in a deep-sea version of the dramatic meeting of surface waves and opposing tidal currents. But these are waves such as never moved at the surface of the ocean. The water masses involved are unthinkably great, some of the waves being as high as three hundred feet.

Of their effect on fishes and other deep-sea life we have only a faint conception. We know that in the open ocean the boundary between water masses of different temperatures or salinities is often a barrier that may not be passed by living creatures, delicately adjusted to certain conditions. Do these creatures then move up and down with the roll of the deep waves? We do not know. We can only sense that in the deep and turbulent recesses of the sea are mysteries far greater than any we have solved.

CHAPTER X: *Wind, Sun, and the Spinning of the Earth*

THE PERMANENT CURRENTS of the ocean are, in a way, the most majestic of her phenomena. Reflecting upon them, our minds are taken out from the earth so that we can regard, as from another planet, the spinning of the globe, the winds that trouble or gently encompass its surface, and the influence of the sun and the moon. For all these cosmic forces are closely linked with the great currents of the ocean, earning for them the adjective I like best of all those applied to them—the planetary currents.

The first thing that impresses us about the ocean currents is their permanence. The forces that produce them show little disposition to change materially over the eons of earthly time. The primary driving power is supplied by the winds; the modifying influences are the sun, the revolving of the earth ever toward the east, and the obstructing masses of the continents.

The surface of the sea is unequally heated by the sun. Probably a slow exchange of polar and equatorial waters is brought about by these differences, the light heated water of the tropics moving poleward in the upper layers, and heavier polar water creeping toward the equator along the floor of the sea. But these movements are obscured in the far greater sweep of the wind-driven currents. The steadiest winds are the trades, blowing diagonally toward the equator from the northeast and southeast. It is the trades that drive the Equatorial Currents around the globe. On wind and water alike, as on all that moves, be it a ship, a bullet or a bird, the spinning earth exerts a deflecting force, turning all moving objects to the right in the Northern Hemisphere and to the left in the Southern. Through the combined action of these and other forces, the resulting current patterns are slowly circulating eddies, turning to the right, or clockwise, in the northern oceans, and to the left, or counterclockwise, in the southern. It is in the Atlantic and Pacific that we see most clearly this interplay of cosmic forces.

The currents of the Atlantic have been longest known to seafaring men and best studied by oceanographers. The strongly running Equatorial Currents, so determined in their set to westward, were familiar to generations of seamen in the days of sail. Ponce de Leon's three ships, sailing south from Cape Canaveral to Tortugas in 1513, sometimes were unable to stem the Gulf Stream, and "although they had great wind, they could not proceed forward, but backward." Later Spanish shipmasters learned to take advantage of the currents, sailing westward in the Equatorial Current, but returning home via the Gulf Stream as far as Cape Hatteras, whence they launched out into the open Atlantic.

The first chart of the Gulf Stream was prepared about 1769 under the direction of Benjamin Franklin, while he was deputy postmaster general of the Colonies. The Board of Customs in Boston had complained that the mail packets coming from England took two weeks longer to make the westward crossing than did the Rhode Island merchant ships. Franklin, perplexed, took the problem to a Nantucket whaling captain, Timothy Folger, who told him the Rhode Island captains were well acquainted with the Gulf Stream from "our pursuit of whales, which keep to the sides of it but are not met within it." Thus they avoided it on the westward crossing, whereas the English captains, unaware, did not. So Franklin asked Folger to mark the current out for him on an old chart.

The Gulf Stream stems from the North Equatorial Current which flows westward from Africa. When it meets the deflecting barrier of the Panamanian Isthmus, it doubles back to the north-east to reenter the Atlantic as the Gulf Stream. If thought of as a "river" in the sea, its width from bank to bank is ninety-five miles. It is a mile deep from surface to riverbed. It flows with a velocity of nearly three knots and its volume is that of several hundred Mississippis.

Even in these days of diesel power, the coastwise shipping off southern Florida shows a wholesome respect for the Gulf Stream. Below Miami, the big freighters and tankers move south in a course surprisingly close to the Keys, risking the almost unbroken wall of submerged reefs lying there within a fathom or two of the surface. To seaward is the Gulf Stream, and while the big boats could fight their way south against it, they would consume much time and fuel in doing so.

Northward, the Stream follows the contours of the continental slope to the offing of Cape Hatteras, whence it deserts the sunken edge of the land, turning northeastward, as a narrow, meandering current, always sharply separated from the water on either side. Near the Grand Banks the line is most sharply drawn between the cold, bottle-green arctic water of the Labrador Current and the warm indigo blue of the Stream. In winter the temperature change across the current boundary is so abrupt that as a ship crosses into the Gulf Stream her bow may be momentarily in water twenty de-grees warmer than that at her stern. One of the densest fogbanks in the world lies in this region—a thick, blanketing whiteness that is the atmospheric response to the Gulf Stream's invasion of the cold northern seas.

Where the Stream feels the rise of the ocean floor known as the "tail" of the Grand Banks, it bends eastward and begins to spread out into many complexly curving tongues. Probably the force of arctic water which comes down from Baffin Bay and Greenland, freighting its icebergs, helps push the Stream to the east—that, and the deflecting force of the earth's rotation, always turning the currents to the right. The Labrador Current itself (being a southward-moving current) is turned in toward the mainland. The next time you wonder why the water is so cold at certain coastal resorts of the eastern United States, remember that the water of the Labrador Current is between you and the Gulf Stream.

Passing across the Atlantic, the Stream becomes less a current than a drift of water, fanning out in three main directions: southward into the Sargasso; northward into the Norwegian Sea; eastward to warm the coast of Europe (some of it even to pass into the Mediterranean) and thence as the Canary Current to rejoin the Equatorial Current and close the circuit.

The Atlantic currents of the Southern Hemisphere are practically a mirror image of those of the Northern. Here the great spiral moves counterclockwise—west, south, east, north. The Benguela Current is a river of cold water moving northward along the west coast of Africa to join the westward-flowing South Equatorial Current. In mid ocean this current is a powerful stream, but it loses a substantial part of its waters to the North Atlantic off the coast of South America. The remainder becomes the Brazil Current, which circles south and then turns east as the South Atlantic or Antarctic Current. The whole is a system of shallow water movements, involving not more than the upper hundred fathoms.

The North Equatorial Current of the Pacific is the longest westerly running current on earth, with nothing to deflect it in its nine-thousand-mile course from Panama to the Philippines. There, meeting the barrier of the islands, most of it swings northward as the Japan Current—Asia's counterpart of the Gulf Stream—flowing along the continental shelf off eastern Asia, until it is driven away from the continent by a mass of icy water—the Oyashio—that pours out of the Sea of Okhotsk and the Bering Sea. The Japan Current and Oyashio meet in a region of fog and tempestuous winds, as, in the North Atlantic, the meeting of the Gulf Stream and the Labrador Current is marked with fog. Drifting toward America, the Japan Current's warm waters become chilled with infusions of cold polar water. When it reaches the mainland of America it is a cool current, moving southward along the coast of California. There it is further cooled by updrafts of deep water and has much to do with the temperate summer climate of the American west coast. Off Lower California it rejoins the North Equatorial Current.

The South Equatorial Current has its course so frequently interrupted by islands, which deflect streams of its water into the central basin, that by the time it approaches Asia it is during most seasons a comparatively feeble current, lost in a confused and ill-defined pattern around the East Indies and Australia.

Only one of the South Pacific currents has been thoroughly studied—the Humboldt—and this has so direct an effect on human affairs that it overshadows all others. The Humboldt Current flows northward along the west coast of South America, carrying waters almost as cold as the Antarctic from which it comes. But its chill is actually that of the deep ocean, for the current is reinforced by almost continuous upwelling from lower oceanic layers.

Upwelling takes place along coastlines when the winds, combined with the deflecting effect of rotation, blow the surface waters offshore, and deep water rises to replace it. Upwelling also occurs in the open sea when two strongly moving currents diverge, and water rises from below to fill the place where streams separate. Upwelling of both types takes place in the Humboldt.

It is because of the Humboldt that penguins live almost under the equator, on the Galápagos Islands. In these cold waters, rich in minerals, there is an abundance of sea life perhaps unparalleled anywhere in the world. The direct harvesters of this sea life are not men, but millions of sea birds. Because their diet links these birds with all the minerals of the sea, their excrement, called guano, is the most valuable and efficient fertilizer in the world, its sun-baked accumulations whitening the coastal cliffs and islands of the continent.

The Humboldt Current carries its cool waters almost to the equator. About the Galápagos Islands it gives rise to a strange mixture of waters—the cool green of the Humboldt and the blue equatorial waters meeting in rips and foam lines, suggesting hidden movements and conflicts deep in the sea.

The conflict between opposing water masses is a dramatic phenomenon. Superficial hissings and sighings, striping of the surface waters with lines of froth, a confused turbulence and boiling, even sounds like distant breakers accompany the displacement of the surface layers by deep water. Creatures that inhabit the deeper places of the sea may be carried up into the surface, there to set off orgies of devouring and being devoured.

Wherever upwelling occurs, it is responsible for a profusion of life. Sardines are abundant off the coast of Algeria because upward streams of deep, cold water provide the minerals to support astronomical numbers of diatoms. Upwelling around the island of South Georgia, east of Cape Horn, makes this one of the world's centers of whaling. On the west coast of the United States the catch of sardines is sometimes as much as a billion pounds in a year, supporting one of the largest fisheries in the world. The fishery could not exist except for upwelling, which sets off the old, familiar biological chain: salts, diatoms, copepods, herring.

The downward movement of surface water into the depths is as dramatic as upwelling, and perhaps it fills the human mind with an even greater sense of awe and mystery, because it cannot be seen but can only be imagined. At several known places the downward flow of enormous quantities of water takes place regularly to feed the deep currents of whose courses we have only the dimmest knowledge. We do know that it is all part of the ocean's system of balances, by which she pays back to one part of her waters what she had borrowed for distribution to another.

The North Atlantic, for example, receives quantities of surface water (some six million cubic meters a second) from the South Atlantic via the Equatorial Current. The return payment is made at deep levels, partly in very cold arctic water, and partly in some of the saltiest, warmest water in the world, that of the Mediterranean. There are two places for the downflow of arctic water, one in the Labrador Sea, another southeast of Greenland. At each the quantity of sinking water is some two million cubic meters a second. The deep Mediterranean water flows out over the sill that separates the Mediterranean basin from the Atlantic. And meeting and mingling with these is water moving northward from the Antarctic Sea.

The flow of these deep, heavy, cold waters is ponderously slow, but the volumes involved are prodigious, and the areas covered worldwide. It may even be that the global wandering of deep-ocean water distributes some of the marine fauna. Some of the same species of deepwater invertebrates and fishes have been collected off the coast of South Africa and off Greenland. And about Bermuda, where a greater variety of deepwater forms has been found than anywhere else, there is a mingling of deep water from the Antarctic, the Arctic and the Mediterranean.

There is, then, no water that is wholly of the Pacific, or wholly of the Atlantic, or of the Indian or the Antarctic. The surf that we find exhilarating at Virginia Beach or at La Jolla today may have lapped at the base of antarctic icebergs or sparkled in the Mediterranean sun years ago. By the deep, hidden currents the oceans are made one.

CHAPTER XI: *The Moving Tides*

THERE IS NO DROP OF ocean water that does not respond to the mysterious forces that create the tide. No other force that affects the sea is so strong. Wind-created waves are felt, at most, no more than a hundred fathoms below the surface. Planetary currents, despite their impressive sweep, seldom involve more than the upper several hundred fathoms. The masses of water affected by tidal movement are enormous. Into little Passamaquoddy Bay—an inlet of the Bay of Fundy—two billion tons of water are carried by the tidal currents twice each day; into the whole Bay of Fundy, one hundred billion tons. And nothing the human mind has invented can control the rhythm of the water's ebb and flow.

The fact that the tides affect the whole ocean from its surface to its floor is dramatically illustrated when opposing tidal currents meet, as in the Strait of Messina, and create whirlpools, like Charybdis of classical fame. These so deeply stir the waters of the strait that fish bearing all the marks of abyssal existence, their eyes atrophied or abnormally large, their bodies studded with phosphorescent organs, frequently are cast up on the lighthouse beach.

The tides are a response of the mobile waters of the ocean to the pull of the moon and the more distant sun. And the moon's power over the tides is more than twice that of the sun. That the sun, with a mass twenty-seven million times that of the moon, should have less influence over the tides than a small satellite of the earth is at first surprising. But in the mechanics of the universe, nearness counts for more than distant mass.

As the moon waxes and wanes in its monthly cycle, so the height of the tide varies. Twice each month, when the moon is a mere thread of silver in the sky, and again when it is full, we have the highest flood tides and the lowest ebb tides of the lunar month. These are called spring tides. At these times sun, moon and earth are directly in line and the pull of the two heavenly bodies is added together to bring the water high on the beaches, and send its surf leaping upward against the sea cliffs. And twice each month, at the quarters of the moon, when sun, moon and earth lie at the apexes of a triangle, and the pull of the sun and moon are opposed, we have neap tides, when there is the least difference between high and lower water.

The force that sets the tides in motion is cosmic, lying wholly outside the earth, but the nature of the tide at any particular place is a local matter, with astonishing differences occurring within a very short geographic distance. On Nantucket Island the range between high water and low is only about a foot or two; the Bay of Fundy has a rise and fall of forty to fifty feet. Yet both places are within the same body of water—the Gulf of Maine. And we may find that the time of high water each day varies by as much as twelve hours in different places on the shores of Chesapeake Bay. The attractive force of the heavenly bodies sets the water in motion, but how far, and how strongly it will rise depend on such things as the slope of the bottom, the depth of a channel, or the width of a bay's entrance.

The fifty-foot tides which occur in the Bay of Fundy are the highest in the world. But at least half a dozen other places have a tidal range of more than thirty feet—Puerto Gallegos in Argentina and Cook Inlet in Alaska, and the Gulf of Saint-Malo in France come to mind. At Tahiti, as on most oceanic islands, "high tide" may mean a gentle rise of only a foot or so, perhaps only a few inches. At the Atlantic end of the Panama Canal the tidal range is not more than one or two feet; at the Pacific end, only forty miles away, it is twelve to sixteen feet.

Tidal rhythms also vary from ocean to ocean. To those who know the Atlantic Ocean, the rhythm of two high tides and two low tides in each day seems "normal." Here, on each flood tide, the water advances about as far as the preceding high; and succeeding ebb tides fall about equally low. But in the Gulf of Mexico a different rhythm prevails. At certain places it is a long, deliberate undulation—one rise and one fall each lunar day—resembling the untroubled breathing of that earth monster to whom the ancients attributed all tides. This "diurnal rhythm" is found in other places scattered about the earth, but most of the world's coasts display a mixture of diurnal and semidiurnal types of tide. There are two high and two low tides in a day, but the succeeding floods may be so unequal that the second scarcely rises to mean sea level; or it may be the ebb tides that are of extreme inequality.

The tides were not always as they are today, and as with all that is earthly, their days are numbered. They reached their greatest grandeur and power in the younger days of Earth, when our moon was much closer to its parent planet. When it was half its present distance away, for instance, its tidal power was eight times as great as now, and the coming in of the tide must have been a stupendous event. Twice each day, the fury of the incoming waters would batter the crest of high cliffs and sweep inland to inundate all the margins of the continents. No living thing could exist on the shores, and, had conditions not changed, life would probably have evolved no further than the fishes.

Over the millions of years the moon has receded more than two hundred thousand miles, and the tides, meanwhile, have grown feebler, and will continue to do so. For they carry within themselves a self-destroying power, tidal friction—that movement of water over the ocean's bed which acts as a constant brake on the earth's rotation.

It once took the earth a much shorter time—perhaps only about four hours—to make a complete rotation on its axis. Since then, the spinning of the globe has been so greatly slowed that a rotation now requires, as everyone knows, about twenty-four hours. This retarding will continue, according to mathematicians, and all the while, tidal friction will be exerting a second effect: pushing the moon farther away; for according to the laws of mechanics, as the earth's turning slows down, the spinning of the moon must speed up, and centrifugal force will carry it farther away. The moon will then have even less power over the tides and they will grow weaker. It will also take the moon longer to complete its orbit around the earth. When finally the length of the day and of the month coincide, the moon will no longer rotate relatively to the earth, and there will be no lunar tides.

All this, of course, will require time on a scale the mind finds it difficult to conceive, and before it happens it is quite probable that the human race will have vanished from the earth. But already, even in our allotted fraction of earthly time, we can see some of the effects of these cosmic processes. Our day is believed to be several seconds longer than that of Babylonian times. Conventional clocks, geared to the earth's rotation, do not show the effect of the tide-induced lengthening of the day. New atomic clocks now being constructed will show actual time and will differ from other clocks.

Although the tides have become tamer, many violent movements and disturbances of the sea are indirectly related to them. In the confinement of narrow passages or when opposed by contrary winds and swells, tidal currents create some of the most dangerous waterways of the world. Around the Aleutians, for instance, strong tidal currents pour through Unalga and Akutan passes, which are among the most-used routes for vessels entering the Bering Sea from the Pacific. "Vessels must be prepared to take seas aboard," warns the *Alaska Pilot*, for a fifteen-foot wave of a tide rip may suddenly rise and sweep across a vessel, and more than one man has thus been carried off to his death.

Edgar Allan Poe, in his "A Descent into the Maelstrom," converted one of the more evil manifestations of the tide into literature. Few who have read it will forget the old man's story of his own descent into the whirlpool and of his miraculous escape. There actually is a maelstrom and it exists where Poe placed it, between two of the islands of the Lofoten group off the west coast of Norway. It is, as he described it, a gigantic whirlpool or series of whirlpools, and men with their boats have actually been drawn down into these spinning funnels of water. Although Poe's account exaggerates certain details, the essential facts on which he based his tale are true.

Among unusual creations of the tide, perhaps the best known are the bores. A bore is created when a great part of the flood tide enters a river as a single wave, or at most two or three waves. To produce a bore there must be a considerable range of tide combined with sandbars or other obstructions in the mouth of the river, so that the tide is held back until it finally gathers itself together and rushes through. The Amazon is remarkable for the distance its bore travels upstream—some two hundred miles—with the result that the bores of as many as five flood tides may actually be moving up the river at one time.

On the Tsientang River, which empties into the China Sea, all shipping is controlled by the bore—the largest, most dangerous in the world. The ancient Chinese used to throw offerings into the river to appease the angry spirit of this bore. During most of the month the bore advances up the river in a wave eight to eleven feet high, moving at a speed of twelve to thirteen knots, its front "a sloping cascade of bubbling foam, falling forward and pounding on itself and on the river." Its full ferocity is reserved for the spring tides, when the crest of the advancing wave is said to rise twenty-five feet above the surface of the river.

The influence of the tide over the affairs of sea creatures may be seen all over the world. Billions upon billions of sessile animals, like oysters, mussels and barnacles, owe their very existence to the sweep of the tides, which brings them food. By marvelous adaptations of form and structure, the inhabitants of the world between the tide lines are enabled to live in a zone where the danger of being dried up is matched against the danger of being washed away, where for every enemy that comes by sea there is another that comes by land, and where the most delicate of living tissues must withstand the assault of storm waves that have the power to shift tons of rock or to crack the hardest granite.

The breeding rhythm of certain marine animals is timed to coincide with stages of the tide. In Europe the spawning activities of oysters reach their peak on the spring tides. In the waters of northern Africa there is a sea urchin that, on the nights when the moon is full, and apparently only then, releases its reproductive cells into the sea. And in many tropical waters there are small marine worms whose spawning behavior is so precisely adjusted to the tidal calendar that, merely from observing them, one could tell the month, the day, and often the time of day as well.

No other creature displays so exquisite an adaptation to the tidal rhythm as the grunion—a small, shimmering fish about as long as a man's hand. Shortly after the full moon of the months from March to August, the grunion appear in the surf on the California beaches, just as the tide begins to ebb. Now on these waves of the ebbing tide the fish come in. Thousands upon thousands of grunion are borne up the beach, lie glittering on the wet sand for a perceptible moment, then fling themselves into the wash of the next wave and are carried back to sea. For about an hour after the turn of the tide this continues.

During the brief interval between successive waves, the male and female have come together, the one to shed her eggs, the other to fertilize them. When the parent fish return to the water, they have left behind a mass of eggs buried in the sand. Succeeding waves on that night do not wash out the eggs because the tide is already ebbing. The next high tide will not reach them, because for a time after the full of the moon each tide will halt its advance a little lower on the beach than the preceding one. The eggs, then, will be undisturbed for at least a fortnight. In the warm, damp incubating sand they undergo the magic change from fertilized egg to larval fishlet. The perfectly formed little grunion, still confined within the membranes of the egg, still buried in the sand, waits for release. With the tides of the new moon it comes. Their waves reach and stir the sand where the little masses of the grunion eggs were buried. As the sand is washed away, and the eggs feel the touch of the cool seawater, the membranes rupture, the fishlets hatch, and the waves that released them bear them away to the sea.

But the link between tide and living creature I find most unforgettable is that of a very small worm named *Convoluta roscoffensis*, which lives by the thousands on the beaches of northern Brittany and the Channel Islands. Convoluta has entered into a remarkable partnership with a green alga, whose cells inhabit its body and supply all its food. So that the guest plants may have life-giving light, Convoluta rises from the damp sands as soon as the tide has ebbed and lies in the sun, while the plants manufacture their starches and sugars. When the tide returns, the worm again sinks into the sand to avoid being washed out into deep water. So the whole lifetime of the worm is a succession of movements conditioned by the tide—upward into sunshine on the ebb, downward on the flood.

Sometimes a whole colony of the worms is transferred into a laboratory aquarium, where there are no tides. But twice each day Convoluta rises out of the sand on the bottom of the aquarium into the light of the sun. Twice each day it sinks again into the sand. Without a brain, or what we would call a memory, Convoluta continues to live out its life in this alien place, remembering, in every fiber of its small green body, the tidal rhythm of the distant sea.

CHAPTER XII: *The Global Thermostat*

THE OCEAN IS THE GREAT regulator, the great stabilizer of temperatures on our earth. Without it, we would have unthinkably harsh extremes of temperature. The water that covers three fourths of the earth's surface is an excellent absorber and radiator of heat, "a savings bank for solar energy." And through the agency of ocean currents, heat and cold may be distributed over thousands of miles, thus tending to make up for the uneven heating of the globe by the sun. Ocean currents carry hot equatorial water toward the poles and return cold water equatorward by such surface drifts as the Labrador Current and Oyashio, and even more importantly by deep currents. The redistribution of heat for the whole earth is accomplished about half by the ocean currents, and half by the winds.

Most of the rains that fall on sea and land alike were raised from the sea. They are carried as vapor in the winds, and then with change of temperature the rains fall. European rain generally comes from evaporation of Atlantic water. In the United States, vapor and warm air from the Gulf of Mexico and the tropical waters of the western Atlantic ride the winds up the Mississippi valley and provide rains for much of the eastern part of North America.

Whether any place will know the harsh extremes of a continental climate or the moderating effect of the sea depends less on its nearness to the ocean than on the pattern of currents and winds and the relief of the continents. The east coast of North America receives little benefit from the sea, because the prevailing winds are from the west. The Pacific coast, on the other hand, lies in the path of the westerly winds that have blown across thousands of miles of ocean. Their moist breath brings climatic mildness and creates the dense rain forests of British Columbia, Washington and Oregon; but its full influence is largely restricted to a narrow strip by the coast ranges that parallel the sea. Europe, in contrast, is wide open to the sea, and "Atlantic weather" carries hundreds of miles into the interior.

The transforming influence of the sea is portrayed with beautiful clarity in the striking differences between the Arctic, a nearly land-locked sea, and the Antarctic, a continent surrounded by ocean. The ice-covered Antarctic continent is bathed by seas of uniform coldness. High winds blow from the land and repel any warming influence that might seek to penetrate it. The mean temperature of this bitter world is never above the freezing point. On exposed rocks the lichens grow, covering the barrenness of cliffs. Mosses hide in valleys and crevices. But of the higher plants only a few impoverished stands of grasses have managed to invade this land. There are no land mammals; the fauna consists only of birds, wingless mosquitoes, a few flies and microscopic mites.

In sharp contrast are the arctic summers, where the tundra is bright with many-colored flowers. Everywhere except on the Greenland ice cap and some of the arctic islands, summer temperatures are high enough for the growth of plants, packing a year's development into the short, warm, arctic summer. The polar limit of plant growth is set not by latitude, but by the sea. Through the one large break in the land girdle, the Greenland Sea, streams of warm Atlantic water enter the Arctic to make it, in climate as well as in geography, a world apart from the Antarctic.

So, day by day and season by season, the ocean dominates the world's climate. Can it also be an agent in bringing about the long-period swings of climatic change that we know have occurred throughout the earth's history—the alternating periods of heat and cold, of drought and flood? The distinguished Swedish oceanographer, Otto Pettersson, who died in 1941, developed just such a fascinating theory. In Pettersson's laboratory atop a sheer cliff overlooking the deep waters of the Gulmarfiord, instruments recorded strange phenomena in the depths of this gateway to the Baltic. As the ocean water presses in toward that inland sea it dips down and lets the fresh surface water roll out above it. Each day Pettersson's instruments revealed a strong, pulsing movement of that deep saltwater layer—the pressing inward of great submarine waves, of moving mountains of water. The movement was strongest every twelfth hour of the day, and Pettersson soon established a link between these submarine waves and the daily tides. "Moon waves," he called them, and as he measured their height—some were giants of nearly a hundred feet—and timed their pulsing beat through the months and years, their relation to the ever-changing cycles of the tides became crystal clear.

Pettersson's mind then moved logically to another problem—the changing fortunes of the Swedish herring fishery. His native Bohuslan had been the site of the great Hanseatic herring fisheries of the Middle Ages, when there seemed no end of the silvery, wealth-bringing fish. Then suddenly the fishery ceased, for the herring withdrew into the North Sea and came no more into the gateways of the Baltic. Why? Pettersson thought he knew, and the reason was intimately related to those movements of the submarine waves far down in the depths of Gulmarfiord.

He had found that the waves varied in height and power as the tide-producing power of the moon and sun varied. From astronomical calculations he learned that the tides must have been at their greatest strength about 1433, when sun, moon and earth came into such a position at the time of the winter solstice that they exerted the greatest possible attracting force upon the sea—the effect being felt, however, for several centuries before and after that date. And it was during those centuries when the Baltic herring fishery was flourishing. Only about every eighteen centuries do the heavenly bodies assume this particular relation. Therefore, Pettersson reasoned, in that period of the Middle Ages the great underwater waves pressed with unusual force into the narrow passages to the Baltic, carrying the herring with them. Later, when the tides became weaker, the herring remained outside the Baltic, in the North Sea.

Then he realized another fact of extreme significance—that those centuries just before, during and after the great tides had been a period of "startling and unusual occurrences" in the world of nature. Polar ice blocked much of the North Atlantic. The coasts of the North Sea and the Baltic were laid waste by violent storm floods. The winters were of "unexplained severity" and in consequence of the climatic rigors political and economic catastrophes occurred all over the populated regions of the earth. Could there be a connection between all these events? Could the deep tides affect the lives of men as well as of herring?

From this germ of an idea, Pettersson's fertile mind evolved a theory of climatic variation, which he set forth in 1912. Marshaling scientific, historic and literary evidence, he showed that there are alternating periods of mild and severe climates which correspond to the long-period cycles of the oceanic tides.

The world's most recent period of minimum tidal effect prevailed about A.D. 550 (and will occur again about the year 2400). It was a period of benevolent climate. Snow and ice were little known on the coast of Europe and in the seas about Iceland and Greenland: the Vikings sailed freely over northern seas; monks went back and forth between Ireland and Iceland. Early Icelandic sagas speak of the abundant fruit growing in Greenland, and of the number of cattle that could be pastured there, and recent Danish excavations indicate clearly that the colonists lived in a climate definitely milder than the present one.

But Greenland's bland climatic conditions began to deteriorate in the thirteenth century. The Eskimos began to make troublesome raids, perhaps because their northern sealing grounds were frozen over and they were hungry. Ships attempting the icy passage between Iceland and Europe found it increasingly difficult to reach Greenland, and eventually the colonists, left to their own resources, were wiped out—sometime about 1418.

Climatic rigors were felt also in Europe. Old Icelandic records say that, in the winters of the early 1300s, packs of wolves crossed on the ice from Norway to Denmark. The Baltic froze over, forming a bridge of ice between Sweden and the Danish islands. Pedestrians and carriages crossed the frozen sea and hostelries were put up on the ice to accommodate them. In southern Europe there were unusual storms, crop failures, famine and distress.

What of the previous era of cold and storms, which should have occurred about the third or fourth century B.C., according to the tidal theory? In literature and folklore there are shadowy hints of great catastrophe. Early history contains striking suggestions that the restless movements of the tribes of northern Europe—the "barbarians" who shook the power of Rome—coincided with periods of storms, floods and other climatic catastrophes.

These ancient records convinced Pettersson that climatic changes are brought about as the tide-induced submarine waves disturb the deep waters of polar seas. In the years or the centuries of strong tidal forces, unusual quantities of warm Atlantic water press into the Arctic Sea at deep levels, moving in under the ice. Then thousands of square miles of ice that normally remain solidly frozen undergo partial thawing and break up. Drift ice, in extraordinary volume, enters the Labrador Current and is carried southward into the Atlantic. This changes the pattern of surface circulation, which is so intimately related to the winds, rainfall and air temperatures. For the drift ice then attacks the Gulf Stream south of Newfoundland and sends it on a more easterly course, deflecting the streams of warm surface water that usually bring a softening effect to the climate of Greenland, Iceland and northern Europe.

Now in our own lifetime we are witnessing a startling alteration of climate, and it is intriguing to apply Otto Pettersson's ideas as a possible explanation. A definite warming of the arctic climate set in about 1900, became astonishingly marked about 1930, and is now spreading into subarctic and temperate regions. During the 1940s the season for shipping coal from ports on Norway's West Spitsbergen Island lengthened to seven months, compared with three at the beginning of the century. Drift ice in the Russian sector of the Arctic Sea decreased by a million square kilometers between 1924 and 1944.

The changed habits and migrations of many fishes, birds, land mammals and whales also reflect arctic warming. Many new birds are appearing in far northern lands for the first time in our records. The long list of southern visitors—birds never reported in Greenland before 1920—includes the greater yellowlegs, cliff swallow, ovenbird, Baltimore oriole and Canada warbler. Iceland has had subtropical avian visitors since 1935: wood warblers, skylarks, scarlet grosbeaks, pipits and thrushes.

The cod first appeared off Greenland in 1912. It was a new and strange fish to the Eskimos and Danes, but by the 1930s it supported so substantial a fishery in the area that the natives had become dependent upon it for food. They were also using its oil as fuel for their lamps and to heat their houses.

The recession of the northern glaciers is now going on at such a rate that many smaller ones have already disappeared. The melting away of the snowfields in the Opdal Mountains in Norway has exposed wooden-shafted arrows of a type used about A.D. 400 to 500. This suggests that the snow cover in this region must now be less than it has been at any time within the past fourteen to fifteen hundred years. Geologists report that most Norwegian glaciers "are living only on their own mass without receiving any annual fresh supply of snow"; and that in the Alps there has been a general retreat and shrinkage of glaciers during the last decades. The glaciers of several East African high volcanoes have also been diminishing rapidly since 1920, and there is glacial shrinkage in the Andes and in the high mountains of central Asia.

The milder arctic and subarctic climate has already resulted in longer growing seasons and better crops. The cultivation of oats has improved in Iceland. In Norway good seed years are now the rule rather than the exception, and in northern Scandinavia the trees have spread above their former timber lines.

Unquestionably, several agents are at work in bringing about these climatic changes. For one thing, we are almost certainly still in the warming-up stage following the last Pleistocene glaciation—and the world's climate, over the next several thousands of years, will grow warmer before beginning a downward swing into another Ice Age. But it is interesting to calculate where our twentieth-century situation fits into the cosmic scheme of the shifting cycles of the tides. The great tides at the close of the Middle Ages, with their accompanying snow, ice, winds and floods, are more than five centuries behind us. The era of weakest tidal movements, with a climate as benign as that of the early Middle Ages, is about four centuries ahead. We have therefore begun to move strongly into a period of milder weather. There will be fluctuations as the tidal power waxes and wanes. But the long trend is toward a warmer earth; the pendulum is swinging.

CHAPTER XIII: *Wealth from the Salt Seas*

THE OCEAN IS THE EARTH'S greatest storehouse of minerals. In a single cubic mile of seawater there are, on the average, a hundred and sixty-six million tons of dissolved salts, and in all the ocean waters of the earth there are about fifty quadrillion tons.

And this quantity gradually increases over the millennia as the rains wear away the rocks and carry their contained minerals to the sea.

Yet it is a curious fact that there is little similarity between the chemical composition of river water and of seawater. The rivers bring into the sea four times as much calcium as chloride, for example, yet in the ocean the proportions are strongly reversed—forty-six times as much chloride as calcium. This is partly due to the immense amounts of calcium salts being constantly withdrawn from the seawater by marine animals for building shells, skeletons and the massive structures of the coral reefs. There is a striking difference, too, in the silicon content of river and seawater—about five hundred percent greater in rivers than in the sea. The silica is required by diatoms to make their shells. Because of the enormous total chemical requirements of all the fauna and flora of the sea, only a small part of the salts annually brought in by rivers goes to increasing the quantity of dissolved minerals in the water.

There are other agencies by which minerals are added to the sea. From every volcano chlorine and other gases escape into the atmosphere and are carried down in rain onto the surface of land and sea alike. And all the submarine volcanoes, discharging through unseen craters directly into the sea, pour in boron, chlorine, sulfur and iodine.

Only to a very limited extent is there any return of minerals to the land. We attempt to recover some directly by chemical extraction and mining, and indirectly by harvesting the sea's plants and animals. And, in the long, recurring cycles of the earth, when ocean waters rise over the lands, deposit sediments and at last withdraw, they leave on the continent another layer of sedimentary rocks containing some of the salts of the sea. But it is only a temporary loan of minerals to the land and the return payment begins at once by way of the old, familiar channels—rain, erosion, runoff to the rivers, transport to the sea.

There are other curious exchanges of materials between sea and land. While evaporation raises water vapor into the air, leaving most of the salts behind, a surprising amount of salt does intrude itself into the atmosphere. These tiny, invisible particles of sea salt drifting in the air are, in fact, one of the many forms of atmospheric nuclei around which raindrops form. Areas nearest the sea receive most of this salt: twenty-four to thirty-six pounds per acre per year for England and more than one hundred pounds for British Guiana. But an astounding example of long-distance, large-scale transport of salts is furnished by Sambhar Salt Lake in northern India. It receives three thousand tons of salt a year, carried to it on the hot dry monsoons of summer from the sea, four hundred miles away.

The plants and animals of the sea are very much better chemists than men, able to find and to utilize elements present in minute traces. We did not know, for example, that vanadium occurred in the sea until it was discovered in the blood of certain sluggish and sedentary sea creatures such as sea cucumbers. Relatively huge quantities of cobalt are extracted by lobsters and mussels; and copper, recoverable only as about a hundredth part in a million of seawater, helps constitute the lifeblood of lobsters as iron does human blood.

We know that there is enough gold in the sea to make every person in the world a millionaire. But how can the sea be made to yield it? The German chemist Fritz Haber, after World War I, conceived the idea of extracting enough gold from the sea to pay the German war debt. His dream resulted in the German South Atlantic Expedition of the *Meteor*. The *Meteor* was equipped with a laboratory and filtration plant, and between 1924 and 1928 it crossed and recrossed the Atlantic, sampling the water. About $93,000,000 in gold was found per cubic mile of water, but the cost of extraction was far greater than the value of the gold recovered.

Most mysterious, perhaps, of all substances in the sea is iodine. In seawater itself it is difficult to detect. Yet it is found in almost every marine plant and animal. Sponges, corals and certain seaweeds accumulate vast quantities of it. From the time living things first made iodine a part of the chemistry of their tissues, they seem to have become increasingly dependent on it; now we ourselves require it as a regulator of our basal metabolism, through the thyroid gland which accumulates it.

All commercial iodine was formerly obtained from seaweeds; then deposits of crude nitrate of soda were discovered in the high deserts of North Chile where they were probably left by some prehistoric sea filled with marine vegetation.

Ninety-nine percent of the world's bromine is concentrated in the ocean. Thanks to bromine we have high-test gasoline for our cars. Other uses include the manufacture of sedatives, fire extinguishers, photographic chemicals, dyestuffs and chemical-warfare materials. We once obtained bromine from the brines left in subterranean pools by prehistoric oceans; now there are large plants on the seacoasts—especially in the United States—which extract the bromine directly from ocean water.

Magnesium is another mineral we now obtain by collecting huge volumes of ocean water and treating it with chemicals, although originally it was derived only from brines or magnesium-containing rocks. Since the direct extraction method was developed about 1941, production has increased enormously. It was magnesium from the sea that made possible the wartime growth of the aviation industry, for every airplane made in the United States (and in most other countries as well) contains about half a ton of magnesium metal. And it has long been useful in printing inks, medicines, toothpastes and tracer ammunition.

Sodium chloride, or common table salt, is by far the most abundant of the ocean's salts. For many centuries, wherever climate has permitted it, men have evaporated salt from seawater. The ancient Greeks, Romans and Egyptians harvested the salt men and animals everywhere must have in order to live. Even today in certain hot, dry parts of the world where drying winds blow, solar evaporation of salt is practiced—on the shores of the Persian Gulf, in China, India and Japan, in the Philippines, and on the coast of California and the alkali flats of Utah.

Here and there are natural basins where the action of sun, wind and sea combine to carry on evaporation of salt on a scale man could not hope to accomplish. Such a natural basin is India's Rann of Cutch, a flat plain, some sixty by one hundred and eighty-five miles, separated from the sea by an island. When the monsoons blow, seawater is carried in by way of a channel to cover the plain. But in summer, in the season when the hot monsoon blows from the desert, no more water enters, and that which is collected in pools over the plain evaporates into a salt crust, in some places several feet thick.

The sea has created some reservoirs of chemicals, upon which we can draw with comparatively little trouble. One of the world's greatest stockpiles of minerals came from the evaporation of an inland sea in the western United States. This is Searles Lake in the Mojave Desert of California, where an arm of the sea was cut off from the ocean by the thrusting up of a range of mountains. As the lake evaporated, the water that remained became ever more salty through the inwash of minerals from all the surrounding land. Perhaps this slow process began only a few thousand years ago; now Searles Lake has a hard crust of salts over which a car may be driven. The crystals of salts form a layer fifty to seventy feet deep. Below that is mud, and a second layer of salts and brine, probably at least as thick as the upper layer, underlies the mud. Searles Lake was first worked in the 1870s for borax; then teams of twenty mules each carried the borax across desert and mountains to the railroads. In the 1930s the recovery of other substances from the lake began—bromine, lithium and salts of potassium and sodium. Now Searles Lake yields forty percent of the production of potassium chloride in the United States and a large share of all the borax and lithium salts produced in the world.

In some future era the Dead Sea will probably repeat the history of Searles Lake. The Dead Sea once filled the entire Jordan Valley. Now it has shrunk to about a fourth its former length and volume. And with the shrinkage and the evaporation in the hot dry climate has come a great concentration of salts. No animal life can exist in the Dead Sea's brine; such luckless fish as are brought down by the River Jordan die and provide food for the seabirds. It is thirteen hundred feet below the Mediterranean, lying farther below sea level than any other body of water in the world. The water of the Dead Sea is warmer than the air, a condition favoring evaporation, and clouds of its vapor float, nebulous and half formed, above it, while its brine grows more bitter and the salts accumulate.

Of all legacies of the ancient seas the most valuable is petroleum. No one can describe with certainty the whole sequence of geologic events which have created the precious pools of liquid deep within the earth. But the origin of petroleum is most likely to be found in the bodies of plants and animals buried under the fine-grained sediments of former seas and there subjected to slow decomposition.

Perhaps the essence of conditions favoring petroleum production is found in the Black Sea. The abundant life of this sea is confined to the upper layers; the deeper and especially the bottom waters are devoid of oxygen and often permeated with hydrogen sulfide. In these poisoned waters there can be no bottom scavengers to devour the bodies of marine animals that drift down from above, so they are entombed in the fine sediments.

Whatever great oil fields are found, they are related to past or present seas. This is true of the inland fields as well as of those near the seacoast. The great quantities of oil that have been obtained from the Oklahoma fields, for example, were trapped in spaces within sedimentary rocks laid down under seas that invaded this part of North America in Paleozoic time.

The search for petroleum has also led geologists to those shallow seas which lie around the margins of the main continental platforms, and between them and the great oceanic depths. The Persian Gulf, the Red, Black, Caspian and Mediterranean seas form one such region between Europe and the Near East. The Gulf of Mexico and the Caribbean Sea lie in another basin of shallow sea between the Americas. A shallow, island-studded sea lies between the continents of Asia and Australia. Lastly, there is the nearly landlocked sea of the Arctic. In past ages all of these areas have been alternately raised and depressed, belonging at one time to the land, at another to the encroaching sea. During their periods of submersion, in their waters a rich marine fauna has lived, died, and drifted down into the soft sediment carpet.

There are vast oil deposits in all these areas. In the Near East are the great fields of Saudi Arabia, Iran and Iraq. The shallow depression between Asia and Australia yields the oil of Java,

Sumatra, Borneo and New Guinea. Half the proved resources of the United States come from the northern shore of the Gulf of Mexico, and Colombia, Venezuela and Mexico have rich oil fields along the western and southern margins of the Gulf. Oil seepages in northern Alaska, on islands north of the Canadian mainland, and along the Arctic coast of Siberia hint that this land may be one of the great oil fields of the future.

In recent years, oil has also been produced from offshore wells, on the continental shelf off Texas and Louisiana. Still, it is no simple matter to obtain oil from undersea fields. Offshore drilling platforms rest on piles that must be driven as far as two hundred and fifty feet into the floor of the Gulf of Mexico to withstand the force of waves. Winds, storm waves, fogs, the corrosive gnawing of seawater upon metal structures— all these are hazards that must be faced and overcome. Yet technical difficulties do not discourage specialists in petroleum engineering.

So our search for mineral wealth often leads us back to the seas of ancient times —to the oil pressed from the bodies of fishes, seaweeds and other forms of plant and animal life, and then stored away in ancient rocks; to the layers of salts those old seas laid down as a covering mantle over the continents. Perhaps in time, as we learn the chemical secrets of the corals and sponges and diatoms, we shall go more and more directly to the ocean and the rocks now forming under its shallow waters.

CHAPTER XIV: *The Encircling Sea*

To the ancient Greeks the ocean was an endless stream that flowed forever around the border of the world, ceaselessly turning upon itself like a wheel. This ocean was boundless and infinite. If a person were to venture far out upon it he would pass through gathering darkness and obscuring fog and would come at last to a dreadful and chaotic blending of sea and sky, a place where whirlpools and yawning abysses waited to draw him down into a dark world from which there was no return.

These ideas are found, in varying form, in much of the ancient literature. To the Greeks the familiar Mediterranean was The Sea. Outside, bathing the periphery of the land world, was Oceanus. Perhaps somewhere in its uttermost expanse was the home of the gods and of departed spirits, the Elysian fields. Ideas of unattainable continents or of beautiful islands in the distant ocean are confusedly mingled with references to a bottomless gulf at the edge of the world—but always around the disk of the habitable world was the vast ocean, encircling all.

Perhaps word-of-mouth tales of the mysterious northern world filtered down by way of merchants who brought tin and amber overland from the Baltic. So the boundary of the land world came to be pictured as a place of fog and storms and darkness. Early poets and historians may also have derived some of their ideas of the ocean from the Phoenicians, whose craft, for at least two thousand years before Christ, roamed the shores of Europe, Asia and Africa in search of gold, silver, gems, spices and wood for their commerce with kings and emperors. It may well be that these sailor-merchants were the first ever to cross an ocean. Herodotus wrote that they circumnavigated Africa from east to west about 600 B.C., reaching Egypt via the Pillars of Hercules and the Mediterranean. But the canny Phoenicians themselves said and wrote little or nothing of their voyaging, keeping their trade routes and the sources of their precious cargoes secret.

So far as historical records are concerned, the first great voyage of marine exploration was by Pytheas of Massilia about 330 B.C. But unfortunately the writings of this Greek astronomer and geographer are preserved for us only in fragmentary quotations passed on by later writers. Pytheas was the first to use astronomical measurements to determine geographic locations. He seems to have sailed around Great Britain, reached the Shetland Islands, and then launched out into the open ocean to the north, coming at last to "Thule," the land of midnight sun where "the nights were very short, in some places two, in others three hours long." The location of Thule is a point much disputed by later authorities, some believing it to have been Iceland, while others believe that Pytheas crossed the North Sea to Norway. Pytheas is also said to have described a "congealed sea" lying north of Thule, which accords better with Iceland. But the Dark Ages were settling over the civilized world, and little of the knowledge of distant places acquired by Pytheas seems to have impressed the learned men who followed him.

More than a century passed before the age of the Vikings dawned. As early as the sixth century A.D. the Vikings must have crossed the North Sea to the land of the Franks, and probably to southern Britain. Later they sailed to the Faroes and to Iceland; in the last quarter of the tenth century they established two colonies in Greenland. Shortly thereafter they steered across the intervening Atlantic waters to North America.

Of the place of these voyages in history Fridtjof Nansen writes:

The shipbuilding and seamanship of the Norwegians mark a new epoch in the history both of navigation and discovery. We find accounts of these voyages in old sagas, put into writing in Iceland. A somber undercurrent runs through these narratives—the silent struggle of hardy men with ice, storms, cold, and want. They had neither compass, nor astronomical instruments for finding their position at sea; they could only sail by the sun, moon, and stars, and it seems incomprehensible how for days and weeks, when these were invisible, they were able to find their course through fog and bad weather; but they found it, and in the open craft of the Norwegian Vikings, with their square sails, fared north and west over the whole ocean, from Novaya Zemlya and Spitsbergen to Greenland, Baffin Bay, Newfoundland, and North America. . . . It was not until five hundred years later that the ships of other nations were to make their way to the same regions.

Only the vaguest rumors of these things reached the "civilized world" of the Mediterranean. While the sagas of the Norsemen were giving clear and factual directions for the passage across oceans, from known to unknown worlds, the writings of the scholars of the medieval world dealt still with that outermost encircling ocean, the dread Sea of Darkness. And even the Norsemen themselves, as they discovered lands across the Atlantic, seem merely to have pushed back the boundaries, for the idea of the outer ocean surrounding the disk of the earth appears in Northern chronicles, too. And so over that Western Ocean into which Columbus and his men set out there hung still the legend of a dead and stagnant sea, of monsters and entrapping weeds, of fog and gloom and ever-present danger.

Yet centuries before Columbus—no one knows how many centuries—men on the opposite side of the world were boldly sailing their craft across the Pacific. We know little of the hardships, the difficulties, and the fears that may have beset the Polynesian colonists. We know only that in open canoes they entrusted themselves to the stars and the signposts of the sea and found their way somehow from the Asiatic mainland to remote islands. There is evidence that their last important colonizing voyage to the Hawaiian Islands was made in the thirteenth century, and that about the middle of the fourteenth century a fleet from Tahiti permanently colonized New Zealand. But long after the Polynesians had mastered the art of navigating unknown seas, European sailors still regarded the Pillars of Hercules as the gateway to a dreaded sea of darkness.

Once Columbus had shown the way to the West Indies and the Americas, once Balboa had seen the Pacific, and Magellan had sailed around the globe, there arose, and long persisted, two new ideas. One concerned the existence of a northern passage by sea to Asia; the other had to do with a great southern continent generally believed to lie below the then-known lands.

Magellan, while sailing through the strait that now bears his name, had seen land to the south of him. At night the lights of many fires glowed from the shores of this land, which Magellan named Tierra del Fuego—Land of Fires. He supposed that these were the near shores of that great land which the theoretical geographers had already decided should lie to the south.

Many voyagers after Magellan reported land they assumed to be outlying regions of the long-sought-for continent, but all proved to be islands. Discovery of the southern land was one of the objects of Captain Cook's voyages, but instead of a continent he discovered an ocean. By making an almost complete circumnavigation of the globe in high southern latitudes, Cook revealed the existence of a stormy ocean running completely around the earth south of Africa, Australia and South America.

American sealers had quite possibly been to some of the islands in that ocean before Cook, yet this chapter of Antarctic exploration contains many blank pages. The Yankee sealers did not want their competitors to find the rich sealing grounds, and they kept the details of their voyages secret. Evidently they had operated in the vicinity for many years, because most of the fur seals in these waters had been exterminated by 1820. It was in this year that the Antarctic continent was first sighted, by Captain N. B. Palmer in command of the *Hero*, one of a fleet of eight sealers from Connecticut ports. A century later, explorers were still making fresh discoveries about the nature of that southern continent, finally established as one of the great continental masses.

Meanwhile, the dream of a northwest passage to the riches of Asia lured one expedition after another into the frozen Arctic. Cabot, Frobisher and Davis sought the passage, failed, and turned back. Hudson was left by a mutinous crew to die in an open boat. Sir John Franklin set out with the *Erebus* and *Terror* in 1845, apparently entered the labyrinth of Arctic islands by what later proved a feasible route, but then lost his ships and perished with all his men. Later rescue ships coming from east and west met in Melville Sound and thus the Northwest Passage was established.

So, little by little, through many voyages undertaken over many centuries, the fog and the frightening obscurity of the unknown were lifted from the Sea of Darkness. How did they accomplish it—those first voyagers, to whom modern loran, radar and sonic sounding would have been fantasies beyond belief? We know only enough to want to know more.

Of the methods of those secretive master mariners, the Phoenicians, we cannot even guess. We have more basis for conjecture about the ancient Polynesians, for we can study their descendants in the South Pacific today and find hints of the methods that led them on their course from island to island. Certainly they seem to have followed the stars, which burned brightly in the heavens over those calm Pacific regions, which are so unlike the stormy and fogbound northern seas. The Polynesians also understood all the language of the sea: the varying color of the water, the haze of surf breaking on rocks yet below the horizon, and the cloud patches that hang over every islet of the tropic seas and sometimes seem even to reflect the color of a lagoon within a coral atoll.

No doubt bird migrations had meaning for the Polynesians, and they learned much from watching the flocks that gathered each spring and fall, launched out over the ocean, and returned later out of the emptiness into which they had vanished. Harold Gatty believes the Hawaiians may have found their islands by following the spring migration of the golden plover from Tahiti to the Hawaiian chain, as the birds returned to the North American mainland. Tradition and written records tell us that primitive navigators often carried with them birds which they would release and follow to land. And in foggy weather, when the Norsemen drifted for days without knowing where they were, they often relied on observing the flight of birds to judge the direction of land.

The first mention of the use of the magnetic needle as a guide to mariners occurs in the twelfth century after Christ, but as much as a century later scholars were expressing doubt that sailors would entrust their lives to an instrument so obviously invented by the devil. There is fair evidence, however, that the compass was in use in the Mediterranean about the end of the twelfth century, and in northern Europe within the next hundred years.

For navigating the known seas, there had been the equivalent of our modern *Sailing Directions* for many centuries. The *portolano* (harbor-finding charts) and the *peripli* (coast pilots) guided the mariners of antiquity about the Mediterranean and Black seas. Sea charts were "keys to empire" and a "way to wealth," however, and as such they were carefully guarded secret documents.

It was a Dutchman who, in 1584, produced the first collection of navigational charts bound together in book form—Lucas Janszoon

Waghenaer. For many years *Waggoners* guided Dutch, English, Scandinavian and German navigators through eastern Atlantic waters. In the sixteenth and seventeenth centuries, under the stimulus of fierce competition, private companies employed their own hydrographers and prepared secret atlases. But in 1795 the East India Company's hydrographer, Alexander Dalrymple, became official hydrographer to the Admiralty; and under his direction the British Admiralty began its survey of the coasts of the world from which the modern *Admiralty Pilots* stem.

Shortly thereafter a young man joined the United States Navy—Matthew Fontaine Maury. In only a few years Lieutenant Maury was to write a book, *The Physical Geography of the Sea*, which is now considered the foundation of the science of oceanography. Maury, as head of the Depot of Charts and Instruments—the forerunner of the present Hydrographic Office—had begun a practical study of winds and currents from the standpoint of the navigator. Through his energy and initiative a worldwide cooperative system was organized. Ships' officers of all nations sent in the logs of their voyages, from which Maury assembled and organized information which he incorporated in navigational charts. In return, the cooperating mariners received copies of the charts. Soon Maury's sailing directions were attracting world notice: he had shortened the passage for American east-coast vessels to Rio de Janeiro by ten days, to Australia by twenty days, and around the Horn to California by thirty days. The cooperative exchange of information sponsored by Maury remains in effect today, and the *Pilot Charts* of the Hydrographic Office carry the inscription: *Founded upon the researches made in the early part of the nineteenth century by Matthew Fontaine Maury, while serving as a Lieutenant in the United States Navy.*

In the *Sailing Directions* and *Coast Pilots* issued by every maritime nation we find the most complete information that is available to guide the navigator over the ocean. In these writings there is a blend of modernity and antiquity, through which we may trace their lineage back to the sagas or the *peripli* of the ancient Mediterranean seamen. It is surprising, but pleasant, that sailing directions which tell how to obtain position by loran should also counsel the navigator to be guided, like the Norsemen a millennium ago, by the flight of birds in foggy weather.

The ultramodern *Sailing Directions for Antarctica* says:

> Navigators should observe the birdlife, for deductions may often be drawn from the presence of certain species. Shags are . . . a sure sign of the close proximity of land. . . . The snow petrel is . . . of great interest to mariners as an augury of ice conditions on their course. . . .

Sometimes the *Sailing Directions* for remote areas of the sea can report only what the whalers or sealers or some oldtime fisherman has said about the navigability of a channel or the set of the tidal currents. In phrases like these we get the feel of the unknown and mysterious that never quite separates itself from the sea: "It is said that there was once an island there . . . Such information as could be secured from reports of men with local knowledge . . . A bank reported by an oldtime sealer."

But the darkness of antiquity is rapidly being dispelled and most of the length and breadth of the ocean is known; it is only in thinking of its depth that we can still apply the concept of the Sea of Darkness. It took centuries to chart the surface of the sea; our progress in delineating the unseen world beneath it seems by comparison phenomenally rapid. But even with all our modern instruments for probing and sampling the deep ocean, no one now can say that we shall ever resolve its last, its ultimate mysteries.

In its broader meaning, that other concept of the ancients remains. For the sea lies all about us. The commerce of all lands must cross it. The winds that move over the lands have been cradled on its broad expanse and seek ever to return to it. The continents dissolve and pass to the sea, in grain after grain of eroded land. The rains that rose from it return again in rivers. In its past it encompasses all the dim origins of life and receives in the end, after, it may be, many transmutations, the dead husks of that same life. For all at last return to the sea—to Oceanus, the ocean river, like the ever-flowing stream of time, the beginning and the end.

ALICE'S ADVENTURES IN WONDERLAND

and

THROUGH THE LOOKING GLASS

ALICE'S ADVENTURES IN WONDERLAND

by Lewis Carroll

**WITH ILLUSTRATIONS
BY JOHN TENNIEL**

LEWIS CARROLL was a bundle of contradictions, like the Wonderland he created. His real name was Charles Lutwidge Dodgson. Grown-ups knew him as the Reverend Mr. Dodgson, Anglican curate and lecturer in mathematics at Oxford University: a shy, sober, scholarly man. But to a few lucky children he was a whimsical friend, a maker of riddles and spinner of fantastic tales.

One of these children was Alice Pleasance Liddell, daughter of an Oxford dean. While she and her sisters were boating with Mr. Dodgson one summer day in 1862, he began to tell them the marvelous dream adventures of an imaginary Alice in a topsy-turvy world. The real Alice was so thrilled with these fancies that Mr. Dodgson spent many sleepless nights writing them in a little book to give her for Christmas. By 1865 he had added more stories, and *Alice's Adventures in Wonderland* was then published under his pen name, with the wonderful illustrations by Sir John Tenniel which to us now seem so inseparable a part of the text. Seven years later came *Through the Looking Glass*. Both books are here presented as they were written.

Since then statesmen with grave responsibilities have turned to these incomparable books for refreshment, and soldiers have drawn strength from them before battle. Queen Victoria was so entranced by *Alice* that she asked Mr. Dodgson to dedicate his next book to her. It turned out to be a ponderous treatise on mathematics!

Alice Liddell's own handwritten copy survives to this day. In 1946, as a gesture of gratitude for England's gallantry during World War II, a group of Americans bought it at auction for $50,000 and gave it to the British Museum.

CHAPTER I: *Down the Rabbit Hole*

ALICE WAS BEGINNING to get very tired of sitting by her sister on the bank and of having nothing to do: once or twice she had peeped into the book her sister was reading, but it had no pictures or conversations in it, "and what is the use of a book," thought Alice, "without pictures or conversations?"

So she was considering, in her own mind (as well as she could, for the hot day made her feel very sleepy and stupid), whether the pleasure of making a daisy chain would be worth the trouble of getting up and picking the daisies, when suddenly a White Rabbit with pink eyes ran close by her.

There was nothing so *very* remarkable in that; nor did Alice think it so *very* much out of the way to hear the Rabbit say to itself, "Oh dear! Oh dear! I shall be too late!" (when she thought it over afterwards it occurred to her that she ought to have wondered at this, but at the time it all seemed quite natural); but, when the Rabbit actually *took a watch out of its waistcoat pocket*, and looked at it, and then hurried on, Alice started to her feet, for it flashed across her mind that she had never before seen a rabbit with either a waistcoat pocket, or a watch to take out of it, and burning with curiosity, she ran across the field after it, and was just in time to see it pop down a large rabbit hole under the hedge.

In another moment down went Alice after it, never once considering how in the world she was to get out again.

The rabbit hole went straight on like a tunnel for some way, and then dipped suddenly down, so suddenly that Alice had not a moment to think about stopping herself before she found herself falling down what seemed to be a very deep well.

Either the well was very deep, or she fell very slowly, for she had plenty of time as she went down to look about her, and to wonder what was going to happen next. First, she tried to look down and make out what she was coming to, but it was too dark to see anything; then she looked at the sides of the well, and noticed that they were filled with cupboards and bookshelves: here and there she saw maps and pictures hung upon pegs. She took a jar from one of the shelves as she passed: it was labeled ORANGE MARMALADE but to her great disappointment it was empty; she did not like to drop the jar, for fear of killing somebody underneath, so managed to put it into one of the cupboards as she fell past it.

"Well!" thought Alice to herself. "After such a fall as this, I shall think nothing of tumbling downstairs! How brave they'll all think me at home! Why, I wouldn't say anything about it, even if I fell off the top of the house!" (Which was very likely true.)

Down, down, down. Would the fall *never* come to an end? "I wonder how many miles I've fallen by this time?" she said aloud. "I must be getting somewhere near the center of the earth. Let me see: that would be four thousand miles down, I think—" (for, you see, Alice had learned several things of this sort in her lessons in the schoolroom, and though this was not a *very* good opportunity for showing off her knowledge, as there was no one to listen to her, still it was good practice to say it over) "—yes, that's about the right distance—but then I wonder what Latitude or Longitude I've got to?" (Alice had not the slightest idea what Latitude was, or Longitude either, but she thought they were nice grand words to say.)

Presently she began again. "I wonder if I shall fall right *through* the earth! How funny it'll seem to come out among the people that walk with their heads downwards! The antipathies, I think—"

(she was rather glad there *was* no one listening, this time, as it didn't sound at all the right word) "— but I shall have to ask them what the name of the country is, you know. Please, Ma'am, is this New Zealand? Or Australia?" (and she tried to curtsy as she spoke— fancy, *curtsying* as you're falling through the air! Do you think you could manage it?) "And what an ignorant little girl she'll think me for asking! No, it'll never do to ask: perhaps I shall see it written up somewhere."

Down, down, down. There was nothing else to do, so Alice soon began talking again. "Dinah'll miss me very much tonight, I should think!" (Dinah was the cat.) "I hope they'll remember her saucer of milk at teatime. Dinah, my dear! I wish you were down here with me! There are no mice in the air, I'm afraid, but you might catch a bat, and that's very like a mouse, you know. But do cats eat bats, I wonder?" And here Alice began to get rather sleepy, and went on saying to herself, in a dreamy sort of way, "Do cats eat bats? Do cats eat bats?" and sometimes "Do bats eat cats?" for, you see, as she couldn't answer either question, it didn't much matter which way she put it. She felt that she was dozing off, and had just begun to dream that she was walking hand in hand with Dinah, and was saying to her, very earnestly, "Now Dinah, tell me the truth: did you ever eat a bat?" when suddenly, thump! thump! down she came upon a heap of sticks and dry leaves, and the fall was over.

Alice was not a bit hurt, and she jumped up onto her feet in a moment. She looked up, but it was all dark overhead; before her was another long passage, and the White Rabbit was still in sight, hurrying down it. There was not a moment to be lost: away went Alice like the wind, and was just in time to hear it say, as it turned a corner, "Oh my ears and whiskers, how late it's getting!" She was close behind it when she turned the corner, but the Rabbit was no longer to be seen; she found herself in a long, low hall, which was lit up by a row of lamps hanging from the roof.

There were doors all round the hall, but they were all locked, and when Alice had been all the way down one side and up the other, trying every door, she walked sadly down the middle, wondering how she was ever to get out again.

Suddenly she came upon a little three-legged table, all made of solid glass. There was nothing on it but a tiny golden key, and Alice's first idea was that this might belong to one of the doors of the hall; but, alas! either the locks were too large, or the key was too small, but at any rate it would not open any of them. However, on the second time round, she came upon a low curtain she had not noticed before, and behind it was a little door about fifteen inches high; she tried the little golden key in the lock, and to her great delight it fitted!

Alice opened the door and found that it led into a small passage, not much larger than a rathole; she knelt down and looked along the passage into the loveliest garden you ever saw. How she longed to get out of that dark hall, and wander about among those beds of bright flowers and those cool fountains, but she could not even get her head through the doorway; "and even if my head *would* go through," thought poor Alice, "it would be of very little use without my shoulders. Oh, how I wish I could shut up like a telescope! I think I could, if I only knew how to begin." For, you see, so many out-of-the-way things had happened lately that Alice had begun to think that very few things indeed were really impossible.

There seemed to be no use in waiting by the little door, so she went back to the table, half hoping she might find another key on it, or at any rate a book of rules for shutting people up like tele-scopes. This time she found a little bottle on it ("which certainly was not here before," said Alice), and tied round the neck of the bottle was a paper label, with the words DRINK ME beautifully printed on it in large letters.

It was all very well to say "Drink me," but the wise little Alice was not going to do *that* in a hurry. "No, I'll look first," she said, "and see whether it's marked 'poison' or not"; for she had read several nice little stories about children who had got burned, and eaten up by wild beasts, and other unpleasant things, all because they *would* not remember the simple rules their friends had taught them: such as, that a red-hot poker will burn you if you hold it too long; and that, if you cut your finger *very* deeply with a knife, it usually bleeds; and she had never forgotten that if you drink much from a bottle marked "poison," it is almost certain to disagree with you, sooner or later.

However, this bottle was *not* marked "poison," so Alice ventured to taste it, and, finding it very nice (it had, in fact, a sort of mixed flavor of cherry tart, custard, pineapple, roast turkey, toffee, and hot buttered toast), she very soon finished it off.

*   *   *   *   *   *   *

"What a curious feeling!" said Alice. "I must be shutting up like a telescope!"

And so it was indeed: she was now only ten inches high, and her face brightened up at the thought that she was now the right size for going through the little door into that lovely garden. First, however, she waited for a few minutes to see if she was going to shrink any further. She felt a little nervous about this; "for it might end, you know," said Alice to herself, "in my going out altogether, like a candle. I wonder what I should be like then?" And she tried to fancy what the flame of a candle looks like after the candle is blown out, for she could not remember ever having seen such a thing.

After a while, finding that nothing more happened, she decided on going into the garden at once; but, alas for poor Alice! when she got to the door, she found she had forgotten the little golden key, and when she went back to the table for it, she found she could not possibly reach it. She could see it quite plainly through the glass, and she tried her best to climb up one of the legs of the table, but it was too slippery; and when she had tired herself out with trying, the poor little thing sat down and cried.

"Come, there's no use in crying like that!" said Alice to herself rather sharply. "I advise you to leave off this minute!" She generally gave herself very good advice (though she very seldom fol-

lowed it), and sometimes she scolded herself
so severely as to bring tears into her eyes;
and once she remembered trying to
box her own ears for having
cheated herself in a game of croquet she was playing against herself, for this curious child was
very fond of pretending to be two
people. "But it's no use now,"
thought poor Alice, "to pretend
to be two people! Why, there's
hardly enough of me left to make
one respectable person!"

Soon her eye fell on a little
glass box that was lying under the
table: she opened it, and found in
it a very small cake, on which the
words EAT ME were beautifully
marked in currants. "Well, I'll
eat it," said Alice, "and if it makes
me grow larger, I can reach the
key; and if it makes me grow
smaller, I can creep under the
door; so either way I'll get into
the garden, and I don't care which
happens!"

She ate a little bit, and said anxiously to herself, "Which way? Which
way?" holding her hand on the top of her
head to feel which way it was growing; and she
was quite surprised to find that she remained the same size. To be
sure, this is what generally happens when one eats cake; but Alice
had got so much into the way of expecting nothing but out-of-the-
way things to happen that it seemed quite dull and stupid for life
to go on in the common way.

So she set to work, and very soon finished off the cake.

"CURIOUSER AND CURIOUSER!" cried Alice (she was so much surprised that for the moment she quite forgot how to speak good English). "Now I'm opening out like the largest telescope that ever was! Good-by, feet!" (For when she looked down at her feet, they seemed to be almost out of sight, they were getting so far off.) "Oh, my poor little feet, I wonder who will put on your shoes and stockings for you now, dears? I'm sure *I* shan't be able! I shall be a great deal too far off to trouble myself about you: you must manage the best way you can—but I must be kind to them," thought Alice, "or perhaps they won't walk the way I want to go! Let me see. I'll give them a new pair of boots every Christmas."

And she went on planning to herself how she would manage it. "They must go by the carrier," she thought; "and how funny it'll seem, sending presents to one's own feet! And how odd the directions will look!

> *Alice's Right Foot, Esq.,*
>   *Hearthrug,*
>   *near the Fender,*
>   (*with Alice's love*).

Oh, dear, what nonsense I'm talking!"

Just at this moment her head struck against the roof of the hall: in fact she was now rather more than nine feet high, and she at once took up the little golden key and hurried off to the garden door.

Poor Alice! It was as much as she could do, lying down on one side, to look through into the garden with one eye; but to get through was more hopeless than ever. She sat down and began to cry again.

"You ought to be ashamed of yourself," said Alice, "a great girl like you," (she might well say this) "to go on crying in this way! Stop this moment, I tell you!" But she went on all the same, shedding gallons of tears, until there was a large pool all around her, about four inches deep and reaching half down the hall.

After a time she heard a little pattering of feet in the distance, and she hastily dried her eyes to see what was coming. It was the White Rabbit returning, splendidly dressed, with a pair of white kid gloves in one hand and a large fan in the other; he came trotting along in a great hurry, muttering to himself, as he came, "Oh! The Duchess, the Duchess! Oh! *Won't* she be savage if I've kept her waiting!"

Alice felt so desperate that she was ready to ask help of anyone: so, when the Rabbit came near her, she began, in a low, timid voice, "If you please, Sir—" The Rabbit started violently, dropped the white kid gloves and the fan, and scurried away into the darkness as hard as he could go.

Alice took up the fan and gloves, and, as the hall was very hot, she kept fanning herself all the time she went on talking. "Dear, dear! How queer everything is today! And yesterday things went on just as usual. I wonder if I've changed in the night? Let me think: *Was* I the same when I got up this morning? I almost think I can remember feeling a little different. But if I'm not the same, the next question is: Who in the world am I? Ah, *that's* the great puzzle!" And she began thinking over all the children she knew that were of the same age as herself, to see if she could have been changed for any of them.

"I'm sure I'm not Ada," she said, "for her hair goes in such long ringlets, and mine doesn't go in ringlets at all; and I'm sure I can't be Mabel, for I know all sorts of things, and she, oh, she knows such a very little! Besides, *she's* she, and *I'm* I, and—oh dear, how puzzling it all is! I'll try if I know all the things I used to know. Let me see: four times five is twelve, and four times six is thirteen, and four times seven is—oh dear! I shall never get to twenty at that rate! However, the Multiplication Table doesn't signify: let's try Geography. London is the capital of Paris, and Paris is the capital of Rome, and Rome—no, *that's* all wrong, I'm certain! I must have been changed for Mabel! I'll try and say *How doth the little*—" and she crossed her hands on her lap, as if she were saying lessons, and began to repeat it, but her voice sounded hoarse and strange, and the words did not come the same as they used to do:

"How doth the little crocodile
Improve his shining tail,
And pour the waters of the Nile
On every golden scale!

How cheerfully he seems to grin,
How neatly spreads his claws,
And welcomes little fishes in,
With gently smiling jaws!"

"I'm sure those are not the right words," said poor Alice, and her eyes filled with tears again as she went on, "I must be Mabel after all, and I shall have to go and live in that poky little house, and have next to no toys to play with, and oh, ever so many lessons to learn! No, I've made up my mind about it: if I'm Mabel, I'll stay down here! It'll be no use their putting their heads down and saying 'Come up again, dear!' I shall only look up and say 'Who am I, then? Tell me that first, and then, if I like being that person, I'll come up; if not, I'll stay down here till I'm somebody else'— but, oh dear!" cried Alice, with a sudden burst of tears, "I do wish they *would* put their heads down! I am so *very* tired of being all alone here!"

As she said this she looked down at her hands, and was surprised to see that she had put on one of the Rabbit's little white kid gloves while she was talking. "How *can* I have done that?" she thought. "I must be growing small again." She got up and went to the table to measure herself by it, and found that, as nearly as she could guess, she was now about two feet high, and was going on shrinking rapidly. She soon found out that the cause of this was the fan she was holding, and she dropped it hastily, just in time to save herself from shrinking away altogether.

"That *was* a narrow escape!" said Alice, a good deal frightened at the sudden change, but very glad to find herself still in existence. "And now for the garden!" And she ran with all speed back to the little door; but, alas! the little door was shut again, and the little golden key was lying on the glass table as before, "and things are worse than ever," thought the poor child, "for I never was so

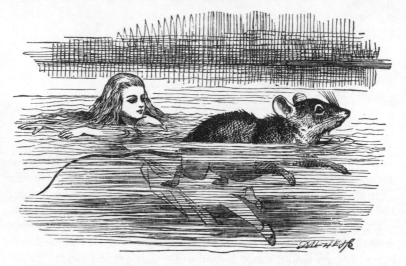

small as this before, never! And I declare it's too bad, that it is!"

As she said these words her foot slipped, and in another moment, splash! she was up to her chin in salt water. Her first idea was that she had somehow fallen into the sea, "and in that case I can go back by railway," she said to herself. (Alice had been to the seaside once in her life, and had come to the general conclusion that wherever you go to on the English coast, you find a number of bathing machines in the sea, some children digging in the sand with wooden spades, then a row of lodging houses, and behind them a railway station.) However, she soon made out that she was in the pool of tears which she had wept when she was nine feet high.

"I wish I hadn't cried so much!" said Alice, as she swam about, trying to find her way out. "I shall be punished for it now, I suppose, by being drowned in my own tears! That *will* be a queer thing, to be sure! However, everything is queer today."

Just then she heard something splashing about in the pool a little way off, and she swam nearer to make out what it was: at first she thought it must be a walrus or hippopotamus, but then she remembered how small she was now, and she soon made out that it was only a mouse that had slipped in like herself.

"Would it be of any use, now," thought Alice, "to speak to this mouse? Everything is so out-of-the-way down here that I should think very likely it can talk; at any rate, there's no harm in trying." So she began: "O Mouse, do you know the way out of this pool? I am very tired of swimming about here, O Mouse!" (Alice thought this must be the right way of speaking to a mouse: she had never done such a thing before, but she remembered having seen, in her brother's Latin Grammar, *A mouse—of a mouse—to a mouse— a mouse—O mouse!*) The Mouse looked at her rather inquisitively, and seemed to her to wink with one of its little eyes, but it said nothing.

"Perhaps it doesn't understand English," thought Alice. "I daresay it's a French mouse, come over with William the Conqueror." (For, with all her knowledge of history, Alice had no very clear notion how long ago anything had happened.) So she began again: "*Où est ma chatte?*" which was the first sentence in her French lesson book. The Mouse gave a sudden leap out of the water, and seemed to quiver all over with fright. "Oh, I beg your pardon!" cried Alice hastily, afraid that she had hurt the poor animal's feelings. "I quite forgot you didn't like cats."

"Not like cats!" cried the Mouse in a shrill, passionate voice. "Would *you* like cats, if you were me?"

"Well, perhaps not," said Alice in a soothing tone; "don't be angry about it. And yet I wish I could show you our cat Dinah. I think you'd take a fancy to cats, if you could only see her. She is such a dear quiet thing," Alice went on, half to herself, as she swam lazily about in the pool, "and she sits purring so nicely by the fire, licking her paws and washing her face—and she is such a nice soft thing to nurse—and she's such a capital one for catching mice—oh, I beg your pardon!" cried Alice again, for this time the Mouse was bristling all over, and she felt certain it must be really offended. "We won't talk about her anymore if you'd rather not."

"We, indeed!" cried the Mouse, who was trembling down to the end of its tail. "As if *I* would talk on such a subject! Our family always *hated* cats: nasty, low, vulgar things! Don't let me hear the name again!"

"I won't indeed!" said Alice, in a great hurry to change the subject of conversation. "Are you—are you fond—of—of dogs?" The Mouse did not answer, so Alice went on eagerly, "There is such a nice little dog, near our house, I should like to show you! A little bright-eyed terrier, you know, with oh, such long curly brown hair! And it'll fetch things when you throw them, and it'll sit up and beg for its dinner, and all sorts of things—I can't remember half of them—and it belongs to a farmer, you know, and he says it's so useful, it's worth a hundred pounds! He says it kills all the rats and—oh dear!" cried Alice in a sorrowful tone. "I'm afraid I've offended it again!" For the Mouse was swimming away from her as hard as it could go, and making quite a commotion in the pool as it went.

So she called softly after it, "Mouse dear! Do come back again, and we won't talk about cats, or dogs either, if you don't like them!" When the Mouse heard this, it turned round and swam slowly back to her; its face was quite pale (with passion, Alice thought), and it said, in a low trembling voice, "Let us get to the shore, and then I'll tell you my history, and you'll understand why it is I hate cats and dogs."

It was high time to go, for the pool was getting quite crowded with the birds and animals that had fallen into it: there was a Duck and a Dodo, a Lory and an Eaglet, and several other curious creatures. Alice led the way, and the whole party swam to the shore.

CHAPTER III: *A Caucus Race and a Long Tale*

THEY WERE INDEED a queer-looking party that assembled on the bank—the birds with draggled feathers, the animals with their fur clinging close to them, and all dripping wet, cross, and uncomfortable.

The first question, of course, was how to get dry again: they had a consultation about this, and after a few minutes it seemed quite natural to Alice to find herself talking familiarly with them, as if she had known them all her life. Indeed, she had quite a long argument with the Lory, who at last turned sulky, and would only say, "I'm older than you, and must know better." And this Alice would not allow, without knowing how old it was, and as the Lory positively refused to tell its age, there was no more to be said.

At last the Mouse, who seemed to be a person of some authority among them, called out, "Sit down, all of you, and listen to me! *I'll* soon make you dry enough!" They all sat down at once, in a large ring, with the Mouse in the middle. Alice kept her eyes anxiously fixed on it, for she felt sure she would catch a bad cold if she did not get dry very soon.

"Ahem!" said the Mouse with an important air. "Are you all ready? This is the driest thing I know. Silence all round, if you please! 'William the Conqueror, whose cause was favored by the Pope, was soon submitted to by the English, who wanted leaders, and had been of late much accustomed to usurpation and conquest. Edwin and Morcar, the earls of Mercia and Northumbria—'"

"Ugh!" said the Lory, with a shiver.

"I beg your pardon!" said the Mouse, frowning, but very politely. "Did you speak?"

"Not I!" said the Lory, hastily.

"I thought you did," said the Mouse. "I proceed. 'Edwin and Morcar, the earls of Mercia and Northumbria, declared for him; and even Stigand, the patriotic Archbishop of Canterbury, found it advisable—'"

"Found *what?*" said the Duck.

"Found *it*," the Mouse replied rather crossly: "of course you know what 'it' means."

"I know what 'it' means well enough, when *I* find a thing," said the Duck: "it's generally a frog, or a worm. The question is, what did the Archbishop find?"

The Mouse did not notice this question, but hurriedly went on, "'—found it advisable to go with Edgar Atheling to meet William and offer him the crown. William's conduct at first was moderate. But the insolence of his Normans—' How are you getting on now, my dear?" it continued, turning to Alice as it spoke.

"As wet as ever," said Alice in a melancholy tone; "it doesn't seem to dry me at all."

"In that case," said the Dodo solemnly, rising to its feet, "I move that the meeting adjourn, for the immediate adoption of more energetic remedies—"

"Speak English!" said the Eaglet. "I don't know the meaning of half those long words, and, what's more, I don't believe you do either!" And the Eaglet bent down its head to hide a smile; some of the other birds tittered audibly.

"What I was going to say," said the Dodo in an offended tone, "was that the best thing to get us dry would be a Caucus Race."

"What *is* a Caucus Race?" said Alice; not that she much wanted to know, but the Dodo had paused as if it thought that *somebody* ought to speak, and no one else seemed inclined to say anything.

"Why," said the Dodo, "the best way to explain it is to do it." (And, as you might like to try the thing yourself some winter day, I will tell you how the Dodo managed it.)

First it marked out a racecourse, in a sort of circle ("the exact shape doesn't matter," it said), and then all the party were placed along the course, here and there. There was no "One, two, three, and away!" but they began running when they liked, and left off when they liked, so that it was not easy to know when the race was over. However, when they had been running half an hour or so, and were quite dry again, the Dodo suddenly called out, "The race is over!" and they all crowded round it, panting, and asking, "But who has won?"

This question the Dodo could not answer without a great deal of thought, and it stood for a long time with one finger pressed upon its forehead (the position in which you usually see Shakespeare, in the pictures of him), while the rest waited in silence. At last the Dodo said, "*Everybody* has won, and *all* must have prizes."

"But who is to give the prizes?" quite a chorus of voices asked.

"Why, *she*, of course," said the Dodo, pointing to Alice with one finger; and the whole party at once crowded round her, calling out, in a confused way, "Prizes! Prizes!"

Alice had no idea what to do, and in despair she put her hand in her pocket, and pulled out a box of comfits (luckily the salt water had not got into it), and handed them round as prizes. There was exactly one apiece, all round.

"But she must have a prize herself, you know," said the Mouse.

"Of course," the Dodo replied very gravely. "What else have you got in your pocket?" it went on, turning to Alice.

"Only a thimble," said Alice sadly.

"Hand it over here," said the Dodo.

Then they all crowded round her once more, while Dodo solemnly presented the thimble, saying, "We beg your acceptance of this elegant thimble"; and, when it had finished this short speech, they all cheered.

Alice thought the whole thing very absurd, but they all looked so grave that she did not dare to laugh; and, as she could not think of anything to say, she simply bowed, and took the thimble, looking as solemn as she could.

The next thing was to eat the comfits: this caused some noise and confusion, as the large birds complained that they could not

taste theirs, and the small ones choked and had to be patted on
the back. However, it was over at last, and they sat down again
in a ring, and begged the Mouse to tell them something more.

"You promised to tell me your history, you know," said Alice,
"and why it is you hate—C and D," she added in a whisper, half
afraid that it would be offended again.

"Mine is a long and a sad tale!" said the Mouse, turning to
Alice, and sighing.

"It *is* a long tail, certainly," said Alice, looking down with wonder at the Mouse's tail; "but why do you call it sad?" And she kept on puzzling about it while the Mouse was speaking, so that her idea of the tale was something like this:

Fury said to a
mouse that
he met in the
house, "Let
us both go
to law: *I*
will prose-
cute *you*—
Come, I'll
take no de-
nial. We
must have
the trial;
for really
this morn-
ing I've
nothing
to do."
Said the
mouse to
the cur,
"Such a
trial, dear
sir, with
no jury
or judge,
would
be wast-
ing our
breath."
"I'll be
judge,
I'll be
jury,"
said
cun-
ning
old
Fury:
"I'll
try
the
whole
cause,
and
con-
demn
you to
death."

"You are not attending!" said the Mouse to Alice, severely. "What are you thinking of?"

"I beg your pardon," said Alice very humbly; "you had got to the fifth bend, I think?"

"I had *not!*" cried the Mouse, sharply and very angrily.

"A knot!" said Alice, always ready to make herself useful, and looking anxiously about her. "Oh, do let me help to undo it!"

"I shall do nothing of the sort," said the Mouse, getting up and walking away. "You insult me by talking such nonsense!"

"I didn't mean it!" pleaded poor Alice. "But you're so easily offended, you know!"

The Mouse only growled in reply.

"Please come back, and finish your story!" Alice called after it. And the others all joined in chorus, "Yes, please do!" But the Mouse only shook its head impatiently, and walked a little quicker.

"What a pity it wouldn't stay!" sighed the Lory, as soon as it was quite out of sight. And an old Crab took the opportunity of saying to her daughter, "Ah, my dear! Let this be a lesson to you never to lose *your* temper!" "Hold your tongue, Ma!" said the young Crab, a little snappishly. "You're enough to try the patience of an oyster!"

"I wish I had our Dinah here, I know I do!" said Alice aloud, addressing nobody in particular. "*She'd* soon fetch it back!"

"And who is Dinah, if I might venture to ask the question?" said the Lory.

Alice replied eagerly, for she was always ready to talk about her pet: "Dinah's our cat. And she's such a capital one for catching mice, you can't think! And oh, I wish you could see her after the birds! Why, she'll eat a little bird as soon as look at it!"

This speech caused a remarkable sensation among the party. Some of the birds hurried off at once: one old Magpie began wrapping itself up very carefully, remarking, "I really must be getting home: the night air doesn't suit my throat!" And a Canary called out in a trembling voice, to its children, "Come away, my dears! It's high time you were all in bed!" On various pretexts they all moved off, and Alice was soon left alone.

"I wish I hadn't mentioned Dinah!" she said to herself in a

melancholy tone. "Nobody seems to like her, down here, and I'm sure she's the best cat in the world! Oh, my dear Dinah! I wonder if I shall ever see you any more!" And here poor Alice began to cry again, for she felt very lonely and low-spirited. In a little while, however, she again heard a little pattering of footsteps in the distance, and she looked up eagerly, half hoping that the Mouse had changed his mind, and was coming back to finish his story.

CHAPTER IV: *The Rabbit Sends in a Little Bill*

IT WAS THE WHITE RABBIT, trotting slowly back again, and looking anxiously about as it went, as if it had lost something; and she heard it muttering to itself, "The Duchess! The Duchess! Oh my dear paws! Oh my fur and whiskers! She'll get me executed, as sure as ferrets are ferrets! Where *can* I have dropped them, I wonder?"

Alice guessed in a moment that it was looking for the fan and the pair of white kid gloves, and she very good-naturedly began hunting about for them, but they were nowhere to be seen—everything seemed to have changed since her swim in the pool; and the great hall, with the glass table and the little door, had vanished completely.

Very soon the Rabbit noticed Alice, as she went hunting about, and called out to her, in an angry tone, "Why, Mary Ann, what *are* you doing out here? Run home this moment, and fetch me a pair of gloves and a fan! Quick, now!" And Alice was so much frightened that she ran off at once in the direction it pointed to, without trying to explain the mistake that it had made.

"He took me for his housemaid," she said to herself as she ran. "How surprised he'll be when he finds out who I am! But I'd better take him his fan and gloves—that is, if I can find them." As she said this, she came upon a neat little house, on the door of which was a bright brass plate with the name W. RABBIT engraved upon it. She went in without knocking, and hurried upstairs, in great fear lest she should meet the real Mary Ann, and be turned out of the house before she had found the fan and gloves.

"How queer it seems," Alice said to herself, "to be going messages for a rabbit! I suppose Dinah'll be sending me on messages next!" And she began fancying the sort of thing that would happen: "'Miss Alice! Come here directly, and get ready for your walk!' 'Coming in a minute, nurse! But I've got to watch this mousehole till Dinah comes back, and see that the mouse doesn't get out.' Only I don't think," Alice went on, "that they'd let Dinah stop in the house if she began ordering people about like that!"

By this time she had found her way into a tidy little room with a table in the window, and on it (as she had hoped) a fan and two or three pairs of tiny white kid gloves; she took up the fan and a pair of the gloves, and was just going to leave the room, when her eye fell upon a little bottle that stood near the looking glass. There was no label this time with the words DRINK ME, but nevertheless she uncorked it and put it to her lips. "I know *something* interesting is sure to happen," she said to herself, "whenever I eat or drink anything, so I'll just see what this bottle does. I do hope it'll make me grow large again, for really I'm quite tired of being such a tiny little thing!"

It did so indeed, and much sooner than she had expected: before she had drunk half the bottle, she found her head pressing against the ceiling, and had to stoop to save her neck from being broken. She hastily put down the bottle, saying to herself, "That's quite enough—I hope I shan't grow any more. As it is, I can't get out at the door—I do wish I hadn't drunk quite so much!"

Alas! It was too late to wish that! She went on growing, and growing, and very soon had to kneel down on the floor; in another minute there was not even room for this, and she tried the effect of lying down with one elbow against the door, and the other arm curled round her head.

Still she went on growing, and, as a last resource, she put one arm out of the window, and one foot up the chimney, and said to herself, "Now I can do no more, whatever happens. What *will* become of me?"

Luckily for Alice, the little magic bottle had now had its full effect, and she grew no larger; still it was very uncomfortable, and, as there seemed to be no sort of chance of her ever getting out of the room again, no wonder she felt unhappy.

"It was much pleasanter at home," thought poor Alice, "when one wasn't always growing larger and smaller, and being ordered about by mice and rabbits. I almost wish I hadn't gone down that rabbit hole—and yet—and yet—it's rather curious, you know, this sort of life! I do wonder what *can* have happened to me! When I used to read fairy tales, I fancied that kind of thing never happened, and now here I am in the middle of one! There ought to be a book written about me, that there ought! And when I grow up, I'll write one—but I'm grown up now," she added in a sorrowful tone. "At least there's no room to grow up any more *here*.

"But then," thought Alice, "shall I *never* get any older than I am now? That'll be a comfort, one way—never to be an old woman—but then—always to have lessons to learn! Oh, I shouldn't like that!

"Oh, you foolish Alice!" she answered herself. "How can you learn lessons in here? Why, there's hardly room for *you*, and no room at all for any lesson books!"

And so she went on, taking first one side and then the other, and making quite a conversation of it altogether; but after a few minutes she heard a voice outside, and stopped to listen.

"Mary Ann! Mary Ann!" said the voice. "Fetch me my gloves this moment!" Then came a little pattering of feet on the stairs. Alice knew it was the Rabbit coming to look for her, and she trembled till she shook the house, quite forgetting that she was now about a thousand times as large as the Rabbit, and had no reason to be afraid of it.

Presently the Rabbit came up to the door, and tried to open it; but, as the door opened inwards, and Alice's elbow was pressed hard against it, that attempt proved a failure. Alice heard it say to itself, "Then I'll go round and get in at the window."

"*That* you won't!" thought Alice, and, after waiting till she fancied she heard the Rabbit just under the window, she suddenly spread out her hand, and made a snatch in the air. She did not get hold of anything, but she heard a little shriek and a fall, and a crash of broken glass, from which she concluded that it was just possible it had fallen into a cucumber frame, or something of the sort.

Next came an angry voice—the Rabbit's: "Pat! Pat! Where are you?" And then a voice she had never heard before, "Sure then I'm here! Digging for apples, yer honor!"

"Digging for apples, indeed!" said the Rabbit angrily. "Here! Come and help me out of *this*!" (Sounds of more broken glass.)

"Now tell me, Pat, what's that in the window?"

"Sure, it's an arm, yer honor!" (He pronounced it "arrum.")

"An arm, you goose! Who ever saw one that size? Why, it fills the whole window!"

"Sure, it does, yer honor; but it's an arm for all that."

"Well, it's got no business there, at any rate. Go and take it away!"

There was a long silence after this, and Alice could only hear whispers now and then; such as "Sure, I don't like it, yer honor, at all, at all!" "Do as I tell you, you coward!" and at last she spread out her hand again, and made another snatch in the air. This time there were *two* little shrieks, and more sounds of broken glass. "What a number of cucumber frames there must be!" thought Alice. "I wonder what they'll do next! As for pulling me out of the window, I only wish *they could!* I'm sure *I* don't want to stay in here any longer!"

She waited for some time without hearing anything more: at last came a rumbling of little cart wheels, and the sound of a good many voices all talking together; she made out the words: "Where's the other ladder?—Why, I hadn't to bring but one. Bill's got the other—Bill! Fetch it here, lad!—Here, put 'em up at this corner. No, tie 'em together first—they don't reach half high enough yet—Oh, they'll do well enough. Don't be particular—Here, Bill! Catch hold of this rope—Will the roof bear?—Mind that loose slate—Oh, it's coming down! Heads below!" (a loud crash)—"Now, who did that?—It was Bill, I fancy—Who's to go down the chimney?—Nay, *I* shan't! *You* do it! *That* I won't, then!—Bill's got to go down—Here, Bill! The master says you've got to go down the chimney!"

"Oh! So Bill's got to come down the chimney, has he?" said Alice to herself. "Why, they seem to put everything upon Bill! I wouldn't be in Bill's place for a good deal; this fireplace is narrow, to be sure; but I *think* I can kick a little!"

She drew her foot as far down the chimney as she could, and waited till she heard a little animal (she couldn't guess of what sort it was) scratching and scrambling about in the chimney close above her; then, saying to herself, "This is Bill," she gave one sharp kick, and waited to see what would happen next.

The first thing she heard was a general chorus of "There goes Bill!" Then the Rabbit's voice alone—"Catch him, you by the hedge!" Then silence, and then another confusion of voices—"Hold up his head—Brandy now—Don't choke him—How was it, old fellow? What happened to you? Tell us all about it!"

Last came a little feeble, squeaking voice. ("That's Bill," thought Alice.) "Well, I hardly know—No more, thank ye; I'm better now—but I'm a deal too flustered to tell you. All I know is, something comes at me like a jack-in-the-box, and up I goes like a skyrocket!"

"So you did, old fellow!" said the others.

"We must burn the house down!" said the Rabbit's voice. And Alice called out, as loud as she could, "If you do, I'll set Dinah at you!"

There was a dead silence instantly, and Alice thought to herself, "I wonder what they *will* do next! If they had any sense, they'd take the roof off." After a minute or two they began moving about again, and Alice heard the Rabbit say, "A barrowful will do, to begin with."

"A barrowful of *what?*" thought Alice. But she had not long to doubt, for the next moment a shower of little pebbles came rattling in at the window, and some of them hit her in the face. "I'll put a stop to this," she said to herself, and shouted out, "You'd better not do that again!" which produced another dead silence.

Alice noticed, with some surprise, that the pebbles were all turning into little cakes as they lay on the floor, and a bright idea came into her head. "If I eat one of these cakes," she thought, "it's sure to make *some* change in my size; and, as it can't possibly make me larger, it must make me smaller, I suppose."

So she swallowed one of the cakes, and was delighted to find that she began shrinking directly. As soon as she was small enough to get through the door, she ran out of the house, and found quite a crowd of little animals and birds waiting outside. The poor little Lizard, Bill, was in the middle, being held up by two guinea pigs, who were giving it something out of a bottle. They all made a rush at Alice the moment she appeared; but she ran off as hard as she could, and soon found herself safe in a thick wood.

"The first thing I've got to do," said Alice to herself, as she wandered about in the wood, "is to grow to my right size again; and the second thing is to find my way into that lovely garden. I think that will be the best plan."

It sounded an excellent plan, no doubt, and very neatly and simply arranged. The only difficulty was that she had not the smallest idea how to set about it; and, while she was peering about anxiously among the trees, a little sharp bark just over her head made her look up in a great hurry.

An enormous puppy was looking down at her with large round eyes, and feebly stretching out one paw, trying to touch her. "Poor little thing!" said Alice, in a coaxing tone, and she tried hard to whistle to it; but she was terribly frightened all the time at the thought that it might be hungry, in which case it would be very likely to eat her up in spite of all her coaxing.

Hardly knowing what she did, she picked up a little bit of stick, and held it out to the puppy; whereupon the puppy jumped into the air off all its feet at once, with a yelp of delight, and rushed at the stick, and made believe to worry it; then Alice dodged behind a great thistle, to keep herself from being run over; and, the moment she appeared on the other side, the puppy made another rush at the stick, and tumbled head over heels in its hurry to get hold of it; then Alice, thinking it was very like having a game of play with a cart horse, and expecting every moment to be trampled under its feet, ran round the thistle again; then the puppy began a series of short charges at the stick, running a very little way forwards each time and a long way back, and barking hoarsely all the while, till at last it sat down a good way off, panting, with its tongue hanging out of its mouth, and its great eyes half shut.

This seemed to Alice a good opportunity for making her escape; so she set off at once, and ran till she was quite tired and out of breath, and till the puppy's bark sounded quite faint in the distance.

"And yet what a dear little puppy it was!" said Alice, as she leaned against a buttercup to rest herself, and fanned herself with one of the leaves. "I should have liked teaching it tricks very much, if—if I'd only been the right size to do it! Oh dear! I'd nearly forgotten that I've got to grow up again! Let me see—how *is* it to be managed? I suppose I ought to eat or drink something or other; but the great question is 'What?'"

The great question certainly was "What?" Alice looked all round her at the flowers and the blades of grass, but she could not see anything that looked like the right thing to eat or drink under the circumstances.

There was a large mushroom growing near her, about the same height as herself; and, when she had looked under it, and on both sides of it, and behind it, it occurred to her that she might as well look and see what was on top of it.

She stretched herself up on tiptoe, and peeped over the edge of the mushroom, and her eyes immediately met those of a large blue caterpillar that was sitting on the top, with its arms folded, quietly smoking a long hookah, and taking not the smallest notice of her or of anything else.

THE CATERPILLAR AND ALICE looked at each other for some time in silence; at last the Caterpillar took the hookah out of its mouth, and addressed her in a languid, sleepy voice.

"Who are *you?*" said the Caterpillar.

This was not an encouraging opening for a conversation. Alice replied, rather shyly, "I—I hardly know, Sir, just at present—at least I know who I *was* when I got up this morning, but I think I must have been changed several times since then."

"What do you mean by that?" said the Caterpillar, sternly. "Explain yourself!"

"I can't explain *myself*, I'm afraid, Sir," said Alice, "because I'm not myself, you see."

"I don't see," said the Caterpillar.

"I'm afraid I can't put it more clearly," Alice replied, very politely, "for I can't understand it myself, to begin with; and being so many different sizes in a day is very confusing."

"It isn't," said the Caterpillar.

"Well, perhaps you haven't found it so yet," said Alice; "but when you have to turn into a chrysalis—you will someday, you know—and then after that into a butterfly, I should think you'll feel it a little queer, won't you?"

"Not a bit," said the Caterpillar.

"Well, perhaps *your* feelings may be different," said Alice; "all I know is, it would feel very queer to *me*."

"You!" said the Caterpillar contemptuously. "Who are *you?*"

Which brought them back again to the beginning of the conversation. Alice felt a little irritated at the Caterpillar's making such *very* short remarks, and she drew herself up and said, very gravely, "I think you ought to tell me who *you* are, first."

"Why?" said the Caterpillar.

Here was another puzzling question; and, as Alice could not think of any good reason, and the Caterpillar seemed to be in a *very* unpleasant state of mind, she turned away.

"Come back!" the Caterpillar called after her. "I've something important to say!" This sounded promising, certainly. Alice turned and came back again.

"Keep your temper," said the Caterpillar.

"Is that all?" said Alice, swallowing down her anger as well as she could.

"No," said the Caterpillar. Alice thought she might as well wait, as she had nothing else to do, and perhaps after all it might tell her something worth hearing. For some minutes it puffed away without speaking; but at last it unfolded its arms, took the hookah out of its mouth again, and said, "So you think you're changed, do you?"

"I'm afraid I am, Sir," said Alice. "I can't remember things as I used—and I don't keep the same size for ten minutes together!"

"Can't remember *what* things?" said the Caterpillar.

"Well, I've tried to say *How doth the little busy bee*, but it all came different!" Alice replied in a very melancholy voice.

"Repeat 'You Are Old, Father William,'" said the Caterpillar. Alice folded her hands, and began:

> "'You are old, Father William,' the young man said,
>   'And your hair has become very white;
> And yet you incessantly stand on your head—
>   Do you think, at your age, it is right?'
>
> 'In my youth,' Father William replied to his son,
>   'I feared it might injure the brain;
> But, now that I'm perfectly sure I have none,
>   Why, I do it again and again.'
>
> 'You are old,' said the youth, 'as I mentioned before,
>   And have grown most uncommonly fat;
> Yet you turned a back somersault in at the door—
>   Pray, what is the reason of that?'
>
> 'In my youth,' said the sage, as he shook his gray locks,
>   'I kept all my limbs very supple
> By the use of this ointment—one shilling the box—
>   Allow me to sell you a couple?'
>
> 'You are old,' said the youth, 'and your jaws are too weak
>   For anything tougher than suet;
> Yet you finished the goose, with the bones and the beak—
>   Pray, how did you manage to do it?'
>
> 'In my youth,' said his father, 'I took to the law,
>   And argued each case with my wife;
> And the muscular strength, which it gave to my jaw
>   Has lasted the rest of my life.'
>
> 'You are old,' said the youth, 'one would hardly suppose
>   That your eye was as steady as ever;
> Yet you balanced an eel on the end of your nose—
>   What made you so awfully clever?'

'*I have answered three questions, and that is enough,*'
   Said his father. '*Don't give yourself airs!*
   Do you think I can listen all day to such stuff?
   Be off, or I'll kick you downstairs!'"

"That is not said right," said the Caterpillar.

"Not *quite* right, I'm afraid," said Alice, timidly; "some of the words have got altered."

"It is wrong from beginning to end," said the Caterpillar, decidedly; and there was silence for some minutes.

The Caterpillar was the first to speak.

"What size do you want to be?" it asked.

"Oh, I'm not particular as to size," Alice hastily replied; "only one doesn't like changing so often, you know."

"I *don't* know," said the Caterpillar.

Alice said nothing: she had never been so much contradicted in all her life before, and she felt that she was losing her temper.

"Are you content now?" said the Caterpillar.

"Well, I should like to be a *little* larger, Sir, if you wouldn't mind," said Alice; "three inches is such a wretched height to be."

"It is a very good height indeed!" said the Caterpillar angrily, rearing itself upright as it spoke (it was exactly three inches high).

"But I'm not used to it!" pleaded poor Alice in a piteous tone. And she thought to herself, "I wish the creatures wouldn't be so easily offended!"

"You'll get used to it in time," said the Caterpillar; and it put the hookah into its mouth, and began smoking again.

This time Alice waited patiently until it chose to speak again. In a minute or two the Caterpillar took the hookah out of its mouth, and yawned once or twice, and shook itself. Then it got down off the mushroom, and crawled away into the grass, merely remarking, as it went, "One side will make you grow taller, and the other side will make you grow shorter."

"One side of *what*? The other side of *what*?" thought Alice to herself.

"Of the mushroom," said the Caterpillar, just as if she

had asked it aloud; and in another moment it was out of sight.

Alice remained looking thoughtfully at the mushroom for a minute, trying to make out which were the two sides of it; and, as it was perfectly round, she found this a very difficult question. However, at last she stretched her arms round it as far as they would go, and broke off a bit of the edge with each hand.

"And now which is which?" she said to herself, and nibbled a little of the right-hand bit to try the effect. The next moment she felt a violent blow underneath her chin: it had struck her foot!

She was a good deal frightened by this very sudden change, but she felt that there was no time to be lost, as she was shrinking rapidly; so she set to work at once to eat some of the other bit. Her chin was pressed so closely against her foot that there was hardly room to open her mouth; but she did it at last, and managed to swallow a morsel of the left-hand bit.

*   *   *   *   *   *   *

"Come, my head's free at last!" said Alice in a tone of delight, which changed into alarm in another moment, when she found that her shoulders were nowhere to be found: all she could see, when she looked down, was an immense length of neck, which seemed to rise like a stalk out of a sea of green leaves that lay far below her. "What *can* all that green stuff be?" said Alice. "And where *have* my shoulders got to? And oh, my poor hands, how is it I can't see you?" She was moving them about, as she spoke, but no result seemed to follow, except a little shaking among the distant green leaves.

As there seemed to be no chance of getting her hands up to her head, she tried to get her head down to *them*, and was delighted to find that her neck would bend about easily in any direction, like a serpent. She had just succeeded in curving it down into a graceful zigzag, and was going to dive in among the leaves, which she found to be nothing but the tops of the trees under which she had been wandering, when a sharp hiss made her draw back in a hurry: a large pigeon had flown into her face, and was beating her violently with its wings.

"Serpent!" screamed the Pigeon.

"I'm *not* a serpent!" said Alice indignantly. "Let me alone!"

"Serpent, I say again!" repeated the Pigeon, but in a more subdued tone, and added, with a kind of sob, "I've tried every way, but nothing seems to suit them!"

"I haven't the least idea what you're talking about," said Alice.

"I've tried the roots of trees, and I've tried banks, and I've tried hedges," the Pigeon went on, without attending to her, "but those serpents! There's no pleasing them!"

Alice was more and more puzzled, but she thought there was no use in saying anything more till the Pigeon had finished.

"As if it wasn't trouble enough hatching the eggs," said the Pigeon; "but I must be on the lookout for serpents, night and day! Why, I haven't had a wink of sleep these three weeks!"

"I'm very sorry you've been annoyed," said Alice, who was beginning to see its meaning.

"And just as I'd taken the highest tree in the wood," continued the Pigeon, raising its voice to a shriek, "and just as I was thinking I should be free of them at last, they must needs come wriggling down from the sky! Ugh, Serpent!"

"But I'm *not* a serpent, I tell you!" said Alice. "I'm a— I'm a—"

"Well! *What* are you?" said the Pigeon. "I can see you're trying to invent something!"

"I—I'm a little girl," said Alice, rather doubtfully, as she remembered the number of changes she had gone through that day.

"A likely story indeed!" said the Pigeon, in a tone of the deepest contempt. "I've seen a good many little girls in my time, but never *one* with such a neck as that! No, no! You're a serpent, and there's no use denying it. I suppose you'll be telling me next that you never tasted an egg!"

"I *have* tasted eggs, certainly," said Alice, who was a very truthful child; "but little girls eat eggs quite as much as serpents do, you know."

"I don't believe it," said the Pigeon; "but if they do, why, then they're a kind of serpent, that's all I can say."

This was such a new idea to Alice that she was quite silent for a minute or two, which gave the Pigeon the opportunity of adding, "You're looking for eggs, I know *that* well enough; and what does it matter to me whether you're a little girl or a serpent?"

"It matters a good deal to *me*," said Alice hastily; "but I'm not looking for eggs, as it happens; and, if I was, I shouldn't want *yours:* I don't like them raw."

"Well, be off, then!" said the Pigeon in a sulky tone, as it settled down again into its nest. Alice crouched down among the trees as well as she could, for her neck kept getting entangled among the branches, and every now and then she had to stop and untwist it. After a while she remembered that she still held the pieces of mushroom in her hands, and she set to work very carefully, nibbling first at one and then at the other, and growing sometimes taller, and sometimes shorter, until she had succeeded in bringing herself down to her usual height.

It was so long since she had been anything near the right size that it felt quite strange at first; but she got used to it in a few minutes, and began talking to herself, as usual, "Come, there's half my plan done now! How puzzling all these changes are! I'm never sure what I'm going to be from one minute to another! However, I've got back to my right size; the next thing is, to get into that beautiful garden—how *is* that to be done, I wonder?" As she said this, she came suddenly upon an open place, with a little house in it about four feet high. "Whoever lives there," thought Alice, "it'll never do to come upon them *this* size; why, I should frighten them out of their wits!" So she began nibbling at the right-hand bit again, and did not venture to go near the house till she had brought herself down to nine inches high.

CHAPTER VI: *Pig and Pepper*

FOR A MINUTE OR TWO she stood looking at the house, and wondering what to do next, when suddenly a footman in livery came running out of the woods (she considered him to be a footman because he was in livery; otherwise, judging by his face only, she would have called him a fish) and rapped loudly at the door with his

knuckles. It was opened by another footman in livery, with a round face, and large eyes like a frog; and both footmen, Alice noticed, had powdered hair that curled all over their heads. She felt very curious to know what it was all about, and crept a little way out of the wood to listen.

The Fish-Footman began by producing from under his arm a

great letter, nearly as large as himself, and this he handed over to the other, saying, in a solemn tone, "For the Duchess. An invitation from the Queen to play croquet." The Frog-Footman repeated, in the same solemn tone, only changing the order of the words a little, "From the Queen. An invitation for the Duchess to play croquet."

Then they both bowed low, and their curls got entangled together.

Alice laughed so much at this that she had to run back into the wood for fear of their hearing her; and, when she next peeped out, the Fish-Footman was gone, and the other was sitting on the ground near the door, staring stupidly up into the sky.

Alice went timidly up to the door, and knocked.

"There's no sort of use in knocking," said the Footman, "and that for two reasons. First, because I'm on the same side of the door as you are; secondly, because they're making such a noise inside, no one could possibly hear you." And certainly there *was* a most extraordinary noise going on within—a constant howling and sneezing, and every now and then a great crash, as if a dish or kettle had been broken to pieces.

"Please, then," said Alice, "how am I to get in?"

"There might be some sense in your knocking," the Footman went on, without attending to her, "if we had the door between us. For instance, if you were *inside*, you might knock, and I could let you out, you know." He was looking up into the sky all the time he was speaking, and this Alice thought decidedly uncivil. "But perhaps he can't help it," she said to herself; "his eyes are so *very* nearly at the top of his head. But at any rate he might answer questions— How am I to get in?" she repeated, aloud.

"I shall sit here," the Footman remarked, "till tomorrow—"

At this moment the door of the house opened, and a large plate came skimming out, straight at the Footman's head; it just grazed his nose, and broke to pieces against one of the trees behind him.

"—or next day, maybe," the Footman continued in the same tone, exactly as if nothing had happened.

"How am I to get in?" asked Alice again, in a louder tone.

"*Are* you to get in at all?" said the Footman. "That's the first question, you know."

It was, no doubt: only Alice did not like to be told so. "It's really dreadful," she muttered to herself, "the way all the creatures argue. It's enough to drive one crazy!"

The Footman seemed to think this a good opportunity for repeating his remark, with variations. "I shall sit here," he said, "on and off, for days and days."

"But what am *I* to do?" said Alice.

"Anything you like," said the Footman, and began whistling.

"Oh, there's no use in talking to him," said Alice desperately; "he's perfectly idiotic!" And she opened the door and went in.

The door led right into a large kitchen, which was full of smoke from one end to the other, the Duchess was sitting on a three-legged stool in the middle, nursing a baby; the cook was leaning over the fire, stirring a large caldron which seemed to be full of soup. "There's certainly too much pepper in that soup!" Alice said to herself, as well as she could for sneezing.

There was certainly too much of it in the *air*. Even the Duchess sneezed occasionally; and as for the baby, it was sneezing and howling alternately without a moment's pause. The only two creatures in the kitchen that did *not* sneeze were the cook, and a large cat, which was lying on the hearth and grinning from ear to ear.

"Please would you tell me," said Alice, a little timidly, for she was not quite sure whether it was good manners for her to speak first, "why your cat grins like that?"

"It's a Cheshire Cat," said the Duchess, "and that's why. Pig!"

She said the last word with such sudden violence that Alice quite jumped; but she saw in another moment that it was addressed to the baby, and not to her, so she took courage, and went on again: "I didn't know that Cheshire Cats always grinned; in fact, I didn't know that cats *could* grin."

"They all can," said the Duchess, "and most of 'em do."

"I don't know of any that do," Alice said very politely, feeling quite pleased to have got into a conversation.

"You don't know much," said the Duchess, "and that's a fact."

Alice did not at all like the tone of this remark, and thought it would be as well to introduce some other subject of conversation. While she was trying to fix on one, the cook took the caldron of soup off the fire, and at once set to work throwing everything within her reach at the Duchess and the baby—the fire irons came first; then followed a shower of saucepans, plates, and dishes. The Duchess took no notice of them even when they hit her; and the baby was howling so much already that it was quite impossible to say whether the blows hurt it or not.

"Oh, *please* mind what you're doing!" cried Alice, jumping up and down in an agony of terror. "Oh, there goes his *precious* nose!" as an unusually large saucepan flew close by it, and very nearly carried it off.

"If everybody minded their own business," the Duchess said,

in a hoarse growl, "the world would go round a deal faster than it does."

"Which would *not* be an advantage," said Alice, who felt very glad to get an opportunity of showing off a little of her knowledge. "Just think what work it would make with the day and night! You see the earth takes twenty-four hours to turn round on its axis—"

"Talking of axes," said the Duchess, "chop off her head!"

Alice glanced rather anxiously at the cook, to see if she meant to take the hint; but the cook was busily stirring the soup, and seemed not to be listening, so she went on again: "Twenty-four hours, I *think;* or is it twelve? I—"

"Oh, don't bother *me!*" said the Duchess. "I never could abide figures!" And with that she began nursing her child again, singing a sort of lullaby to it as she did so, and giving it a violent shake at the end of every line:

> *"Speak roughly to your little boy,*
> *And beat him when he sneezes;*
> *He only does it to annoy,*
> *Because he knows it teases."*

Chorus

(in which the cook and the baby joined):

> *"Wow! Wow! Wow!"*

While the Duchess sang the second verse of the song, she kept tossing the baby violently up and down, and the poor little thing howled so that Alice could hardly hear the words:

> *"I speak severely to my boy,*
> *I beat him when he sneezes;*
> *For he can thoroughly enjoy*
> *The pepper when he pleases!"*

Chorus

> *"Wow! Wow! Wow!"*

"Here! You may nurse it a bit, if you like!" the Duchess said to Alice, flinging the baby at her as she spoke. "I must go and get ready to play croquet with the Queen," and she hurried out of the room. The cook threw a frying pan after her as she went, but it just missed her.

Alice caught the baby with some difficulty, as it was a queer-shaped little creature, and held out its arms and legs in all directions, "just like a starfish," thought Alice. The poor little thing was snorting like a steam engine when she caught it, and kept doubling itself up and straightening itself out again, so that altogether, for the first minute or two, it was as much as she could do to hold it.

As soon as she had made out the proper way of nursing it (which was to twist it up into a sort of knot, and then keep tight hold of its right ear and left foot, so as to prevent its undoing itself), she carried it out into the open air.

"If I don't take this child away with me," thought Alice, "they're sure to kill it in a day or two. Wouldn't it be murder to leave it behind?" She said the last words out loud, and the little thing grunted in reply (it had left off sneezing by this time). "Don't grunt," said Alice; "that's not at all a proper way of expressing yourself."

The baby grunted again, and Alice looked very anxiously into its face to see what was the matter with it. There could be no doubt that it had a *very* turn-up nose, much more like a snout than a real nose; also its eyes were getting extremely small for a baby: altogether Alice did not like the look of the thing at all. "But perhaps it was only sobbing," she thought, and looked into its eyes again, to see if there were any tears.

No, there were no tears. "If you're going to turn into a pig, my dear," said Alice, seriously, "I'll have nothing more to do with you. Mind now!" The poor little thing sobbed again (or grunted, it was impossible to say which), and they went on for some while in silence.

Alice was just beginning to think to herself, "Now, what am I to do with this creature, when I get it home?" when it grunted again, so violently that she looked down into its face in some alarm. This time there could be *no* mistake about it: it was neither more nor less than a pig, and she felt that it would be quite absurd for her to carry it any further.

So she set the little creature down, and felt quite relieved to see it trot away quietly into the wood. "If it had grown up," she said to herself, "it would have made a dreadfully ugly child; but it makes rather a handsome pig, I think."

And she began thinking over other children she knew who might do very well as pigs, and was just saying to herself, "If one only knew the right way to change them—" when she was a little startled by seeing the Cheshire Cat sitting on a bough of a tree a few yards off. The Cat only grinned when it saw Alice. It looked good-natured, she thought; still it had *very* long claws and a great many teeth, so she felt that it ought to be treated with respect.

"Cheshire Puss," she began, rather timidly, as she did not at all know whether it would like the name; however, it only grinned a little wider. "Come, it's pleased so far," thought Alice, and she went on. "Would you tell me, please, which way I ought to go from here?"

"That depends a good deal on where you want to get to," said the Cat.

"I don't much care where—" said Alice.

"Then it doesn't matter which way you go," said the Cat.

"—so long as I get *somewhere*," Alice added as an explanation.

"Oh, you're sure to do that," said the Cat, "if you only walk long enough."

Alice felt that this could not be denied, so she tried another question. "What sort of people live about here?"

"In *that* direction," the Cat said, waving its right paw round, "lives a Hatter; and in *that* direction," waving the other paw, "lives a March Hare. Visit either you like; they're both mad."

"But I don't want to go among mad people," Alice remarked.

"Oh, you can't help that," said the Cat: "we're all mad here. I'm mad. You're mad."

"How do you know I'm mad?" said Alice.

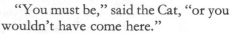

"You must be," said the Cat, "or you wouldn't have come here."

Alice didn't think that proved it at all; however, she went on: "And how do you know that you're mad?"

"To begin with," said the Cat, "a dog's not mad. You grant that?"

"I suppose so," said Alice.

"Well, then," the Cat went on, "you see a dog growls when it's angry, and wags its tail when it's pleased. Now *I* growl when I'm pleased, and wag my tail when I'm angry. Therefore I'm mad."

"*I* call it purring, not growling," said Alice.

"Call it what you like," said the Cat. "Do you play croquet with the Queen today?"

"I should like it very much," said Alice, "but I haven't been invited yet."

"You'll see me there," said the Cat, and vanished.

Alice was not much surprised at this, she was getting so well used to queer things happening. While she was still looking at the place where it had been, it suddenly appeared again.

"By the by, what became of the baby?" said the Cat. "I'd nearly forgotten to ask."

"It turned into a pig," Alice answered very quietly, just as if the Cat had come back in a natural way.

"I thought it would," said the Cat, and vanished again.

Alice waited a little, half expecting to see it again, but it did not appear, and after a minute or two she walked on in the direction in which the March Hare was said to live. "I've seen hatters before," she said to herself; "the March Hare will be much the most interesting, and perhaps, as this is May, it won't be raving mad—at least not so mad as it was in March." As she said this, she looked up, and there was the Cat again, sitting on a branch of a tree.

"Did you say 'pig,' or 'fig'?" said the Cat.

"I said 'pig,'" replied Alice; "and I wish you wouldn't keep appearing and vanishing so suddenly—you make one quite giddy!"

"All right," said the Cat; and this time it vanished quite slowly, beginning with the end of the tail, and ending with the grin, which remained some time after the rest of it had gone.

"Well! I've often seen a cat without a grin," thought Alice; "but a grin without a cat! It's the most curious thing I ever saw in all my life!"

She had not gone much farther before she came in sight of the house of the March Hare; she thought it must be the right house, because the chimneys were shaped like ears and the roof was thatched with fur. It was so large a house that she did not like to go nearer till she had nibbled some more of the left-hand bit of mushroom, and raised herself to about two feet high. Even then she walked up towards it rather timidly, saying to herself, "Suppose it should be raving mad after all! I almost wish I'd gone to see the Hatter instead!"

THERE WAS A TABLE SET OUT under a tree in front of the house, and the March Hare and the Hatter were having tea at it; a Dormouse was sitting between them, fast asleep, and the other two were using it as a cushion, resting their elbows on it, and talking over its head. "Very uncomfortable for the Dormouse," thought Alice; "only as it's asleep, I suppose it doesn't mind."

The table was a large one, but the three were all crowded together at one corner of it. "No room! No room!" they cried out when they saw Alice coming. "There's *plenty* of room!" said Alice indignantly, and she sat down in a large armchair at one end of the table.

"Have some wine," the March Hare said in an encouraging tone.

Alice looked all round the table, but there was nothing on it but tea. "I don't see any wine," she remarked.

"There isn't any," said the March Hare.

"Then it wasn't very civil of you to offer it," said Alice angrily.

"It wasn't very civil of you to sit down without being invited," said the March Hare.

"I didn't know it was *your* table," said Alice; "it's laid for a great many more than three."

"Your hair wants cutting," said the Hatter. He had been looking at Alice for some time with great curiosity, and this was his first speech.

"You should learn not to make personal remarks," Alice said with some severity. "It's very rude."

The Hatter opened his eyes very wide on hearing this; but all he *said* was, "Why is a raven like a writing desk?"

"Come, we shall have some fun now!" thought Alice. "I'm glad they've begun asking riddles. I believe I can guess that," she added aloud.

"Do you mean that you think you can find out the answer to it?" said the March Hare.

"Exactly so," said Alice.

"Then you should say what you mean," the March Hare went on.

"I do," Alice hastily replied; "at least—at least I mean what I say—that's the same thing, you know."

"Not the same thing a bit!" said the Hatter. "Why, you might just as well say that 'I see what I eat' is the same thing as 'I eat what I see!'"

"You might just as well say," added the March Hare, "that 'I like what I get' is the same thing as 'I get what I like!'"

"You might just as well say," added the Dormouse, which seemed to be talking in its sleep, "that 'I breathe when I sleep' is the same thing as 'I sleep when I breathe!'"

"It *is* the same thing with you," said the Hatter, and here the conversation dropped, and the party sat silent for a minute, while Alice thought over all she could remember about ravens and writing desks, which wasn't much.

The Hatter was the first to break the silence. "What day of the

343

month is it?" he said, turning to Alice. He had taken his watch out of his pocket, and was looking at it uneasily, shaking it every now and then, and holding it to his ear.

Alice considered a little, and then said, "The fourth."

"Two days wrong!" sighed the Hatter. "I told you butter wouldn't suit the works!" he added, looking angrily at the March Hare.

"It was the *best* butter," the March Hare meekly replied.

"Yes, but some crumbs must have got in as well," the Hatter grumbled. "You shouldn't have put it in with the bread knife."

The March Hare took the watch and looked at it gloomily; then he dipped it into his cup of tea, and looked at it again; but he could think of nothing better to say than his first remark, "It was the *best* butter, you know."

Alice had been looking over his shoulder with some curiosity. "What a funny watch!" she remarked. "It tells the day of the month, and doesn't tell what o'clock it is!"

"Why should it?" muttered the Hatter. "Does *your* watch tell you what year it is?"

"Of course not," Alice replied very readily; "but that's because it stays the same year for such a long time together."

"Which is just the case with *mine*," said the Hatter.

Alice felt dreadfully puzzled. The Hatter's remark seemed to her to have no sort of meaning in it, and yet it was certainly English. "I don't quite understand you," she said, as politely as she could.

"The Dormouse is asleep again," said the Hatter, and he poured a little hot tea upon its nose.

The Dormouse shook its head impatiently, and said, without opening its eyes, "Of course, of course: just what I was going to remark myself."

"Have you guessed the riddle yet?" the Hatter said, turning to Alice again.

"No, I give it up," Alice replied. "What's the answer?"

"I haven't the slightest idea," said the Hatter.

"Nor I," said the March Hare.

Alice sighed wearily. "I think you might do something better with the time," she said, "than wasting it in asking riddles that have no answers."

"If you knew Time as well as I do," said the Hatter, "you wouldn't talk about wasting *it*. It's *him*."

"I don't know what you mean," said Alice.

"Of course you don't!" the Hatter said, tossing his head contemptuously. "I daresay you never even spoke to Time!"

"Perhaps not," Alice cautiously replied; "but I know I have to beat time when I learn music."

"Ah! That accounts for it," said the Hatter. "He won't stand beating. Now, if you only kept on good terms with him, he'd do almost anything you liked with the clock. For instance, suppose it were nine o'clock in the morning, just time to begin lessons: you'd only have to whisper a hint to Time, and round goes the clock in a twinkling! Half past one, time for dinner!"

("I only wish it was," the March Hare said to itself in a whisper.)

"That would be grand, certainly," said Alice thoughtfully; "but then—I shouldn't be hungry for it, you know."

"Not at first, perhaps," said the Hatter; "but you could keep it to half past one as long as you liked."

"Is that the way *you* manage?" Alice asked.

The Hatter shook his head mournfully. "Not I!" he replied. "We quarreled last March—just before *he* went mad, you know—" (pointing with his teaspoon at the March Hare) "—it was at the great concert given by the Queen of Hearts, and I had to sing

> *"Twinkle, twinkle, little bat!*
> *How I wonder what you're at!*

You know the song, perhaps?"

"I've heard something like it," said Alice.

"It goes on, you know," the Hatter continued, "in this way:

> *"Up above the world you fly,*
> *Like a tea tray in the sky.*
> *Twinkle, twinkle—"*

345

Here the Dormouse shook itself, and began singing in its sleep, "*Twinkle, twinkle, twinkle, twinkle*—" and went on so long that they had to pinch it to make it stop.

"Well, I'd hardly finished the first verse," said the Hatter, "when the Queen bawled out, 'He's murdering the time! Off with his head!'"

"How dreadfully savage!" exclaimed Alice.

"And ever since that," the Hatter went on in a mournful tone, "he won't do a thing I ask! It's always six o'clock now."

A bright idea came into Alice's head. "Is that the reason so many tea things are put out here?" she asked.

"Yes, that's it," said the Hatter with a sigh; "it's always tea-time, and we've no time to wash the things betweenwhiles."

"Then you keep moving round, I suppose?" said Alice.

"Exactly so," said the Hatter, "as the things get used up."

"But what happens when you come to the beginning again?" Alice ventured to ask.

"Suppose we change the subject," the March Hare interrupted, yawning. "I'm getting tired of this. I vote the young lady tells us a story."

"I'm afraid I don't know one," said Alice, rather alarmed at the proposal.

"Then the Dormouse shall!" they both cried. "Wake up, Dormouse!" And they pinched it on both sides at once.

The Dormouse slowly opened its eyes. "I wasn't asleep," it said in a hoarse, feeble voice, "I heard every word you fellows were saying."

"Tell us a story!" said the March Hare.

"Yes, please do!" pleaded Alice.

"And be quick about it," added the Hatter, "or you'll be asleep again before it's done."

"Once upon a time there were three little sisters," the Dormouse began in a great hurry, "and their names were Elsie, Lacie, and Tillie; and they lived at the bottom of a well—"

"What did they live on?" said Alice, who always took a great interest in questions of eating and drinking.

"They lived on treacle," said the Dormouse, after thinking a minute or two.

"They couldn't have done that, you know," Alice gently remarked. "They'd have been ill."

"So they were," said the Dormouse, "*very* ill."

Alice tried to fancy to herself what such an extraordinary way of living would be like, but it puzzled her too much, so she went on:

"But why did they live at the bottom of a well?"

"Take some more tea," the March Hare said to Alice, very earnestly.

"I've had nothing yet," Alice replied in an offended tone, "so I can't take more."

"You mean you can't take *less*," said the Hatter; "it's very easy to take *more* than nothing."

"Nobody asked *your* opinion," said Alice.

"Who's making personal remarks now?" the Hatter asked triumphantly.

Alice did not quite know what to say to this, so she helped herself to some tea and bread and butter, and then turned to the Dormouse, and repeated her question. "Why did they live at the bottom of a well?"

The Dormouse again took a minute or two to think about it, and then said, "It was a treacle well."

"There's no such thing!" Alice was beginning very angrily, but the Hatter and the March Hare went "Sh! Sh!" and the Dormouse sulkily remarked, "If you can't be civil, you'd better finish the story for yourself."

"No, please go on!" Alice said very humbly. "I won't interrupt you again. I daresay there may be *one*."

"One, indeed!" said the Dormouse indignantly. However, he

consented to go on. "And so these three little sisters—they were learning to draw, you know—"

"What did they draw?" said Alice, quite forgetting her promise.

"Treacle," said the Dormouse, without considering at all, this time.

"I want a clean cup," interrupted the Hatter; "let's all move one place on."

He moved on as he spoke, and the Dormouse followed him; the March Hare moved into the Dormouse's place, and Alice rather unwillingly took the place of the March Hare. The Hatter was the only one who got any advantage from the change; and Alice was a good deal worse off than before, as the March Hare had just upset the milk jug into his plate.

Alice did not wish to offend the Dormouse again, so she began very cautiously: "But I don't understand. Where did they draw the treacle from?"

"You can draw water out of a water well," said the Hatter; "so I should think you could draw treacle out of a treacle well— eh, stupid?"

"But they were *in* the well," Alice said to the Dormouse, not choosing to notice this last remark.

"Of course they were," said the Dormouse, "well in."

This answer so confused poor Alice that she let the Dormouse go on for some time without interrupting it.

"They were learning to draw," the Dormouse went on, yawning and rubbing its eyes, for it was getting very sleepy; "and they drew all manner of things—everything that begins with an *M*—"

"Why with an *M?*" said Alice.

"Why not?" said the March Hare.

Alice was silent.

The Dormouse had closed its eyes by this time, and was going off into a doze; but, on being pinched by the Hatter, it woke up again with a little shriek, and went on: "—that begins with an *M*, such as mousetraps, and the moon, and memory, and muchness—you know you say things are 'much of a muchness'—did you ever see such a thing as a drawing of a muchness!"

"Really, now you ask me," said Alice, very much confused, "I don't think—"

"Then you shouldn't talk," said the Hatter. This piece of rudeness was more than Alice could bear; she got up in great disgust, and walked off. The Dormouse fell asleep instantly, and neither of the others took the least notice of her going, though she looked back once or twice, half hoping that they would call after her.

The last time she saw them, they were trying to put the Dormouse into the teapot.

"At any rate I'll never go *there* again!" said Alice, as she picked her way through the wood. "It's the stupidest tea party I ever was at in all my life!"

Just as she said this, she noticed that one of the trees had a door leading right into it. "That's very curious!" she thought. "But everything's curious today. I think I may as well go in at once." And in she went.

Once more she found herself in the long hall, and close to the little glass table.

"Now, I'll manage better this time," she said to herself, and began by taking the little golden key, and unlocking the door that led into the garden. Then she set to work nibbling at the mushroom (she had kept a piece of it in her pocket) till she was about a foot high; then she walked down the little passage, and *then*— she found herself at last in the beautiful garden, among the bright flower beds and the cool fountains.

A LARGE ROSE TREE STOOD near the entrance of the garden; the roses growing on it were white, but there were three gardeners at it, busily painting them red. Alice thought this a very curious thing, and she went nearer to watch them, and, just as she came up to them, she heard one of them say, "Look out now, Five! Don't go splashing paint over me like that!"

"I couldn't help it," said Five, in a sulky tone. "Seven jogged my elbow."

On which Seven looked up and said, "That's right, Five! Always lay the blame on others!"

"*You'd* better not talk!" said Five. "I heard the Queen say only yesterday you deserved to be beheaded."

"What for?" said the one who had spoken first.

"That's none of *your* business, Two!" said Seven.

"Yes, it *is* his business!" said Five. "And I'll tell him—it was for bringing the cook tulip roots instead of onions."

Seven flung down his brush, and had just begun, "Well, of all the unjust things—" when his eye chanced to fall upon Alice, as she stood watching them, and he checked himself suddenly; the others looked round also, and all of them bowed low.

"Would you tell me, please," said Alice, a little timidly, "why you are painting those roses?"

Five and Seven said nothing, but looked at Two. Two began, in a low voice, "Why, the fact is, you see, Miss, this here ought to have been a *red* rose tree, and we put a white one in by mistake; and, if the Queen was to find it out, we should all have our heads cut off, you know. So you see, Miss, we're doing our best, afore she comes, to—" At this moment, Five, who had been anxiously looking across the garden, called out, "The Queen! The Queen!" and the three gardeners instantly threw themselves flat upon their faces. There was a sound of many footsteps, and Alice looked round, eager to see the Queen.

First came ten soldiers carrying clubs: these were all shaped like the three gardeners, oblong and flat, with their hands and feet at the corners; next the ten courtiers: these were ornamented all over with diamonds, and walked two and two, as the soldiers did. After these came the royal children: there were ten of them, and the little dears came jumping merrily along, hand in hand, in couples; they were all ornamented with hearts. Next came the guests, mostly kings and queens, and among them Alice recognized the White Rabbit: it was talking in a hurried nervous manner, smiling at everything that was said, and went by without noticing her. Then followed the Knave of Hearts, carrying the King's crown on a crimson velvet cushion; and, last of all this grand procession, came THE KING AND THE QUEEN OF HEARTS.

Alice was rather doubtful whether she ought not to lie down on her face like the three gardeners, but she could not remember ever having heard of such a rule at processions; "and besides, what would be the use of a procession," thought she, "if people had all to lie down on their faces, so that they couldn't see it?" So she stood where she was, and waited.

When the procession came opposite to Alice, they all stopped and looked at her, and the Queen said, severely, "Who is this?" She said it to the Knave of Hearts, who only bowed and smiled in reply.

"Idiot!" said the Queen, tossing her head impatiently; and, turning to Alice, she went on, "What's your name, child?"

"My name is Alice, so please your Majesty," said Alice very politely; but she added, to herself, "Why, they're only a pack of cards, after all. I needn't be afraid of them!"

"And who are *these*?" said the Queen, pointing to the three gardeners who were lying round the rose tree; for, you see, as they were lying on their faces, and the pattern on their backs was the same as the rest of the pack, she could not tell whether they were gardeners, or soldiers, or courtiers, or three of her own children.

"How should *I* know?" said Alice, surprised at her own courage. "It's no business of *mine*."

The Queen turned crimson with fury, and, after glaring at her

for a moment like a wild beast, began screaming, "Off with her head! Off with—"

"Nonsense!" said Alice, very loudly and decidedly, and the Queen was silent.

The King laid his hand upon her arm, and timidly said, "Consider, my dear: she is only a child!"

The Queen turned angrily away from him, and said to the Knave, "Turn them over!"

The Knave did so, very carefully, with one foot.

"Get up!" said the Queen in a shrill, loud voice, and the three gardeners instantly jumped up, and began bowing to the King, the Queen, the royal children, and everybody else.

"Leave off that!" screamed the Queen. "You make me giddy." And then, turning to the rose tree, she went on, "What *have* you been doing here?"

"May it please your Majesty," said Two, in a very humble tone, going down on one knee as he spoke, "we were trying—"

"*I* see!" said the Queen, who had meanwhile been examining the roses. "Off with their heads!" and the procession moved on, three of the soldiers remaining behind to execute the unfortunate gardeners, who ran to Alice for protection.

"You shan't be beheaded!" said Alice, and she put them into a large flowerpot that stood near. The three soldiers wandered about for a minute or two, looking for them, and then quietly marched off after the others.

"Are their heads off?" shouted the Queen.

"Their heads are gone, if it please your Majesty!" the soldiers shouted in reply.

"That's right!" shouted the Queen. "Can you play croquet?"

The soldiers were silent, and looked at Alice, as the question was evidently meant for her. "Yes!" shouted Alice.

"Come on, then!" roared the Queen, and Alice joined the procession, wondering very much what would happen next.

"It's—it's a very fine day!" said a timid voice at her side. She was walking by the White Rabbit, who was peeping anxiously into her face.

"Very," said Alice. "Where's the Duchess?"

"Hush! Hush!" said the Rabbit in a low hurried tone. He looked anxiously over his shoulder as he spoke, and then raised himself upon tiptoe, put his mouth close to her ear, and whispered, "She's under sentence of execution."

"What for?" said Alice.

"Did you say 'What a pity'?" the Rabbit asked.

"No, I didn't," said Alice. "I don't think it's at all a pity. I said 'What for?'"

"She boxed the Queen's ears—" the Rabbit began. Alice gave a little scream of laughter. "Oh, hush!" the Rabbit whispered in a frightened tone. "The Queen will hear you! You see she came rather late, and the Queen said—"

"Get to your places!" shouted the Queen in a voice of thunder, and people began running about in all directions, tumbling up against each other; however, they got settled down in a minute or two, and the game began.

Alice thought she had never seen such a curious croquet ground in her life: it was all ridges and furrows, the croquet balls were live hedgehogs, and the mallets live flamingos, and the soldiers had to double themselves up and stand on their hands and feet, to make the arches.

The chief difficulty Alice found at first was in managing her flamingo: she succeeded in getting its body tucked away, comfortably enough, under her arm, with its legs hanging down, but generally, just as she had got its neck nicely straightened out, and was going to give the hedgehog a blow with its head, it *would* twist itself round and look up in her face, with such a puzzled expression that she could not help bursting out laughing; and, when she had got its head down, and was going to begin again, it was very provoking to find that the hedgehog had unrolled itself, and was in the act of crawling away; besides all this, there was generally a ridge or a furrow in the way wherever she wanted to send the hedgehog to, and, as the doubled-up soldiers were always getting up and walking off to other parts of the ground, Alice soon came to the conclusion that it was a very difficult game indeed.

The players all played at once, without waiting for turns, quarreling all the while, and fighting for the hedgehogs; and in a very short time the Queen was in a furious passion, and went stamping about, and shouting, "Off with his head!" or "Off with her head!" about once in a minute.

Alice began to feel very uneasy: to be sure, she had not as yet

had any dispute with the Queen, but she knew that it might happen any minute, "and then," thought she, "what would become of me? They're dreadfully fond of beheading people here; the great wonder is that there's anyone left alive!"

She was looking about for some way of escape, and wondering whether she could get away without being seen, when she noticed a curious appearance in the air; it puzzled her very much at first, but after watching it a minute or two she made it out to be a grin, and she said to herself, "It's the Cheshire Cat; now I shall have somebody to talk to."

"How are you getting on?" said the Cat, as soon as there was mouth enough for it to speak with.

Alice waited till the eyes appeared, and then nodded. "It's no use speaking to it," she thought, "till its ears have come, or at least one of them." In another minute the whole head appeared, and then Alice put down her flamingo, and began an account of the game, feeling very glad she had someone to listen to her. The Cat seemed to think that there was enough of it now in sight, and no more of it appeared.

"I don't think they play at all fairly," Alice began, in rather a complaining tone, "and they all quarrel so dreadfully one can't hear oneself speak—and they don't seem to have any rules in particular; at least, if there are, nobody attends to them—and you've no idea how confusing it is all the things being alive. For instance, there's the arch I've got to go through next walking about at the other end of the ground—and I should have croqueted the Queen's hedgehog just now, only it ran away when it saw mine coming!"

"How do you like the Queen?" said the Cat in a low voice.

"Not at all," said Alice; "she's so extremely—" Just then she noticed that the Queen was close behind her, listening, so she went on "—likely to win, that it's hardly worthwhile finishing the game." The Queen smiled and passed on.

"Who *are* you talking to?" said the King, coming up to Alice, and looking at the Cat's head with great curiosity.

"It's a friend of mine—a Cheshire Cat," said Alice. "Allow me to introduce it."

"I don't like the look of it at all," said the King. "However, it may kiss my hand, if it likes."

"I'd rather not," the Cat remarked.

"Don't be impertinent," said the King, "and don't look at me like that!" He got behind Alice as he spoke.

"A cat may look at a king," said Alice. "I've read that in some book, but I don't remember where."

"Well, it must be removed," said the King very decidedly; and he called to the Queen, who was passing at the moment, "My dear! I wish you would have this cat removed!"

The Queen had only one way of settling all difficulties, great or small. "Off with his head!" she said without even looking around.

"I'll fetch the executioner myself," said the King eagerly, and he hurried off.

Alice thought she might as well go back and see how the game was going on, as she heard the Queen's voice in the distance, screaming with passion. She had already heard her sentence three of the players to be executed for having missed their turns, and she did not like the look of things at all, as the game was in such confusion that she never knew whether it was her turn or not. So she went off in search of her hedgehog.

The hedgehog was engaged in a fight with another hedgehog, which seemed to Alice an excellent opportunity for croqueting one of them with the other; the only difficulty was that her flamingo was gone across the other side of the garden, where Alice could see it trying in a helpless sort of way to fly up into a tree.

By the time she had caught the flamingo and brought it back, the fight was over, and both the hedgehogs were out of sight; "but it doesn't matter much," thought Alice, "as all the arches are gone from this side of the ground." So she tucked it away under her arm, that it might not escape again, and went back to have a little more conversation with her friend.

When she got back to the Cheshire Cat, she was surprised to find quite a large crowd collected round it; there was a dispute going on between the executioner, the King, and the Queen, who were all talking at once, while all the rest were quite silent, and looked very uncomfortable.

The moment Alice appeared, she was appealed to by all three to settle the question, and they repeated their arguments to her, though, as they all spoke at once, she found it very hard to make out exactly what they said.

The executioner's argument was that you couldn't cut off a head unless there was a body to cut it off from; that he had never had to do such a thing before, and he wasn't going to begin at *his* time of life.

The King's argument was that anything that had a head could be beheaded, and that you weren't to talk nonsense.

The Queen's argument was that if something wasn't done about it in less than no time, she'd have everybody executed, all round. (It was this last remark that had made the whole party look so grave and anxious.)

Alice could think of nothing else to say but, "It belongs to the Duchess; you'd better ask *her* about it."

"She's in prison," the Queen said to the executioner. "Fetch her here." And the executioner went off like an arrow.

The Cat's head began fading away the moment he was gone, and, by the time he had come back with the Duchess, it had entirely disappeared; so the King and the executioner ran wildly up and down, looking for it, while the rest of the party went back to the game.

"You can't think how glad I am to see you again, you dear old thing!" said the Duchess, as she tucked her arm affectionately into Alice's, and they walked off together.

Alice was very glad to find her in such a pleasant temper, and thought to herself that perhaps it was only the pepper that had made her so savage when they met in the kitchen.

"When *I'm* a duchess," she said to herself (not in a very hopeful tone, though), "I won't have any pepper in my kitchen *at all*. Soup does very well without— Maybe it's always pepper that makes people hot-tempered," she went on, very much pleased at having found out a new kind of rule, "and vinegar that makes them sour—and camomile that makes them bitter—and—and barley sugar and such things that make children sweet-tempered. I only wish people knew *that;* then they wouldn't be so stingy about it, you know—"

She had quite forgotten the Duchess by this time, and was a little startled when she heard her voice close to her ear. "You're thinking about something, my dear, and that makes you forget to talk. I can't tell you just now what the moral of that is, but I shall remember it in a bit."

"Perhaps it hasn't one," Alice ventured to remark.

"Tut, tut, child!" said the Duchess. "Everything's got a moral, if only you can find it." And she squeezed herself up closer to Alice's side as she spoke.

Alice did not much like her keeping so close to her: first, because the Duchess was *very* ugly; and secondly, because she was exactly the right height to rest her chin on Alice's shoulder, and it was an uncomfortably sharp chin. However, she did not like to be rude, so she bore it as well as she could.

"The game's going on rather better now," she said, by way of keeping up the conversation a little.

"'Tis so," said the Duchess; "and the moral of that is— 'Oh, 'tis love, 'tis love, that makes the world go round!'"

"Somebody said," Alice whispered, "that it's done by everybody minding their own business!"

"Ah well! It means much the same thing," said the Duchess, digging her sharp little chin into Alice's shoulder as she added, "and the moral of *that* is—'Take care of the sense, and the sounds will take care of themselves.'"

"How fond she is of finding morals in things!" Alice thought to herself.

"I daresay you're wondering why I don't put my arm round your waist," the Duchess said, after a pause. "The reason is that I'm doubtful about the temper of your flamingo. Shall I try the experiment?"

"He might bite," Alice cautiously replied, not feeling at all anxious to have the experiment tried.

"Very true," said the Duchess: "flamingos and mustard both bite. And the moral of that is—'Birds of a feather flock together.'"

"Only mustard isn't a bird," Alice remarked.

"Right, as usual," said the Duchess; "what a clear way you have of putting things!"

"It's a mineral, I *think*," said Alice.

"Of course it is," said the Duchess, who seemed ready to agree to everything that Alice said. "There's a large mustard machine near here. And the moral of that is—'The more there is of mine, the less there is of yours.'"

"Oh, I know!" exclaimed Alice, who had not attended to this last remark. "It's a vegetable. It doesn't look like one, but it is."

"I quite agree with you," said the Duchess; "and the moral of that is—'Be what you would seem to be'—or, if you'd like it put more simply—'Never imagine yourself not to be otherwise than what it might appear to others that what you were or might have been was not otherwise than what you had been would have appeared to them to be otherwise.'"

"I think I should understand that better," Alice said very politely, "if I had it written down; but I can't quite follow it as you say it."

"That's nothing to what I could say if I chose," the Duchess replied, in a pleased tone.

"Pray don't trouble yourself to say it any longer than that," said Alice.

"Oh, don't talk about trouble!" said the Duchess. "I make you a present of everything I've said as yet."

"A cheap sort of present!" thought Alice. "I'm glad people don't give birthday presents like that!" But she did not venture to say it out loud.

"Thinking again?" the Duchess asked, with another dig of her sharp little chin.

"I've a right to think," said Alice sharply, for she was beginning to feel a little worried.

"Just about as much right," said the Duchess, "as pigs have to fly; and the m—"

But here, to Alice's great surprise, the Duchess's voice died away, even in the middle of her favorite word 'moral,' and the arm that was linked into hers began to tremble. Alice looked up, and there stood the Queen in front of them, with her arms folded, frowning like a thunderstorm.

"A fine day, your Majesty!" the Duchess began in a low, weak voice.

"Now, I give you fair warning," shouted the Queen, stamping on the ground as she spoke; "either you or your head must be off, and that in about half no time! Take your choice!"

The Duchess took her choice, and was gone in a moment.

"Let's go on with the game," the Queen said to Alice; and Alice was too much frightened to say a word, but slowly followed her back to the croquet ground.

The other guests had taken advantage of the Queen's absence, and were resting in the shade; however, the moment they saw her, they hurried back to the game, the Queen merely remarking that a moment's delay would cost them their lives.

All the time they were playing the Queen never left off quarreling with the other players and shouting, "Off with his head" or "Off with her head!" Those whom she sentenced were taken into custody by the soldiers, who of course had to leave off being arches to do this, so that, by the end of half an hour or so, there were no arches left, and all the players, except the King, the Queen, and Alice, were in custody and under sentence of execution.

Then the Queen left off, quite out of breath, and said to Alice, "Have you seen the Mock Turtle yet?"

"No," said Alice. "I don't even know what a Mock Turtle is."

"It's the thing Mock Turtle Soup is made from," said the Queen.

"I never saw one, or heard of one," said Alice.

"Come on, then," said the Queen, "and he shall tell you his history."

As they walked off together, Alice heard the King say in a low voice, to the company, generally, "You are all pardoned." "Come, *that's* a good thing!" she said to herself, for she had felt quite unhappy at the number of executions the Queen had ordered.

They very soon came upon a Gryphon, lying fast asleep in the sun. (If you don't know what a Gryphon is, look at the picture on the next page.) "Up, lazy thing!" said the Queen, "and take this young lady to see the Mock Turtle, and to hear his history. I must go back and see after some executions I have ordered"; and she walked off, leaving Alice alone with the Gryphon. Alice did not quite like the look of the creature, but on the whole she thought it would be quite as safe to stay with it as to go after that savage Queen; so she waited.

The Gryphon sat up and rubbed its eyes; then it watched the Queen till she was out of sight; then it chuckled. "What fun!" said the Gryphon, half to itself, half to Alice.

"What *is* the fun?" said Alice.

"Why, *she*," said the Gryphon. "It's all her fancy, that: they never executes nobody, you know. Come on!"

"Everybody says 'come on!' here," thought Alice, as she went slowly after it; "I never was so ordered about before, in all my life, never!"

They had not gone far before they saw the Mock Turtle in the distance, sitting sad and lonely on a little ledge of rock, and, as they came nearer, Alice could hear him sighing as if his heart

would break. She pitied him deeply. "What is his sorrow?" she asked the Gryphon. And the Gryphon answered, very nearly in the same words as before, "It's all his fancy, that: he hasn't got no sorrow, you know. Come on!"

So they went up to the Mock Turtle, who looked at them with large eyes full of tears, but said nothing.

"This here young lady," said the Gryphon, "she wants for to know your history, she do."

"I'll tell it her," said the Mock Turtle in a deep, hollow tone. "Sit down, both of you, and don't speak a word till I've finished."

So they sat down, and nobody spoke for some minutes. Alice thought to herself, "I don't see how he can *ever* finish, if he doesn't begin." But she waited patiently.

"Once," said the Mock Turtle at last, with a deep sigh, "I was a real Turtle."

These words were followed by a very long silence, broken only by an occasional exclamation of "Hjckrrh!" from the Gryphon, and the constant heavy sobbing of the Mock Turtle. Alice was very nearly getting up and saying, "Thank you, Sir, for your interesting story," but she could not help thinking there *must* be more to come, so she sat still and said nothing.

"When we were little," the Mock Turtle went on at last, more calmly, though still sobbing a little now and then, "we went to school in the sea. The master was an old Turtle—we used to call him Tortoise—"

"Why did you call him Tortoise, if he wasn't one?" Alice asked.

"We called him Tortoise because he taught us," said the Mock Turtle angrily. "Really you are very dull!"

"You ought to be ashamed of yourself for asking such a simple question," added the Gryphon; and then they both sat silent and looked at poor Alice, who felt ready to sink into the earth. At last the Gryphon said to the Mock Turtle, "Drive on, old fellow! Don't be all day about it!" and he went on in these words: "Yes, we went to school in the sea, though you mayn't believe it—"

"I never said I didn't!" interrupted Alice.

"You did," said the Mock Turtle.

"Hold your tongue!" added the Gryphon, before Alice could speak again. The Mock Turtle went on. "We had the best of educations—in fact, we went to school every day—"

"*I've* been to a day school, too," said Alice. "You needn't be so proud as all that."

"With extras?" asked the Mock Turtle, a little anxiously.

"Yes," said Alice; "we learned French and music."

"And washing?" said the Mock Turtle.

"Certainly not!" said Alice indignantly.

"Ah! Then yours wasn't a really good school," said the Mock Turtle in a tone of great relief. "Now, at *ours* they had, at the end of the bill, 'French, music, *and washing*—extra.'"

"You couldn't have wanted it much," said Alice, "living at the bottom of the sea."

"I couldn't afford to learn it," said the Mock Turtle with a sigh. "I only took the regular course."

"What was that?" inquired Alice.

"Reeling and Writhing, of course, to begin with," the Mock Turtle replied; "and then the different branches of Arithmetic—Ambition, Distraction, Uglification, and Derision."

"I never heard of Uglification," Alice ventured to say. "What is it?"

The Gryphon lifted up both its paws in surprise. "Never heard of uglifying!" it exclaimed. "You know what to beautify is, I suppose?"

"Yes," said Alice doubtfully: "it means—to—make—anything—prettier."

"Well, then," the Gryphon went on, "if you don't know what to uglify is, you *are* a simpleton."

Alice did not feel encouraged to ask any more questions about it; so she turned to the Mock Turtle, and said, "What else had you to learn?"

"Well, there was Mystery," the Mock Turtle replied, counting off the subjects on his flappers—"Mystery, ancient and modern, with Seaography; then Drawling—the Drawling master was an old conger eel that used to come once a week; *he* taught us Drawling, Stretching, and Fainting in Coils."

"What was *that* like?" said Alice.

"Well, I can't show it to you, myself," the Mock Turtle said; "I'm too stiff. And the Gryphon never learned it."

"Hadn't time," said the Gryphon; "I went to the Classical master, though. He was an old crab, *he* was."

"I never went to him," the Mock Turtle said with a sigh. "He taught Laughing and Grief, they used to say."

"So he did, so he did," said the Gryphon, sighing in his turn; and both creatures hid their faces in their paws.

"And how many hours a day did you do lessons?" said Alice, in a hurry to change the subject.

"Ten hours the first day," said the Mock Turtle; "nine the next, and so on."

"What a curious plan!" exclaimed Alice.

"That's the reason they're called lessons," the Gryphon remarked; "because they lessen from day to day."

This was quite a new idea to Alice, and she thought it over a little before she made her next remark. "Then the eleventh day must have been a holiday?"

"Of course it was," said the Mock Turtle.

"And how did you manage on the twelfth?" Alice went on eagerly.

"That's enough about lessons," the Gryphon interrupted in a very decided tone. "Tell her something about the games now."

CHAPTER X: *The Lobster Quadrille*

THE MOCK TURTLE SIGHED DEEPLY, and drew the back of one flapper across his eyes. He looked at Alice and tried to speak, but, for a minute or two, sobs choked his voice. "Same as if he had a bone in his throat," said the Gryphon; and it set to work shaking him and punching him in the back. At last the Mock Turtle recovered his voice, and, with tears running down his cheeks, he went on again:

"You may not have lived much under the sea—" ("I haven't," said Alice) "—and perhaps you were never even introduced to a lobster—" (Alice began to say, "I once tasted—" but checked herself hastily, and said, "No, never") "—so you can have no idea what a delightful thing a Lobster Quadrille is!"

"No, indeed," said Alice. "What sort of a dance is it?"

"Why," said the Gryphon, "you first form into a line along the seashore—"

"Two lines!" cried the Mock Turtle. "Seals, turtles, salmon, and so on; then, when you've cleared all the jellyfish out of the way—"

"*That* generally takes some time," interrupted the Gryphon.

"—you advance twice—"

"Each with a lobster as a partner!" cried the Gryphon.

"Of course," the Mock Turtle said. "Advance twice, set to partners—"

"—change lobsters, and retire in same order," continued the Gryphon.

"Then, you know," the Mock Turtle went on, "you throw the—"

"The lobsters!" shouted the Gryphon, with a bound into the air.

"—as far out to sea as you can—"

"Swim after them!" screamed the Gryphon.

"Turn a somersault in the sea!" cried the Mock Turtle, capering wildly about.

"Change lobsters again!" yelled the Gryphon at the top of its voice.

"Back to land again, and—that's all the first figure," said the Mock Turtle, suddenly dropping his voice; and the two creatures, who had been jumping about like mad things all this time, sat down again very sadly and quietly, and looked at Alice.

"It must be a very pretty dance," said Alice timidly.

"Would you like to see a little of it?" said the Mock Turtle.

"Very much indeed," said Alice.

"Come, let's try the first figure!" said the Mock Turtle to the Gryphon. "We can do it without lobsters, you know. Which shall sing?"

"Oh, *you* sing," said the Gryphon. "I've forgotten the words."

So they began solemnly dancing round and round Alice, every now and then treading on her toes when they passed too close, and waving their forepaws to mark the time, while the Mock Turtle sang this, very slowly and sadly:

"'*Will you walk a little faster?*' *said a whiting to a snail,*
'*There's a porpoise close behind us, and he's treading
  on my tail.*
See how eagerly the lobsters and the turtles all advance!
*They are waiting on the shingle—will you come and
  join the dance?*
*Will you, won't you, will you, won't you, will you
  join the dance?*
*Will you, won't you, will you, won't you, won't you
  join the dance?**

'*You can really have no notion how delightful it will be
When they take us up and throw us, with the lobsters,
  out to sea!*'
*But the snail replied, '*Too far, too far!*' and gave a
  look askance—*
*Said he thanked the whiting kindly, but he would not join
  the dance.*
*Would not, could not, would not, could not, would
  not join the dance.*
*Would not, could not, would not, could not, could not
  join the dance.*

'*What matters it how far we go?*' *his scaly friend replied.*
'*There is another shore, you know, upon the other side.*
The further off from England the nearer is to France—
*Then turn not pale, beloved snail, but come and join
  the dance.*
*Will you, won't you, will you, won't you, will you
  join the dance?*
*Will you, won't you, will you, won't you, won't you
  join the dance?*'"

"Thank you, it's a very interesting dance to watch," said Alice, feeling very glad that it was over at last; "and I do so like that curious song about the whiting!"

"Oh, as to the whiting," said the Mock Turtle, "they—you've seen them, of course?"

"Yes," said Alice, "I've often seen them at dinn—" she checked herself hastily.

"I don't know where Dinn may be," said the Mock Turtle; "but, if you've seen them so often, of course you know what they're like?"

"I believe so," Alice replied thoughtfully. "They have their tails in their mouths—and they're all over crumbs."

"You're wrong about the crumbs," said the Mock Turtle; "crumbs would all wash off in the sea. But they *have* their tails in their mouths; and the reason is—" Here the Mock Turtle yawned and shut his eyes. "Tell her about the reason and all that," he said to the Gryphon.

"The reason is," said the Gryphon, "that they *would* go with the lobsters to the dance. So they got thrown out to sea. So they had to fall a long way. So they got their tails fast in their mouths. So they couldn't get them out again. That's all."

"Thank you," said Alice, "it's very interesting. I never knew so much about a whiting before."

"I can tell you more than that, if you like," said the Gryphon. "Do you know why it's called a whiting?"

"I never thought about it," said Alice. "Why?"

"*It does the boots and shoes*," the Gryphon replied very solemnly.

Alice was thoroughly puzzled. "Does the boots and shoes!" she repeated in a wondering tone.

"Why, what are *your* shoes done with?" said the Gryphon. "I mean, what makes them so shiny?"

Alice looked down at them, and considered a little before she gave her answer. "They're done with blacking, I believe."

"Boots and shoes under the sea," the Gryphon went on in a deep voice, "are done with whiting. Now you know."

"And what are they made of?" Alice asked in a tone of great curiosity.

"Soles and eels, of course," the Gryphon replied, rather impatiently; "any shrimp could have told you that."

"If I'd been the whiting," said Alice, whose thoughts were still running on the song, "I'd have said to the porpoise 'Keep back, please! We don't want *you* with us!'"

"They were obliged to have him with them," the Mock Turtle

said. "No wise fish would go anywhere without a porpoise."

"Wouldn't it, really?" said Alice, in a tone of great surprise.

"Of course not," said the Mock Turtle. "Why if a fish came to *me*, and told me he was going a journey, I should say, 'With what porpoise?'"

"Don't you mean 'purpose?'" said Alice.

"I mean what I say," the Mock Turtle replied, in an offended tone. And the Gryphon added, "Come, let's hear some of *your* adventures."

"I could tell you my adventures—beginning from this morning," said Alice a little timidly; "but it's no use going back to yesterday, because I was a different person then."

"Explain all that," said the Mock Turtle.

"No, no! The adventures first," said the Gryphon in an impatient tone; "explanations take such a dreadful time."

So Alice began telling them her adventures from the time when she first saw the White Rabbit. She was a little nervous about it, just at first, the two creatures got so close to her, one on each side, and opened their eyes and mouths so *very* wide; but she gained courage as she went on.

Her listeners were perfectly quiet till she got to the part about her repeating "You Are Old, Father William" to the Caterpillar, and the words all coming different, and then the Mock Turtle drew a long breath and said, "That's very curious!"

"It's all about as curious as it can be," said the Gryphon.

"It all came different!" the Mock Turtle repeated thoughtfully. "I should like to hear her try and repeat something now. Tell her to begin." He looked at the Gryphon as if he thought it had some kind of authority over Alice.

"Stand up and repeat ' 'Tis the Voice of the Sluggard,' " said the Gryphon.

"How the creatures order one about, and make one repeat lessons!" thought Alice. "I might just as well be at school at once." However, she got up, and began to repeat it, but her head was so full of the Lobster Quadrille, that she hardly knew what she was saying; and the words came very queer indeed:

> *"'Tis the voice of the Lobster: I heard him declare,*
> *'You have baked me too brown, I must sugar my hair.'*
> *As a duck with his eyelids, so he with his nose*
> *Trims his belt and his buttons, and turns out his toes.*
> *When the sands are all dry, he is gay as a lark,*
> *And will talk in contemptuous tones of the Shark;*
> *But, when the tide rises and sharks are around,*
> *His voice has a timid and tremulous sound."*

"That's different from what *I* used to say when I was a child," said the Gryphon.

"Well, *I* never heard it before," said the Mock Turtle; "but it sounds uncommon nonsense."

Alice said nothing; she had sat down with her face in her hands, wondering if anything would *ever* happen in a natural way again.

"I should like to have it explained," said the Mock Turtle.

"She can't explain it," said the Gryphon hastily. "Go on with the next verse."

"But about his toes?" the Mock Turtle persisted. "How *could* he turn them out with his nose, you know?"

"It's the first position in dancing," Alice said; but she was dreadfully puzzled by the whole thing, and longed to change the subject.

"Go on with the next verse," the Gryphon repeated. "It begins *I passed by his garden.*"

Alice did not dare to disobey, though she felt sure it would all come wrong, and she went on in a trembling voice:

> *"I passed by his garden, and marked, with one eye,*
> *How the Owl and the Panther were sharing a pie:*
> *The Panther took piecrust, and gravy, and meat,*
> *While the Owl had the dish as its share of the treat.*
> *When the pie was all finished, the Owl, as a boon,*
> *Was kindly permitted to pocket the spoon;*
> *While the Panther received knife and fork with a growl,*
> *And concluded the banquet by—"*

"What *is* the use of repeating all that stuff," the Mock Turtle interrupted, "if you don't explain it as you go on? It's by far the most confusing thing that *I* ever heard!"

"Yes, I think you'd better leave off," said the Gryphon, and Alice was only too glad to do so.

"Shall we try another figure of the Lobster Quadrille?" the Gryphon went on. "Or would you like the Mock Turtle to sing you another song?"

"Oh, a song, please, if the Mock Turtle would be so kind," Alice replied, so eagerly that the Gryphon said, in a rather offended tone, "Hm! No accounting for tastes! Sing her 'Turtle Soup,' will you, old fellow?"

The Mock Turtle sighed deeply, and began, in a voice choked with sobs, to sing this:

> *"Beautiful Soup, so rich and green,*
> *Waiting in a hot tureen!*
> *Who for such dainties would not stoop?*
> *Soup of the evening, beautiful Soup!*
> *Soup of the evening, beautiful Soup!*
> *Beau—ootiful Soo—oop!*
> *Beau—ootiful Soo—oop!*
> *Soo—oop of the e—e—evening,*
> *Beautiful, beautiful Soup!*
>
> *Beautiful Soup! Who cares for fish,*
> *Game, or any other dish?*
> *Who would not give all else for two p*
> *ennyworth only of beautiful Soup?*
> *Pennyworth only of beautiful Soup?*
> *Beau—ootiful Soo—oop!*
> *Beau—ootiful Soo—oop!*
> *Soo—oop of the e—e—evening,*
> *Beautiful, beauti—FUL SOUP!"*

"Chorus again!" cried the Gryphon, and the Mock Turtle had just begun to repeat it, when a cry of "The trial's beginning!" was heard in the distance.

"Come on!" cried the Gryphon, and, taking Alice by the hand, it hurried off, without waiting for the end of the song.

"What trial is it?" Alice panted as she ran; but the Gryphon only answered, "Come on!" and ran the faster, while more and more faintly came, carried on the breeze that followed them, the melancholy words:

> "Soo—oop of the e—e—evening,
>   Beautiful, beautiful Soup!"

CHAPTER XI: *Who Stole the Tarts?*

THE KING AND QUEEN OF HEARTS were seated on their throne when they arrived, with a great crowd assembled about them— all sorts of little birds and beasts, as well as the whole pack of cards; the Knave was standing before them, in chains, with a soldier on each side to guard him; and near the King was the White Rabbit, with a trumpet in one hand, and a scroll of parchment in the other.

In the very middle of the court was a table, with a large dish of tarts upon it; they looked so good that it made Alice quite hungry to look at them— "I wish they'd get the trial done," she thought, "and hand round the refreshments!" But there seemed to be no chance of this; so she began looking at everything about her to pass away the time.

Alice had never been in a court of justice before, but she had read about them in books, and she was quite pleased to find that she knew the name of nearly everything there. "That's the judge," she said to herself, "because of his great wig."

The judge, by the way, was the King; and, as he wore his crown over the wig, he did not look at all comfortable, and it was certainly not becoming.

"And that's the jury box," thought Alice; "and those twelve creatures," (she was obliged to say "creatures," you see, because some of them were animals, and some were birds) "I suppose they are the jurors." She said this last word two or three times over to herself, being rather proud of it; for she thought, and rightly too, that very few little girls of her age knew the meaning of it all. However, "jurymen" would have done just as well.

The twelve jurors were all writing very busily on slates. "What are they doing?" Alice whispered to the Gryphon. "They can't have anything to put down yet, before the trial's begun."

"They're putting down their names," the Gryphon whispered in reply, "for fear they should forget them before the end of the trial."

"Stupid things!" Alice began in a loud, indignant voice; but she stopped herself hastily, for the White Rabbit cried out, "Silence in the court!" and the King put on his spectacles and looked anxiously round, to make out who was talking.

Alice could see, as well as if she were looking over their shoulders, that all the jurors were writing down "Stupid things!" on their slates, and she could even make out that one of them didn't know how to spell "stupid," and that he had to ask his neighbor to tell him. "A nice muddle their slates'll be in before the trial's over!" thought Alice.

One of the jurors had a pencil that squeaked. This, of course, Alice could *not* stand, and she went round the court and got behind him, and very soon found an opportunity of taking it away. She did it so quickly that the poor little juror (it was Bill, the Lizard) could not make out at all what had become of it; so, after hunting all about for it, he was obliged to write with one finger for the rest of the day; and this was of very little use, as it left no mark on the slate.

"Herald, read the accusation!" said the King.

On this the White Rabbit blew three blasts on the trumpet, and then unrolled the parchment scroll, and read as follows:

"The Queen of Hearts, she made some tarts,
All on a summer day;
The Knave of Hearts, he stole those tarts
And took them quite away!"

"Consider your verdict," the King said to the jury.

"Not yet, not yet!" the Rabbit hastily interrupted. "There's a great deal to come before that!"

"Call the first witness," said the King; and the White Rabbit blew three blasts on the trumpet, and called out, "First witness!"

The first witness was the Hatter. He came in with a teacup in one hand and a piece of bread and butter in the other. "I beg pardon, your Majesty," he began, "for bringing these in; but I hadn't quite finished my tea when I was sent for."

"You ought to have finished," said the King. "When did you begin?"

The Hatter looked at the March Hare, who had followed him into court, arm in arm with the Dormouse. "Fourteenth of March, I *think* it was," he said.

"Fifteenth," said the March Hare.

"Sixteenth," said the Dormouse.

"Write that down," the King said to the jury; and the jury eagerly wrote down all three dates on their slates, and then added them up, and reduced the answer to shillings and pence.

"Take off your hat," the King said to the Hatter.

"It isn't mine," said the Hatter.

"*Stolen!*" the King exclaimed, turning to the jury, who instantly made a memorandum of the fact.

"I keep them to sell," the Hatter added as an explanation. "I've none of my own. I'm a hatter."

Here the Queen put on her spectacles, and began staring hard at the Hatter, who turned pale, and fidgeted.

"Give your evidence," said the King; "and don't be nervous, or I'll have you executed on the spot."

This did not seem to encourage the witness at all: he kept shifting from one foot to the other, looking uneasily at the Queen, and in his confusion he bit a large piece out of his tea-cup instead of the bread and butter.

Just at this moment Alice felt a very curious sensation, which puzzled her a good deal until she made out what it was: she was beginning to grow larger again, and she thought at first she would get up and leave the court; but on second thoughts she decided to remain where she was as long as there was room for her.

"I wish you wouldn't squeeze so," said the Dormouse, who was sitting next to her. "I can hardly breathe."

"I can't help it," said Alice very meekly; "I'm growing."

"You've no right to grow *here*," said the Dormouse.

"Don't talk nonsense," said Alice more boldly; "you know you're growing too."

"Yes, but *I* grow at a reasonable pace," said the Dormouse, "not in that ridiculous fashion." And he got up very sulkily and crossed over to the other side of the court.

All this time the Queen had never left off staring at the Hatter, and, just as the Dormouse crossed the court, she said to one of the officers of the court, "Bring me the list of the singers in the last concert!" on which the wretched Hatter trembled so that he shook off both his shoes.

"Give your evidence," the King repeated angrily, "or I'll have you executed, whether you are nervous or not."

"I'm a poor man, your Majesty," the Hatter began, in a trembling voice, "and I hadn't begun my tea—not above a week or so—and what with the bread and butter getting so thin—and the twinkling of the tea—"

"The twinkling of *what?*" said the King.

"It *began* with the tea," the Hatter replied.

"Of course twinkling *begins* with a *T!*" said the King sharply. "Do you take me for a dunce? Go on!"

"I'm a poor man," the Hatter went on, "and most things twinkled after that—only the March Hare said—"

"I didn't!" the March Hare interrupted in a great hurry.

"You did!" said the Hatter.

"I deny it!" said the March Hare.

"He denies it," said the King. "Leave out that part."

"Well, at any rate, the Dormouse said—" the Hatter went on, looking anxiously round to see if he would deny it too; but the Dormouse denied nothing, being fast asleep.

"After that," continued the Hatter, "I cut some more bread and butter—"

"But what did the Dormouse say?" one of the jury asked.

"That I can't remember," said the Hatter.

"You *must* remember," remarked the King, "or I'll have you executed."

The miserable Hatter dropped his teacup and bread and butter, and went down on one knee. "I'm a poor man, your Majesty," he began.

"You're a *very* poor *speaker*," said the King.

Here one of the guinea pigs cheered, and was immediately suppressed by the officers of the court. (As that is rather a hard word, I will just explain to you how it was done. They had a large canvas bag, which tied up at the mouth with strings; into this they slipped the guinea pig, head first, and then sat upon it.)

"I'm glad I've seen that done," thought Alice. "I've so often read in the newspapers, at the end of trials, 'There was some attempt at applause, which was immediately suppressed by the officers of the court,' and I never understood what it meant till now."

"If that's all you know about it, you may stand down," continued the King.

"I can't go no lower," said the Hatter: "I'm on the floor, as it is."

"Then you may *sit* down," the King replied.

Here the other guinea pig cheered, and was suppressed.

"Come, that finishes the guinea pigs!" thought Alice. "Now we shall get on better."

"I'd rather finish my tea," said the Hatter, with an anxious look at the Queen, who was reading the list of singers.

"You may go," said the King, and the Hatter hurriedly left the court, without even waiting to put his shoes on.

"—and just take his head off outside," the Queen added to one of the officers; but the Hatter was out of sight before the officer could get to the door.

"Call the next witness!" said the King.

The next witness was the Duchess's cook. She carried the pepper-box in her hand, and Alice guessed who it was, even before she got into the court, by the way the people near the door began sneezing all at once.

"Give your evidence," said the King.

"Shan't," said the cook.

The King looked anxiously at the White Rabbit, who said, in a low voice, "Your Majesty must cross-examine *this* witness."

"Well, if I must, I must," the King said with a melancholy air, and, after folding his arms and frowning at the cook till his eyes were nearly out of sight, he said, in a deep voice, "What are tarts made of?"

"Pepper, mostly," said the cook.

"Treacle," said a sleepy voice behind her.

"Collar that Dormouse!" the Queen shrieked out. "Behead that Dormouse! Turn that Dormouse out of court! Suppress him! Pinch him! Off with his whiskers!"

For some minutes the whole court was in confusion, getting the Dormouse turned out, and, by the time they had settled down again, the cook had disappeared.

"Never mind!" said the King, with an air of great relief. "Call the next witness."

And he added in an undertone to the Queen, "Really, my dear, *you* must cross-examine the next witness. It quite makes my forehead ache!"

Alice watched the White Rabbit as he fumbled over the list,

feeling very curious to see what the next witness would be like— "For they haven't got much evidence *yet*," she said to herself. Imagine her surprise, when the White Rabbit read out, at the top of his shrill little voice, the name "Alice!"

CHAPTER XII: *Alice's Evidence*

"HERE!" CRIED ALICE, quite forgetting in the flurry of the moment how large she had grown in the last few minutes, and she jumped up in such a hurry that she tipped over the jury box with the edge of her skirt, upsetting all the jurymen onto the heads of the crowd below, and there they lay sprawling about, reminding her very much of a globe of goldfish she had accidentally upset the week before.

"Oh, I *beg* your pardon!" she exclaimed in a tone of great dismay, and began picking them up again as quickly as she could, for the accident of the goldfish kept running in her head, and she had a vague sort of idea that they must be collected at once and put back into the jury box, or they would die.

"The trial cannot proceed," said the King in a very grave voice, "until all the jurymen are back in their proper places— *all*," he repeated with great emphasis, looking hard at Alice as he said so.

Alice looked at the jury box, and saw that, in her haste, she had put the Lizard in head downwards, and the poor little thing was waving its tail about in a melancholy way, being quite unable to move. She soon got it out again, and put it right; "not that it signifies much," she said to herself; "I think it would be *quite* as much use in the trial one way up as the other."

As soon as the jury had a little recovered from the shock of being upset, and their slates and pencils had been found and handed back to them, they set to work very diligently to write out a history of the accident, all except the Lizard, who seemed too much overcome to do anything but sit with its mouth open, gazing up into the roof of the court.

"What do you know about this business?" the King said to Alice.

"Nothing," said Alice.

"Nothing *whatever?*" persisted the King.

"Nothing whatever," said Alice.

"That's very important," the King said, turning to the jury. They were just beginning to write this down on their slates, when the White Rabbit interrupted: "*Un*important, your Majesty means, of course," he said in a very respectful tone, but frowning and making faces at him as he spoke.

"*Un*important, of course, I meant," the King hastily said, and went on to himself in an undertone, "important—unimportant— unimportant—important—" as if he were trying which word sounded best.

Some of the jury wrote it down "important," and some "unimportant." Alice could see this, as she was near enough to look over their slates; "but it doesn't matter a bit," she thought to herself.

At this moment the King, who had been for some time busily writing in his notebook, called out, "Silence!" and read out from his book, "Rule Forty-two. *All persons more than a mile high to leave the court.*"

Everybody looked at Alice.

"*I'm* not a mile high," said Alice.

"You are," said the King.

"Nearly two miles high," added the Queen.

"Well, I shan't go, at any rate," said Alice. "Besides, that's not a regular rule: you invented it just now."

"It's the oldest rule in the book," said the King.

"Then it ought to be Number One," said Alice.

The King turned pale, and shut his notebook hastily. "Consider your verdict," he said to the jury, in a low trembling voice.

"There's more evidence to come yet, please your Majesty," said the White Rabbit, jumping up in a great hurry; "this paper has just been picked up."

"What's in it?" said the Queen.

"I haven't opened it yet," said the White Rabbit; "but it seems to be a letter, written by the prisoner to—to somebody."

"It must have been that," said the King, "unless it was written to nobody, which isn't usual, you know."

"Who is it directed to?" said one of the jurymen.

"It isn't directed at all," said the White Rabbit; "in fact, there's nothing written on the *outside*." He unfolded the paper as he spoke, and added, "It isn't a letter, after all; it's a set of verses."

"Are they in the prisoner's handwriting?" asked another of the jurymen.

"No, they're not," said the White Rabbit, "and that's the queerest thing about it." (The jury all looked puzzled.)

"Please, your Majesty," said the Knave, "I didn't write it, and they can't prove that I did; there's no name signed at the end."

"If you didn't sign it," said the King, "that only makes the matter worse. You *must* have meant some mischief, or else you'd have signed your name like an honest man."

There was a general clapping of hands at this: it was the first really clever thing the King had said that day.

"That *proves* his guilt, of course," said the Queen; "so, off with—"

"It doesn't prove anything of the sort!" said Alice. "Why, you don't even know what they're about!"

"Read them," said the King.

The White Rabbit put on his spectacles. "Where shall I begin, please your Majesty?" he asked.

"Begin at the beginning," the King said, very gravely, "and go on till you come to the end; then stop."

There was dead silence in the court, whilst the White Rabbit read out these verses:

> *"They told me you had been to her,*
> *And mentioned me to him;*
> *She gave me a good character,*
> *But said I could not swim.*
>
> *He sent them word I had not gone*
> *(We know it to be true);*
> *If she should push the matter on,*
> *What would become of you?*

I gave her one, they gave him two,
You gave us three or more;
They all returned from him to you,
Though they were mine before.

If I or she should chance to be
Involved in this affair,
He trusts to you to set them free,
Exactly as we were.

My notion was that you had been
(Before she had this fit)
An obstacle that came between
Him, and ourselves, and it.

Don't let him know she liked them best,
For this must ever be
A secret, kept from all the rest,
Between yourself and me."

"That's the most important piece of evidence we've heard yet," said the King, rubbing his hands; "so now let the jury—"

"If anyone of them can explain it," said Alice (she had grown so large in the last few minutes that she wasn't a bit afraid of interrupting him), "I'll give him sixpence. *I* don't believe there's an atom of meaning in it."

The jury all wrote down on their slates, "*She* doesn't believe there's an atom of meaning in it," but none of them attempted to explain the paper.

"If there's no meaning in it," said the King, "that saves a world of trouble, you know, as we needn't try to find any. And yet I don't know," he went on, spreading out the verses on his knee, and looking at them with one eye; "I seem to see some meaning in them, after all.—*Said I could not swim*—you can't swim, can you?" he added, turning to the Knave.

The Knave shook his head sadly. "Do I look like it?" he said. (Which he certainly did *not*, being made entirely of cardboard.)

"All right, so far," said the King; and he went on muttering over the verses to himself: "*We know it to be true*—that's the jury, of course— *If she should push the matter on*—that must be the Queen— *What would become of you?*— What, indeed!— *I gave her one, they gave him two*—why, that must be what he did with the tarts, you know—"

"But it goes on, *They all returned from him to you*," said Alice.

"Why, there they are!" said the King triumphantly, pointing to the tarts on the table. "Nothing can be clearer than *that*. Then again—*Before she had this fit*—you never had *fits*, my dear, I think?" he said to the Queen.

"Never!" said the Queen furiously, throwing an inkstand at the Lizard as she spoke. (The unfortunate little Bill had left off writing on his slate with one finger, as he found it made no mark; but he now hastily began again, using the ink that was trickling down his face, as long as it lasted.)

"Then the words don't *fit* you," said the King, looking round the court with a smile. There was a dead silence.

"It's a pun!" the King added in an angry tone, and everybody laughed. "Let the jury consider their verdict," the King said, for about the twentieth time that day.

"No, no!" said the Queen. "Sentence first—verdict afterwards."

"Stuff and nonsense!" said Alice loudly. "The idea of having the sentence first!"

"Hold your tongue!" said the Queen, turning purple.

"I won't!" said Alice.

"Off with her head!" the Queen shouted at the top of her voice. Nobody moved.

"Who cares for *you?*" said Alice (she had grown to her full size by this time). "You're nothing but a pack of cards!"

At this the whole pack rose up into the air, and came flying down upon her; she gave a little scream, half of fright and half of anger, and tried to beat them off, and found herself lying on the bank, with her head in the lap of her sister, who was gently brushing away some dead leaves that had fluttered down from the trees upon her face.

"Wake up, Alice dear!" said her sister. "Why, what a long sleep you've had!"

"Oh, I've had such a curious dream!" said Alice. And she told her sister, as well as she could remember them, all these strange Adventures of hers that you have just been reading about; and, when she had finished, her sister kissed her, and said, "It *was* a curious dream, dear, certainly; but now run in to your tea; it's getting late." So Alice got up and ran off, thinking while she ran, as well she might, what a wonderful dream it had been.

But her sister sat still just as she left her, leaning her head on her hand, watching the setting sun, and thinking of little Alice and all her wonderful Adventures, till she too began dreaming after a fashion, and this was her dream:

First, she dreamed about little Alice herself: once again the tiny hands were clasped upon her knee, and the bright eager eyes were looking up into hers—she could hear the very tones of her voice, and see that queer little toss of her head to keep back the wandering hair that *would* always get into her eyes—and still, as she listened, or seemed to listen, the whole place around her became alive with the strange creatures of her little sister's dream.

The long grass rustled at her feet as the White Rabbit hurried by—the frightened Mouse splashed his way through the neighboring pool—she could hear the rattle of the teacups as the March Hare and his friends shared their never-ending meal, and the shrill voice of the Queen ordering off her unfortunate guests to execution—once more the pig baby was sneezing on the Duchess's knee, while plates and dishes crashed around it—once more the shriek of the Gryphon, the squeaking of the Lizard's slate pencil, and the choking of the suppressed guinea pigs, filled the air, mixed up with the distant sob of the miserable Mock Turtle.

So she sat on, with closed eyes, and half believed herself in Wonderland, though she knew she had but to open them again, and all would change to dull reality—the grass would be only rustling in the wind, and the pool rippling to the waving of the reeds—the rattling teacups would change to tinkling sheep bells, and the Queen's shrill cries to the voice of the shepherd boy—and the sneeze of the baby, the shriek of the Gryphon, and all the other queer noises, would change (she knew) to the confused clamor of the busy farmyard—while the lowing of the cattle in the distance would take the place of the Mock Turtle's heavy sobs.

Lastly, she pictured to herself how this same little sister of hers would, in the aftertime, be herself a grown woman; and how she would keep, through all her riper years, the simple and loving heart of her childhood; and how she would gather about her other little children, and make *their* eyes bright and eager with many a strange tale, perhaps even with the dream of Wonderland of long ago; and how she would feel with all their simple sorrows, and find a pleasure in all their simple joys, remembering her own child life, and the happy summer days.

THROUGH
THE LOOKING
GLASS

And What Alice Found There

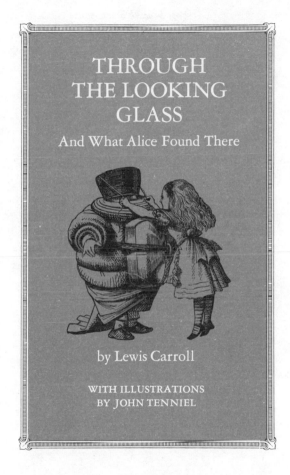

by Lewis Carroll

WITH ILLUSTRATIONS
BY JOHN TENNIEL

A boat, beneath a sunny sky
Lingering onward dreamily
In an evening of July—

Children three that nestle near,
Eager eye and willing ear,
Pleased a simple tale to hear—

Long has paled that sunny sky;
Echoes fade and memories die;
Autumn frosts have slain July.

Still she haunts me, phantomwise,
Alice moving under skies
Never seen by waking eyes.

Children yet, the tale to hear,
Eager eye and willing ear,
Lovingly shall nestle near.

In a Wonderland they lie,
Dreaming as the days go by,
Dreaming as the summers die.

Ever drifting down the stream—
Lingering in the golden gleam—
Life, what is it but a dream?

Editor's note: The initial letters of this poem
when read downward give the full name of
the original Alice—Alice Pleasance Liddell.

CHAPTER I: *Looking-Glass House*

ONE THING WAS CERTAIN, that the *white* kitten had had nothing to do with it—it was the black kitten's fault entirely. For the white kitten had been having its face washed by the old cat for the last quarter of an hour (and bearing it pretty well, considering); so you see that it *couldn't* have had any hand in the mischief.

The way Dinah washed her children's faces was this: first she held the poor thing down by its ear with one paw, and then with the other paw she rubbed its face all over, the wrong way, beginning at the nose; and just now, as I said, she was hard at work on the white kitten, which was lying quite still and trying to purr—no doubt feeling that it was all meant for its good.

But the black kitten had been finished with earlier in the afternoon, and so, while Alice was sitting curled up in a corner of the great armchair half talking to herself and half asleep, the kitten had been having a grand game of romps with the ball of worsted Alice had been trying to wind up, and had been rolling it up and down till it had all come undone again; and there it was, spread over the hearthrug, all knots and tangles, with the kitten running after its own tail in the middle.

"Oh, you wicked, wicked little thing!" cried Alice, catching up the kitten, and giving it a little kiss to make it understand that it was in disgrace. "Really, Dinah ought to have taught you better manners! You *ought*, Dinah, you know you ought!" she added, looking reproachfully at the old cat, and speaking in as cross a voice as she could manage—and then she scrambled back into the armchair, taking the kitten and the worsted with her, and began winding up the ball again. But she didn't get on very fast, as she was talking all the time, sometimes to the kitten, and sometimes to herself.

Kitty sat very demurely on her knee, pretending to watch the progress of the winding, and now and then putting out one paw and gently touching the ball, as if it would be glad to help if it might.

"Do you know what tomorrow is, Kitty?" Alice began. "You'd have guessed if you'd been up in the window with me—only Dinah was making you tidy, so you couldn't. I was watching the boys getting in sticks for the bonfire—and it wants plenty of sticks, Kitty! Only it got so cold, and it snowed so, they had to leave off. Never mind, we'll go and see the bonfire tomorrow." Here Alice wound two or three turns of the worsted round the kitten's neck, just to see how it would look; this led to a scramble, in which the ball rolled down upon the floor, and yards and yards of it got unwound again.

"Do you know, I was so angry, Kitty," Alice went on, as soon as they were comfortably settled again, "when I saw all the mischief you had been doing, I was very nearly opening the window, and putting you out into the snow! And you'd have deserved it, you little mischievous darling! What have you got to say for yourself? Now don't interrupt me!" she went on, holding up one finger. "I'm going to tell you all your faults. Number one: you squeaked twice while Dinah was washing your face this morning. Now you can't deny it. Kitty, I heard you! What's that you say?" (pretending that the kitten was speaking.) "Her paw went into your eye? Well, that's *your* fault, for keeping your eyes open—if you'd shut them tight up, it wouldn't have happened. Now don't make any more excuses, but listen! Number two: you pulled Snowdrop away by the tail just as I had put down the saucer of milk before her! What, you were thirsty, were you? How do you know she wasn't thirsty too? Now for number three: you unwound every bit of the worsted while I wasn't looking!

"That's three faults, Kitty, and you've not been punished for any of them yet. You know I'm saving up all your punishments for Wednesday week— Suppose they had saved up all *my* punishments?" she went on, talking more to herself than the kitten. "What *would* they do at the end of a year? I should be sent to prison, I suppose, when the day came. Or—let me see—suppose each punishment was to be going without a dinner; then, when the miserable day came, I should have to go without fifty dinners at once! Well, I shouldn't mind *that* much! I'd far rather go without them than eat them!

"Do you hear the snow against the windowpanes, Kitty? How nice and soft it sounds! Just as if someone was kissing the window all over outside. I wonder if the snow *loves* the trees and fields, that it kisses them so gently? And then it covers them up snug, you know, with a white quilt; and perhaps it says, 'Go to sleep, darlings, till the summer comes again.' And when they wake up in the summer, Kitty, they dress themselves all in green, and dance about— whenever the wind blows—oh, that's very pretty!" cried Alice, dropping the ball of worsted to clap her hands. "And I do so *wish* it was true! I'm sure the woods look sleepy in the autumn, when the leaves are getting brown.

"Kitty, can you play chess? Now, don't smile, my dear, I'm asking it seriously. Because when we were playing just now, you watched just as if you understood it; and when I said 'Check!' you purred! Well, it *was* a nice check, Kitty, and really I might have won, if it hadn't been for that nasty Knight that came wriggling down among my pieces. Kitty, dear, let's pretend " And here I wish I could tell you half the things Alice used to say, beginning with her favorite phrase, "Let's pretend." She had had quite a long argument with her sister only the day before—all because Alice had begun with "Let's pretend we're kings and queens"; and her sister, who liked being very exact, had argued that they couldn't, because there were only two of them, and Alice had been reduced at last to say, "Well, *you* can be one of them, then, and I'll be all the rest." And once she had really frightened her old nurse by shouting suddenly in her ear, "Nurse! Do let's pretend that I'm a hungry hyena, and you're a bone!"

But this is taking us away from Alice's speech to the kitten. "Let's pretend that you're the Red Queen, Kitty! Do you know, I think if you sat up and folded your arms, you'd look exactly like her. Now do try, there's a dear!" And Alice got the Red Queen off the table, and set it up before the kitten as a model for it to imitate; however, the thing didn't succeed, principally, Alice said, because the kitten wouldn't fold its arms properly. So, to punish it, she held it up to the Looking Glass, that it might see how sulky it was. "—And if you're not good directly," she added, "I'll put you through into Looking-Glass House. How would you like *that?*

"Now, if you'll only attend, Kitty, and not talk so much, I'll tell you all my ideas about Looking-Glass House. First, there's the room you can see through the glass—that's just the same as our drawing room, only the things go the other way. I can see all of it when I get upon a chair—all but the bit just behind the fireplace. Oh! I do so wish I could see *that* bit! I want so much to know whether they've a fire in the winter; you never *can* tell, you know, unless our fire smokes, and then smoke comes up in that room too—but that may be only pretense, just to make it look as if they had a fire. Well then, the books are something like our books, only the words go the wrong way: I know *that*, because I've held up one of our books to the glass, and then they hold up one in the other room.

"How would you like to live in Looking-Glass House, Kitty? I wonder if they'd give you milk in there? Perhaps Looking-Glass milk isn't good to drink—but oh, Kitty! now we come to the passage. You can just see a little *peep* of the passage in Looking-Glass House, if you leave the door of our drawing room wide open, and it's very like our passage as far as you can see, only you know it may be quite different on beyond. Oh, Kitty, how nice it would be if we could only get through into Looking-Glass House! I'm sure

it's got, oh! such beautiful things in it! Let's pretend there's a way
of getting through into it, somehow, Kitty. Let's pretend the glass
has got all soft, like gauze, so that we can get through. Why, it's
turning into a sort of mist now, I declare! It'll be easy enough to
get through—" She was up on the chimneypiece while she said
this, though she hardly knew how she had got there. And certainly the glass *was* beginning to melt away, just like a bright
silvery mist.

In another moment Alice was through the glass, and had jumped lightly down into the Looking-Glass room. The very first thing she did was to look whether there was a fire in the fireplace, and she was quite pleased to find that there was a real one, blazing away as brightly as the one she had left behind. "So I shall be as warm here as I was in the old room," thought Alice; "warmer, in fact, because there'll be no one here to scold me away from the fire. Oh, what fun it'll be, when they see me through the glass in here, and can't get at me!" Then she began looking about, and noticed that what could be seen from the old room was quite common and uninteresting, but that all the rest was as different as possible. For instance, the pictures on the wall next the fire seemed to be all alive, and the very clock on the chimneypiece (you know you can only see the back of it in the Looking Glass) had got the face of a little old man, and grinned at her.

"They don't keep this room so tidy as the other," Alice thought to herself, as she noticed several of the chessmen down in the hearth among the cinders; but in another moment, with a little "Oh!" of surprise, she was down on her hands and knees watching them. The chessmen were walking about, two and two!

"Here are the Red King and the Red Queen," Alice said (in a whisper, for fear of frightening them), "and there are the White King and the White Queen sitting on the edge of the shovel—and here are two Castles walking arm in arm— I don't think they can hear me," she went on, as she put her head closer down, "and I'm nearly sure they can't see me. I feel somehow as if I was getting invisible—"

Here something began squeaking on the table behind Alice, and made her turn her head just in time to see one of the White Pawns roll over and begin kicking; she watched it with great curiosity to see what would happen next.

"It is the voice of my child!" the White Queen cried out, as she rushed past the King so violently that she knocked him over among the cinders. "My precious Lily! My imperial kitten!" and she began scrambling wildly up the side of the fender.

"Imperial fiddlestick!" said the King, rubbing his nose, which had been hurt by the fall. He had a right to be a *little* annoyed with the Queen, for he was covered with ashes from head to foot.

Alice was very anxious to be of use, and, as the poor little Lily was nearly screaming herself into a fit, she hastily picked up the Queen and set her on the table by the side of her noisy little daughter.

The Queen gasped, and sat down; the rapid journey through the air had quite taken away her breath, and for a minute or two she could do nothing but hug the little Lily in silence. As soon as she had recovered her breath a little, she called out to the White King, who was sitting sulkily among the ashes, "Mind the volcano!"

"What volcano?" said the King, looking up anxiously into the fire, as if he thought that was the most likely place to find one.

"Blew—me—up," panted the Queen, who was still a little out of breath. "Mind you come up—the regular way—don't get blown up!"

Alice watched the White King as he slowly struggled up from bar to bar, till at last she said, "Why, you'll be hours and hours getting to the table, at that rate. I'd far better help you, hadn't I?" But the King took no notice of the question: it was quite clear that he could neither hear her nor see her.

So Alice picked him up very gently, and lifted him across more slowly than she had lifted the Queen, that she mightn't take his breath away; but, before she put him on the table, she thought she might as well dust him a little, he was so covered with ashes.

She said afterwards that she had never seen in all her life such a face as the King made, when he found himself held in the air by an invisible hand, and being dusted: he was far too much astonished to cry out, but his eyes and his mouth went on getting larger and larger, and rounder and rounder, till her hand shook so with laughing that she nearly let him drop upon the floor.

"Oh, _please_ don't make such faces, my dear!" she cried out, quite forgetting that the King couldn't hear her. "You make me laugh so that I can hardly hold you! And don't keep your mouth so wide open! All the ashes will get into it— There, now I think you're tidy

394

enough!" she added, as she smoothed his hair, and set him upon the table near the Queen.

The King immediately fell flat on his back, and lay perfectly still; and Alice was a little alarmed at what she had done, and went round the room to see if she could find any water to throw over him. However, she could find nothing but a bottle of ink, and when she got back with it she found he had recovered, and he and the Queen were talking together in a frightened whisper—so low that Alice could hardly hear what they said.

The King was saying, "I assure you, my dear, I turned cold to the very ends of my whiskers!"

To which the Queen replied, "You haven't got any whiskers."

"The horror of that moment," the King went on, "I shall never, *never* forget!"

"You will, though," the Queen said, "if you don't make a memorandum of it."

Alice looked on with great interest as the King took an enormous memorandum book out of his pocket, and began writing. A sudden thought struck her, and she took hold of the end of the pencil, which came some way over his shoulder, and began writing for him.

The poor King looked puzzled and unhappy, and struggled with the pencil for some time without saying anything; but Alice was too strong for him, and at last he panted out, "My dear! I really *must* get a thinner pencil. I can't manage this one a bit: it writes all manner of things that I don't intend—"

"What manner of things?" said the Queen, looking over the book (in which Alice had put *The White Knight is sliding down the poker. He balances very badly.*). "That's not a memorandum of *your* feelings!"

There was a book lying near Alice on the table, and while she sat watching the White King (for she was still a little anxious about him, and had the ink all ready to throw over him, in case he fainted again), she turned over the leaves, to find some part that she could read "—for it's all in some language I don't know," she said to herself.

It was like this:

ЈАВВЕ****ЯWOCKY

'Тwas brillig, and the slithy toves
Did gyre and gimble in the wabe;
All mimsy were the borogoves,
And the mome raths outgrabe.

She puzzled over this for some time, but at last a bright thought struck her. "Why, it's a Looking-Glass book, of course! And, if I hold it up to a glass, the words will all go the right way again." This was the poem that Alice read:

JABBERWOCKY

'Twas brillig, and the slithy toves
    Did gyre and gimble in the wabe;
All mimsy were the borogoves,
    And the mome raths outgrabe.

"Beware the Jabberwock, my son!
    The jaws that bite, the claws that catch!
Beware the Jubjub bird, and shun
    The frumious Bandersnatch!"

He took his vorpal sword in hand:
    Long time the manxome foe he sought—
So rested he by the Tumtum tree,
    And stood awhile in thought.

And, as in uffish thought he stood,
    The Jabberwock, with eyes of flame,
Came whiffling through the tulgey wood,
    And burbled as it came!

One, two! One, two! And through and through
    The vorpal blade went snicker-snack!
He left it dead, and with its head
    He went galumphing back.

"And hast thou slain the Jabberwock?
  Come to my arms, my beamish boy!
O frabjous day! Callooh! Callay!"
  He chortled in his joy.

'Twas brillig, and the slithy toves
  Did gyre and gimble in the wabe;
All mimsy were the borogoves,
  And the mome raths outgrabe.

"It seems very pretty," she said when she had finished it, "but it's *rather* hard to understand!" (You see, she didn't like to confess, even to herself, that she couldn't make it out at all.) "Somehow it seems to fill my head with ideas—only I don't exactly know what they are! However, *somebody* killed *something*: that's clear, at any rate—

"But oh," thought Alice, suddenly jumping up, "if I don't make haste, I shall have to go back through the Looking Glass before I've seen what the rest of the house is like! Let's have a look at the garden first!" She was out of the room in a moment, and ran downstairs—or, at least, it wasn't exactly running, but a new invention for getting downstairs quickly and easily, as Alice said to herself. She just kept the tips of her fingers on the handrail, and floated gently down without even touching the stairs with her feet; then she floated on through the hall, and would have gone straight out at the door in the same way, if she hadn't caught hold of the doorpost. She was getting a little giddy with so much floating in the air, and was rather glad to find herself walking again in the natural way.

CHAPTER II: *The Garden of Live Flowers*

"I SHOULD SEE THE GARDEN far better," said Alice to herself, "if I could get to the top of that hill; and here's a path that leads straight to it—at least, no, it doesn't do *that*—" (after going a few yards along the path, and turning several sharp corners) "but I suppose it will at last. But how curiously it twists! It's more like a cork-screw than a path! Well *this* turn goes to the hill, I suppose—no, it doesn't! This goes straight back to the house! Well then, I'll try it the other way."

And so she did: wandering up and down, and trying turn after turn, but always coming back to the house, do what she would. Indeed, once, when she turned a corner rather more quickly than usual, she ran against it before she could stop herself.

"It's no use talking about it," Alice said, looking up at the house and pretending it was arguing with her. "I'm *not* going in again yet. I know I should have to get through

the Looking Glass again—back into the old room—and there'd be
an end of all my adventures!"

So, resolutely turning her back upon the house, she set out once
more down the path, determined to keep straight on till she got
to the hill. For a few minutes all went on well, and she was just
saying, "I really *shall* do it this time—" when the path gave a sudden twist and shook itself (as she described it afterwards), and the
next moment she found herself actually walking in at the door.

"Oh, it's too bad!" she cried. "I never saw such a house for getting in the way! Never!"

However, there was the hill full in sight, so there was nothing
to be done but start again. This time she came upon a large
flower bed, with a border of daisies, and a willow tree growing
in the middle.

"O Tiger Lily," said Alice, addressing herself to one that was
waving gracefully about in the wind, "I *wish* you could talk!"

"We *can* talk," said the Tiger Lily, "when there's anybody worth
talking to."

Alice was so astonished that she couldn't speak for a minute: it
quite seemed to take her breath away. At length, as the Tiger Lily
only went on waving about, she spoke again, in a timid voice—
almost in a whisper. "And can *all* the flowers talk?"

"As well as *you* can," said the Tiger Lily. "And a great deal
louder."

"It isn't manners for us to begin, you know," said the Rose, "and
I really was wondering when you'd speak! Said I to myself, 'Her
face has got *some* sense in it, though it's not a clever one!' Still,
you're the right color, and that goes a long way."

"I don't care about the color," the Tiger Lily remarked. "If
only her petals curled up a little more, she'd be all right."

Alice didn't like being criticized, so she began asking questions.
"Aren't you sometimes frightened at being planted out here, with
nobody to take care of you?"

"There's the tree in the middle," said the Rose. "What else is it
good for?"

"But what could it do, if any danger came?" Alice asked.

"It could bark," said the Rose.

"It says 'Boughwough!'" cried a Daisy. "That's why its branches are called boughs!"

"Didn't you know *that?*" cried another Daisy. And here they all began shouting together, till the air seemed quite full of little shrill voices. "Silence, every one of you!" cried the Tiger Lily, waving itself passionately from side to side, and trembling with excitement. "They know I can't get at them," it panted, bending its quivering head towards Alice, "or they wouldn't dare to do it!"

"Never mind!" Alice said in a soothing tone, and, stooping down to the daisies, who were just beginning again, she whispered, "If you don't hold your tongues, I'll pick you!"

There was silence in a moment, and several of the pink daisies turned white.

"That's right!" said the Tiger Lily. "The daisies are worst of all. When one speaks, they all begin together, and it's enough to make one wither to hear the way they go on!"

"How is it you can all talk so nicely?" Alice said, hoping to get it into a better temper by a compliment. "I've been in many gardens before, but none of the flowers could talk."

"Put your hand down, and feel the ground," said the Tiger Lily. "Then you'll know why."

Alice did so. "It's very hard," she said, "but I don't see what that has to do with it."

"In most gardens," the Tiger Lily said, "they make the beds too soft—so that the flowers are always asleep."

This sounded a very good reason, and Alice was quite pleased to know it. "I never thought of that before!" she said.

"It's *my* opinion that you never think *at all*," the Rose said, in a rather severe tone.

"I never saw anybody that looked stupider," a Violet said, so suddenly that Alice quite jumped, for it hadn't spoken before.

"Hold *your* tongue!" cried the Tiger Lily. "As if *you* ever saw anybody! You keep your head under the leaves, and snore away there, till you know no more what's going on in the world than if you were a bud!"

"Are there any more people in the garden besides me?" Alice said, not choosing to notice the Rose's last remark.

"There's one other flower in the garden that can move about like you," said the Rose. "I wonder how you do it—" ("You're always wondering," said the Tiger Lily) "—but she's more bushy than you are."

"Is she like me?" Alice asked eagerly, for the thought crossed her mind, "There's another little girl in the garden, somewhere!"

"Well, she has the same awkward shape as you," the Rose said; "but she's redder—and her petals are shorter, I think."

"They're done up close, like a dahlia," said the Tiger Lily; "not tumbled about, like yours."

"But that's not *your* fault," the Rose added kindly. "You're beginning to fade, you know—and then one can't help one's petals getting a little untidy."

Alice didn't like this idea at all; so, to change the subject, she asked, "Does she ever come out here?"

"I daresay you'll see her soon," said the Rose. "She's one of the kind that has nine spikes, you know."

"Where does she wear them?" Alice asked with some curiosity.

"Why, all round her head, of course," the Rose replied. "I was wondering *you* hadn't got some too. I thought it was the regular rule."

"She's coming!" cried the Larkspur. "I hear her footstep, thump, thump, along the gravel walk!"

Alice looked round eagerly and found that it was the Red Queen. "She's grown a good deal!" was her first remark. She had indeed: when Alice first found her in the ashes, she had been only three inches high—and here she was, half a head taller than Alice herself!

"It's the fresh air that does it," said the Rose; "wonderfully fine air it is, out here."

"I think I'll go and meet her," said Alice, for, though the flowers were interesting enough, she felt that it would be far grander to have a talk with a real Queen.

"You can't possibly do that," said the Rose. "I should advise you to walk the other way."

This sounded nonsense to Alice, so she said nothing, but set off at once towards the Red Queen. To her surprise she lost sight of her in a moment, and found herself walking in at the front door again. A little provoked, she drew back, and, after looking everywhere for the Queen (whom she spied out at last, a long way off), she thought she would try the plan, this time, of walking in the opposite direction.

It succeeded beautifully. She had not been walking a minute before she found herself face-to-face with the Red Queen, and full in sight of the hill she had been so long aiming at.

"Where do you come from?" said the Red Queen. "And where are you going? Look up, speak nicely, and don't twiddle your fingers all the time."

Alice attended to all these directions, and explained, as well as she could, that she had lost her way.

"I don't know what you mean by *your* way," said the Queen; "all the ways about here belong to *me*—but why did you come out here at all?" she added in a kinder tone. "Curtsy while you're thinking what to say. It saves time."

Alice wondered a little at this, but she was too much in awe of the Queen to disbelieve it. "I'll try it when I go home," she thought to herself, "the next time I'm a little late for dinner."

"It's time for you to answer now," the Queen said, looking at her watch; "open your mouth a *little* wider when you speak, and always say 'your Majesty.' "

"I only wanted to see what the garden was like, your Majesty—"

"That's right," said the Queen, patting her on the head, which Alice didn't like at all; "though, when you say 'garden'—*I've* seen gardens, compared with which this would be a wilderness."

Alice didn't dare to argue the point, but went on: "—and I thought I'd try and find my way to the top of that hill—"

"When you say 'hill,' " the Queen interrupted, "*I* could show you hills, in comparison with which you'd call that a valley."

"No, I shouldn't," said Alice, surprised into contradicting her at last; "a hill *can't* be a valley, you know. That would be nonsense—"

The Red Queen shook her head. "You may call it 'nonsense' if you like," she said, "but *I've* heard nonsense, compared with which that would be as sensible as a dictionary!"

Alice curtsied again, as she was afraid from the Queen's tone that she was a *little* offended; and they walked on in silence till they got to the top of the little hill.

For some minutes Alice stood without speaking, looking out in

all directions over the country—and a most curious country it was. There were a number of tiny little brooks running straight across it from side to side, and the ground between was divided up into squares by a number of little green hedges that reached from brook to brook.

"I declare it's marked out just like a large chessboard!" Alice said at last. "There ought to be some men moving about somewhere—and so there are!" she added in a tone of delight, and her heart began to beat quick with excitement as she went on. "It's a great huge game of chess that's being played—all over the world— if this *is* the world at all, you know. Oh, what fun it is! How I *wish*

I was one of them! I wouldn't mind being a Pawn, if only I might join—though of course I should *like* to be a Queen, best."

She glanced rather shyly at the real Queen as she said this, but her companion only smiled pleasantly, and said, "That's easily managed. You can be the White Queen's Pawn, if you like, as Lily's too young to play; and you're in the Second Square to begin with; when you get to the Eighth Square you'll be a Queen—" Just at this moment, somehow or other, they began to run.

Alice never could quite make out, in thinking it over afterwards, how it was that they began; all she remembers is that they were running hand in hand, and the Queen went so fast that it was all she could do to keep up with her; and still the Queen kept crying, "Faster! Faster!" but Alice felt she *could not* go faster, though she had no breath left to say so.

The most curious part of the thing was that the trees and the other things round them never changed their places at all: however fast they went, they never seemed to pass anything. "I wonder if all the things move along with us?" thought poor puzzled Alice. And the Queen seemed to guess her thoughts, for she cried, "Faster! Don't try to talk!"

Not that Alice had any idea of doing *that*. She felt as if she would never be able to talk again, she was getting so much out of breath; and still the Queen cried, "Faster! Faster!" and dragged her along. "Are we nearly there?" Alice managed to pant out at last.

"Nearly there!" the Queen repeated. "Why, we passed it ten minutes ago! Faster!" And they ran on for a time in silence, with the wind whistling in Alice's ears, and almost blowing her hair off her head, she fancied.

"Now! Now!" cried the Queen. "Faster! Faster!" And they went so fast that at last they seemed to skim through the air, hardly touching the ground with their feet, till suddenly, just as Alice was getting quite exhausted, they stopped, and she found herself sitting on the ground, breathless and giddy.

The Queen propped her up against a tree, and said kindly, "You may rest a little, now."

Alice looked round her in great surprise. "Why, I do believe

we've been under this tree the whole time! Everything's just as it was!"

"Of course it is," said the Queen. "What would you have it?"

"Well, in *our* country," said Alice, still panting a little, "you'd generally get to somewhere else—if you ran very fast for a long time as we've been doing."

"A slow sort of country!" said the Queen. "Now, *here*, you see, it takes all the running *you* can do, to keep in the same place. If you want to get somewhere else, you must run at least twice as fast as that!"

"I'd rather not try, please!" said Alice. "I'm quite content to stay here—only I *am* so hot and thirsty!"

"I know what *you'd* like!" the Queen said good-naturedly, taking a little box out of her pocket. "Have a biscuit?"

Alice thought it would not be civil to say "No," though it wasn't at all what she wanted. So she took it, and ate it as well as she could; and it was *very* dry; and she thought she had never been so nearly choked in all her life.

"While you're refreshing yourself," said the Queen, "I'll just take the measurements." And she took a ribbon out of her pocket, marked in inches, and began measuring the ground, and sticking little pegs in here and there.

"At the end of two yards," she said, putting in a peg to mark the distance, "I shall give you your directions—have another biscuit?"

"No, thank you," said Alice; "one's *quite* enough!"

"Thirst quenched, I hope?" said the Queen.

Alice did not know what to say to this, but luckily the Queen did not wait for an answer, but went on. "At the end of *three* yards I shall repeat them—for fear of your forgetting them. At the end of *four*, I shall say good-by. And at the end of *five*, I shall go!"

She had got all the pegs put in by this time, and Alice looked on with great interest as she returned to the tree, and then began slowly walking down the row.

At the two-yard peg she faced round, and said, "A Pawn goes two squares in its first move, you know. So you'll go *very* quickly through the Third Square—by railway, I should think—and you'll find yourself in the Fourth Square in no time. Well, *that* square belongs to Tweedledum and Tweedledee—the Fifth is mostly water—the Sixth belongs to Humpty Dumpty— But you make no remark?"

"I—I didn't know I had to make one—just then," Alice faltered out.

"You *should* have said," the Queen went on in a tone of grave reproof, " 'It's extremely kind of you to tell me all this'—however, we'll suppose it said—the Seventh Square is all forest—however, one of the Knights will show you the way—and in the Eighth Square we shall be Queens together, and it's all feasting and fun!" Alice got up and curtsied, and sat down again.

At the next peg the Queen turned again, and this time she said, "Speak in French when you can't think of the English for a thing—turn out your toes as you walk—and remember who you are!" She did not wait for Alice to curtsy, this time, but walked on quickly to the next peg, where she turned for a moment to say "Good-by," and then hurried on to the last.

How it happened, Alice never knew, but exactly as she came to the last peg she was gone. Whether she vanished into the air, or whether she ran quickly into the wood ("and she *can* run very fast!" thought Alice), there was no way of guessing, but she was gone, and Alice began to remember that she was a Pawn, and that it would soon be time for her to move.

CHAPTER III: *Looking-Glass Insects*

OF COURSE THE FIRST THING to do was to make a grand survey of the country she was going to travel through. "It's something very like learning geography," thought Alice, as she stood on tiptoe in hopes of being able to see a little further. "Principal rivers—there *are* none. Principal mountains—I'm on the only one, but I don't think it's got any name. Principal towns—why, what *are* those creatures, making honey down there? They can't be bees—nobody ever saw bees a mile off, you know—" and for some time she stood silent, watching one of them that was bustling about among the flowers, poking its proboscis into them, "just as if it was a regular bee," thought Alice.

However, this was anything but a regular bee: in fact, it was an elephant—as Alice soon found out, though the idea quite took her breath away at first. "And what enormous flowers they must be!" was her next idea. "Something like cottages with the roofs taken off, and stalks put to them—and what quantities of honey they must make! I think I'll go down and—no, I won't go *just* yet," she went on, checking herself just as she was beginning to run down the hill, and trying to find some excuse for turning shy so suddenly.

"It'll never do to go down among them without a good long branch to brush them away—and what fun it'll be when they ask me how I liked my walk. I shall say, 'Oh, I liked it well enough—' (here came the favorite little toss of the head) 'only it *was* so dusty and hot, and the elephants *did* tease so!'

"I think I'll go down the other way," she said after a pause; "and perhaps I may visit the elephants later on. Besides, I *do* so want to get into the Third Square!"

So, with this excuse, she ran down the hill, and jumped over the first of the six little brooks.

*　　*　　*　　*　　*　　*　　*

"Tickets, please!" said the Guard, putting his head in at the window. In a moment everybody was holding out a ticket; they were about the same size as the people, and quite seemed to fill the carriage.

"Now then! Show your ticket, child!" the Guard went on, looking angrily at Alice. And a great many voices all said together ("like the chorus of a song," thought Alice), "Don't keep him waiting, child! Why, his time is worth a thousand pounds a minute!"

"I'm afraid I haven't got one," Alice said in a frightened tone; "there wasn't a ticket office where I came from." And again the chorus of voices went on. "There wasn't room for one where she came from. The land there is worth a thousand pounds an inch!"

"Don't make excuses," said the Guard; "you should have bought one from the engine driver." And once more the chorus of voices went on with, "The man that drives the engine. Why, the smoke alone is worth a thousand pounds a puff!"

Alice thought to herself, "Then there's no use in speaking." The voices didn't join in, *this* time, as she hadn't spoken, but, to her great surprise, they all *thought* in chorus (I hope you understand what *thinking in chorus* means, for I must confess that *I* don't), "Better say nothing at all. Language is worth a thousand pounds a word!"

"I shall dream about a thousand pounds tonight, I know I shall!" thought Alice.

All this time the Guard was looking at her, first through a telescope, then through a microscope, and then through an opera glass. At last he said, "You're traveling the wrong way," and shut up the window, and went away.

"So young a child," said the gentleman sitting opposite to her (he was dressed in white paper), "ought to know which way she's going, even if she doesn't know her own name!"

A Goat, that was sitting next to the gentleman in white, shut his eyes and said in a loud voice, "She ought to know her way to the ticket office, even if she doesn't know her alphabet!"

There was a Beetle sitting next to the Goat (it was a very queer carriage-full of passengers altogether), and, as the rule seemed to be that they should all speak in turn, *he* went on with, "She'll have to go back from here as luggage!"

Alice couldn't see who was sitting beyond the Beetle, but a hoarse voice spoke next. "Change engines—" it said, and there it choked and was obliged to leave off.

"It sounds like a horse," Alice thought to herself. And an extremely small voice, close to her ear, said, "You might make a joke on that—something about 'horse' and 'hoarse,' you know."

Then a very gentle voice in the distance said, "She must be labeled 'Lass, with care,' you know—"

And after that other voices went on ("What a number of people

there are in the carriage!" thought Alice), saying, "She must go by post, as she's got a head on her—" "She must be sent as a message by the telegraph—" "She must draw the train herself the rest of the way—" and so on.

But the gentleman dressed in white paper leaned forwards and whispered in her ear, "Never mind what they all say, my dear, but take a return ticket every time the train stops."

"Indeed I shan't!" Alice said rather impatiently. "I don't belong to this railway journey at all—I was in a wood just now—and I wish I could get back there!"

"You might make a joke on *that*," said the little voice close to her ear; "something about 'you *would* if you could,' you know."

"Don't tease so," said Alice, looking about in vain to see where the voice came from. "If you're so anxious to have a joke made, why don't you make one yourself?"

The little voice sighed deeply. It was *very* unhappy, evidently, and Alice would have said something pitying to comfort it, "if it would only sigh like other people!" she thought. But this was such a wonderfully small sigh that she wouldn't have heard it at all if it hadn't come *quite* close to her ear. The consequence of this was that it tickled her ear very much, and quite took off her thoughts from the unhappiness of the poor little creature.

"I know you are a friend," the little voice went on; "a dear friend, and an old friend. And you won't hurt me, though I am an insect."

"What kind of insect?" Alice inquired, a little anxiously. What she really wanted to know was whether it could sting or not, but she thought this wouldn't be quite a civil question to ask.

"What, then you don't—" the little voice began, when it was drowned by a shrill scream from the engine, and everybody jumped up in alarm, Alice among the rest.

The Horse, who had put his head out of the window, quietly drew it in and said, "It's only a brook we have to jump over." Everybody seemed satisfied with this, though Alice felt a little nervous at the idea of trains jumping at all. "However, it'll take us into the Fourth Square, that's some comfort!" she said to herself.

In another moment she felt the carriage rise straight up into the air, and in her fright she caught at the thing nearest to her hand, which happened to be the Goat's beard.

*   *   *   *   *   *   *

But the beard seemed to melt away as she touched it, and she found herself sitting quietly under a tree—while the Gnat (for that was the insect she had been talking to) was balancing itself on a twig just over her head, and fanning her with its wings.

It certainly was a *very* large Gnat; "about the size of a chicken," Alice thought. Still, she couldn't feel nervous with it, after they had been talking together so long.

"—then you don't like *all* insects?" the Gnat went on, as quietly as if nothing had happened.

"I like them when they can talk," Alice said. "None of them ever talk, where *I* come from."

"What sort of insects do you rejoice in, where *you* come from?" the Gnat inquired.

"I don't *rejoice* in insects at all," Alice explained, "because I'm rather afraid of them—at least the large kinds. But I can tell you the names of some of them."

"Of course they answer to their names?" the Gnat remarked carelessly.

"I never knew them to do it."

"What's the use of their having names," the Gnat said, "if they won't answer to them?"

"No use to *them*," said Alice; "but it's useful to the people that name them, I suppose. If not, why do things have names at all?"

"I can't say," the Gnat replied. "Further on, in the wood down there, they've got no names—however, go on with your list of insects; you're wasting time."

"Well, there's the Horse-fly," Alice began, counting off the names on her fingers.

"All right," said the Gnat. "Halfway up that bush, you'll see a Rocking-horse-fly, if you look. It's made entirely of wood, and gets about by swinging itself from branch to branch."

"What does it live on?" Alice asked, with great curiosity.

"Sap and sawdust," said the Gnat. "Go on with the list."

Alice looked at the Rocking-horse-fly with great interest, and made up her mind that it must have been just repainted, it looked so bright and sticky; and then she went on.

"And there's the Dragon-fly."

"Look on the branch above your head," said the Gnat, "and there you'll find a Snap-dragon-fly. Its body is made of plum pudding, its wings of holly leaves, and its head is a raisin burning in brandy."

"And what does it live on?" Alice asked, as before.

"Frumenty and mince pie," the Gnat replied; "and it makes its nest in a Christmas box."

"And then there's the Butterfly," Alice went on, after she had taken a good look at the insect with its head on fire, and had thought to herself, "I wonder if that's the reason insects are so fond of flying into candles—because they want to turn into Snap-dragon-flies!"

"Crawling at your feet," said the Gnat (Alice drew her feet back in some alarm), "you may observe a Bread-and-butter-fly. Its wings are thin slices of bread and butter, its body is a crust, and its head is a lump of sugar."

"And what does *it* live on?"

"Weak tea with cream in it."

A new difficulty came into Alice's head. "Supposing it couldn't find any?" she suggested.

"Then it would die, of course."

"But that must happen very often," Alice remarked thoughtfully.

"It always happens," said the Gnat.

After this, Alice was silent for a minute or two, pondering. The Gnat amused itself meanwhile by humming round and round her head; at last it settled again and remarked, "I suppose you don't want to lose your name?"

"No, indeed," Alice said, a little anxiously.

"And yet I don't know," the Gnat went on in a careless tone; "only think how convenient it would be if you could manage to go home without it! For instance, if the governess wanted to call you to your lessons, she would call out 'Come here—' and there she would have to leave off, because there wouldn't be any name for her to call, and of course you wouldn't have to go, you know."

"That would never do, I'm sure," said Alice; "the governess would never think of excusing me lessons for that. If she couldn't remember my name, she'd call me 'Miss,' as the servants do."

"Well, if she said 'Miss,' and didn't say anything more," the Gnat remarked, "of course you'd miss your lessons. That's a joke. I wish *you* had made it."

"Why do you wish *I* had made it?" Alice asked. "It's a very bad one." But the Gnat only sighed deeply while two large tears came rolling down its cheeks.

"You shouldn't make jokes," Alice said, "if it makes you so unhappy."

Then came another of those melancholy little sighs, and this time the poor Gnat really seemed to have sighed itself away, for, when Alice looked up, there was nothing whatever to be seen on the twig, and, as she was getting quite chilly with sitting so long, she got up and walked on.

She very soon came to an open field, with a wood on the other side of it; it looked much darker than the last wood, and Alice felt a *little* timid about going into it. However, on second thoughts, she made up her mind to go on; "for I certainly won't go *back*," she thought to herself, and this was the only way to the Eighth Square.

"This must be the wood," she said thoughtfully to herself, "where things have no names. I wonder what'll become of *my* name when I go in? I shouldn't like to lose it at all—because they'd have to give me another, and it would be almost certain to be an ugly one. But then the fun would be trying to find the creature that had got my old name! That's just like the advertisements, you know, when people lose dogs—*answers to the name of 'Dash'; had on a brass collar*—just fancy calling everything you met 'Alice,' till one of them answered! Only they wouldn't answer at all, if they were wise."

She was rambling on in this way when she reached the wood; it looked very cool and shady. "Well, at any rate it's a great comfort," she said as she stepped under the trees, "after being so hot, to get into the—into the—into *what?*" she went on, rather surprised at not being able to think of the word. "I mean to get under the—under the—under *this*, you know!" putting her hand on the trunk of the tree. "What *does* it call itself, I wonder? I do believe it's got no name—why, to be sure it hasn't!"

She stood silent for a minute, thinking; then suddenly began again. "Then it really *has* happened, after all! And now, who am I? I *will* remember, if I can! I'm determined to do it!" But being determined didn't help her much, and all she could say, after a great deal of puzzling, was, "*L, I know* it begins with *L!*"

Just then a Fawn came wandering by; it looked at Alice with its large gentle eyes, but didn't seem at all frightened.

"Here then! Here then!" Alice said, as she held out her hand and tried to stroke it; but it only started back a little, and then stood looking at her again.

"What do you call your-self?" the Fawn said at last. Such a soft sweet voice it had!

"I wish I knew!" thought poor Alice. She answered, rather sadly, "Nothing, just now."

"Think again," it said; "that won't do."

Alice thought, but nothing came of it. "Please, would you tell me what *you* call yourself?" she said timidly. "I think that might help a little."

"I'll tell you, if you'll come a little further on," the Fawn said. "I can't remember *here*."

415

So they walked on together through the wood, Alice with her arms clasped lovingly round the soft neck of the Fawn, till they came out into another open field, and here the Fawn gave a sudden bound into the air, and shook itself free from Alice's arm. "I'm a Fawn!" it cried out in a voice of delight. "And, dear me, you're a human child!" A sudden look of alarm came into its beautiful brown eyes, and in another moment it had darted away at full speed.

Alice stood looking after it, almost ready to cry with vexation at having lost her dear little fellow traveler so suddenly. "However, I know my name now," she said, "that's *some* comfort. Alice— Alice—I won't forget it again. And now, which of these fingerposts ought I to follow, I wonder?"

It was not a very difficult question to answer, as there was only one road through the wood, and the two fingerposts both pointed along it. "I'll settle it," Alice said to herself, "when the road divides and they point different ways." But this did not seem likely to happen. She went on and on, a long way, but wherever the road divided, there were sure to be two fingerposts pointing the same way, one marked TO TWEEDLEDUM'S HOUSE, and the other TO THE HOUSE OF TWEEDLEDEE.

"I do believe," said Alice at last, "that they live in the *same* house! I wonder I never thought of that before— But I can't stay there long. I'll just call and say 'How d'ye do?' and ask them the way out of the wood. If I could only get to the Eighth Square before it gets dark!" So she wandered on, talking to herself as she went, till, on turning a sharp corner, she came upon two fat little men, so suddenly that she could not help starting back, but in another moment she recovered herself, feeling sure that they must be.

CHAPTER IV: *Tweedledum and Tweedledee*

THEY WERE STANDING UNDER a tree, each with an arm round the other's neck, and Alice knew which was which in a moment, because one of them had DUM embroidered on his collar, and the other DEE.

"I suppose they've each got TWEEDLE round at the back of the collar," she said to herself.

They stood so still that she quite forgot they were alive, and she was just going round to see if the word TWEEDLE was written at the back of each collar, when she was startled by a voice coming from the one marked DUM.

"If you think we're waxworks," he said, "you ought to pay, you know. Waxworks weren't made to be looked at for nothing. Nohow!"

"Contrariwise," added the one marked DEE, "if you think we're alive, you ought to speak."

"I'm sure I'm very sorry," was all Alice could say; for the words of the old song kept ringing through her head like the ticking of a clock, and she could hardly help saying them out loud:

"Tweedledum and Tweedledee
Agreed to have a battle;
For Tweedledum said Tweedledee
Had spoiled his nice new rattle.

Just then flew down a monstrous crow,
As black as a tar barrel;
Which frightened both the heroes so,
They quite forgot their quarrel."

"I know what you're thinking about," said Tweedledum; "but it isn't so, nohow."

"Contrariwise," continued Tweedledee, "if it was so, it might be; and if it were so, it would be; but as it isn't, it ain't. That's logic."

"I was thinking," Alice said very politely, "which is the best way out of this wood; it's getting so dark. Would you tell me, please?"

But the fat little men only looked at each other and grinned.

They looked so exactly like a couple of great schoolboys that Alice couldn't help pointing her finger at Tweedledum, and saying, "First Boy!"

"Nohow!" Tweedledum cried out briskly, and shut his mouth up again with a snap.

"Next Boy!" said Alice, passing on to Tweedledee, though she felt quite certain he would only shout out "Contrariwise!" and so he did.

"You've begun wrong!" cried Tweedledum. "The first thing in a visit is to say 'How d'ye do?' and shake hands!" And here the two brothers gave each other a hug, and then they held out the two hands that were free, to shake hands with her.

Alice did not like shaking hands with either of them first, for fear of hurting the other one's feelings; so, as the best way out of the difficulty, she took hold of both hands at once; the next moment they were dancing round in a ring. This seemed quite natural (she remembered afterwards), and she was not even surprised to hear music playing; it seemed to come from the tree under which they were dancing, and it was done (as well as she could make it out) by the branches rubbing one across the other, like fiddles and fiddlesticks.

"But it certainly *was* funny," (Alice said afterwards, when she was telling her sister the history of all this) "to find myself singing *Here we go round the mulberry bush*. I don't know when I began it, but somehow I felt as if I'd been singing it a long time!"

The other two dancers were fat, and very soon out of breath. "Four times round is enough for one dance," Tweedledum panted out, and they left off dancing as suddenly as they had begun; the music stopped at the same moment.

Then they let go of Alice's hands, and stood looking at her for a minute; there was a rather awkward pause, as Alice didn't know how to begin a conversation with people she had just been dancing with. "It would never do to say 'How d'ye do?' *now*," she said to herself; "we seem to have got beyond that, somehow!"

"I hope you're not much tired?" she said at last.

"Nohow. And thank you *very* much for asking," said Tweedledum.

"So *much* obliged!" added Tweedledee. "You like poetry?"

"Ye-es, pretty well—*some* poetry," Alice said doubtfully. "Would you tell me which road leads out of the wood?"

"What shall I repeat to her?" said Tweedledee, looking round at Tweedledum with great solemn eyes, and not noticing Alice's question.

"'The Walrus and the Carpenter' is the longest," Tweedledum replied, giving his brother an affectionate hug.

Tweedledee began instantly:

"*The sun was shining—*"

Here Alice ventured to interrupt him. "If it's *very* long," she said, as politely as she could, "would you please tell me first which road—"

Tweedledee smiled gently, and began again:

"The sun was shining on the sea,
Shining with all his might:
He did his very best to make
The billows smooth and bright—
And this was odd, because it was
The middle of the night.

The moon was shining sulkily,
Because she thought the sun
Had got no business to be there
After the day was done—
'It's very rude of him,' she said,
'To come and spoil the fun!'

The sea was wet as wet could be,
The sands were dry as dry.
You could not see a cloud, because
No cloud was in the sky;
No birds were flying overhead—
There were no birds to fly.

The Walrus and the Carpenter
Were walking close at hand;
They wept like anything to see
Such quantities of sand;
'If this were only cleared away,'
They said, 'it would be grand!'

'If seven maids with seven mops
Swept it for half a year,
Do you suppose,' the Walrus said,
'That they could get it clear?'
'I doubt it,' said the Carpenter,
And shed a bitter tear.

'O Oysters, come and walk with us!'
The Walrus did beseech.
'A pleasant walk, a pleasant talk,
Along the briny beach;
We cannot do with more than four,
To give a hand to each.'

The eldest Oyster looked at him,
But never a word he said;
The eldest Oyster winked his eye,
And shook his heavy head—
Meaning to say he did not choose
To leave the oyster bed.

But four young Oysters hurried up,
All eager for the treat;
Their coats were brushed, their faces washed,
Their shoes were clean and neat—
And this was odd, because, you know,
They hadn't any feet.

Four other Oysters followed them,
And yet another four;
And thick and fast they came at last,
And more, and more, and more—
All hopping through the frothy waves,
And scrambling to the shore.

The Walrus and the Carpenter
Walked on a mile or so,
And then they rested on a rock
Conveniently low;
And all the little Oysters stood
And waited in a row.

'The time has come,' the Walrus said,
'To talk of many things:
Of shoes—and ships—and sealing wax—
Of cabbages—and kings—
And why the sea is boiling hot—
And whether pigs have wings.'

'But wait a bit,' the Oysters cried,
'Before we have our chat;
For some of us are out of breath,
And all of us are fat!'
'No hurry!' said the Carpenter.
They thanked him much for that.

'*A loaf of bread,*' *the Walrus said,*
  '*Is what we chiefly need;*
Pepper and vinegar besides
  Are very good indeed—
Now, if you're ready, Oysters dear,
  We can begin to feed.'

'*But not on us!*' *the Oysters cried,*
  Turning a little blue.
'*After such kindness, that would be*
  A dismal thing to do!'
'*The night is fine,*' *the Walrus said.*
  '*Do you admire the view?*

'*It was so kind of you to come!*
  And you are very nice!'
The Carpenter said nothing but,
  '*Cut us another slice.*
I wish you were not quite so deaf—
  I've had to ask you twice!'

'*It seems a shame,*' *the Walrus said,*
  '*To play them such a trick.*
After we've brought them out so far,
  And made them trot so quick!'
The Carpenter said nothing but,
  '*The butter's spread too thick!*'

'*I weep for you,*' *the Walrus said,*
  '*I deeply sympathize.*'
With sobs and tears he sorted out
  Those of the largest size,
Holding his pocket handkerchief
  Before his streaming eyes.

'*O Oysters,*' *said the Carpenter,*
  '*You've had a pleasant run!*
Shall we be trotting home again?'
  But answer came there none—
And this was scarcely odd, because
  They'd eaten every one."

"I like the Walrus best," said Alice; "because he was a *little* sorry for the poor oysters."

"He ate more than the Carpenter, though," said Tweedledee. "You see, he held his handkerchief in front, so that the Carpenter couldn't count how many he took. Contrariwise."

"That was mean!" Alice said indignantly. "Then I like the Carpenter best—if he didn't eat so many as the Walrus."

"But he ate as many as he could get," said Tweedledum.

This was a puzzler. After a pause, Alice began, "Well! They were *both* very unpleasant characters—" Here she checked herself in some alarm, at hearing something that sounded to her like the puffing of a large steam engine in the wood near them, though she feared it was more likely to be a wild beast. "Are there any lions or tigers about here?" she asked timidly.

"It's only the Red King snoring," said Tweedledee.

"Come and look at him!" the brothers cried, and they each took one of Alice's hands, and led her up to where the King was sleeping.

"Isn't he a *lovely* sight?" said Tweedledum.

Alice couldn't say honestly that he was. He had a tall red night-cap on, with a tassel, and he was lying crumpled up into a sort of untidy heap, and snoring loud—"fit to snore his head off!" as Tweedledum remarked.

"I'm afraid he'll catch cold with lying on the damp grass," said Alice, who was a very thoughtful little girl.

"He's dreaming now," said Tweedledee; "and what do you think he's dreaming about?"

Alice said, "Nobody can guess that."

"Why, about *you!*" Tweedledee exclaimed, clapping his hands triumphantly. "And if he left off dreaming about you, where do you suppose you'd be?"

"Where I am now, of course," said Alice.

"Not you!" Tweedledee retorted contemptuously. "You'd be nowhere. Why, you're only a sort of thing in his dream!"

"If that there King was to wake," added Tweedledum, "you'd go out—bang!—just like a candle!"

"I shouldn't!" Alice exclaimed indignantly. "Besides, if *I'm* only a sort of thing in his dream, what are *you*, I should like to know?"

"Ditto," said Tweedledum.

"Ditto, ditto!" cried Tweedledee.

He shouted this so loud that Alice couldn't help saying, "Hush! You'll be waking him, I'm afraid, if you make so much noise."

"Well, it's no use *your* talking about waking him," said Tweedledum, "when you're only one of the things in his dream. You know very well you're not real."

"I *am* real!" said Alice, and began to cry.

"You won't make yourself a bit realer by crying," Tweedledee remarked; "there's nothing to cry about."

"If I wasn't real," Alice said—half laughing through her tears, it all seemed so ridiculous—"I shouldn't be able to cry."

"I hope you don't suppose those are *real* tears?" Tweedledum interrupted in a tone of great contempt.

"I know they're talking nonsense," Alice thought to herself; "and it's foolish to cry about it." So she brushed away her tears, and went on, as cheerfully as she could, "At any rate I'd better be getting out of the wood, for really it's coming on very dark. Do you think it's going to rain?"

Tweedledum spread a large umbrella over himself and his brother, and looked up into it. "No, I don't think it is," he said; "at least—not under *here*. Nohow."

"But it may rain *outside?*"

"It may—if it chooses," said Tweedledee; "we've no objection. Contrariwise."

"Selfish things!" thought Alice, and she was just going to say "Good night" and leave them when Tweedledum sprang out from under the umbrella, and seized her by the wrist.

"Do you see *that?*" he said, in a voice choking with passion, and his eyes grew large and yellow all in a moment, as he pointed with a trembling finger at a small white thing lying under the tree.

"It's only a rattle," Alice said, after a careful examination of the little white thing. "Not a rattle*snake*, you know," she added hastily, thinking that he was frightened; "only an old rattle—quite old and broken."

"I knew it was!" cried Tweedledum, beginning to stamp about wildly and tear his hair. "It's spoiled, of course!" Here he looked

425

at Tweedledee, who immediately sat down on the ground, and tried to hide himself under the umbrella.

Alice laid her hand upon his arm and said, in a soothing tone, "You needn't be so angry about an old rattle."

"But it *isn't* old!" Tweedledum cried, in a greater fury than ever. "It's *new*, I tell you—I bought it yesterday—my nice NEW RATTLE!" and his voice rose to a perfect scream.

All this time Tweedledee was trying his best to fold up the umbrella, with himself in it; which was such an extraordinary thing to do that it quite took off Alice's attention from the angry brother. But he couldn't quite succeed, and it ended in his rolling over, bundled up in the umbrella, with only his head out; and there he lay, opening and shutting his mouth and his large eyes—"looking more like a fish than anything else," Alice thought.

"Of course you agree to have a battle?" Tweedledum said in a calmer tone.

"I suppose so," the other sulkily replied, as he crawled out of the umbrella; "only *she* must help us to dress up, you know."

So the two brothers went off hand in hand into the wood, and returned in a minute with their arms full of things—such as bolsters, blankets, hearthrugs, tablecloths, dish covers, and coal scuttles. "I hope you're a good hand at pinning and tying strings?" Tweedledum remarked. "Every one of these things has got to go on, somehow or other."

Alice said afterwards she had never seen such a fuss made about anything in all her life—the way those two bustled about— and the quantity of things they put on—and the trouble they gave her in tying strings and fastening buttons— "Really they'll be more like bundles of old clothes than anything else, by the time they're ready!" she said to herself, as she arranged a bolster round the neck of Tweedledee, "to keep his head from being cut off," as he said. "You know," he added very gravely, "it's one of the most serious things that can possibly happen to one in a battle—to get one's head cut off."

Alice laughed loud; but she managed to turn it into a cough, for fear of hurting his feelings.

"Do I look very pale?" said Tweedledum, coming up to have his helmet tied on. (He *called* it a helmet, though it certainly looked much more like a saucepan.)

"Well—yes—a *little*," Alice replied gently.

"I'm very brave, generally," he went on in a low voice; "only today I happen to have a headache."

"And *I've* got a toothache!" said Tweedledee, who had overheard the remark. "I'm far worse than you!"

"Then you'd better not fight today," said Alice, thinking it a good opportunity to make peace.

"We *must* have a bit of a fight, but I don't care about going on long," said Tweedledum. "What's the time now?"

Tweedledee looked at his watch, and said, "Half past four."

"Let's fight till six, and then have dinner," said Tweedledum.

"Very well," the other said, rather sadly; "and *she* can watch us— only you'd better not come *very* close," he added; "I generally hit everything I can see—when I get really excited."

"And *I* hit everything within reach," cried Tweedledum, "whether I can see it or not!"

Alice laughed. "You must hit the *trees* pretty often, I should think," she said.

Tweedledum looked round him with a satisfied smile. "I don't suppose," he said, "there'll be a tree left standing, for ever so far round, by the time we've finished!"

"And all about a rattle!" said Alice, still hoping to make them a *little* ashamed of fighting for such a trifle.

"I shouldn't have minded it so much," said Tweedledum, "if it hadn't been a new one."

"I wish the monstrous crow would come!" thought Alice.

"There's only one sword, you know," Tweedledum said to his brother; "but *you* can have the umbrella—it's quite as sharp. Only we must begin quick. It's getting as dark as it can."

"And darker," said Tweedledee.

It was getting dark so suddenly that Alice thought there must be a thunderstorm coming on. "What a thick black cloud that is!" she said. "And how fast it comes! Why, I do believe it's got wings!"

"It's the crow!" Tweedledum cried out in a shrill voice of alarm; and the two brothers took to their heels and were out of sight in a moment.

Alice ran a little way into the wood, and stopped under a large tree. "It can never get at me *here*," she thought; "it's far too large to squeeze itself in among the trees. But I wish it wouldn't flap its wings so—it makes quite a hurricane in the wood—here's somebody's shawl being blown away!"

CHAPTER V: *Wool and Water*

SHE CAUGHT THE SHAWL as she spoke, and looked about for the owner; in another moment the White Queen came running wildly through the wood, with both arms stretched out wide, as if she were flying, and Alice very civilly went to meet her with the shawl.

"I'm very glad I happened to be in the way," Alice said, as she helped her to put on her shawl again.

The White Queen only looked at her in a helpless frightened

sort of way, and kept repeating something in a whisper to herself that sounded like "Bread and butter, bread and butter," and Alice felt that if there was to be any conversation at all, she must manage it herself. So she began rather timidly: "Am I addressing the White Queen?"

"Well, yes, if you call that a-dressing," the Queen said. "It isn't *my* notion of the thing, at all."

Alice thought it would never do to have an argument at the very beginning of their conversation, so she smiled and said, "If your Majesty will only tell me the right way to begin, I'll do it as well as I can."

"But I don't want it done at all!" groaned the poor Queen. "I've been a-dressing myself for the last two hours."

It would have been all the better, as it seemed to Alice, if she had got someone else to dress her, she was so dreadfully untidy. "Every single thing's crooked," Alice thought to herself, "and she's all over pins!— May I put your shawl straight for you?" she added aloud.

"I don't know what's the matter with it!" the Queen said, in a melancholy voice. "It's out of temper, I think. I've pinned it here, and I've pinned it there, but there's no pleasing it!"

"It *can't* go straight, you know, if you pin it all on one side," Alice said, as she gently put it right for her; "and, dear me, what a state your hair is in!"

"The brush has got entangled in it!" the Queen said with a sigh. "And I lost the comb yesterday."

Alice carefully released the brush, and did her best to get

the hair into order. "Come, you look rather better now!" she said, after altering most of the pins. "But really you should have a lady's maid!"

"I'm sure I'll take *you* with pleasure!" the Queen said. "Twopence a week, and jam every other day."

Alice couldn't help laughing as she said, "I don't want you to hire *me*—and I don't care for jam."

"It's very good jam," said the Queen.

"Well, I don't want any *today*, at any rate."

"You couldn't have it if you *did* want it," the Queen said. "The rule is, jam tomorrow and jam yesterday—but never jam *today*."

"It *must* come sometimes to 'jam today,'" Alice objected.

"No, it can't," said the Queen. "It's jam every *other* day; today isn't any other day, you know."

"I don't understand you," said Alice. "It's dreadfully confusing!"

"That's the effect of living backwards," the Queen said kindly; "it always makes one a little giddy at first—"

"Living backwards!" Alice repeated in great astonishment. "I never heard of such a thing!"

"—but there's one advantage in it, that one's memory works both ways."

"I'm sure *mine* only works one way," Alice remarked. "I can't remember things before they happen."

"It's a poor sort of memory that only works backwards," the Queen remarked.

"What sort of things do *you* remember best?" Alice ventured to ask.

"Oh, things that happened the week after next," the Queen replied in a careless tone. "For instance, now," she went on, sticking a large piece of plaster on her finger as she spoke, "there's the King's Messenger. He's in prison now, being punished; and the trial doesn't even begin till next Wednesday; and of course the crime comes last of all."

"Suppose he never commits the crime?" said Alice.

"That would be all the better, wouldn't it?" the Queen said, as she bound the plaster round her finger with a bit of ribbon.

Alice felt there was no denying *that*. "Of course it would be all the better," she said; "but it wouldn't be all the better his being punished."

"You're wrong *there*, at any rate," said the Queen. "Were *you* ever punished?"

"Only for faults," said Alice.

"And you were all the better for it, I know!" the Queen said triumphantly.

"Yes, but then I *had* done the things I was punished for," said Alice; "that makes all the difference."

"But if you *hadn't* done them," the Queen said, "that would have been better still; better, and better, and better!" Her voice went higher with each "better," till it got quite to a squeak at last.

Alice was just beginning to say, "There's a mistake somewhere—" when the Queen began screaming, so loud that she had to leave the sentence unfinished. "Oh, oh, oh!" shouted the Queen, shaking her hand about as if she wanted to shake it off. "My finger's bleeding! Oh, oh, oh, oh!"

Her screams were so exactly like the whistle of a steam engine  that Alice had to hold both her hands over her ears. "What *is* the matter?" she said, as soon as there was a chance of making herself heard. "Have you pricked your finger?"

"I haven't pricked it *yet*," the Queen said, "but I soon shall— oh, oh, oh!"

"When do you expect to do it?" Alice asked, feeling very much inclined to laugh.

"When I fasten my shawl again," the poor Queen groaned out; "the brooch will come undone directly. Oh, oh!" As she said the words the brooch flew open, and the Queen clutched wildly at it, and tried to clasp it again.

"Take care!" cried Alice. "You're holding it all crooked!" And she caught at the brooch; but it was too late: the pin had slipped, and the Queen had pricked her finger.

"That accounts for the bleeding, you see," she said to Alice with a smile. "Now you understand the way things happen here."

"But why don't you scream *now?*" Alice asked, holding her hands ready to put over her ears again.

"Why, I've done all the screaming already," said the Queen. "What would be the good of having it all over again?"

By this time it was getting light. "The crow must have flown away, I think," said Alice; "I'm so glad it's gone. I thought it was the night coming on."

"I wish *I* could manage to be glad!" the Queen said. "Only I never can remember the rule. You must be very happy, living in this wood, and being glad whenever you like!"

"Only it is so *very* lonely here!" Alice said in a melancholy voice; and, at the thought of her loneliness, two large tears came rolling down her cheeks.

"Oh, don't go on like that!" cried the poor Queen, wringing her hands in despair. "Consider what a great girl you are. Consider what a long way you've come today. Consider what o'clock it is. Consider anything, only don't cry!"

Alice could not help laughing at this, even in the midst of her tears. "Can *you* keep from crying by considering things?" she asked.

"That's the way it's done," the Queen said with great decision; "nobody can do two things at once, you know. Let's consider your age to begin with—how old are you?"

"I'm seven and a half, exactly."

"You needn't say 'exactually,'" the Queen remarked. "I can believe it without that. Now I'll give *you* something to believe. I'm just one hundred and one, five months and a day."

"I can't believe *that!*" said Alice.

"Can't you?" the Queen said in a pitying tone. "Try again; draw a long breath, and shut your eyes."

Alice laughed. "There's no use trying," she said; "one *can't* believe impossible things."

"I daresay you haven't had much practice," said the Queen. "When I was your age, I always did it for half an hour a day. Why, sometimes I've believed as many as six impossible things before breakfast. There goes the shawl again!"

The brooch had come undone as she spoke, and a sudden gust of wind blew the Queen's shawl across a little brook. The Queen spread out her arms again and went flying after it, and this time she succeeded in catching it for herself. "I've got it!" she cried in a triumphant tone. "Now you shall see me pin it on again, all by myself!"

"Then I hope your finger is better now?" Alice said very politely, as she crossed the little brook after the Queen.

*   *   *   *   *   *   *

"Oh, much better!" cried the Queen, her voice rising into a squeak as she went on. "Much be-etter! Be-etter! Be-e-e-etter! Be-e-ehh!" The last word ended in a long bleat, so like a sheep that Alice quite started.

She looked at the Queen, who seemed to have suddenly wrapped herself up in wool. Alice rubbed her eyes, and looked again. She couldn't make out what had happened at all. Was she in a shop? And was that really— was it really a *sheep* that was sitting on the other side of the counter? Rub as she would, she could make nothing more of it; she was in a little dark shop, leaning with her elbows on the counter, and opposite to her was an old Sheep, sitting in an armchair, knitting, and every now and then leaving off to look at her through a great pair of spectacles.

"What is it you want to buy?" the Sheep said at last, looking up for a moment from her knitting.

"I don't *quite* know yet," Alice said very gently. "I should like to look all round me first, if I might."

"You may look in front of you, and on both sides, if you like," said the Sheep; "but you can't look *all* round you—unless you've got eyes at the back of your head."

But these, as it happened, Alice had *not* got; so she contented herself with turning round, looking at the shelves as she came to them.

The shop seemed to be full of all manner of curious things— but the oddest part of it all was that, whenever she looked hard at any shelf, to make out exactly what it had on it, that particular shelf was always quite empty, though the others round it were crowded as full as they could hold. "Things flow about so here!" she said at last in a plaintive tone, after she had spent a minute or so in vainly pursuing a large bright thing that looked sometimes like a doll and sometimes like a workbox, and was always in the shelf next above the one she was looking at. "And this one is the most provoking of all—but I'll tell you what—" she added, as a sudden thought struck her. "I'll follow it up to the very top shelf of all. It'll puzzle it to go through the ceiling, I expect!"

But even this plan failed: the "thing" went through the ceiling as quietly as possible, as if it were quite used to it.

"Are you a child or a teetotum?" the Sheep said, as she took up another pair of needles. "You'll make me giddy soon, if you go on turning round like that." She was now working with fourteen pairs at once, and Alice couldn't help looking at her in great astonishment.

"How *can* she knit with so many?" the puzzled child thought to herself. "She gets more and more like a porcupine every minute!"

"Can you row?" the Sheep asked, handing her a pair of knitting needles as she spoke.

"Yes, a little—but not on land—and not with needles—" Alice was beginning to say, when suddenly the needles turned into oars in her hands, and she found they were in a little boat, gliding along between banks, so there was nothing for it but to do her best.

"Feather," cried the Sheep, as she took up another pair of needles.

This didn't sound like a remark that needed any answer; so Alice said nothing, but pulled away. There was something very queer about the water, she thought, as every now and then the oars got fast in it, and would hardly come out again.

"Feather! Feather!" the Sheep cried again, taking more needles. "You'll be catching a crab directly."

"A dear little crab!" thought Alice. "I should like that."

"Didn't you hear me say 'Feather'?" the Sheep cried angrily, taking up quite a bunch of needles.

"Indeed I did," said Alice; "you've said it very often—and very loud. Please, where *are* the crabs?"

"In the water, of course!" said the Sheep, sticking some of the needles into her hair, as her hands were full. "Feather, I say!"

"*Why* do you say 'Feather' so often?" Alice asked at last, rather vexed. "I'm not a bird!"

"You are," said the Sheep; "you're a little goose."

This offended Alice a little, so there was no more conversation for a minute or two, while the boat glided gently on, sometimes among beds of weeds (which made the oars stick fast in the water, worse than ever), and sometimes under trees, but always with the same tall riverbanks frowning over their heads.

"Oh, please! There are some scented rushes!" Alice cried in a sudden transport of delight. "There really are—and *such* beauties!"

"You needn't say 'please' to *me* about 'em," the Sheep said, without looking up from her knitting; "I didn't put 'em there, and I'm not going to take 'em away."

"No, but I meant—please, may we wait and pick some?" Alice pleaded. "If you don't mind stopping the boat for a minute."

"How am *I* to stop it?" said the Sheep. "If you leave off rowing, it'll stop of itself."

So the boat was left to drift down the stream as it would, till it

glided gently in among
the waving rushes. And
then the little sleeves
were carefully rolled
up, and the little arms
were plunged in elbow-
deep, to get hold of the
rushes a good long way
down before breaking
them off—and for a
while Alice forgot all
about the Sheep and
the knitting, as she
bent over the side of
the boat, with just the
ends of her tangled hair
dipping into the wa-
ter—while with bright
eager eyes she caught

at one bunch after another of the darling scented rushes.

"I only hope the boat won't tipple over!" she said to herself.
"Oh, *what* a lovely one! Only I couldn't quite reach it." And it certainly *did* seem a little provoking ("almost as if it happened on
purpose," she thought) that, though she managed to pick plenty
of beautiful rushes as the boat glided by, there was always a more
lovely one that she couldn't reach.

"The prettiest are always further!" she said at last with a sigh at
the obstinacy of the rushes in growing so far off, as, with flushed
cheeks and dripping hair and hands, she scrambled back into her
place, and began to arrange her newfound treasures. What mat-
tered it to her just then that the rushes had begun to fade, and to
lose all their scent and beauty, from the very moment that she
picked them? Even real scented rushes, you know, last only a very
little while—and these, being dream rushes, melted away almost
like snow, as they lay in heaps at her feet—but Alice hardly noticed
this, there were so many other curious things to think about.

They hadn't gone much farther before the blade of one of the oars got fast in the water and *wouldn't* come out again (so Alice explained it afterwards), and the consequence was that the handle of it caught her under the chin, and, in spite of a series of little shrieks of "Oh, oh, oh!" from poor Alice, it swept her straight off the seat, and down among the heap of rushes.

However, she wasn't a bit hurt, and was soon up again; the Sheep went on with her knitting all the while, just as if nothing had happened. "That was a nice crab you caught!" she remarked, as Alice got back into her place, very much relieved to find herself still in the boat.

"Was it? I didn't see it," said Alice, peeping cautiously over the side of the boat into the dark water. "I wish it hadn't let go—I should so like a little crab to take home with me!" But the Sheep only laughed scornfully, and went on with her knitting.

"Are there many crabs here?" said Alice.

"Crabs, and all sorts of things," said the Sheep; "plenty of choice, only make up your mind. Now, what *do* you want to buy?"

"To buy!" Alice echoed in a tone that was half astonished and half frightened—for the oars, and the boat, and the river, had vanished all in a moment, and she was back again in the little dark shop. "I should like to buy an egg, please," she said timidly. "How do you sell them?"

"Fivepence farthing for one—twopence for two," the Sheep replied.

"Then two are cheaper than one?" Alice said in a surprised tone, taking out her purse.

"Only you *must* eat them both, if you buy two," said the Sheep.

"Then I'll have *one*, please," said Alice, as she put the money down on the counter. For she thought to herself, "They mightn't be at all nice, you know."

The Sheep took the money, and put it away in a box; then she said, "I never put things into people's hands—that would never do—you must get it for yourself." And so saying, she went off to the other end of the shop, and set the egg upright on a shelf.

"I wonder *why* it wouldn't do?" thought Alice, as she groped her way among the tables and chairs, for the shop was very dark towards the end. "The egg seems to get further away the more I walk towards it. Let me see, is this a chair? Why, it's got branches, I declare! How very odd to find trees growing here! And actually here's a little brook! Well, this is the very queerest shop I ever saw!"

*   *   *   *   *   *   *

So she went on, wondering more and more at every step, as everything turned into a tree the moment she came up to it, and she quite expected the egg to do the same.

CHAPTER VI: *Humpty Dumpty*

HOWEVER, THE EGG ONLY GOT larger and larger, and more and more human; when she had come within a few yards of it, she saw that it had eyes and a nose and mouth; and, when she had come close to it, she saw clearly that it was HUMPTY DUMPTY himself. "It can't be anybody else!" she said to herself. "I'm as certain of it as if his name were written all over his face!"

It might have been written a hundred times, easily, on that enormous face. Humpty Dumpty was sitting, with his legs crossed like a Turk, on the top of a high wall—such a narrow one that Alice quite wondered how he could keep his balance—and, as his eyes were steadily fixed in the opposite direction, and he didn't take the least notice of her, she thought he must be a stuffed figure, after all.

"And how exactly like an egg he is!" she said aloud, standing with her hands ready to catch him, for she was every moment expecting him to fall.

"It's *very* provoking," Humpty Dumpty said after a long silence, looking away from Alice as he spoke, "to be called an egg—*very!*"

"I said you *looked* like an egg, Sir," Alice gently explained. "And some eggs are very pretty, you know," she added, hoping to turn her remark into a sort of compliment.

"Some people," said Humpty Dumpty, looking away from her as usual, "have no more sense than a baby!"

Alice didn't know what to say to this; it wasn't at all like conversation, she thought, as he never said anything to *her;* in fact, his last remark was evidently addressed to a tree—so she stood and softly repeated to herself:

> "*Humpty Dumpty sat on a wall;*
> *Humpty Dumpty had a great fall.*
> *All the King's horses and all the King's men*
> *Couldn't put Humpty Dumpty in his place again.*

"That last line is much too long for the poetry," she added, almost out loud, forgetting that Humpty Dumpty would hear her.

"Don't stand chattering to yourself like that," Humpty Dumpty said, looking at her for the first time, "but tell me your name and your business."

"My *name* is Alice, but—"

"It's a stupid name enough!" Humpty Dumpty interrupted impatiently. "What does it mean?"

"*Must* a name mean something?" Alice asked doubtfully.

"Of course it must," Humpty Dumpty said with a short laugh; "*my* name means the shape I am—and a good handsome shape it is, too. With a name like yours, you might be any shape, almost."

"Why do you sit out here all alone?" said Alice, not wishing to begin an argument.

"Why, because there's nobody with me!" cried Humpty Dumpty. "Did you think I didn't know the answer to *that?* Ask another."

"Don't you think you'd be safer down on the ground?" Alice went on, not with any idea of making another riddle, but simply in her good-natured anxiety for the queer creature. "That wall is so *very* narrow!"

"What tremendously easy riddles you ask!" Humpty Dumpty growled. "Of course I don't think so! Why, if ever I *did* fall off—which there's no chance of—but *if* I did—" Here he pursed up his lips, and looked so solemn and grand that Alice could hardly help laughing. "*If* I *did* fall," he went on, "*the King has promised me*—ah, you may turn pale, if you like! You didn't think I was going to say that, did you? *The King has promised me—with his very own mouth—to—to—*"

"To send all his horses and all his men," Alice interrupted, rather unwisely.

"Now I declare that's too bad!" Humpty Dumpty cried, breaking into a sudden passion. "You've been listening at doors—and behind trees—and down chimneys—or you couldn't have known it!"

"I haven't, indeed!" Alice said very gently. "It's in a book."

"Ah, well! They may write such things in a *book*," Humpty Dumpty said in a calmer tone. "That's what you call a History of England, that is. Now, take a good look at me! I'm one that has spoken to a King, *I* am; mayhap you'll never see such another; and, to show you I'm not proud, you may shake hands with me!" And he grinned almost from ear to ear, as he leaned forwards (and as nearly as possible fell off the wall in doing so) and offered Alice his hand. She watched him a little anxiously as she took it. "If he smiled much more the ends of his mouth might meet behind," she thought. "And then I don't know *what* would happen to his head! I'm afraid it would come off!"

"Yes, all his horses and all his men," Humpty Dumpty went on. "They'd pick me up again in a minute, *they* would! However, this conversation is going on a little too fast; let's go back to the last remark but one."

"I'm afraid I can't quite remember it," Alice said, very politely.

"In that case we start afresh," said Humpty Dumpty, "and it's my turn to choose a subject—" ("He talks about it just as if it was a game!" thought Alice.) "So here's a question for you. How old did you say you were?"

Alice made a short calculation, and said, "Seven years and six months."

"Wrong!" Humpty Dumpty exclaimed triumphantly. "You never said a word like it!"

"I thought you meant 'How old *are* you?'" Alice explained.

"If I'd meant that, I'd have said it," said Humpty Dumpty.

Alice didn't want to begin another argument, so she said nothing.

"Seven years and six months!" Humpty Dumpty repeated thoughtfully. "An uncomfortable sort of age. Now if you'd asked *my* advice, I'd have said 'Leave off at seven'—but it's too late now."

"I never ask advice about growing," Alice said indignantly.

"Too proud?" the other inquired.

Alice felt even more indignant at this suggestion. "I mean," she said, "that one can't help growing older."

"*One* can't, perhaps," said Humpty Dumpty, "but *two* can. With proper assistance, you might have left off at seven."

"What a beautiful belt you've got on!" Alice suddenly remarked. (They had had quite enough of the subject of age, she thought; and, if they really were to take turns in choosing subjects, it was *her* turn now.) "At least," she corrected herself on second thoughts, "a beautiful cravat, I should have said—no, a belt, I mean— I beg your pardon!" she added in dismay, for Humpty Dumpty looked thoroughly offended, and she began to wish she hadn't chosen that subject. "If only I knew," she thought to herself, "which was neck and which was waist!"

Evidently Humpty Dumpty was very angry, though he said nothing for a minute or two. When he *did* speak again, it was in a deep growl. "It is a—*most—provoking*—thing," he said at last, "when a person doesn't know a cravat from a belt!"

"I know it's very ignorant of me," Alice said, in so humble a tone that Humpty Dumpty relented.

"It's a cravat, child, and a beautiful one, as you say. It's a present from the White King and Queen. There now!"

"Is it really?" said Alice, quite pleased to find that she *had* chosen a good subject after all.

"They gave it me," Humpty Dumpty continued thoughtfully as he crossed one knee over the other and clasped his hands round it, "they gave it me—for an unbirthday present."

"I beg your pardon?" Alice said with a puzzled air.

"I'm not offended," said Humpty Dumpty.

"I mean, what *is* an unbirthday present?"

"A present given when it isn't your birthday, of course."

Alice considered a little. "I like birthday presents best," she said at last.

"You don't know what you're talking about!" cried Humpty Dumpty. "How many days are there in a year?"

"Three hundred and sixty-five," said Alice.

"And how many birthdays have you?"

"One."

"And if you take one from three hundred and sixty-five what remains?"

"Three hundred and sixty-four, of course."

Humpty Dumpty looked doubtful. "I'd rather see that done on paper," he said.

Alice couldn't help smiling as she took out her memorandum book, and worked the sum for him:

$$365$$
$$\underline{1}$$
$$364$$

Humpty Dumpty took the book and looked at it carefully.

"That seems to be done right—" he began.

"You're holding it upside down!" Alice interrupted.

"To be sure I was!" Humpty Dumpty said gaily as she turned it round for him. "I thought it looked a little queer. As I was saying, that *seems* to be done right—though I haven't time to look it over thoroughly just now—and that shows that there are three hundred and sixty-four days when you might get unbirthday presents—"

"Certainly," said Alice.

"And only *one* for birthday presents, you know. There's glory for you!"

"I don't know what you mean by 'glory,'" Alice said.

Humpty Dumpty smiled contemptuously. "Of course you don't—till I tell you. I meant 'there's a nice knockdown argument for you!'"

"But 'glory' doesn't mean 'a nice knockdown argument,'" Alice objected.

"When *I* use a word," Humpty Dumpty said, in rather a scornful tone, "it means just what I choose it to mean—neither more nor less."

"The question is," said Alice, "whether you *can* make words mean so many different things."

"The question is," said Humpty Dumpty, "which is to be master—that's all."

Alice was too much puzzled to say anything; so after a minute Humpty Dumpty began again.

"They've a temper, some of them—particularly verbs: they're the proudest—adjectives you can do anything with, but not verbs—however, *I* can manage the whole lot of them! Impenetrability! That's what *I* say!"

"Would you tell me please," said Alice, "what that means?"

"Now you talk like a reasonable child," said Humpty Dumpty, looking very much pleased. "I meant by 'impenetrability' that we've had enough of that subject, and it would be just as well if you'd mention what you mean to do next, as I suppose you don't mean to stop here all the rest of your life."

"That's a great deal to make one word mean," Alice said in a thoughtful tone.

"When I make a word do a lot of work like that," said Humpty Dumpty, "I always pay it extra."

"Oh!" said Alice. She was too much puzzled to make any other remark.

"Ah, you should see 'em come round me of a Saturday night," Humpty Dumpty went on, wagging his head gravely from side to side, "for to get their wages, you know." (Alice didn't venture to ask what he paid them with; and so you see I can't tell *you*.)

"You seem very clever at explaining words, Sir," said Alice. "Would you kindly tell me the meaning of the poem called 'Jabberwocky'?"

"Let's hear it," said Humpty Dumpty. "I can explain all the poems that ever were invented—and a good many that haven't been invented just yet."

This sounded very hopeful, so Alice repeated the first verse:

> "'*Twas brillig, and the slithy toves*
> *Did gyre and gimble in the wabe;*
> *All mimsy were the borogoves,*
> *And the mome raths outgrabe.*"

"That's enough to begin with," Humpty Dumpty interrupted: "there are plenty of hard words there. *Brillig* means four o'clock in the afternoon—the time when you begin *broiling* things for dinner."

"That'll do very well," said Alice; "and *slithy?*"

"Well, *slithy* means lithe and slimy. Lithe is the same as active. You see it's like a portmanteau—there are two meanings packed up into one word."

"I see it now," Alice remarked thoughtfully; "and what are *toves?*"

"Well, *toves* are something like badgers—they're something like lizards—and they're something like corkscrews."

"They must be very curious-looking creatures."

"They are that," said Humpty Dumpty; "also they make their nests under sundials—also they live on cheese."

"And what's to *gyre* and to *gimble?*"

"To *gyre* is to go round and round like a gyroscope. To *gimble* is to make holes like a gimlet."

"And *the wabe* is the grass plot round a sundial, I suppose?" said Alice, surprised at her own ingenuity.

"Of course it is. It's called *wabe*, you know, because it goes a long way before it, and a long way behind it—"

"And a long way beyond it on each side," Alice added.

"Exactly so. Well then, *mimsy* is flimsy and miserable (there's another portmanteau for you). And a *borogove* is a thin shabby-looking bird with its feathers sticking out all round—something like a live mop."

"And then *mome raths?*" said Alice. "I'm afraid I'm giving you a great deal of trouble."

"Well, a *rath* is a sort of green pig; but *mome* I'm not certain about. I think it's short for from home—meaning that they'd lost their way, you know."

"And what does *outgrabe* mean?"

"Well, *outgribing* is something between bellowing and whistling, with a kind of sneeze in the middle; however, you'll hear it done, maybe—down in the wood yonder—and, when you've once heard it, you'll be *quite* content. Who's been repeating all that hard stuff to you?"

"I read it in a book," said Alice. "But I *had* some poetry repeated to me much easier than that, by—Tweedledee, I think it was."

"As to poetry, you know," said Humpty Dumpty, stretching out one of his great hands, "*I* can repeat poetry as well as other folk, if it comes to that—"

"Oh, it needn't come to that!" Alice hastily said, hoping to keep him from beginning.

"The piece I'm going to repeat," he went on without noticing her remark, "was written entirely for your amusement."

Alice felt that in that case she really *ought* to listen to it; so she sat down, and said "Thank you" rather sadly.

> *"In winter, when the fields are white,*
> *I sing this song for your delight—*

Only I don't sing it," he added, as an explanation.

"I see you don't," said Alice.

"If you can *see* whether I'm singing or not, you've sharper eyes than most," Humpty Dumpty remarked severely. Alice was silent.

> *"In spring, when woods are getting green,*
> *I'll try and tell you what I mean;"*

"Thank you very much," said Alice.

> *"In summer, when the days are long,*
> *Perhaps you'll understand the song;*
> *In autumn, when the leaves are brown,*
> *Take pen and ink, and write it down."*

"I will, if I can remember it so long," said Alice.

"You needn't go on making remarks like that," Humpty Dumpty said; "they're not sensible, and they put me out.

> *"I sent a message to the fish:*
> *I told them 'This is what I wish.'*
>
> *The little fishes of the sea,*
> *They sent an answer back to me.*
>
> *The little fishes' answer was*
> *'We cannot do it, Sir, because—'"*

"I'm afraid I don't quite understand," said Alice.

"It gets easier further on," Humpty Dumpty replied.

> "*I sent to them again to say,*
> '*It will be better to obey.*'
>
> *The fishes answered, with a grin,*
> '*Why, what a temper you are in!*'
>
> *I told them once, I told them twice:*
> *They would not listen to advice.*
>
> *I took a kettle large and new,*
> *Fit for the deed I had to do.*
>
> *My heart went hop, my heart went thump;*
> *I filled the kettle at the pump.*
>
> *Then someone came to me and said,*
> '*The little fishes are in bed.*'
>
> *I said to him, I said it plain,*
> '*Then you must wake them up again.*'
>
> *I said it very loud and clear:*
> *I went and shouted in his ear.*"

Humpty Dumpty raised his voice almost to a scream as he repeated this verse, and Alice thought, with a shudder, "I wouldn't have been the messenger for *anything!*"

> "*But he was very stiff and proud:*
> *He said, 'You needn't shout so loud!'*
>
> *And he was very proud and stiff:*
> *He said, 'I'd go and wake them, if—'*
>
> *I took a corkscrew from the shelf;*
> *I went to wake them up myself.*
>
> *And when I found the door was locked,*
> *I pulled and pushed and kicked and knocked.*
>
> *And when I found the door was shut,*
> *I tried to turn the handle, but—*"

There was a long pause.

"Is that all?" Alice timidly asked.

"That's all," said Humpty Dumpty. "Good-by."

This was rather sudden, Alice thought; but, after such a *very* strong hint that she ought to be going, she felt that it would hardly be civil to stay. So she got up, and held out her hand. "Good-by, till we meet again!" she said as cheerfully as she could.

"I shouldn't know you again if we *did* meet," Humpty Dumpty replied in a discontented tone, giving her one of his fingers to shake; "you're so exactly like other people."

"The face is what one goes by, generally," Alice remarked in a thoughtful tone.

"That's just what I complain of," said Humpty Dumpty. "Your face is the same as everybody has—the two eyes, so—" (marking their places in the air with his thumb) "nose in the middle, mouth under. It's always the same. Now if you had the two eyes on the same side of the nose, for instance—or the mouth at the top—that would be *some* help."

"It wouldn't look nice," Alice objected. But Humpty Dumpty only shut his eyes, and said, "Wait till you've tried."

Alice waited a minute to see if he would speak again, but, as he never opened his eyes or took any further notice of her, she said "Good-by!" once more, and, getting no answer to this, she quietly walked away; but she couldn't help saying to herself, as she went, "Of all the unsatisfactory—" (she repeated this aloud, as it was a great comfort to have such a long word to say) "of all the unsatisfactory people I *ever* met—" She never finished the sentence, for at this moment a heavy crash shook the forest from end to end.

CHAPTER VII: *The Lion and the Unicorn*

THE NEXT MOMENT SOLDIERS came running through the wood, at first in twos and threes, then ten or twenty together, and at last in such crowds that they seemed to fill the whole forest. Alice got behind a tree, for fear of being run over, and watched them go by.

She thought that in all her life she had never seen soldiers so uncertain on their feet: they were always tripping over something or other, and whenever one went down, several more always fell over him, so that the ground was soon covered with little heaps of men.

Then came the horses. Having four feet, these managed rather better than the foot soldiers; but even *they* stumbled now and then; and it seemed to be a regular rule that, whenever a horse stumbled, the rider fell off instantly. The confusion got worse every moment, and Alice was very glad to get out of the wood into an open place, where she found the White King seated on the ground, busily writing in his memorandum book.

"I've sent them all!" the King cried in a tone of delight, on seeing Alice. "Did you happen to meet any soldiers, my dear, as you came through the wood?"

"Yes, I did," said Alice; "several thousand, I should think."

"Four thousand two hundred and seven, that's the exact number," the King said, referring to his book. "I couldn't send all the horses, you know, because two of them are wanted in the game. And I haven't sent the two Messengers, either. They're both gone to the town. Just look along the road, and tell me if you can see either of them."

"I see nobody on the road," said Alice.

"I only wish *I* had such eyes," the King remarked in a fretful tone. "To be able to see Nobody! And at that distance too! Why, it's as much as *I* can do to see real people, by this light!"

All this was lost on Alice, who was still looking intently along the road, shading her eyes with one hand. "I see somebody now!" she exclaimed at last. "But he's coming very slowly—and what curious attitudes he goes into!" (For the Messenger kept skipping up and down, and wriggling like an eel, as he came along, with his great hands spread out like fans on each side.)

"Not at all," said the King. "He's an Anglo-Saxon Messenger—and those are Anglo-Saxon attitudes. He only does them when he's happy. His name is Haigha." (He pronounced it so as to rhyme with "mayor.")

"I love my love with an *H*," Alice couldn't help beginning, "because he is Happy. I hate him with an *H*, because he is Hideous. I fed him with—with—with Ham sandwiches and Hay. His name is Haigha, and he lives—"

"He lives on the Hill," the King remarked simply, without the least idea that he was joining in the game, while Alice was still hesitating for the name of a town beginning with *H*. "The other Messenger's called Hatta. I must have *two*, you know—to come and go. One to come, and one to go."

"I beg your pardon?" said Alice.

"It isn't respectable to beg," said the King.

"I only meant that I didn't understand," said Alice. "Why one to come and one to go?"

"Don't I tell you?" the King repeated impatiently. "I must have *two*—to fetch and carry. One to fetch, and one to carry."

At this moment the Messenger arrived; he was far too much out of breath to say a word, and could only wave his hands about, and make the most fearful faces at the poor King.

"This young lady loves you with an *H*," the King said, introducing Alice in the hope of turning off the Messenger's attention from himself—but it was of no use—the Anglo-Saxon attitudes only got more extraordinary every moment, while the great eyes rolled wildly from side to side.

"You alarm me!" said the King. "I feel faint— Give me a ham sandwich!" On which the Messenger, to Alice's great amusement, opened a bag that hung round his neck, and handed a sandwich to the King, who devoured it greedily.

"Another sandwich!" said the King.

"There's nothing but hay left now," the Messenger said, peeping into the bag.

"Hay, then," the King murmured in a faint whisper.

Alice was glad to see that it revived him a good deal.

"There's nothing like eating hay when you're faint," he remarked to her, as he munched away.

"I should think throwing cold water over you would be better," Alice suggested, "or some sal volatile."

"I didn't say there was nothing *better*," the King replied. "I said there was nothing *like* it." Which Alice did not venture to deny.

"Who did you pass on the road?" the King went on, holding out his hand to the Messenger for some hay.

"Nobody," said the Messenger.

"Quite right," said the King; "this young lady saw him too. So of course Nobody walks slower than you."

"I do my best," the Messenger said in a sullen tone. "I'm sure nobody walks much faster than I do!"

"He can't do that," said the King, "or else he'd have been here first. However, now you've got your breath, you may tell us what's happened in the town."

"I'll whisper it," said the Messenger, putting his hands to his mouth in the shape of a trumpet and stooping so as to get close to the King's ear. Alice was sorry for this, as she wanted to hear the news too. However, instead of whispering, he simply shouted, at the top of his voice, "They're at it again!"

"Do you call *that* a whisper?" cried the poor King, jumping up and shaking himself. "If you do such a thing again, I'll have you buttered! It went through and through my head like an earthquake!"

"It would have to be a very tiny earthquake!" thought Alice "Who are at it again?" she ventured to ask.

"Why, the Lion and the Unicorn, of course," said the King.

"Fighting for the crown?"

"Yes, to be sure," said the King; "and the best of the joke is that it's *my* crown all the while! Let's run and see them." And they trotted off, Alice repeating to herself, as she ran, the words of the old song:

> *"The Lion and the Unicorn were fighting for the crown;*
> *The Lion beat the Unicorn all round the town.*
> *Some gave them white bread, some gave them brown;*
> *Some gave them plum cake and drummed them out of town.*

"Does—the one—that wins—get the crown?" she asked, as well as she could, for the run was putting her quite out of breath.

"Dear me, no!" said the King. "What an idea!"

"Would you—be good enough—" Alice panted out, after running a little further, "to stop a minute—just to get—one's breath again?"

"I'm *good* enough," the King said, "only I'm not *strong* enough. You see, a minute goes by so fearfully quick. You might as well try to stop a Bandersnatch!"

Alice had no more breath for talking; so they trotted on in silence, till they came into sight of a great crowd, in the middle of which the Lion and Unicorn were fighting. They were in such a cloud of dust that at first Alice could not make out which was which; but she soon managed to distinguish the Unicorn by his horn.

They placed themselves close to where Hatta, the other Mes-

senger, was standing watching the fight, with a cup of tea in one
hand and a piece of bread and butter in the other.

"He's only just out of prison, and he hadn't finished his tea
when he was sent in," Haigha whispered to Alice; "and they only
give them oystershells in there—so you see he's very hungry and
thirsty. How are you, dear child?" he went on, putting his arm
affectionately round Hatta's neck.

Hatta looked round and nodded, and went on with his bread
and butter.

"Were you happy in prison, dear child?" said Haigha.

Hatta looked round once more, and this time a tear or two
trickled down his cheek; but not a word would he say.

"Speak, can't you!" Haigha cried impatiently. But Hatta only
munched away, and drank some more tea.

"Speak, won't you!" cried the King. "How are they getting on
with the fight?"

Hatta made a desperate effort, and swallowed a large piece of
bread and butter. "They're getting on very well," he said in a chok-

ing voice; "each of them has been down about eighty-seven times."

"Then I suppose they'll soon bring the white bread and the brown?" Alice ventured to remark.

"It's waiting for 'em now," said Hatta; "this is a bit of it as I'm eating."

There was a pause in the fight just then, and the Lion and the Unicorn sat down, panting, while the King called out, "Ten minutes allowed for refreshments!" Haigha and Hatta set to work at once, carrying round trays of white and brown bread. Alice took a piece to taste, but it was *very* dry.

"I don't think they'll fight any more today," the King said to Hatta; "go and order the drums to begin." And Hatta went bounding away like a grasshopper.

For a minute or two Alice stood silent, watching him. Suddenly she brightened up. "Look, look!" she cried, pointing eagerly. "There's the White Queen running across the country! She came flying out of the wood over yonder— How fast those Queens *can* run!"

"There's some enemy after her, no doubt," the King said, without even looking round. "That wood's full of them."

"But aren't you going to run and help her?" Alice asked, very much surprised at his taking it so quietly.

"No use, no use!" said the King. "She runs so fearfully quick. You might as well try to catch a Bandersnatch! But I'll make a memorandum about her, if you like— She's a dear good creature," he repeated softly to himself, as he opened his memorandum book. "Do you spell creature with a double e?"

At this moment the Unicorn sauntered by them, with his hands in his pockets. "I had the best of it this time?" he said to the King, just glancing at him as he passed.

"A little—a little," the King replied, rather nervously. "You shouldn't have run him through with your horn, you know."

"It didn't hurt him," the Unicorn said carelessly, and he was going on, when his eye happened to fall upon Alice; he turned round instantly, and stood for some time looking at her with an air of the deepest disgust. "What—is—this?" he said at last.

"This is a child!" Haigha replied eagerly, coming in front of Alice to introduce her, and spreading out both his hands towards her in an Anglo-Saxon attitude. "We only found it today. It's as large as life, and twice as natural!"

"I always thought they were fabulous monsters!" said the Unicorn. "Is it alive?"

"It can talk," said Haigha solemnly.

The Unicorn looked dreamily at Alice, and said, "Talk, child."

Alice could not help her lips curling up into a smile as she began: "Do you know, I always thought Unicorns were fabulous monsters, too? I never saw one alive before!"

"Well, now that we *have* seen each other," said the Unicorn, "if you'll believe in me, I'll believe in you. Is that a bargain?"

"Yes, if you like," said Alice.

"Come, fetch out the plum cake, old man!" the Unicorn went on, turning from her to the King. "None of your brown bread for me!"

"Certainly—certainly!" the King muttered, and beckoned to Haigha. "Open the bag!" he whispered. "Quick! Not that one— that's full of hay!"

Haigha took a large cake out of the bag, and gave it to Alice to hold, while he got out a dish and carving knife. How they all came out of it Alice couldn't guess. It was just like a conjuring trick, she thought.

The Lion had joined them while this was going on; he looked very tired and sleepy, and his eyes were half shut. "What's this!" he said, blinking lazily at Alice, and speaking in a deep hollow tone that sounded like the tolling of a great bell.

"Ah, what *is* it, now?" the Unicorn cried eagerly. "You'll never guess! *I* couldn't."

The Lion looked at Alice wearily. "Are you animal—or vegetable—or mineral?" he said, yawning at every other word.

"It's a fabulous monster!" the Unicorn cried out, before Alice could reply.

"Then hand round the plum cake, Monster," the Lion said, lying down and putting his chin on his paws. "And sit down, both of you" (to the King and the Unicorn); "fair play with the

cake, you know!" The King was evidently very uncomfortable at having to sit down between the two great creatures; but there was no other place for him.

"What a fight we might have for the crown, *now!*" the Unicorn said, looking slyly up at the crown, which the poor King was nearly shaking off his head, he trembled so much.

"I should win easy," said the Lion.

"I'm not so sure of that," said the Unicorn.

"Why, I beat you all round the town, you chicken!" the Lion replied angrily, half getting up as he spoke.

Here the King interrupted, to prevent the quarrel going on; he was very nervous, and his voice quite quivered. "All round the town?" he said. "That's a good long way. Did you go by the old bridge, or the marketplace? You get the best view by the old bridge."

"I'm sure I don't know," the Lion growled out as he lay down again. "There was too much dust to see anything. What a time the Monster is, cutting up that cake!"

Alice had seated herself on the bank of a little brook, with the great dish on her knees, and was sawing away diligently with the knife. "It's very provoking!" she said, in reply to the Lion (she was getting quite used to being called "the Monster"). "I've cut several slices already, but they always join on again!"

"You don't know how to manage Looking-Glass cakes," the Unicorn remarked. "Hand it round first, and cut it afterwards."

This sounded nonsense, but Alice very obediently got up, and carried the dish round, and the cake divided itself into three pieces as she did so. "*Now* cut it up," said the Lion, as she returned to her place with the empty dish.

"I say, this isn't fair!" cried the Unicorn, as Alice sat with the knife in her hand, very much puzzled how to begin. "The Monster has given the Lion twice as much as me!"

"She's kept none for herself, anyhow," said the Lion. "Do you like plum cake, Monster?"

But before Alice could answer him, the drums began.

Where the noise came from she couldn't make out; the air seemed full of it, and it rang through and through her head till she felt quite deafened. She started to her feet and sprang across the little brook in her terror, and had just time to see the Lion and the Unicorn rise to their feet, with angry looks at being interrupted in their feast, before she dropped to her knees, and put her hands over her ears, vainly trying to shut out the dreadful uproar.

"If *that* doesn't drum them out of town," she thought to herself, "nothing ever will!"

CHAPTER VIII: *"It's My Own Invention"*

AFTER A WHILE THE NOISE seemed gradually to die away, till all was dead silence, and Alice lifted up her head in some alarm. There was no one to be seen, and her first thought was that she must have been dreaming about the Lion and the Unicorn and those queer Anglo-Saxon Messengers. However, there was the great dish still lying at her feet, on which she had tried to cut the plum cake. "So

I wasn't dreaming, after all," she said to herself, "unless—unless we're all part of the same dream. Only I do hope it's *my* dream and not the Red King's! I don't like belonging to another person's dream," she went on in a rather complaining tone; "I've a great mind to go and wake him, and see what happens!"

At this moment her thoughts were interrupted by a loud shouting of "Ahoy! Ahoy! Check!" and a Knight, dressed in crimson armor, came galloping down upon her, brandishing a great club. Just as he reached her, the horse stopped suddenly. "You're my prisoner!" the Knight cried, as he tumbled off his horse.

Startled as she was, Alice was more frightened for him than for herself at the moment, and watched him with some anxiety as he mounted again. As soon as he was comfortably in the saddle, he began once more, "You're my—" but here another voice broke in: "Ahoy! Ahoy! Check!" and Alice looked round in some surprise for the new enemy.

This time it was a White Knight. He drew up at Alice's side, and tumbled off his horse just as the Red Knight had done; then he got on again, and the two Knights sat and looked at each other for some time without speaking. Alice looked from one to the other in some bewilderment.

"She's *my* prisoner, you know!" the Red Knight said at last.

"Yes, but then *I* came and rescued her!" the White Knight replied.

"Well, we must fight for her, then," said the Red Knight, as he took up his helmet (which hung from the saddle, and was something the shape of a horse's head) and put it on.

"You will observe the Rules of Battle, of course?" the White Knight remarked, putting on his helmet too.

"I always do," said the Red Knight, and they began banging away at each other with such fury that Alice got behind a tree to be out of the way of the blows.

"I wonder, now, what the Rules of Battle are," she said to herself, as she watched the fight, timidly peeping out from her hiding place. "One Rule seems to be that if one Knight hits the other, he knocks him off his horse; and, if he misses, he tumbles off himself—and another Rule seems to be that they hold their clubs with their arms, as if they were Punch and Judy— What a noise they make when they tumble! Just like a whole set of fire irons falling into the fender! And how quiet the horses are. They let them get on and off them just as if they were tables!"

Another Rule of Battle that Alice had not noticed seemed to be that they always fell on their heads; and the battle ended with their both falling off in this way, side by side. When they got up again, they shook hands, and then the Red Knight mounted and galloped off.

"It was a glorious victory, wasn't it?" said the White Knight, as he came up panting.

"I don't know," Alice said doubtfully. "I don't want to be anybody's prisoner. I want to be a Queen."

"So you will, when you've crossed the next brook," said the White Knight. "I'll see you safe to the end of the wood—and then I must go back, you know. That's the end of my move."

"Thank you very much," said Alice. "May I help you off with your helmet?" It was evidently more than he could manage by himself; however she managed to shake him out of it at last.

"Now one can breathe more easily," said the Knight, putting back his shaggy hair with both hands, and turning his gentle face and large mild eyes to Alice. She thought she had never seen such a strange-looking soldier in all her life.

He was dressed in tin armor, which seemed to fit him very

badly, and he had a queer-shaped little deal box fastened across his shoulders, upside down, and with the lid hanging open. Alice looked at it with great curiosity. "I see you're admiring my little box," the Knight said in a friendly tone. "It's my own invention—to keep clothes and sandwiches in. You see, I carry it upside down so that the rain can't get in."

"But the things can get *out*," Alice gently remarked. "Do you know the lid's open?"

"I didn't know it," the Knight said, a shade of vexation passing over his face. "Then all the things must have fallen out! And the box is no use without them."

He unfastened it as he spoke, and was just going to throw it into the bushes, when a sudden thought seemed to strike him, and he hung it carefully on a tree. "Can you guess why I did that?" he said to Alice.

Alice shook her head.

"In hopes some bees may make a nest in it—then I should get the honey."

"But you've got a beehive—or something like one—fastened to the saddle," said Alice.

"Yes, it's a very good beehive," the Knight said in a discontented tone, "one of the best kind. But not a single bee has come near it yet. And the other thing is a mousetrap. I suppose the mice keep the bees out—or the bees keep the mice out, I don't know which."

"I was wondering what the mousetrap was for," said Alice. "It isn't very likely there would be any mice on the horse's back."

"Not very likely, perhaps," said the Knight; "but, if they *do* come, I don't choose to have them running all about.

"You see," he went on after a pause, "it's as well to be provided for *everything*. That's the reason the horse has all those anklets round his feet."

"But what are they for?" Alice asked in a tone of great curiosity.

"To guard against the bites of sharks," the Knight replied. "It's an invention of my own. And now help me on. I'll go with you to the end of the wood— What's that dish for?"

"It's meant for plum cake," said Alice.

"We'd better take it with us," the Knight said. "It'll come in handy if we find any plum cake. Help me to get it into this bag."

This took a long time to manage, though Alice held the bag open very carefully, because the Knight was so *very* awkward in putting in the dish; the first two or three times that he tried he fell in himself instead.

"It's rather a tight fit, you see," he said, as they got it in at last; "there are so many candlesticks in the bag." And he hung it to the saddle, which was already loaded with bunches of carrots, and fire irons, and many other things.

"I hope you've got your hair well fastened on?" he continued, as they set off.

"Only in the usual way," Alice said, smiling.

"That's hardly enough," he said, anxiously. "You see, the wind is so *very* strong here. It's as strong as soup."

"Have you invented a plan for keeping the hair from being blown off?" Alice inquired.

"Not yet," said the Knight. "But I've got a plan for keeping it from *falling* off."

"I should like to hear it, very much."

"First you take an upright stick," said the Knight. "Then you make your hair creep up it, like a fruit tree. Now the reason hair falls off is because it hangs *down*—things never fall *upwards*, you know. It's a plan of my own invention. You may try it if you like."

It didn't sound a comfortable plan, Alice thought, and for a few minutes she walked on in silence, puzzling over the idea, and every now and then stopping to help the poor Knight, who certainly was *not* a good rider.

Whenever the horse stopped (which it did very often), he fell off in front; and, whenever it went on again (which it generally did

rather suddenly), he fell off behind. Otherwise he kept on pretty well, except that he had a habit of now and then falling off sideways; and, as he generally did this on the side on which Alice was walking, she soon found that it was the best plan not to walk *quite* close to the horse.

"I'm afraid you've not had much practice in riding," she ventured to say, as she was helping him up from his fifth tumble.

The Knight looked very much surprised, and a little offended at the remark. "What makes you say that?" he asked, as he scrambled back into the saddle, keeping hold of Alice's hair with one hand, to save himself from falling over on the other side.

"Because people don't fall off quite so often, when they've had much practice."

"I've had plenty of practice," the Knight said very gravely; "plenty of practice!"

Alice could think of nothing better to say than "Indeed?" but she said it as heartily as she could. They went on a little way in silence after this, the Knight with his eyes shut, muttering to himself, and Alice watching anxiously for the next tumble.

"The great art of riding," the Knight suddenly began in a loud voice, waving his right arm as he spoke, "is to keep—" Here the sentence ended as suddenly as it had begun, as the Knight fell heavily on the top of his head exactly in the path where Alice was walking. She was quite frightened this time, and said in an anxious tone, as she picked him up, "I hope no bones are broken?"

"None to speak of," the Knight said, as if he didn't mind breaking two or three of them. "The great art of riding, as I was saying, is—to keep your balance properly. Like this, you know—"

He let go the bridle, and stretched out both his arms to show Alice what he meant, and this time he fell flat on his back, right under the horse's feet.

"Plenty of practice!" he went on repeating, all the time that Alice was getting him on his feet again. "Plenty of practice!"

"It's too ridiculous!" cried Alice, losing all her patience this time. "You ought to have a wooden horse on wheels, that you ought!"

"Does that kind go smoothly?" the Knight asked in a tone of great interest, clasping his arms round the horse's neck as he spoke, just in time to save himself from tumbling off again.

"Much more smoothly than a live horse," Alice said, with a little scream of laughter, in spite of all she could do to prevent it.

"I'll get one," the Knight said thoughtfully to himself. "One or two—several."

There was a short silence after this, and then the Knight went on again. "I'm a great hand at inventing things. Now, I daresay you noticed, the last time you picked me up, that I was looking rather thoughtful?"

"You *were* a little grave," said Alice.

"Well, just then I was inventing a new way of getting over a gate—would you like to hear it?"

"Very much indeed," Alice said politely.

"I'll tell you how I came to think of it," said the Knight. "You see, I said to myself, 'The only difficulty is with the feet; the *head* is high enough already.' Now, first I put my head on the top of the gate—then the head's high enough—then I stand on my head—then the feet are high enough, you see—then I'm over, you see."

"Yes, I suppose you'd be over when that was done," Alice said thoughtfully; "but don't you think it would be rather hard?"

"I haven't tried it yet," the Knight said, gravely; "so I can't tell for certain—but I'm afraid it *would* be a little hard."

He looked so vexed at the idea that Alice changed the subject hastily. "What a curious helmet you've got!" she said cheerfully. "Is that your invention too?"

The Knight looked down proudly at his helmet, which hung from the saddle. "Yes," he said; "but I've invented a better one than that—like a sugarloaf. When I used to wear it, if I fell off the horse, it always touched the ground directly. So I had a *very* little way to fall, you see— But there *was* the danger of falling *into* it, to be sure. That happened to me once—and the worst of it was, before I could get out again, the other White Knight came and put it on. He thought it was his own helmet."

The Knight looked so solemn about it that Alice did not dare to laugh. "I'm afraid you must have hurt him," she said in a trembling voice, "being on the top of his head."

"I had to kick him, of course," the Knight said, very seriously. "And then he took the helmet off again –but it took hours and hours to get me out. I was as fast as—as lightning, you know."

"But that's a different kind of fastness," Alice objected.

The Knight shook his head. "It was all kinds of fastness with me, I can assure you!" he said. He raised his hands in some excitement as he said this, and instantly rolled out of the saddle, and fell headlong into a deep ditch.

Alice ran to the side of the ditch to look for him. She was rather startled by the fall, as for some time he had kept on very well, and she was afraid that he really *was* hurt this time.

However, though she could see nothing but the soles of his feet, she was much relieved to hear that he was talking on in his usual tone. "All kinds of fastness," he repeated; "but it was careless of him to put another man's helmet on—with the man in it, too."

"How *can* you go on talking so quietly, head downwards?" Alice asked, as she dragged him out by the feet, and laid him in a heap on the bank.

The Knight looked surprised at the question. "What does it matter where my body happens to be?" he said. "My mind goes on working all the same. In fact, the more head downwards I am, the more I keep inventing new things.

"Now the cleverest thing of the sort that I ever did," he went on after a pause, "was inventing a new pudding during the meat course."

"In time to have it cooked for the next course?" said Alice. "Well, that *was* quick work, certainly!"

"Well, not the *next* course," the Knight said in a slow thoughtful tone; "no, certainly not the next *course*."

"Then it would have to be the next day. I suppose you wouldn't have two pudding courses in one dinner?"

"Well, not the *next* day," the Knight repeated as before; "not the next *day*.

"In fact," he went on, holding his head down, and his voice getting lower and lower, "I don't believe that pudding ever *was* cooked! In fact, I don't believe that pudding ever *will* be cooked! And yet it was a very clever pudding to invent."

"What did you mean it to be made of?" Alice asked, hoping to cheer him up, for the poor Knight seemed quite low-spirited about it.

"It began with blotting paper," the Knight answered with a groan.

"That wouldn't be very nice, I'm afraid—"

"Not very nice *alone*," he interrupted, quite eagerly; "but you've no idea what a difference it makes, mixing it with other things—such as gunpowder and sealing wax. And here I must leave you." They had just come to the end of the wood.

Alice could only look puzzled; she was thinking of the pudding.

"You are sad," the Knight said in an anxious tone; "let me sing you a song to comfort you."

"Is it very long?" Alice asked, for she had heard a good deal of poetry that day.

"It's long," said the Knight, "but it's very, *very* beautiful. Everybody that hears me sing it—either it brings the *tears* into their eyes, or else—"

"Or else what?" said Alice, for the Knight had made a sudden pause.

"Or else it doesn't, you know. The name of the song is called 'Haddocks' Eyes.'"

"Oh, that's the name of the song, is it?" Alice said, trying to feel interested.

"No, you don't understand," the Knight said, looking a little vexed. "That's what the name is *called*. The name really *is* 'The Aged Aged Man.'"

"Then I ought to have said, 'That's what the *song* is called?'" Alice corrected herself.

"No, you oughtn't; that's quite another thing! The *song* is called 'Ways and Means'; but that's only what it's *called*, you know!"

"Well, what *is* the song, then?" said Alice, who was by this time completely bewildered.

"I was coming to that," the Knight said. "The song really *is* 'A-sitting On a Gate'; and the tune's my own invention."

So saying, he stopped his horse and let the reins fall on its neck; then, slowly beating time with one hand, and with a faint smile lighting up his gentle, foolish face, as if he enjoyed the music of his song, he began.

Of all the strange things that Alice saw in her journey Through the Looking Glass, this was the one that she always remembered most clearly. Years afterwards she could bring the whole scene back again, as if it had been only yesterday—the mild blue eyes and kindly smile of the Knight—the setting sun gleaming through his hair and shining on his armor in a blaze of light that quite dazzled her—the horse quietly moving about, with the reins hanging loose on his neck, cropping the grass at her feet—and the black shadows of the forest behind—all this she took in like a picture, as, with one hand shading her eyes, she leaned against a tree, watching the strange pair, and listening, in a half dream, to the melancholy music of the song.

"But the tune *isn't* his own invention," she said to herself; "it's 'I Give Thee All, I Can No More.'"

She stood and listened very attentively, but no tears came into her eyes.

> "*I'll tell thee everything I can:*
> *There's little to relate.*
> *I saw an aged aged man,*
> *A-sitting on a gate.*
> *'Who are you, aged man?' I said.*
> *'And how is it you live?'*
> *And his answer trickled through my head,*
> *Like water through a sieve.*
>
> *He said, 'I look for butterflies*
> *That sleep among the wheat;*
> *I make them into mutton pies,*
> *And sell them in the street.*
> *I sell them unto men,' he said,*
> *'Who sail on stormy seas;*
> *And that's the way I get my bread—*
> *A trifle, if you please.'*
>
> *But I was thinking of a plan*
> *To dye one's whiskers green,*
> *And always use so large a fan*
> *That they could not be seen.*
> *So, having no reply to give*
> *To what the old man said,*
> *I cried, 'Come, tell me how you live!'*
> *And thumped him on the head.*

His accents mild took up the tale:
　He said, 'I go my ways,
And when I find a mountain rill,
　I set it in a blaze;
And thence they make a stuff they call
　Rowland's Macassar Oil—
Yet twopence-halfpenny is all
　They give me for my toil.'

But I was thinking of a way
　To feed oneself on batter,
And so go on from day to day
　Getting a little fatter.
I shook him well from side to side,
　Until his face was blue;
'Come, tell me how you live,' I cried,
　'And what it is you do!'
He said, 'I hunt for haddocks' eyes
　Among the heather bright,

And work them into waistcoat buttons
  In the silent night.
And these I do not sell for gold
  Or coin of silvery shine,
But for a copper halfpenny,
  And that will purchase nine.

'I sometimes dig for buttered rolls,
  Or set limed twigs for crabs;
I sometimes search the grassy knolls
  For wheels of hansom cabs.
And that's the way' (he gave a wink)
  'By which I get my wealth—
And very gladly will I drink
  Your Honor's noble health.'

I heard him then, for I had just
  Completed my design
To keep the Menai bridge from rust
  By boiling it in wine.
I thanked him much for telling me
  The way he got his wealth,
But chiefly for his wish that he
  Might drink my noble health.

And now, if e'er by chance I put
  My fingers into glue,
Or madly squeeze a right-hand foot
  Into a left-hand shoe,
Or if I drop upon my toe
  A very heavy weight,
I weep, for it reminds me so
Of that old man I used to know—
Whose look was mild, whose speech was slow,
Whose hair was whiter than the snow,
Whose face was very like a crow,
With eyes, like cinders, all aglow,
Who seemed distracted with his woe,
Who rocked his body to and fro.

And muttered mumblingly and low,
As if his mouth were full of dough,
Who snorted like a buffalo—
That summer evening long ago,
A-sitting on a gate."

As the Knight sang the last words of the ballad, he gathered up the reins, and turned his horse's head along the road by which they had come.

"You've only a few yards to go," he said, "down the hill and over that little brook, and then you'll be a Queen— But you'll stay and see me off first?" he added as Alice turned with an eager look in the direction to which he pointed. "I shan't be long. You'll wait and wave your handkerchief when I get to that turn in the road! I think it'll encourage me, you see."

"Of course I'll wait," said Alice; "and thank you very much for coming so far—and for the song— I liked it very much."

"I hope so," the Knight said doubtfully; "but you didn't cry so much as I thought you would." So they shook hands, and then the Knight rode slowly away into the forest.

"It won't take long to see him *off*, I expect," Alice said to herself, as she stood watching him. "There he goes! Right on his head as usual! However, he gets on again pretty easily—that comes of having so many things hung round the horse—" So she went on talking to herself, as she watched the horse walking leisurely along the road, and the Knight tumbling off, first on one side and then on the other. After the fourth or fifth tumble he reached the turn, and then she waved her handkerchief to him, and waited till he was out of sight.

470

"I hope it encouraged him," she said, as she turned to run down the hill; "and now for the last brook, and to be a Queen! How grand it sounds!" A very few steps brought her to the edge of the brook. "The Eighth Square at last!" she cried as she bounded across, and threw herself down to rest on a lawn as soft as moss, with little flower beds dotted about it here and there. "Oh, how glad I am to get here! And what *is* this on my head?" she exclaimed in a tone of dismay, as she put her hands up to something very heavy that fitted tight all round her head.

"But how *can* it have got there without my knowing it?" she said to herself, as she lifted it off, and set it on her lap to make out what it could possibly be.

It was a golden crown.

CHAPTER IX: *Queen Alice*

"WELL, THIS IS GRAND!" said Alice. "I never expected I should be a Queen so soon—and I'll tell you what it is, your Majesty," she went on, in a severe tone (she was always rather fond of scolding herself), "it'll never do for you to be lolling about on the grass like that! Queens have to be dignified, you know!"

So she got up and walked about—rather stiffly just at first, as she was afraid that the crown might come off; but she comforted herself with the thought that there was nobody to see her, "and if I really am a Queen," she said as she sat down again, "I shall be able to manage it quite well in time."

Everything was happening so oddly that she didn't feel a bit surprised at finding the Red Queen and the White Queen sitting close to her, one on each side; she would have liked very much to ask them how they came there, but she feared it would not be quite civil. However, there would be no harm, she thought, in asking if the game was over. "Please, would you tell me—" she began, looking timidly at the Red Queen.

"Speak when you're spoken to!" the Queen sharply interrupted her.

"But if everybody obeyed that rule," said Alice, who was always ready for a little argument, "and if you only spoke when you were spoken to, and the other person always waited for *you* to begin, you see nobody would ever say anything, so that—"

"Ridiculous!" cried the Queen. "Why, don't you see, child—" Here she broke off with a frown, and, after thinking for a minute, suddenly changed the subject of the conversation. "What do you mean by 'If you really are a Queen?' What right have you to call yourself so? You can't be a Queen, you know, till you've passed the proper examination. And the sooner we begin it, the better."

"I only said 'if'!" poor Alice pleaded in a piteous tone.

The two Queens looked at each other, and the Red Queen remarked, with a little shudder, "She *says* she only said 'if'—"

"But she said a great deal more than that!" the White Queen moaned, wringing her hands. "Oh, ever so much more than that!"

"So you did, you know," the Red Queen said to Alice. "Always speak the truth—think before you speak—and write it down afterwards."

"I'm sure I didn't mean—" Alice was beginning, but the Red Queen interrupted her impatiently.

"That's just what I complain of! You *should* have meant! What do you suppose is the use of a child without any meaning? Even a joke should have some meaning—and a child's more important than a joke, I hope. You couldn't deny that, even if you tried with both hands."

"I don't deny things with my *hands*," Alice objected.

"Nobody said you did," said the Red Queen. "I said you couldn't if you tried."

"She's in that state of mind," said the White Queen, "that she wants to deny *something*—only she doesn't know what to deny!"

"A nasty, vicious temper," the Red Queen remarked; and then there was an uncomfortable silence for a minute or two.

The Red Queen broke the silence by saying, to the White Queen, "I invite you to Alice's dinner party this afternoon."

The White Queen smiled feebly, and said, "And I invite *you.*"

"I didn't know I was to have a party at all," said Alice; "but, if there *is* to be one, I think *I* ought to invite the guests."

"We gave you the opportunity of doing it," the Red Queen remarked; "but I daresay you've not had many lessons in manners yet."

"Manners are not taught in lessons," said Alice. "Lessons teach you to do sums, and things of that sort."

"Can you do Addition?" the White Queen asked. "What's one and one and one and one and one and one and one and one and one and one and one?"

"I don't know," said Alice. "I lost count."

"She can't do Addition," the Red Queen interrupted. "Can you do Subtraction? Take nine from eight."

"Nine from eight I can't, you know," Alice replied very readily; "but—

"She can't do Subtraction," said the White Queen. "Can you do Division? Divide a loaf by a knife—what's the answer to *that?*"

"I suppose—" Alice was beginning, but the Red Queen answered for her.

473

"Bread and butter, of course. Try another Subtraction sum. Take a bone from a dog; what remains?"

Alice considered. "The bone wouldn't remain, of course, if I took it—and the dog wouldn't remain: it would come to bite me—and I'm sure *I* shouldn't remain!"

"Then you think nothing would remain?" said the Red Queen.

"I think that's the answer."

"Wrong, as usual," said the Red Queen; "the dog's temper would remain."

"But I don't see how—"

"Why, look here!" the Red Queen cried. "The dog would lose its temper, wouldn't it?"

"Perhaps it would," Alice replied cautiously.

"Then if the dog went away, its temper would remain!" the Queen exclaimed triumphantly.

Alice said, as gravely as she could, "They might go different ways." But she couldn't help thinking to herself, "What dreadful nonsense we *are* talking!"

"She can't do sums a *bit!*" the Queens said together, with great emphasis.

"Can *you* do sums?" Alice said, turning suddenly on the White Queen, for she didn't like being found fault with so much.

The Queen gasped and shut her eyes. "I can do Addition," she said, "if you give me time—but I can't do Subtraction under *any* circumstances!"

"Of course you know your ABC?" said the Red Queen.

"To be sure I do," said Alice.

"So do I," the White Queen whispered; "we'll often say it over together, dear. And I'll tell you a secret—I can read words of one letter! Isn't *that* grand? However, don't be discouraged. You'll come to it in time."

Here the Red Queen began again. "Can you answer useful questions?" she said. "How is bread made?"

"I know *that!*" Alice cried eagerly. "You take some flour—"

"Where do you pick the flower," the White Queen asked; "in a garden or in the hedges?"

THROUGH THE LOOKING GLASS

"Well, it isn't *picked* at all," Alice explained; "it's *ground*—"

"How many acres of ground?" said the White Queen. "You mustn't leave out so many things."

"Fan her head!" the Red Queen anxiously interrupted. "She'll be feverish after so much thinking." So they set to work and fanned her with bunches of leaves, till she had to beg them to leave off, it blew her hair about so.

"She's all right again now," said the Red Queen. "Do you know Languages? What's the French for fiddledeedee?"

"Fiddledeedee's not English," Alice replied gravely.

"Who ever said it was?" said the Red Queen.

Alice thought she saw a way out of the difficulty, this time. "If you'll tell me what language fiddledeedee is, I'll tell you the French for it!" she exclaimed triumphantly.

But the Red Queen drew herself up rather stiffly, and said, "Queens never make bargains."

"I wish Queens never asked questions," Alice thought to herself.

"Don't let us quarrel," the White Queen said in an anxious tone. "What is the cause of lightning?"

"The cause of lightning," Alice said very decidedly, for she felt quite certain about this, "is the thunder—no, no!" she hastily corrected herself. "I meant the other way."

"It's too late to correct it," said the Red Queen; "when you've once said a thing, that fixes it, and you must take the consequences."

"Which reminds me—" the White Queen said, looking down and nervously clasping and unclasping her hands, "we had *such* a thunderstorm last Tuesday—I mean one of the last set of Tuesdays, you know."

Alice was puzzled. "In *our* country," she remarked, "there's only one day at a time."

The Red Queen said, "That's a poor thin way of doing things. Now *here*, we mostly have days and nights two or three at a time, and sometimes in the winter we take as many as five nights together—for warmth, you know."

475

"Are five nights warmer than one night, then?" Alice ventured to ask.

"Five times as warm, of course."

"But they should be five times as *cold*, by the same rule—"

"Just so!" cried the Red Queen. "Five times as warm, *and* five times as cold—just as I'm five times as rich as you are, *and* five times as clever!"

Alice sighed and gave it up. "It's exactly like a riddle with no answer!" she thought.

"Humpty Dumpty saw it too," the White Queen went on in a low voice, more as if she were talking to herself. "He came to the door with a corkscrew in his hand—"

"What did he want?" said the Red Queen.

"He said he *would* come in," the White Queen went on, "because he was looking for a hippopotamus. Now, as it happened, there wasn't such a thing in the house, that morning."

"Is there generally?" Alice asked in an astonished tone.

"Well, only on Thursdays," said the Queen.

"I know what he came for," said Alice; "he wanted to punish the fish, because—"

Here the White Queen began again. "It was *such* a thunderstorm, you can't think!" ("She *never* could, you know," said the Red Queen.)

"And part of the roof came off, and ever so much thunder got in—and it went rolling round the room in great lumps—and knocking over the tables and things—till I was so frightened, I couldn't remember my own name!"

Alice thought to herself, "I never should *try* to remember my name in the middle of an accident! Where would be the use of it?" but she did not say this aloud, for fear of hurting the poor Queen's feelings.

"Your Majesty must excuse her," the Red Queen said to Alice, taking one of the White Queen's hands in her own, and gently stroking it; "she means well, but she can't help saying foolish things, as a general rule."

The White Queen looked timidly at Alice, who felt she *ought*

to say something kind, but really couldn't think of anything at the moment.

"She never was really well brought up," the Red Queen went on; "but it's amazing how good-tempered she is! Pat her on the head, and see how pleased she'll be!" But this was more than Alice had courage to do.

"A little kindness—and putting her hair in papers—would do wonders with her—"

The White Queen gave a deep sigh, and laid her head on Alice's shoulder. "I *am* so sleepy!" she moaned.

"She's tired, poor thing!" said the Red Queen. "Smooth her hair—lend her your nightcap—and sing her a soothing lullaby."

"I haven't got a nightcap with me," said Alice, as she tried to obey the first direction; "and I don't know any soothing lullabies."

"I must do it myself, then," said the Red Queen, and she began:

> *"Hush-a-bye lady, in Alice's lap!*
> *Till the feast's ready, we've time for a nap.*
> *When the feast's over, we'll go to the ball—*
> *Red Queen, and White Queen, and Alice, and all!"*

"And now you know the words," she added, as she put her head down on Alice's other shoulder, "just sing it through to *me*. I'm getting sleepy, too." In another moment both Queens were fast asleep, and snoring loud.

"What *am* I to do?" exclaimed Alice, looking about in great perplexity, as first one round head, and then the other, rolled down from her shoulder, and lay like a heavy lump in her lap. "I don't think it *ever* happened before, that anyone had to take care of two Queens asleep at once! No, not in all the History of England—it couldn't, you know, because there never was more than one Queen at a time. Do wake up, you heavy things!" she went on in an impatient tone; but there was no answer but a gentle snoring.

The snoring got more distinct every minute, and sounded more like a tune; at last she could even make out words, and she listened so eagerly that, when the two great heads suddenly vanished from her lap, she hardly missed them.

She was standing before an arched doorway, over which were the words QUEEN ALICE in large letters, and on each side of the arch there was a bell handle; one was marked VISITORS' BELL, and the other SERVANTS' BELL.

"I'll wait till the song's over," thought Alice, "and then I'll ring the—the—*which* bell must I ring?" she went on, very much puzzled by the names. "I'm not a visitor, and I'm not a servant. There *ought* to be one marked QUEEN, you know—"

Just then the door opened a little way, and a creature with a long beak put its head out for a moment and said, "No admittance till the week after next!" and shut the door again with a bang.

Alice knocked and rang in vain for a long time; but at last a very old Frog, who was sitting under a tree, got up and hobbled slowly towards her; he was dressed in bright yellow, and had enormous boots on.

"What is it, now?" the Frog said in a deep hoarse whisper.

Alice turned round, ready to find fault with anybody. "Where's the servant whose business it is to answer the door?" she began angrily.

"Which door?" said the Frog.

Alice almost stamped with irritation at the slow drawl in which he spoke. "*This* door, of course!"

The Frog looked at the door with his large dull eyes for a minute; then he went nearer and rubbed it with his thumb, as if he were trying whether the paint would come off; then he looked at Alice.

"To answer the door?" he said. "What's it been asking of?" He was so hoarse that Alice could scarcely hear him.

"I don't know what you mean," she said.

"I speaks English, doesn't I?" the Frog went on. "Or are you deaf? What did it ask you?"

"Nothing!" Alice said impatiently. "I've been knocking at it!"

"Shouldn't do that—shouldn't do that—" the Frog muttered. "Wexes it, you know." Then he went up and gave the door a kick with one of his great feet. "You let *it* alone," he panted out, as he hobbled back to his tree, "and it'll let *you* alone, you know."

At this moment the door was flung open, and a shrill voice was heard singing:

"*To the Looking-Glass world it was Alice that said,*
  'I've a scepter in hand, I've a crown on my head.
  Let the Looking-Glass creatures, whatever they be,
  Come and dine with the Red Queen, the White Queen, and me!'"

And hundreds of voices joined in the chorus:

  "*Then fill up the glasses as quick as you can,*
    And sprinkle the table with buttons and bran;
    Put cats in the coffee, and mice in the tea—
    And welcome Queen Alice with thirty times three!"

Then followed a confused noise of cheering, and Alice thought to herself, "Thirty times three makes ninety. I wonder if anyone's counting?" In a minute there was silence again, and the same shrill voice sang another verse:

> "'O Looking-Glass creatures,' quoth Alice, 'draw near!
> 'Tis an honor to see me, a favor to hear;
> 'Tis a privilege high to have dinner and tea
> Along with the Red Queen, the White Queen, and me!'"

Then came the chorus again:

> "Then fill up the glasses with treacle and ink,
> Or anything else that is pleasant to drink;
> Mix sand with the cider, and wool with the wine—
> And welcome Queen Alice with ninety times nine!"

"Ninety times nine!" Alice repeated in despair. "Oh, that'll never be done! I'd better go in at once—" and in she went, and there was a dead silence the moment she appeared.

Alice glanced nervously along the table, as she walked up the large hall, and noticed that there were about fifty guests, of all kinds: some were animals, some birds, and there were even a few flowers among them. "I'm glad they've come without waiting to be asked," she thought; "I should never have known who were the right people to invite!"

There were three chairs at the head of the table: the Red and White Queens had already taken two of them, but the middle one was empty. Alice sat down in it, rather uncomfortable at the silence, and longing for someone to speak.

At last the Red Queen began. "You've missed the soup and fish," she said. "Put on the joint!" And the waiters set a leg of mutton before Alice, who looked at it rather anxiously, as she had never had to carve a joint before.

"You look a little shy; let me introduce you to that leg of mutton," said the Red Queen. "Alice—Mutton; Mutton—Alice."

The leg of mutton got up in the dish and made a little bow to Alice; and Alice returned the bow, not knowing whether to be frightened or amused. "May I give you a slice?" she said, taking up the knife and fork, and looking from one Queen to the other.

"Certainly not," the Red Queen said, very decidedly; "it isn't etiquette to cut anyone you've been introduced to. Remove the joint!" And the waiters carried it off, and brought a large plum pudding in its place.

"I won't be introduced to the pudding, please," Alice said rather hastily, "or we shall get no dinner at all. May I give you some?"

But the Red Queen looked sulky, and growled, "Pudding—Alice; Alice—Pudding. Remove the pudding!" and the waiters took it away so quickly that Alice couldn't return its bow.

However, she didn't see why the Red Queen should be the only one to give orders; so, as an experiment, she called out, "Waiter! Bring back the pudding!" and there it was again in a moment, like a conjuring trick. It was so large that she couldn't help feeling a *little* shy with it, as she had been with the mutton; however, she conquered her shyness by a great effort, and cut a slice and handed it to the Red Queen.

"What impertinence!" said the Pudding. "I wonder how you'd like it if I were to cut a slice out of *you*, you creature!"

It spoke in a thick, suety sort of voice, and Alice hadn't a word to say in reply; she could only sit and look at it and gasp.

"Make a remark," said the Red Queen; "it's ridiculous to leave all the conversation to the pudding!"

"Do you know, I've had such a quantity of poetry repeated to me today," Alice began, a little frightened at finding that, the moment she opened her lips, there was dead silence, and all eyes were fixed upon her; "and it's a very curious thing, I think—every poem was about fishes in some way. Do you know why they're so fond of fishes, all about here?"

She spoke to the Red Queen, whose answer was a little wide of the mark.

"As to fishes," she said, very slowly and solemnly, putting her mouth close to Alice's ear, "her White Majesty knows a lovely riddle—all in poetry—all about fishes. Shall she repeat it?"

"Her Red Majesty's very kind to mention it," the White Queen murmured into Alice's other ear, in a voice like the cooing of a pigeon. "It would be *such* a treat! May I?"

"Please do," Alice said very politely.

The White Queen laughed with delight, and stroked Alice's cheek. Then she began:

> "'First, the fish must be caught.'
> *That is easy: a baby, I think, could have caught it.*
> *'Next, the fish must be bought.'*
> *That is easy: a penny, I think, would have bought it.*
>
> *'Now cook me the fish!'*
> *That is easy, and will not take more than a minute.*
> *'Let it lie in a dish!'*
> *That is easy, because it already is in it.*
>
> *'Bring it here! Let me sup!'*
> *It is easy to set such a dish on the table.*
> *'Take the dish cover up!'*
> *Ah, that is so hard that I fear I'm unable!*
>
> *For it holds it like glue—*
> *Holds the lid to the dish, while it lies in the middle;*
> *Which is easiest to do,*
> *Un-dish-cover the fish, or dishcover the riddle?'"*

"Take a minute to think about it, and then guess," said the Red Queen. "Meanwhile, we'll drink your health—Queen Alice's health!" she screamed at the top of her voice, and all the guests began drinking it directly, and very queerly they managed it: some of them put their glasses upon their heads like extinguishers, and drank all that trickled down their faces—others upset the decanters, and drank the wine as it ran off the edges of the table—and three of them (who looked like kangaroos) scrambled into the dish of roast mutton, and began eagerly lapping up the gravy, "just like pigs in a trough!" thought Alice.

"You ought to return thanks in a neat speech," the Red Queen said, frowning at Alice as she spoke.

"We must support you, you know," the White Queen whis-

pered, as Alice got up to do it, very obediently, but a little frightened.

"Thank you very much," she whispered in reply, "but I can do quite well without."

"That wouldn't be at all the thing," the Red Queen said very decidedly; so Alice tried to submit to it with a good grace.

("And they *did* push so!" she said afterwards, when she was telling her sister the history of the feast.

"You would have thought they wanted to squeeze me flat!")

In fact it was rather difficult for her to keep in her place while she made her speech: the two Queens pushed her so, one on each side, that they nearly lifted her up into the air. "I rise to return thanks—" Alice began; and she really *did* rise as she spoke, several inches; but she got hold of the edge of the table, and managed to pull herself down again.

"Take care of yourself!" screamed the White Queen, seizing Alice's hair with both her hands. "Something's going to happen!"

And then (as Alice afterwards described it) all sorts of things happened in a moment. The candles all grew up to the ceiling, looking something like a bed of rushes with fireworks at the top. As to the bottles, they each took a pair of plates, which they hastily fitted on as wings, and so, with forks for legs, went fluttering about in all directions; "and very like birds they look," Alice thought to herself, as well as she could in the dreadful confusion that was beginning.

At this moment she heard a hoarse laugh at her side, and turned to see what was the matter with the White Queen; but, instead of the Queen, there was the leg of mutton sitting in the chair.

"Here I am!" cried a voice from the soup tureen, and Alice turned again, just in time to see the Queen's broad good-natured face grinning at her for a moment over the edge of the tureen, before she disappeared into the soup.

There was not a moment to be lost. Already several of the guests were lying down in the dishes, and the soup ladle was walking up the table towards Alice's chair, and beckoning to her impatiently to get out of its way.

"I can't stand this any longer!" she cried, as she jumped up and seized the tablecloth with both hands; one good pull, and plates, dishes, guests, and candles came crashing down together in a heap on the floor.

"And as for *you*," she went on, turning fiercely upon the Red Queen, whom she considered as the cause of all the mischief— but the Queen was no longer at her side—she had suddenly dwindled down to the size of a little doll, and was now on the table, merrily running round and round after her own shawl, which was trailing behind her.

At any other time, Alice would have felt surprised at this, but she was far too much excited to be surprised at anything *now*. "As for *you*," she repeated, catching hold of the little creature in the very act of jumping over a bottle which had just lighted upon the table, "I'll shake you into a kitten, that I will!"

CHAPTER X: *Shaking*

SHE TOOK HER OFF THE TABLE as she spoke, and shook her backwards and forwards with all her might.

The Red Queen made no resistance whatever: only her face grew very small, and her eyes got large and green; and still, as Alice went on shaking her, she kept on growing shorter—and fatter—and softer—and rounder—and—

CHAPTER XI: *Waking*

—and it really *was* a kitten, after all.

CHAPTER XII: *Which Dreamed It?*

"YOUR RED MAJESTY SHOULDN'T purr so loud," Alice said, rubbing her eyes, and addressing the kitten, respectfully, yet with some severity. "You woke me out of oh, such a nice dream! And you've been along with me, Kitty—all through the Looking-Glass world. Did you know it, dear?"

It is a very inconvenient habit of kittens (Alice had once made the remark) that, whatever you say to them, they *always* purr. "If they would only purr for 'yes,' and mew for 'no,' or any rule of that sort," she had said, "so that one could keep up a conversation! But how *can* you talk with a person if they *always* say the same thing?" On this occasion the kitten only purred; and it was impossible to guess whether it meant yes or no.

So Alice hunted among the chessmen on the table till she had found the Red Queen; then she went down on her knees on the hearthrug, and put the kitten and the Queen to look at each other. "Now, Kitty!" she cried, clapping her hands triumphantly. "Confess that was what you turned into!"

("But it wouldn't look at it," she said, when she was explaining the thing afterwards to her sister; "it turned away its head, and pretended not to see it; but it looked a *little* ashamed of itself, so I think it *must* have been the Red Queen.")

"Sit up a little more stiffly, dear!" Alice cried with a merry laugh. "And curtsy while you're thinking what to—what to purr. It saves time, remember!" And she caught it up and gave it one little kiss, "just in honor of its having been a Red Queen."

"Snowdrop, my pet!" she went on, looking over her shoulder at the White Kitten, which was still patiently undergoing its toilet, "when *will* Dinah have finished with your White Majesty, I wonder? That must be the reason you were so untidy in my dream. Dinah! Do you know that you're scrubbing a White Queen? Really, it's most disrespectful of you!

"And what did *Dinah* turn to, I wonder?" she prattled on, as she settled comfortably down, with one elbow on the rug, and her chin in her hand, to watch the kittens. "Tell me, Dinah, did you turn to Humpty Dumpty? I *think* you did— however, you'd better not mention it to your friends just yet, for I'm not sure.

"By the way, Kitty, if only you'd been really

with me in my dream, there was one thing you *would* have enjoyed—
I had such a quantity of poetry said to me, all about fishes! Tomorrow morning you shall have a real treat. All the time you're
eating your breakfast, I'll repeat 'The Walrus and the Carpenter'
to you; and then you can make believe it's oysters, dear!

"Now, Kitty, let's consider who it was that dreamed it all. This
is a serious question, my dear, and you should *not* go on licking
your paw like that—as if Dinah hadn't washed you this morning!
You see, Kitty, it *must* have been either me or the Red King. He
was part of my dream, of course—but then I was part of his dream,
too! *Was* it the Red King, Kitty? You were his wife, my dear, so
you ought to know— Oh, Kitty, *do* help to settle it! I'm sure your
paw can wait!"

But the provoking kitten only began on the other paw, and pretended it hadn't heard the question.

Which do *you* think it was?

THE PRISONER
OF ZENDA

THE
PRISONER
OF
ZENDA

A CONDENSATION OF THE BOOK BY

Anthony Hope

ILLUSTRATED BY

JEAN LEON HUENS

HORSEMEN galloping through the night, weapons gleaming in the moonlight, the Royal House of Elphberg threatened by a usurper's plot—these are the elements of *The Prisoner of Zenda,* one of the most entertaining of all cloak-and-dagger romances. The place is the mythical kingdom of Ruritania, the time the eve of Prince Rudolph's coronation. On this fantastic scene appears Rudolf Rassendyll, scion of an ancient English house, rumored by family scandal to have Elphberg blood in his veins. In a land where chivalry, courage and untarnished honor are valued above all else, our hero plays out a noble and dangerous role.

The author of *The Prisoner of Zenda* was born in London in 1863. Anthony Hope Hawkins was a cousin of Kenneth Grahame, who wrote *The Wind in the Willows.* He was trained for the bar and admitted to practice; but with clients scarce he fell to writing adventure stories in his spare time.

The Prisoner of Zenda was published in 1894, and its great success, together with an encouraging note from Robert Louis Stevenson, decided the young barrister to pack up his lawbooks and embark on a writing career. A lecture tour took him to the United States, where he met and soon afterward married an American girl named Elizabeth Sheldon.

Anthony Hope wrote many books popular in their time, but the only other one still read today is *Rupert of Hentzau,* a worthy sequel to *The Prisoner of Zenda.* In 1918 he was knighted for his services during the war. He died in 1933 at his home in Surrey.

CHAPTER I

The Rassendylls—with a Word on the Elphbergs

"I wonder when in the world you're going to do anything, Rudolf?" said my brother's wife.

"My dear Rose," I answered, laying down my egg spoon, "why in the world should I do anything? My position is a comfortable one. I have an income sufficient for my wants, and I enjoy an enviable social position: I am brother to Lord Burlesdon, and brother-in-law to that most charming lady, his countess. Behold, it is enough!"

"You are nine-and-twenty," she observed, "and you've done nothing but—"

"Knock about? It is true. Our family doesn't need to do things."

This remark of mine rather annoyed Rose, for, pretty and accomplished as she herself is, her family is hardly of the same standing as the Rassendylls. Ancestry is, however, a matter concerning which Rose's next observation has some truth.

"Good families are generally worse than any others," she said. Upon this I stroked my hair: I knew well what she meant.

"I'm so glad Robert's is black!" she cried.

At this moment Robert, who rises early and works before breakfast, came in. He glanced at his wife: her cheek was slightly flushed; he patted it caressingly.

"What's the matter, my dear?" he asked.

"She objects to my doing nothing and having red hair," said I in an injured tone.

"Oh! Of course he can't help his hair," admitted Rose.

"It generally crops out once in a generation," said my brother. "So does the nose. Rudolf has got them both."

"I wish they didn't crop out," said Rose, still flushed.

"I rather like them myself," said I, and, rising, I bowed to the portrait of Countess Amelia.

My brother's wife uttered an exclamation of impatience.

"I wish you'd take that picture away, Robert," said she.

"My dear!" he cried.

"Good Heavens!" I added.

"Then it might be forgotten," she continued.

"Hardly—with Rudolf about," said Robert, shaking his head.

"Why should it be forgotten?" I asked.

"Rudolf!" exclaimed my brother's wife, blushing very prettily.

I laughed, and went on with my egg. At least I had shelved the question of what (if anything) I ought to do. And, by way of closing the discussion—and also, I must admit, of exasperating my strict little sister-in-law a trifle more—I observed:

"I rather like being an Elphberg myself."

It is manifest that I must explain why my sister-in-law was vexed with my nose and hair, and why I ventured to call myself an Elphberg. For, eminent as the Rassendylls have been for many generations, this blood of course does not, at first sight, justify the boast of a connection with the royal house of the Elphbergs. For what relationship is there between Ruritania and Burlesdon, between the Palace at Strelsau or the Castle of Zenda and Number 305 Park Lane, W.?

Well, then—and I must premise that I am going to rake up the very scandal which my dear Lady Burlesdon wishes forgotten—in the year 1733, George II sitting then on the throne, and peace reigning for the moment, there came on a visit to the English court a certain prince, who was afterwards known to history as Rudolf the Third of Ruritania. The prince was a tall, handsome young fellow, marked by an unusually long, sharp and straight nose, and a mass of dark red hair—in fact, the nose and the hair which have stamped the Elphbergs time out of mind. He stayed some months in England, where he was most courteously received; yet, in the end, he left rather under a cloud. For he fought a duel with a nobleman, well known not only for his own merits, but as the husband of a very beautiful wife. In that duel Prince Rudolf received a severe wound, and, recovering therefrom, was adroitly smuggled off by the Ruritanian ambassador, who had found him a pretty handful. The nobleman was not wounded in the duel; but the morning being raw and damp on the occasion of the meeting, he contracted a severe chill, and, failing to throw it off, he died some six months after the departure of Prince Rudolf, without having found leisure to adjust his relations with his wife—who, after another two months, bore an heir to the title and estates of the family of Burlesdon. This lady was the Countess Amelia, whose picture my sister-in-law wished to remove from the dining room in Park Lane; and her husband was James, fifth Earl of Burlesdon and twenty second Baron Rassendyll, both in the peerage of England, and a Knight of the Garter. As for Rudolf, he went back to Ruritania, married a wife and ascended the throne, whereon his progeny in the direct line have sat from then till this very hour. And, finally, if you walk through the picture galleries at Burlesdon, among the fifty portraits or so of the last century and a half, you will find five or six, including that of the sixth earl, distinguished by long, sharp, straight noses and a quantity of dark red hair; these five or six have also blue eyes, whereas among the Rassendylls dark eyes are the commoner.

That is the explanation, and I am glad to have finished it: the blemishes on honorable lineage are a delicate subject.

It will be observed that my sister in law treated my complexion almost as an offense for which I was responsible, hastening to assume from that external sign inward qualities of which I protest my entire innocence; and this unjust inference she sought to buttress by pointing to the uselessness of the life I had led. Well, be that as it may, I had picked up a good deal of pleasure and a good deal of knowledge. I had been to a German school and a German university, and spoke German as perfectly as English; I was thoroughly at home in French; I had a smattering of Italian and enough Spanish to swear by. I was, I believe, a strong, though hardly a fine swordsman and a good shot. I could ride anything that had a back to sit on; and my head was as cool a one as you could find, for all its flaming cover. If you say that I ought to have spent my time in useful labor, I have nothing to say, save that my parents had no business to leave me two thousand pounds a year and a roving disposition.

"The difference between you and Robert," said my sister-in-law, "is that he recognizes the duties of his position, and you only see the opportunities of yours."

"To a man of spirit, my dear Rose," I answered, "opportunities are duties."

"Nonsense!" said she, tossing her head; and after a moment she went on: "Now, Sir Jacob Borrodaile is to have an embassy somewhere in six months, and Robert says he is sure that he'll take you as an attaché. Do take it, Rudolf—to please me."

Now, when my sister-in-law puts the matter in that way, wrinkling her pretty brows, twisting her little hands and growing wistful in the eyes, all on account of an idle scamp like myself, I am visited with compunction. Therefore I said:

"My dear sister, if in six months' time no unforeseen obstacle has arisen, and Sir Jacob invites me, hang me if I don't go with Sir Jacob!"

"Oh, Rudolf, how good of you! I am glad!"

My promise, then, was given; but six months are six months, and, inasmuch as they stretched between me and my prospective industry (I suppose attachés are industrious; but I know not, for I never became attaché to Sir Jacob or anybody else), I cast about for some desirable mode of spending them. And it occurred to me suddenly that I would visit Ruritania. It may seem strange that I had never visited that country yet; but my father (in spite of a sneaking fondness for the Elphbergs, which led him to give me, his second son, the famous Elphberg name of Rudolf) had always been averse to my going, and, since his death, my brother had accepted the family tradition which taught that a wide berth was to be given to that country. But the moment Ruritania had come into my head I was eaten up with a curiosity to see it; and the old story seemed a preposterously insufficient reason for debarring myself from a highly interesting and important kingdom, one which had played no small part in European history, and might do the like again under the sway of a young and vigorous ruler, such as the new King was rumored to be.

My determination was clinched by reading in *The Times* that Rudolf the Fifth was to be crowned at Strelsau in the course of the next three weeks, and that great magnificence was to mark the occasion. At once I made up my mind to be present, and began my preparations. But, inasmuch as it has never been my practice to furnish my relatives with an itinerary of my journeys, and in this case I anticipated opposition to my wishes, I gave out that I was going for a ramble in the Tyrol—an old haunt of mine—and propitiated Rose's wrath by declaring that I intended to study the political and social problems of the inhabitants.

"Perhaps," I hinted darkly, "there is a gap that might be filled by an exhaustive work on—"

"Oh, will you write a book?" she cried, clapping her hands. "That would be splendid, wouldn't it, Robert?"

"It's the best of introductions to political life nowadays," observed my brother.

"Now promise you'll do it," said Rose earnestly.

This time Rose could get no more than a qualified promise out of me. To tell the truth, I would have wagered a handsome sum that the story of my expedition that summer would stain no paper and spoil not a single pen. And that shows how little we know what the future holds; for here I am, fulfilling my qualified promise, and writing, as I never thought to write, a book—though it will hardly serve as an introduction to political life, and has not a jot to do with the Tyrol.

Neither would it, I fear, please Lady Burlesdon, if I were to submit it to her critical eye—a step which I have no intention of taking.

CHAPTER II

Concerning the Color of Men's Hair

IT WAS A MAXIM OF my Uncle William's that no man should pass through Paris without spending four-and-twenty hours there. My uncle spoke out of a ripe experience of the world, and I honored his advice by putting up for a day and a night at the Continental on my way to—the Tyrol. I called on George Featherly at the embassy, and we had a bit of dinner together at Durand's, and afterwards dropped in to the Opera; and after that we called on Bertram Bertrand, a versifier of some repute and Paris correspondent to *The Critic*. He had a very comfortable suite of rooms, and we found some pleasant fellows smoking and talking. It struck me, however, that Bertram himself was in low spirits, and when everybody except ourselves had gone, I rallied him for a while on his moping preoccupation. At length, flinging himself on a sofa, he exclaimed:

"I am in love—infernally in love!"

"Oh, you'll write the better poetry," said I by way of consolation.

He ruffled his hair with his hand and smoked furiously.

"If it's the old affair," said George Featherly, smiling unkindly, "you may as well throw it up, Bert. She's leaving Paris tomorrow."

"I know that," snapped Bertram.

"It would make it more interesting for me," I ventured to observe, "if I knew whom you were talking about."

"Antoinette de Mauban," said George.

"Oho!" said I. "Where's she going to?" for the lady was something of a celebrity.

George jingled his money, smiled cruelly at poor Bertram and answered pleasantly:

"Nobody knows. By the way, Bert, I met a great and accomplished man at her house about a month ago. Did you ever meet him—the Duke of Strelsau?"

"Yes, I did," growled Bertram.

From this exchange I drew the inference that the duke had distinguished Madame de Mauban by his attentions. She was a widow, rich, handsome and, according to repute, ambitious. The duke was everything he could be, short of enjoying strictly royal rank: for he was the son of the late King of Ruritania by a second and morganatic marriage, and half brother to the new King. He had been his father's favorite, and it had occasioned some unfavorable comment when he had been created a duke, with a title derived from no less a city than the capital itself.

"He's not in Paris now, is he?" I asked.

"Oh, no! He's gone back to be present at the King's coronation; a ceremony which, I should say, he'll not enjoy much."

A few moments later I rose, and leaving the hapless Bertram in George's hands, I went home to bed.

The next day George Featherly went with me to the station, where I took a ticket for Dresden.

"Going to see the pictures?" asked George, with a grin.

George is an inveterate gossip, and had I told him that I was off to Ruritania the news would have been in Park Lane in a week. I was therefore about to return an evasive answer when he left me suddenly. Following him with my eyes, I saw him lift his hat and accost a graceful, fashionably dressed woman. She was perhaps a year or two over thirty, tall, dark and of rather full figure. As George talked, I saw her glance at me, and a moment later George rejoined me.

"You've got a charming traveling companion," he said. "That's poor Bert Bertrand's goddess, Antoinette de Mauban, and, like you, she's going to Dresden. It's very queer, though, that she doesn't at present desire the honor of your acquaintance."

"I didn't ask to be introduced," I observed, a little annoyed.

"Well, I offered to bring you to her; but she said, 'Another time.' Never mind, old fellow, perhaps there'll be a smash, and you'll have a chance of rescuing her and cutting out the Duke of Strelsau!"

No smash, however, happened, either to me or to Madame de Mauban. When, after a night's rest in Dresden, I continued my journey, she got into the same train. Understanding that she wished to be let alone, I avoided her carefully, but I saw that she went the same way as I did to the very end of my journey.

As soon as we reached the Ruritanian frontier I bought the papers, and found in them news which affected my movements. For some reason, which was not clearly explained and seemed to be something of a mystery, the date of the coronation had been suddenly advanced, and the ceremony was to take place on the next day but one. It was evident that Strelsau was thronged. Rooms were all let and hotels overflowing; there would be very little chance of my obtaining a lodging, so I made up my mind to stop at Zenda, a small town fifty miles short of the capital, and about ten from the frontier. My train reached there in the evening; I would spend the next day, Tuesday, in a wander over the hills, which were said to be very fine, and in taking a glance at the famous castle, and go over by train to Strelsau on the Wednesday morning, returning at night to sleep at Zenda.

Accordingly at Zenda I got out, and as the train passed where I stood on the platform, I saw my friend Madame de Mauban in her place; clearly she was going through to Strelsau.

I was very kindly received at the inn, kept by a fat old lady and her two daughters. The old lady's hero was the duke, for he was master of the Zenda estates and of the castle, which rose grandly on its steep hill a mile or so from the inn. The old lady, indeed, did not hesitate to express regret that the duke was not on the throne instead of his half brother.

"We know Duke Michael," said she. "Every Ruritanian knows Duke Michael. But the King is almost a stranger; he has been so much abroad not one in ten knows him even by sight."

"And now," chimed in one of the young women, "they say he has shaved off his beard, so that no one at all knows him."

"Shaved his beard!" exclaimed her mother. "Who says so?"

"Johann, the duke's keeper. He has seen the King."

"Ah, yes. The King, sir, is now at the duke's hunting lodge in the forest here; from here he goes to Strelsau to be crowned on Wednesday morning."

I was interested to hear this, and made up my mind to walk next day in the direction of the lodge on the chance of coming across the King. The old lady ran on garrulously:

"Ah, and I wish he would stay at his hunting—that and wine (and one thing more) are all he loves, they say—and suffer our duke to be crowned on Wednesday. That I wish, and I don't care who knows it."

"Hush, mother!" urged the daughters.

"Oh, there's many to think as I do!" cried the old woman stubbornly.

I threw myself back in my deep armchair and laughed at her zeal.

"For my part," said the younger of the two daughters, a pretty, buxom, smiling wench, "I hate Black Michael! A red Elphberg for me, mother! The King, they say, is as red as a fox or as . . ." And she laughed mischievously as she cast a glance at me.

"Many a man has cursed their red hair before now," muttered the old lady—and I remembered James, fifth Earl of Burlesdon.

"How comes the King here?" I asked. "It is the duke's land here, you say."

"The duke invited him, sir, to rest here till Wednesday. The duke is at Strelsau, preparing the King's reception."

"Then they're friends?"

"None better," said the old lady.

But my rosy damsel tossed her head; she was not to be repressed for long, and she broke out, "Ay, they love one another as men do who want the same place and the same wife!"

The old woman glowered; but the last words pricked my curiosity, and I interposed before she could begin scolding:

"What, the same wife, too! How's that, young lady?"

"All the world knows that Black Michael—well then, mother, the duke—would give his soul to marry his cousin, the Princess Flavia, and that she is to be the queen."

"Upon my word," said I, "I begin to be sorry for your duke." And then I thought of Antoinette de Mauban.

"Black Michael has—" began the girl, braving her mother's anger; but as she spoke a heavy step sounded on the floor, and a gruff voice asked in a threatening tone:

"Who talks of 'Black Michael' in His Highness' own burgh?"

The girl gave a little shriek, half of fright—half, I think, of amusement.

The man who had spoken came forward.

"We have company, Johann," said my hostess, and the fellow plucked off his cap. A moment later he saw me and started back a step, as though he had seen something wonderful.

"What ails you, Johann?" asked the elder girl. "This is a gentleman on his travels, come to see the coronation."

The man had recovered himself, but he was staring at me with an intense, searching, almost fierce glance.

"Good evening to you," said I.

"Good evening, sir," he muttered, still scrutinizing me, and the girl began to laugh as she called:

"See, Johann, it is the color you love! He started to see your hair, sir. It's not the color we see most of here in Zenda."

"I crave your pardon, sir," stammered the fellow, with puzzled eyes. "I expected to see no one."

"Give him a glass to drink my health in; and I'll bid you good night, and thanks to you, ladies, for your courtesy and pleasant conversation."

So speaking, I rose to my feet, and with a slight bow turned to the door. The young girl ran to light me on the way, and the man fell back to let me pass, his eyes following me till the door closed behind me. My saucy conductor, looking over her shoulder at me as she preceded me upstairs, said:

"There's no pleasing Master Johann for one of your color, sir."

"What," asked I, taking hold of the other side of the candlestick, "does color matter in a man?"

"Nay, but I love yours—it's the Elphberg red."

"Color in a man," said I, "is a matter of no more moment than that!" and I gave her something of no value.

"God send the kitchen door be shut!" said she.

"Amen!" said I, and left her.

In fact, however, as I now know, color is sometimes of considerable moment to a man.

CHAPTER III

A Merry Evening with a Distant Relative

I WAS NOT SO UNREASONABLE as to be prejudiced against the duke's keeper because he disliked my complexion; and if I had been, his most civil and obliging conduct next morning would have disarmed me. Hearing that I was bound for Strelsau, he came to see me while I was breakfasting, and told me that a sister of his who lived in the capital had invited him to occupy a room in her house. He had gladly accepted, but now found that his duties would not permit of his absence. He begged therefore that, if such humble (though, as he added, clean and comfortable) lodgings would satisfy me, I would take his place. I accepted his offer without a moment's hesitation, and he went off to telegraph to his sister, while I packed up and prepared to take the next train. But I still hankered after the forest and the hunting lodge, and when my little maid told me that I could, by walking through the forest, hit the railway at a roadside station, I decided to send my luggage direct to the address which Johann had given, take my walk, and follow to Strelsau myself.

I took an early luncheon, and having bid my kind entertainers farewell, I set out to climb the hill that led to the castle, and thence to the forest of Zenda. Half an hour's leisurely walking brought me to the castle. It had been a fortress in old days, and the ancient keep was still in good preservation and very imposing. Behind it stood another portion of the original castle, and behind that again, and separated from it by a deep and broad moat, which ran all round the old buildings, was a handsome modern château, erected by the last king, and now forming the country residence of the Duke of Strelsau. The old and the new portions were connected by a drawbridge, and this formed the only passage between the old building and the outer world; but leading to the modern château there was a broad and handsome avenue. It was an ideal residence: when Black Michael desired company he could dwell in his château; if a fit of misanthropy seized him he had merely to cross the bridge and draw it up after him (it ran on rollers), and nothing short of a regiment and a train of artillery could fetch him out.

Soon I entered the forest, and walked on for an hour or more in its cool somber shade. The great trees enlaced with one another over my head, and the sunshine stole through in patches as bright as diamonds. I was enchanted with the place, and finding a felled tree trunk, propped my back against it, and gave myself up to undisturbed contemplation of the solemn beauty of the woods. Soon I went off into the most delightful sleep, regardless of my train to Strelsau and of the fast-waning afternoon. I fell to dreaming that I was married to the Princess Flavia and dwelt in the Castle of Zenda, and beguiled whole days with my love in the glades of the forest. In fact, I was just impressing a fervent kiss on the charming lips of the princess when I heard (and the voice seemed at first a part of the dream) someone exclaim in rough, strident tones:

"Why, the devil's in it! Shave him and he'd be the King!"

I opened my eyes, and found two men regarding me with much curiosity. Both wore shooting costumes and carried guns. One was rather short and very stoutly built, with a big bullet-shaped head, a bristly gray mustache, and small pale blue eyes, a trifle blood-shot. The other was a slender young fellow, of middle height, dark in complexion, and bearing himself with grace and distinction.

The elder man approached me, beckoning the younger to follow. He did so, courteously raising his hat. I rose slowly to my feet.

"He's the height, too!" I heard the elder murmur as he surveyed my six feet two inches of stature. Then, with a cavalier touch of the cap, he addressed me. "May I ask your name?"

"As you have taken the first step in the acquaintance, gentlemen," said I, with a smile, "suppose you give me a lead in the matter of names."

The young man stepped forward with a pleasant smile.

"This," said he, "is Colonel Sapt, and I am called Fritz von Tarlenheim; we are both in the service of the King of Ruritania."

I bowed and, baring my head, answered:

"I am Rudolf Rassendyll. I am a traveler from England; and once I held a commission from Her Majesty the Queen."

"Then we are all brethren of the sword," answered Tarlenheim, holding out his hand, which I took readily.

"Rassendyll, Rassendyll!" muttered Colonel Sapt; then a gleam of intelligence flitted across his face.

"By Heaven!" he cried. "You're one of the Burlesdons?"

"My brother is now Lord Burlesdon," said I.

"Thy head betrayeth thee," he chuckled, pointing to my uncovered poll. "Why, Fritz, you know the story?"

The young man glanced apologetically at me. To put him at his ease, I remarked with a smile:

"Ah, the story is known here as well as among us, it seems."

"Known!" cried Sapt. "If you stay here not a man in all Ruritania will doubt of it—or a woman either."

I began to feel uncomfortable. Had I realized what a very plainly written pedigree I carried about with me, I should have thought long before I visited Ruritania. However, I was in for it now.

At this moment a ringing voice sounded from behind us:

"Fritz, Fritz! Where are you, man?"

Tarlenheim started, and said hastily:

"It's the King!"

Then a young man jumped out from behind the trunk of a tree and stood beside us. As I looked on him I uttered an astonished cry; and he, seeing me, drew back in sudden wonder. Saving the hair on my face and also that he lacked perhaps half an inch of my height, the King of Ruritania might have been Rudolf Rassendyll, and I Rudolf the King.

For an instant we stood motionless, looking at one another. Then I bared my head again and bowed respectfully. The King found his voice, and asked in bewilderment:

"Colonel—Fritz—who is this gentleman?"

I was about to answer when Colonel Sapt stepped between the King and me, and began to talk to His Majesty in a low growl. I looked at him long and carefully. The King's face was slightly more fleshy than mine, the oval of its contour the least trifle more pronounced, and his mouth lacking something of the firmness of my close-shutting lips. But for all that, the likeness rose striking, salient, wonderful.

Sapt ceased speaking, and the King still frowned. Then, gradually, his nose came down (as mine does when I laugh), his eyes twinkled, and he burst into the merriest fit of irrepressible laughter.

"Well met, cousin!" he cried, stepping up to me, clapping me on the back. "You must forgive me if I was taken aback. A man doesn't expect to see double at this time of day, eh, Fritz?"

"I must pray pardon, sire, for my presumption," said I. "I trust it will not forfeit Your Majesty's favor."

"By Heaven, you'll always enjoy the King's countenance!" He laughed. "Where are you traveling to?"

"To Strelsau, sire—to the coronation."

The King still smiled, though his expression hinted some uneasiness. But the humorous side of the matter caught him again.

"Fritz, Fritz!" he cried. "A thousand crowns for a sight of brother Michael's face when he sees a pair of us!"

"Seriously," observed Fritz von Tarlenheim, "I question Mr. Rassendyll's wisdom in visiting Strelsau just now."

"Well, Sapt?" said the King questioningly.

"He mustn't go," growled the old fellow.

"Come, colonel, you mean that I should be in Mr. Rassendyll's debt, if—"

"Oh, ay! Wrap it up in the right way," said Sapt.

"Enough, sire," said I. "I'll leave Ruritania today."

"Now, by thunder, you shan't. For you shall dine with me tonight. Come, man, you don't meet a new relation every day!"

"We dine sparingly tonight," said Fritz von Tarlenheim.

"Not we—with our new cousin for a guest!" cried the King; and as Fritz shrugged his shoulders, he added, "Oh, I'll remember our early start, Fritz."

"So will I—tomorrow morning," said old Sapt.

"Oh, wise old Sapt!" cried the King. "Come, Mr. Rassendyll—by the way, what name did they give you?"

"Your Majesty's," I answered, bowing.

"Well, that shows they weren't ashamed of us." He laughed.

"Come, then, cousin Rudolf. I've got no house of my own here, but my dear brother Michael lends us a place of his, and we'll make shift to entertain you there"; and he put his arm through mine, and signing to the others to accompany us, walked me off, westerly, through the forest.

We walked for more than half an hour, and the King smoked cigarettes and chattered incessantly. He was full of interest in my family, and laughed heartily when I told him of the portraits with Elphberg hair in our galleries.

Suddenly emerging from the wood, we came on a small and rude hunting lodge. As we approached it, a little man in a plain livery came out to meet us. The only other person I saw about the place was a fat elderly woman, whom I afterwards discovered to be the mother of Johann, the duke's keeper.

"Well, is dinner ready, Josef?" asked the King.

The little servant informed us that it was, and we soon sat down to a plentiful meal. I played a good knife and fork, as my custom is; the King noticed my performance with approval.

"We're all good trenchermen, we Elphbergs," said he. "But what? We're eating dry! Wine, Josef! Wine, man! Are we beasts, to eat without drinking? Are we cattle, Josef?"

At this reproof Josef hastened to load the table with bottles.

"Remember tomorrow!" said Fritz.

"Ay—tomorrow!" said old Sapt.

The King drained a bumper to his "Cousin Rudolf," and I drank its fellow to the "Elphberg red," whereat he laughed loudly. The wine we drank was beyond all price or praise, and we did it justice. Fritz ventured once to stay the King's hand.

"What?" cried the King. "Remember you start before I do, Master Fritz—you must be more sparing by two hours than I."

Fritz saw that I did not understand.

"The colonel and I," he explained, "leave here at six; we ride down to Zenda and return with the guard of honor to fetch the King at eight, and then we all ride together to the station."

"Come, cousin," said the King, "you need not start early. Another bottle, man!"

I had another bottle—or, rather, a part of one, for the larger half traveled quickly down His Majesty's throat. Fritz gave up his attempts at persuasion, and soon we were all as full of wine as we had any right to be. We all talked at once, and followed to the letter Sapt's exhortation to let the morrow take care of itself.

At last the King set down his glass and leaned back in his chair.

"I have drunk enough," said he. Indeed, his remark was most absolutely true—so far as it went. But as he spoke, Josef came and set before the King a marvelous old wicker-covered flagon. It had lain so long in some darkened cellar that it seemed to blink in the candlelight.

"His Highness the Duke of Strelsau bade me set this wine before the King when the King was weary of all other wines."

"Well done, Black Michael!" said the King. "Out with the cork, Josef. Hang him! Did he think I'd flinch from his bottle?"

The bottle was opened, and Josef filled the King's glass. The King tasted it. Then, with a solemnity born of the hour and his own condition, he looked round on us.

"Gentlemen, my friends—Rudolf, my cousin—everything is yours to the half of Ruritania. But ask me not for a single drop of this divine bottle which I will drink to the health of that—that sly knave, my brother, Black Michael."

And the King seized the bottle and turned it over his mouth, and drained it and flung it from him, and laid his head on his arms on the table. We drank pleasant dreams to His Majesty—and that is all I remember of the evening. Perhaps it is enough.

CHAPTER IV

The King Keeps His Appointment

I AWOKE WITH A START AND a shiver; my face, hair and clothes dripped water, and opposite me stood old Sapt, an empty bucket in his hand. On the table by him sat Fritz von Tarlenheim, pale as a ghost and black as a crow under the eyes.

I leaped to my feet in anger. "Your joke goes too far, sir!" I cried.

"Tut, man, we've no time for quarreling. Nothing else would rouse you. It's five o'clock."

"I'll thank you, Colonel Sapt—" I began.

"Rassendyll," interrupted Fritz, getting down from the table and taking my arm, "look here."

The King lay full length on the floor. His face was red as his hair, and he breathed heavily. I saw that his face and head were wet with water, as were mine.

"We've spent half an hour on him," said Fritz.

"He drank three times what either of you did," growled Sapt.

I knelt down and felt his pulse. It was alarmingly languid and slow. We three looked at one another.

"Was it drugged—that last bottle?" I asked in a whisper.

"I don't know," said Sapt.

"We must get a doctor."

"There's none within ten miles," said Fritz, "and a thousand doctors wouldn't take him to Strelsau today. I know the look of it. He'll not move for six or seven hours yet."

"But the coronation!" I cried in horror.

Fritz shrugged his shoulders. "We must send word that he's ill," he said.

Old Sapt, who seemed as fresh as a daisy, had lit his pipe and was puffing hard at it. "If he's not crowned today," said he, "I'll lay a crown he's never crowned. The whole nation's there to meet him; half the army—and Black Michael at the head. Shall we send word that the King's drunk?"

"That he's ill," said I, in correction.

"Ill!" echoed Sapt, with a scornful laugh. "They know his illnesses too well. He's been 'ill' before!"

"Well, we must chance what they think," said Fritz helplessly. "I'll carry the news and make the best of it."

"Tell me," said Sapt, "do you think the King was drugged?"

"I do," said I.

"That damned hound, Black Michael," said Fritz between his teeth.

"Ay," said Sapt, "that he might not come to be crowned.

Rassendyll here doesn't know our pretty Michael. As God's alive, man, the throne's lost if the King show himself not in Strelsau today. I know Black Michael."

"We could carry him there," said I.

"And a very pretty picture he makes," sneered Sapt.

Fritz von Tarlenheim buried his face in his hands. The King breathed loudly and heavily. Sapt stirred him with his foot.

"The drunken dog!" he said. "But he's an Elphberg and the son of his father, and may I rot in hell before Black Michael sits in his place!"

For a moment or two we were all silent; then Sapt, knitting his bushy gray brows, took the pipe from his mouth and said to me:

"As a man grows old he believes in Fate. Fate sent you here. Fate sends you now to Strelsau."

I staggered back, murmuring, "Good God!"

Fritz looked up with an eager, bewildered gaze.

"Impossible!" I muttered. "I should be known."

"It's a risk—against a certainty," said Sapt. "If you shave I'll wager you'll not be known. Are you afraid?"

"Sir!"

"Come, lad, there, there; but it's your life, you know, if you're known—and mine—and Fritz's here. But if you don't go I swear to you Black Michael will sit tonight on the throne, and the King lie in prison or his grave."

The clock ticked fifty times, and sixty and seventy times, as I stood in thought. Then I suppose a look came over my face, for old Sapt caught me by the hand, crying, "You'll go?"

"Yes, I'll go," said I, and I turned my eyes on the prostrate figure of the King on the floor.

"Tonight," Sapt went on in a hasty whisper, "we are to lodge in the palace. The moment they leave us you and I will mount our horses—Fritz must stay there and guard the King's room—and ride here at a gallop. The King will be ready—Josef will tell him—and he must ride back with me to Strelsau, and you ride as if the devil were behind you to the frontier."

I took it all in in a second, and nodded my head.

"There's a chance," said Fritz, with his first sign of hopefulness.

"If I escape detection," said I.

"If we're detected," said Sapt, "I'll send Black Michael down below before I go myself, so help me! Sit in that chair, man."

I obeyed him, and he darted from the room, calling, "Josef! Josef!" In three minutes he was back, and Josef with him. The latter carried a jug of hot water, soap and razors. He was trembling as Sapt told him how the land lay, and bade him shave me.

Suddenly Fritz smote on his thigh. "But the guard! They'll know! They'll know!"

"Pooh! We shan't wait for the guard. We'll ride to Hofbau and catch a train there. When they come the bird'll be flown."

"But the King?"

"The King will be in the wine cellar. I'm going to carry him there now."

"If they find him?"

"They won't. How should they? Josef will put them off."

"But—"

"My God!" roared Sapt. "Don't I know the risk? If they do find him he's no worse off than if he isn't crowned today in Strelsau."

So speaking, he flung the door open and, stooping, lifted the King in his arms. And as he did so the old woman, Johann the keeper's mother, stood in the doorway. For a moment she stood, then she turned and clattered down the passage.

"Has she heard?" cried Fritz.

"I'll shut her mouth!" said Sapt grimly, and he bore off the King in his arms.

For me, I sat half dazed as Josef clipped and scraped me till my face was as bare as the King's. And when Fritz saw me thus he drew a long breath and exclaimed:

"By Jove, we shall do it!"

It was six o'clock now, and we had no time to lose. Sapt hurried me into the King's room, and I dressed myself in the uniform of a colonel of the Guard, finding time as I slipped on the King's boots to ask Sapt what he had done with the old woman.

"She swore she'd heard nothing," said he; "but to make sure

I tied her hands and legs and put a handkerchief in her mouth, and locked her up in the coal cellar, next door to the King."

Then I burst out laughing, and even old Sapt grimly smiled.

I put the King's helmet on my head. Old Sapt handed me the King's sword, looking at me long and carefully.

"Thank God, he shaved his beard!" he exclaimed.

"Why did he?" I asked.

"Because Princess Flavia said he grazed her cheek when he gave her a cousinly kiss. Come, though, we must ride."

Fritz now rejoined us in the uniform of a captain. In four minutes Sapt had arrayed himself in his uniform. Josef called that the horses were ready. We jumped on their backs and started at a rapid trot. The game had begun.

The cool morning air cleared my head, and I was able to take in all Sapt said to me. He was wonderful. He began at once to instruct me most minutely in the history of my past life, of my family, of my tastes, pursuits, weaknesses, friends, companions and servants. He told me the etiquette of the Ruritanian court, promising to be constantly at my elbow to point out everybody whom I ought to know, and give me hints with what degree of favor to greet them.

"By the way," he said, "you're a Catholic, I suppose?"

"Not I," I answered.

"Lord, he's a heretic!" groaned Sapt, and forthwith he fell to a rudimentary lesson in the practices of the Romish faith.

"Luckily," said he, "you won't be expected to know much. The King's notoriously lax about such matters. But you must be as civil as butter to the cardinal. We hope to win him over, because he and Michael have a standing quarrel about precedence."

We were by now at the station. Fritz explained to the astonished stationmaster that the King had changed his plans. The train steamed up. We got into a first-class carriage, and Sapt, leaning back on the cushions, went on with his lesson. I looked at my watch—the King's watch it was. It was just eight.

The train traveled well, and at half past nine, looking out of the window, I saw the towers and spires of a great city.

"Your capital, my liege," grinned old Sapt, with a wave of his hand, and, leaning forward, he laid his finger on my pulse. "A little too quick," said he in his grumbling tone.

"I'm not made of stone!" I exclaimed.

"You'll do," said he, with a nod. "We're an hour early. We'll send word forward of Your Majesty's arrival. And meanwhile—"

"Meanwhile," said I, "the King'll be hanged if he doesn't have some breakfast."

Old Sapt chuckled, and held out his hand. "You're an Elphberg, every inch of you," said he. Then he paused, and said quietly, "God send we may be alive tonight!"

"Amen!" said Fritz von Tarlenheim.

The train stopped. Fritz and Sapt leaped out, uncovered, and held the door for me. I settled my helmet firmly on my head and (I'm not ashamed to say it) breathed a short prayer to God. Then I stepped on the platform of the station at Strelsau.

A moment later all was bustle and confusion: men hurrying up, hats in hand, and hurrying off again; men conducting me to the buffet. Even as I swallowed the last drop of my cup of coffee the bells throughout all the city broke into a joyful peal, and the sound of a military band and of men cheering smote upon my ear.

"God save the King!" they shouted.

Old Sapt's mouth wrinkled into a smile. "God save 'em both!" he whispered. "Courage, lad!" and I felt his hand press my knee.

CHAPTER V

The Adventures of an Understudy

WITH FRITZ VON TARLENHEIM and Colonel Sapt close behind me, I stepped out of the buffet onto the platform. The last thing I did was to feel if my revolver were handy and my sword loose in the scabbard. A gay group of officers and dignitaries stood awaiting me, at their head a tall old man covered with medals. He wore the yellow and red ribbon of the Red Rose of Ruritania—which, by the way, decorated my unworthy breast also.

"Marshal Strakencz," whispered Sapt, and I knew I was in the presence of the most famous veteran of the Ruritanian army.

Just behind the marshal stood a short spare man, in flowing robes of black and crimson.

"The chancellor of the kingdom," whispered Sapt.

The marshal greeted me in a few loyal words, and proceeded to deliver an apology from the Duke of Strelsau. The duke, it seemed, had been afflicted with a sudden indisposition which made it impossible for him to come to the station, but he craved leave to await His Majesty at the cathedral. I accepted the marshal's excuses very suavely, and received the compliments of a large number of distinguished personages. No one betrayed the least suspicion, and I felt my nerve returning.

Once outside the station I mounted my horse, the marshal holding my stirrup. The civil dignitaries went off to their carriages, and I started to ride through the streets with the marshal on my right and Sapt, as my chief aide-de-camp, on my left. The city of Strelsau is partly old and partly new. Spacious modern boulevards and residential quarters surround the narrow, tortuous and picturesque streets of the original town. In the outer circles the upper classes live; in the inner the shops are situated; and behind their prosperous fronts lie wretched lanes and alleys, filled with a poverty-stricken, turbulent and (in large measure) criminal class. These social and local divisions corresponded, as I knew from Sapt's information, to another division more important to me. The New Town was for the King; but to the Old Town, Michael of Strelsau was a hope, a hero and a darling.

The scene was very brilliant as we passed along the Grand Boulevard. Here I was in the midst of my devoted adherents. Every house was hung with red and bedecked with flags. The streets were lined with raised seats on each side, and I passed along, bowing this way and that, under a shower of cheers and blessings. The balconies were full of gaily dressed ladies, who clapped and curtsied and threw their brightest glances at me. A torrent of red roses fell on me; one bloom lodged in my horse's mane, and I took it and stuck it in my coat.

"The red rose for the Elphbergs, marshal," said I gaily, and he nodded, smiling grimly.

I have written "gaily," and a strange word it must seem. But the truth is that I was drunk with excitement. At that moment I almost believed that I was in very truth the King. I raised my eyes to the beauty-laden balconies again . . . and then I started. For looking down on me was the lady who had been my fellow traveler—Antoinette de Mauban; and I saw her also start. And I, collecting myself, met her eyes full and square, while again I felt my revolver. Suppose she had cried aloud, "That's not the King!"

Well, we went by; and then the marshal, turning in his saddle, waved his hand, and the cuirassiers closed round us. We were leaving my quarter and entering Duke Michael's. But if Fate made me a king, the least I could do was to play the part handsomely.

"Why this change in our order, marshal?" said I.

"It is more prudent, sire," he murmured.

"Let those in front ride on," said I, drawing rein, "till they are fifty yards ahead. But do you, marshal, and Colonel Sapt and my friends wait here till I have ridden fifty yards. And see that no one is nearer to me. I will have my people see that their King trusts them."

The marshal hesitated.

"Am I not understood?" said I; and biting his mustache, the marshal gave the orders. I saw old Sapt smiling into his beard, but he shook his head at me.

Perhaps I ought to say that I was dressed all in white, except my boots. I wore a silver helmet with gilt ornaments, and the broad ribbon of the Rose looked well across my chest. I should be paying a poor compliment to the King if I did not set modesty aside and admit that I made a very fine figure. So the people thought; for when I, riding alone, entered the dingy streets of the Old Town there was first a murmur, then a cheer, and a woman, from a window above a cookshop, cried the old local saying:

"If he's red he's right!" whereat I laughed and took off my helmet that she might see that I was of the right color, and they cheered me again at that.

It was more interesting riding thus alone, for I heard the comments of the crowd.

"He looks paler than his wont," said one.

"You'd look pale if you lived as he does," was the highly disrespectful retort.

"He's a bigger man than I thought," said another.

"So he had a good jaw under that beard after all," commented a third.

"The pictures of him aren't handsome enough," declared a pretty girl, taking great care that I should hear.

But in spite of these signs of approval the mass of the people received me in silence and with sullen looks, and my dear brother's portrait ornamented most of the windows—which was an ironical sort of greeting to the King.

At last we were at the cathedral. Its great gray front, embellished with hundreds of statues, rose for the first time before me, and the sudden sense of my audacity almost overcame me. Everything was in a mist as I dismounted. I saw the marshal and Sapt dimly, and dimly the gorgeously robed priests who awaited me. And my eyes were still dim as I walked up the great nave, with the pealing of the organ in my ears. I saw nothing of the brilliant throng that filled it, I hardly distinguished the stately figure of the cardinal as he rose from the archiepiscopal throne to greet me. Two faces only stood out clearly before my eyes—the face of a girl, pale and lovely, surmounted by a crown of the glorious Elphberg hair (for in a woman it is glorious), and the face of a man whose black hair and dark deep eyes told me that at last I was in the presence of my brother, Black Michael. And when he saw me his red cheeks went pale all in a moment, and his helmet fell with a clatter on the floor. Till that moment I believe that he had not realized that the King was in very truth come to Strelsau.

Of what followed next I remember nothing. I knelt before the altar and the cardinal anointed my head. Then I rose to my feet and took from him the crown of Ruritania and set it on my head, and I swore the old oath of the King; and (if it were a sin, may it be forgiven me) I received the Holy Sacrament. Then the great organ pealed out again, the marshal bade the heralds proclaim me, and Rudolf the Fifth was crowned King; of which imposing ceremony

an excellent picture hangs now in my dining room. The portrait of the King is very good.

Then the lady with the pale face and the glorious hair, her train held by two pages, stepped from her place and came to where I stood. And a herald cried:

"Her Royal Highness the Princess Flavia!"

She curtsied low, and put her hand under mine and raised my hand and kissed it. Then I drew her to me and kissed her twice on the cheek, and she blushed red; and then His Eminence the Cardinal Archbishop kissed my hand and presented me with a letter from the Pope—the first and last which I have ever received from that exalted quarter!

And then came the Duke of Strelsau. His step trembled, I swear, and he looked to the right and to the left, as a man looks who thinks on flight; and his hand shook so that it jumped under mine, and I felt his lips dry and parched. And I glanced at Sapt, who was smiling again into his beard, and resolutely doing my duty in that station of life to which I had been marvelously called, I took my dear Michael by both hands and kissed him on the cheek. I think we were both glad when that was over!

But neither in the face of the princess nor in that of any other did I see the least doubt or questioning. So the likeness served, and for an hour I stood there, feeling as though I had been a king all my life; and everybody kissed my hand, and the ambassadors paid me their respects, among them old Lord Topham, at whose house in Grosvenor Square I had danced a score of times. Thank Heaven, the old man was blind as a bat.

Then back we went through the streets to the palace. I was in a carriage now, side by side with the Princess Flavia, and a rough fellow cried out, "And when's the wedding?" and as he spoke another struck him in the face, crying, "Long live Duke Michael!" and the princess colored—it was an admirable tint—and looked straight in front of her.

Now I felt in a difficulty, because I had forgotten to ask Sapt the state of my affections, or how far matters had gone between the princess and myself. Frankly, had I been the King, the further they had gone the better should I have been pleased. These thoughts passed through my head, but not being sure of my ground, I said nothing; and in a moment or two the princess turned to me.

"Do you know, Rudolf," said she, "you look somehow different today?"

The fact was not surprising, but the remark was disquieting.

"You look," she went on, "more sober, more sedate. Surely it's not possible that you've begun to take anything seriously?"

The princess seemed to hold of the King much the same opinion that Lady Burlesdon held of me.

I braced myself up to the conversation.

"I assure you, my dear cousin, that nothing in my life has affected me more than the reception I've been greeted with today."

She smiled brightly, but in an instant grew grave again, and whispered, "Did you notice Michael?"

"Yes," said I, adding, "he wasn't enjoying himself."

"Do be careful!" she went on. "You don't keep enough watch on him. You know—"

"I know," said I, "that he wants what I've got."

Then—and I can't justify it, for I committed the King far beyond what I had a right to do—I suppose she carried me off my feet—I went on:

"And perhaps also something which I haven't got yet, but hope to win someday."

This was my answer, and had I been the King I should have thought it encouraging:

"Haven't you enough responsibilities for one day, cousin?"

Bang, bang! Blare, blare! We were at the palace. Guns were firing and trumpets blowing. Rows of lackeys stood waiting, and handing the princess up the broad marble staircase, I took formal possession of the house of my ancestors, and sat down at my own table, with my cousin on my right hand, on her other side Black Michael, and on my left the cardinal. Behind my chair stood Sapt; and at the end of the table I saw Fritz von Tarlenheim drain his glass of champagne rather sooner than he decently should.

I wondered what the King of Ruritania was doing.

CHAPTER VI

The Secret of a Cellar

WE WERE IN THE KING's dressing room—Fritz von Tarlenheim, Sapt and I. I flung myself exhausted into an armchair. Sapt lit his pipe. He uttered no congratulations on the marvelous success of our wild risk, but his whole bearing was eloquent of satisfaction. The triumph, aided perhaps by good wine, had made a new man of Fritz.

"What a day for you to remember!" he cried. "But, Rassendyll, you mustn't throw your heart too much into the part. I don't wonder Black Michael looked blacker than ever—you and the princess had so much to say to one another."

"How beautiful she is!" I exclaimed.

"Never mind the woman," growled Sapt. "Are you ready to start?"

"Yes," said I, with a sigh.

It was five o'clock, and at twelve I should be no more than Rudolf Rassendyll. I remarked on it in a joking tone.

"You'll be lucky," observed Sapt grimly, "if you're not the late Rudolf Rassendyll. Do you know, friend, that Michael has had news from Zenda? He went into a room alone to read it—and he came out looking like a man dazed."

"I'm ready," said I, this news making me none the more eager to linger.

Sapt sat down.

"I must write us an order to leave the city, and you must sign it. Michael's governor, you know, and we must be prepared for hindrances."

"My dear colonel, I've not been bred a forger!"

Out of his pocket Sapt produced a piece of paper.

"There's the King's signature," he said, "and here is some tracing paper. If you can't manage a 'Rudolf' in ten minutes, why—I can."

"Your education has been more comprehensive than mine," said I. "You write it."

And a very tolerable forgery did this versatile hero produce.

"Now, Fritz," said he, "the King goes to bed. He is upset. No one is to see him till nine tomorrow. You understand—no one?"

"I understand," answered Fritz.

"Michael may come, and claim immediate audience. You'll answer that only princes of the blood are entitled to it."

"That'll annoy Michael," laughed Fritz.

"You quite understand?" asked Sapt again. "If the door of this room is opened while we're away you're not to be alive to tell us about it."

"I need no schooling, colonel," said Fritz, a trifle haughtily.

"Here, wrap yourself in this big cloak," Sapt continued to me, "and put on this flatcap. My orderly rides with me tonight."

"There's an obstacle," I observed. "The horse doesn't live that can carry me forty miles."

"Oh, yes, he does—two of him: one here—one at the lodge. Now, are you ready?"

"I'm ready," said I.

Fritz held out his hand.

"In case," said he; and we shook hands heartily.

"Damn your sentiment!" growled Sapt. "Come along."

He went, not to the door, but to a panel in the wall. I followed him, and we walked near two hundred yards along a narrow passage. Then we came to a stout oak door. Sapt unlocked it. We passed through, and found ourselves in a quiet street that ran along the back of the palace gardens. A man was waiting with two horses. One was a magnificent bay, up to any weight; the other a sturdy brown. Sapt signed to me to mount the bay. Without a word to the man we mounted and rode away. The town was full of noise and merriment, but we took secluded ways. My cloak was wrapped over half my face; the capacious flatcap hid every lock of my telltale hair. Down a long narrow lane we went, meeting some wanderers and some roisterers. It was half past six, and still light. At last we came to the city wall and to a gate.

"Have your weapon ready," whispered Sapt. "We must stop his mouth if he talks."

I put my hand on my revolver. Sapt hailed the doorkeeper. The stars fought for us! A little girl of fourteen tripped out.

"Please, sir, father's gone to see the King."

"He'd better have stayed here," said Sapt to me, grinning.

"But he said I wasn't to open the gate, sir."

"Did he, my dear?" said Sapt, dismounting. "Then give me the key."

The key was in the child's hand. Sapt gave her a crown.

"Here's an order from the King. Orderly, open the gate!"

I leaped down. Between us we rolled back the great gate, led our horses out and closed it again.

"Now, then, lad, for a canter. We mustn't go too fast while we're near the town."

Once outside the city, however, we ran little danger, for everybody else was inside, merrymaking; and as the evening fell we quickened our pace, my splendid horse bounding along under me as though I had been a feather. It was a fine night, and presently the moon appeared. We talked little on the way, and chiefly about the progress we were making. We stopped for a draft of wine and to bait our horses, losing half an hour thus. Then we went ahead again, and had covered some five-and-twenty miles when Sapt abruptly stopped.

"Hark!" he cried.

I listened. Away, far behind us, in the still of the evening—it was just half past nine—we heard the beat of horses' hoofs. The wind, blowing strong behind us, carried the sound.

"Come on!" cried Sapt, and spurred his horse into a gallop. When we next paused to listen the hoofbeats were not audible, and we relaxed our pace. Then we heard them again. Sapt jumped down and laid his ear to the ground.

"There are two," he said. "They're only a mile behind."

We galloped on. We seemed to be holding our own. We had entered the forest of Zenda, and the trees, closing in behind us as the track zigged and zagged, prevented us seeing our pursuers, and them from seeing us.

Another half hour brought us to a divide of the road.

"To the right is our road," said Sapt, drawing rein. "To the left, to the castle. Each about eight miles. Get down."

"But they'll be on us!" I cried.

"Get down!" he repeated brusquely; and I obeyed. The wood was dense up to the very edge of the road. We led our horses into the covert, bound handkerchiefs over their eyes and stood beside them.

"You want to see who they are?" I whispered.

"Ay, and where they're going," he answered.

I saw that his revolver was in his hand.

Nearer and nearer came the hoofs. The moon shone out now clear and full, so that the road was white with it. The ground was hard and we had left no traces.

"Here they come!" whispered Sapt.

It was the duke; and with him a burly fellow who had cause to know me afterward—Max Holf, brother to Johann the keeper, and body servant to His Highness. They were up to us: the duke reined up. I saw Sapt's finger curl lovingly toward the trigger. I believe he would have given ten years of his life for a shot.

"Which way?" asked Black Michael.

"To the castle, Your Highness," urged his companion. "There we shall learn the truth."

For an instant the duke hesitated.

"Why shouldn't we go to the lodge?"

"I fear a trap. If all is well, why go to the lodge? If not, it's a snare to trap us."

Suddenly the duke's horse neighed. In an instant we folded our cloaks close round our horses' heads, and holding them thus, covered the duke and his attendant with our revolvers.

Michael waited a moment longer. Then he cried:

"To Zenda, then!" and setting spurs to his horse, galloped on.

Sapt raised his weapon after him, and there was such an expression of wistful regret on his face that I had much ado not to burst out laughing.

For ten minutes we stayed where we were.

"You see," said Sapt, "they've sent him news that all is well."

"What does that mean?" I asked.

"God knows," said Sapt, frowning heavily. Then we mounted, and rode as fast as our weary horses could lay their feet to the ground. For those last eight miles we spoke no more. Our minds were full of apprehension.

At last the lodge came in sight. Spurring our horses to a last gallop, we rode up to the gate. All was still and quiet. We dismounted in haste. Suddenly Sapt caught me by the arm.

"Look there!" he said, pointing to the ground.

I looked down. At my feet lay five or six silk handkerchiefs, torn and slashed. I turned to him questioningly.

"They're what I tied the old woman up with," said he. "Fasten the horses and come along."

The handle of the door turned without resistance. We passed into the room which had been the scene of last night's bout. It was still strewn with the remnants of our meal and with empty bottles. We rushed down the passage toward the cellars. The door of the coal cellar where we had put the old woman stood wide open, but the door of the wine cellar was shut. It looked in all respects as it had looked when we left it that morning.

A loud oath from Sapt rang out. His face turned pale, and he pointed at the floor. From under the door a red stain had spread over the floor of the passage and dried there. Sapt sank against the opposite wall. I tried the door. It was locked. Sapt took out a flask and put it to his lips. I ran back to the dining room, and seized a heavy poker from the fireplace. In my terror and excitement I rained blows on the lock of the door, and I fired a cartridge into it. It gave way, and the door swung open.

"Give me a light," said I; but Sapt still leaned against the wall.

He was, of course, more moved than I, for he loved his master. Afraid for himself he was not—no man ever saw him that; but to think what might lie in that dark cellar was enough to turn any man's face pale. I went myself, and took a silver candlestick from the dining table, struck a light, and returned to the door of the cellar. The red stain, turning more and more to a dull brown, stretched inside. I walked two yards into the cellar, and held the candle high above my head. I saw the full bins of wine; I saw too a couple of empty bottles lying on the floor; and then, away in the corner, I saw the body of a man, lying flat on his back, with his arms stretched wide, and a crimson gash across his throat. I walked to him and knelt down beside him, and commended to God the soul of a faithful man. For it was the body of Josef, the little servant, slain in guarding the King.

I felt a hand on my shoulder, and turning, saw Sapt, eyes glaring and terror-struck, beside me.

"The King? My God! The King?" he whispered hoarsely.

I threw the candle's gleam over every inch of the cellar.

"The King is not here," said I.

CHAPTER VII

His Majesty Sleeps in Strelsau

I PUT MY ARM ROUND SAPT'S WAIST and supported him out of the cellar, drawing the battered door close after me. For ten minutes or more we sat silent in the dining room. Then old Sapt rubbed his knuckles into his eyes, gave one great gasp and was himself again. As the clock on the mantelpiece struck one he stamped his foot on the floor, saying, "They've got the King!"

"Yes," said I, "'all's well!' as Black Michael's dispatch said. We must get back and rouse every soldier in Strelsau. We ought to be in pursuit of Michael before midday."

Old Sapt pulled out his pipe and carefully lit it from the candle which guttered on the table.

"The King may be murdered while we sit here!" I urged.

Sapt smoked on for a moment in silence.

"That cursed old woman!" he broke out. "She must have attracted their attention somehow. I see the game. They came up to kidnap the King, and—as I say—somehow they found him. Who knows where the King is now?"

"Come, let's be off!" said I; but he sat still. And suddenly he burst into one of his grating chuckles.

"By Jove, we've shaken up Black Michael! And we'll shake him

527

up a bit more," he added, a cunning smile broadening on his wrinkled, weather-beaten face. "Ay, lad, we'll go back to Strelsau. The King shall be in his capital again tomorrow."

"The King?"

"The crowned King!"

"You're mad!" I cried.

"If we go back and tell the trick we played, what would you give for our lives?"

"Just what they're worth," said I.

"And for the King's throne? Do you think that the nobles and the people will enjoy being fooled as you've fooled them? Do you think they'll love a King who was too drunk to be crowned, and sent a servant to impersonate him?"

"He was drugged—and I'm no servant."

He rose, came to me, and laid his hand on my shoulder.

"Lad," he said, "if you play the man you may save the King yet. Go back and keep his throne warm for him."

"But the duke knows—the villains he has employed know—"

"Ay, but they can't speak!" roared Sapt in grim triumph. "We've got 'em! How can they denounce you without denouncing themselves? 'This is not the King, because we kidnaped the King and murdered his servant.' Can they say that?"

The position flashed on me. Whether Michael knew me or not, he could not speak. Unless he produced the King, what could he do? For a moment I was carried away headlong; but in an instant the difficulties came strong upon me.

"I must be found out," I urged.

"Perhaps; but every hour's something. Above all, we must have a King in Strelsau, or the city will be Michael's in four-and-twenty hours, and what would the King's life be worth then—or his throne? Lad, you must do it!"

"Suppose they kill the King?"

"They'll kill him if you don't."

"Sapt, suppose they have killed the King?"

"Then, by Heaven, you're as good an Elphberg as Black Michael, and you shall reign in Ruritania! But I don't believe they have; nor will they kill him if you're on the throne. Will they kill him to put you in?"

It was a wild plan—wilder even and more hopeless than the trick we had already carried through; but as I listened to Sapt I saw the strong points in our game. And then I was a young man and I loved action, and I was offered such a hand in such a game as perhaps never man played yet.

"Sapt," I cried, "I'll try it!"

"Well played!" said he. "I hope they've left us the horses. I'll go and see."

"We must bury that poor fellow," said I.

"No time," said Sapt.

"I'll do it."

"Hang you!" He grinned. "I make you a King, and— Well, do it. Go and fetch him, while I look to the horses. He can't lie very deep, but I doubt if he'll care about that. Poor little Josef! He was an honest bit of a man."

He went out, and I went to the cellar. I raised poor Josef in my arms and bore him into the passage and thence toward the door of the house. At this instant Sapt came up.

"The horses are all right; there's the own brother to the one that brought you here. But you may save yourself that job."

"I'll not go before he's buried."

"Yes, you will."

"Not I, Colonel Sapt; not for all Ruritania."

"You fool!" said he. "Come here."

He drew me to the door. The moon was sinking, but about three hundred yards away, coming along the road from Zenda, I made out a party of seven or eight men. Four were on horseback and the rest were walking, and I saw that they carried long implements, which I guessed to be spades, on their shoulders.

"They'll save you the trouble," said Sapt. "Come along."

He was right. The approaching party must, beyond doubt, be Duke Michael's men, come to remove the traces of their evil work. I hesitated no longer, but an irresistible desire seized me. Pointing to the corpse of poor little Josef, I said to Sapt:

"Colonel, we ought to strike a blow for him!"

"You'd like to give him some company, eh? But it's too risky work, Your Majesty."

"I must have a slap at 'em," said I.

Sapt wavered.

"Well," said he, "you've been a good boy—and if we come to grief, why, hang me, it'll save us a lot of thinking!"

We retreated through the house and made our way to the back entrance. Here our horses were standing. A carriage drive swept all round the lodge.

"Revolver ready?" asked Sapt.

"No: steel for me," said I.

"Gad, you're thirsty tonight," chuckled Sapt. "So be it."

We mounted, drawing our swords, and waited silent for a minute or two. Then we heard the tramp of men on the drive the other side of the house. They came to a stand, and one cried:

"Now, then, fetch him out!"

"Now!" whispered Sapt. Driving the spurs into our horses, we rushed at a gallop round the house, and in a moment we were among the ruffians. Sapt told me afterward that he killed a man; but I saw no more of him. With a cut I split the head of a fellow on a brown horse, and he fell to the ground. Then I found myself opposite a big man, and I was half conscious of another to my right. It was too warm to stay, and with a simultaneous action I drove my spurs into my horse again and my sword full into the big man's breast. His bullet whizzed past my ear—I could almost swear it touched it. I wrenched at the sword, but it would not come, and I dropped it and galloped after Sapt, whom I now saw about twenty yards ahead. I waved my hand in farewell and dropped it a second later with a yell, for a bullet had grazed my finger and I felt the blood. Old Sapt turned round in the saddle. Someone fired again, but they had no rifles, and we were out of range. Sapt fell to laughing.

"That's one to me and two to you, with decent luck," said he. "Little Josef will have company."

"Ay, they'll be a foursome," said I.

"Well, a pleasant night's work to the rest!" said he. "I wonder if they noticed you?"

"The big fellow did; as I stuck him I heard him cry, 'The King!'"

"Good! Good! Oh, we'll give Black Michael some work before we've done!"

Pausing an instant, we made a bandage for my wounded finger, which was bleeding freely and ached severely. Then we rode on, asking of our good horses all that was in them. Day broke clear and cold. We found a farmer just up, and made him give us sustenance for ourselves and our horses. I, feigning a toothache, muffled my face closely. Then ahead again, till Strelsau lay before us. It was eight o'clock or nearing nine, and the gates were all open. We rode in by the same way as we had come out the evening before. The streets were even quieter than when we had gone: everyone was sleeping off last night's revelry, and we met hardly a soul till we reached the little gate of the palace. There Sapt's old groom was waiting for us.

"Is all well, sir?" he asked.

"All's well," said Sapt, and the man, coming to me, took my hand to kiss.

"The King's hurt!" he cried.

"It's nothing," said I as I dismounted.

"Remember—silence!" said Sapt. "Ah, but, my good Freyler, I do not need to tell you that!"

We went in and reached the dressing room. Flinging open the door, we saw Fritz von Tarlenheim stretched, fully dressed, on the sofa. He leaped to his feet, gave one glance at me, and with a joyful cry threw himself on his knees before me.

"Thank God, sire! Thank God, you're safe!" he cried, stretching his hand up to catch hold of mine.

I confess that I was moved. This King, whatever his faults, made people love him. For a moment I could not bear to speak or break the poor fellow's illusion. But tough old Sapt had no such feeling. He slapped his hand on his thigh delightedly.

"Bravo, lad!" cried he. "We shall do!"

Fritz looked up in bewilderment. I held out my hand.

"You're wounded, sire!" he exclaimed.

"It's only a scratch," said I, "but—" I paused.

He rose to his feet with a bewildered air. Holding my hand, he looked me up and down, and down and up. Then suddenly he dropped my hand and reeled back.

"Where's the King? Where's the King? Is he dead?" he cried.

"Please God, no," said I. "But he's in the hands of Black Michael!"

CHAPTER VIII

A Fair Cousin and a Dark Brother

A REAL KING'S LIFE IS PERHAPS a hard one; but a pretended king's is, I warrant, much harder. On the next day Sapt instructed me in my duties for three hours; then I snatched breakfast, with Sapt still opposite me, telling me that the King always took white wine in the morning and was known to detest all highly seasoned dishes. Then came the chancellor for another three hours; and to him I had to explain that the hurt to my finger (we turned that bullet to happy account) prevented me from writing—whence arose great to-do, hunting of precedents and so forth, ending in my "making my mark," and the chancellor attesting it with a superfluity of solemn oaths.

Then, at last, I was left alone. I called my new servant (we had chosen, to succeed poor Josef, a young man who had never known the King), had a brandy and soda brought to me and observed to Sapt that I trusted that I might now have a rest.

Fritz von Tarlenheim was standing by.

"By Heaven," he cried, "we waste time! Aren't we going to throw Black Michael by the heels? Are we to do nothing?"

"We're to do nothing stupid," growled Sapt.

"In fact, Fritz," said I, "I am reminded of two men, each covering the other with a revolver. For I can't expose Michael without exposing myself—"

"And the King," put in Sapt.

"And hang me if Michael won't expose himself if he tries to expose me!"

"It's very pretty," said old Sapt.

"If I'm found out," I pursued, "I will make a clean breast of it, but at present I'm waiting for a move from the duke."

"He'll kill the King," said Fritz.

"Not he," said Sapt.

"Half of the Six are in Strelsau," said Fritz.

"Then the King's alive," said Sapt eagerly, "for the other three are guarding him!"

"Yes—you're right!" exclaimed Fritz, his face brightening. "If the King were dead and buried they'd all be here with Michael. You know Michael's back, colonel?"

"I know, curse him!"

"Gentlemen, gentlemen," said I, "who are the Six?"

"I think you'll make their acquaintance soon," said Sapt. "They are six gentlemen whom Michael maintains in his household; they belong to him body and soul. There are three Ruritanians; then there's a Frenchman, a Belgian and one of your countrymen."

"They'd all cut a throat if Michael told them," said Fritz.

"Perhaps they'll cut mine," I suggested.

"Nothing more likely," agreed Sapt. "Who are here, Fritz?"

"De Gautet, Bersonin and Detchard."

"The foreigners! It's as plain as a pikestaff. He's brought them, and left the Ruritanians with the King."

"They were none of them among our friends at the lodge, then?" I asked.

"I wish they had been," said Sapt wistfully.

I had already developed one attribute of royalty—a feeling that I need not reveal all my mind or my secret designs even to my intimate friends. I had fully resolved on my course of action. I meant to make myself as popular as I could, and at the same time to show no disfavor to Michael. By these means I hoped to allay the hostility of his adherents, and make it appear, if an open conflict came about, that he was ungrateful and not oppressed.

I ordered my horse, and attended by Fritz von Tarlenheim, rode in the grand New Avenue of the royal park, returning with punctilious politeness all the salutes which I received. Then, having attracted the desired amount of attention (for I had a trail of half a thousand people after me), I rode to the residence of the Princess Flavia, and asked if she would receive me. This step created much interest, and was met with shouts of approval. The princess was very popular, and the chancellor himself had not scrupled to hint to me that the more I pressed my suit, and the more rapidly I brought it to a prosperous conclusion, the stronger should I be in the affections of my subjects. The chancellor, of course, did not understand the difficulties which lay in the way of following his loyal and excellent advice. However, I thought I could do no harm by calling; and in this view Fritz supported me with a cordiality that surprised me, until he confessed that he also had his motive for liking a visit to the princess' house, which motive was no other than a great desire to see the princess' lady-in-waiting and bosom friend, the Countess Helga von Strofzin.

Etiquette seconded Fritz's hopes. While I was ushered into the princess' room, he remained with the countess in the antechamber; in spite of the people and servants who were hanging about, I doubt not that they managed a tête-à-tête; but I had no leisure to think of them, for I was playing the most delicate move in all my difficult game. I had to keep the princess devoted to me—and yet indifferent to me; I had to show affection for her—and not feel it. I had to make love for another, and that to a girl who—princess or no princess—was the most beautiful I had ever seen.

"You are gaining golden laurels," she said. "You are like the prince in Shakespeare who was transformed by becoming king. But I'm not forgetting you are King, sire."

"I ask you to speak nothing but what your heart tells you—and to call me nothing but my name."

She looked at me for a moment.

"Then I'm glad and proud, Rudolf," said she. "Why, as I told you, your very face is changed."

I acknowledged the compliment, but I disliked the topic; so I said:

"My brother is back, I hear. He made an excursion, didn't he?"

"Yes, he is here," she said, frowning a little.

"He can't stay long from Strelsau, it seems," I observed, smiling. "Well, we are all glad to see him. The nearer he is the better, don't you agree?"

The princess glanced at me with amusement in her eyes. "I do not mind a snap of my fingers where the Duke of Strelsau is."

"You don't care where cousin Michael—"

"Ah, cousin Michael! I call him the Duke of Strelsau."

"You call him Michael when you meet him?"

"Yes—by the orders of your father."

"I see. And now by mine?"

"If those are your orders."

"Oh, decidedly! We must all be pleasant to our dear Michael."

As I spoke there came a cheer from the street. The princess ran to the window.

"It is he!" she cried. "It is—the Duke of Strelsau!"

I smiled, but said nothing. She returned to her seat. For a few moments we sat in silence. The noise outside subsided, but I heard the tread of feet in the anteroom. I began to talk on general subjects. This went on for some minutes. All at once, to my great surprise, Flavia, clasping her hands, asked in an agitated voice:

"Are you wise to make him angry by keeping him waiting?"

"My dear cousin, I don't want to keep him—"

"Well, then, is he to come in?"

"Of course, if you wish it."

She looked at me curiously. "How funny you are," she said. "Of course no one could be announced while I was with you."

Here was a charming attribute of royalty! "An excellent etiquette!" I cried. "But I had clean forgotten it; and if I were alone with someone else couldn't you be announced?"

"You know as well as I do. I could be, because I am of the Blood"; and she still looked puzzled.

"I never could remember all these silly rules," said I rather feebly, as I inwardly cursed Fritz for not posting me up. "But I'll repair my fault."

I jumped up, flung open the door, and entered the anteroom. Michael was sitting at a table, a heavy frown on his face. Everyone else was standing, save that impudent young dog Fritz, who was lounging easily in an armchair, and flirting with the Countess Helga. He leaped up as I entered, with a deferential alacrity that lent point to his former nonchalance.

I held out my hand, Michael took it, and I embraced him. Then I drew him with me into the inner room.

"Brother," I said, "if I had known you were here you should not have waited a moment before I asked the princess to permit me to bring you to her."

He thanked me, but coldly. The man had many qualities, but he could not hide his feelings. A mere stranger could have seen that he hated me, and hated worse to see me with Princess Flavia; yet I am persuaded that he tried to conceal both feelings. How he must have loathed paying me deference, and hearing my "Michael" and my "Flavia"!

"Your hand is hurt, sire," he observed with concern.

"Yes, I was playing a game with a mongrel dog" (I meant to stir him), "and you know, brother, such have uncertain tempers."

He smiled sourly, his dark eyes resting on me for a moment.

"But is there no danger from the bite?" cried Flavia anxiously.

"None from this," said I. "If I gave him a chance to bite deeper it would be different, cousin."

"But surely he has been destroyed?" said she.

"Not yet. We're waiting to see if his bite is harmful."

"And if it is?" asked Michael, with his sour smile.

"He'll be knocked on the head, brother," said I.

Then, fearing Michael would say something which I must appear to resent, I began to compliment him on the magnificent condition of his regiment and of their loyal greeting to me on the day of my coronation. But he rose suddenly to his feet. His temper was failing him, and with an excuse he said farewell. However, as he reached the door he stopped, saying:

"Three friends of mine are very anxious to have the honor of being presented to you, sire. They are here in the antechamber."

I joined him directly, passing my arm through his. We entered the antechamber in fraternal fashion. Michael beckoned, and three men came forward.

"These gentlemen," said Michael, with a stately courtesy which, to do him justice, he could assume with perfect grace and ease, "are the loyalest and most devoted of Your Majesty's servants, and are my very faithful and attached friends."

"On the last ground as much as the first," said I, "I am very pleased to see them."

They came one by one and kissed my hand—De Gautet, a tall, lean fellow with hair standing straight up and waxed mustache; Bersonin, the Belgian, a portly man of middle height with a bald head; and last, the Englishman, Detchard, a narrow-faced fellow with close-cut fair hair and a bronzed complexion. He was a finely made man, broad in the shoulders and slender in the hips. A good fighter, but a crooked customer, I put him down for. I spoke to him in English, with a slight foreign accent, and I swear the fellow smiled, though he hid the smile in an instant.

So Mr. Detchard is in the secret, thought I.

Having got rid of my dear brother and his friends, I returned to make my adieu to my cousin. I bade her farewell, taking her hand in mine.

"Rudolf," she said, very low, "be careful, won't you?"

"Of what?"

"You know—I can't say. But think what your life is to—"

"Well, to—?"

"To Ruritania."

Was I right or wrong to play the part? I know not; evil lay both ways, and I dared not tell her the truth.

"Only to Ruritania?" I asked softly.

A sudden flush spread over her incomparable face.

"To your friends, too," she said.

"Friends?"

"And to your cousin," she whispered, "and loving servant."

I could not speak. I kissed her hand, and went out cursing myself.

Outside I found Master Fritz, quite reckless of the footmen, playing at cat's cradle with the Countess Helga.

"Hang it," said he, "we can't always be plotting! Love claims his share."

"I'm inclined to think he does," said I; and Fritz, who had been by my side, dropped respectfully behind.

CHAPTER IX

A New Use for a Tea Table

IF I WERE TO DETAIL THE ordinary events of my daily life at this time, they might prove instructive to people who are not familiar with the inside of palaces; if I revealed some of the secrets I learned, they might prove of interest to the statesmen of Europe. I intend to do neither of these things. I feel that I had far better confine myself strictly to the underground drama which was being played beneath the surface of Ruritanian politics. I need only say that the secret of my imposture defied detection. I made mistakes; I had bad minutes. But I escaped, and I attribute my escape most of all to the very audacity of the enterprise.

One day Sapt came into my room. He threw me a letter, saying, "That's for you—a woman's hand, I think. But I've some news for you first."

"What's that?"

"The King's at the Castle of Zenda," said he.

"How do you know?"

"Because the other half of Michael's Six are there. I had inquiries made, and they're all there—Lauengram, Krafstein and young Rupert Hentzau: three rogues as fine as live in Ruritania."

"You think it's certain he's there?"

"Very probable. Besides the fact of those three being there, the drawbridge is kept up and no one goes in without an order from young Hentzau or Black Michael himself."

"I'll go to Zenda," said I.

"You'll very likely stay there if you do."

"That may be, my friend," said I carelessly.

538

"His Majesty looks sulky," observed Sapt. "How's the love affair?"

"Damn you, hold your tongue!" I said.

He looked at me for a moment, then he lit his pipe. It was quite true that I was in a bad temper, and I went on perversely:

"Wherever I go, I'm dogged by half a dozen fellows."

"I know you are; I send 'em," he replied composedly.

"What for?"

"Well," said Sapt, puffing away, "it wouldn't be exactly inconvenient for Black Michael if you disappeared."

"I can take care of myself."

"De Gautet, Bersonin and Detchard are in Strelsau; and any one of them would cut your throat as readily as I would Black Michael's and a deal more treacherously. What's the letter?"

I opened it and read it aloud:

"If the King desires to know what deeply concerns him, let him do as this letter bids him. At the end of the New Avenue there stands a house in large grounds. A wall encloses the garden; there is a gate in the wall at the back. At twelve o'clock tonight, if the King enters *alone* by that gate, turns to the right, and walks twenty yards, he will find a summer house, approached by a flight of six steps. If he mounts and enters, he will find someone who will tell him what touches most dearly his life and his throne. This is written by a faithful friend. He must be alone. If he neglects the invitation his life will be in danger. Let him show this to no one, or he will ruin a woman who loves him: Black Michael does not pardon."

"No," observed Sapt, as I ended, "but he can dictate a very pretty letter."

I had arrived at the same conclusion, and was about to throw the letter away, when I saw there was more writing on the other side.

"Hallo! There's some more."

The writer continued:

"If you hesitate consult Colonel Sapt—"

"Eh!" exclaimed that gentleman, genuinely astonished. "Does she take me for a greater fool than you?"

I waved to him to be silent.

"Ask him what woman would do most to prevent the duke from marrying his cousin, and therefore most to prevent him becoming king? And ask if her name begins with *A*."

I sprang to my feet. Sapt laid down his pipe.

"Antoinette de Mauban, by Heaven!" I cried.

"How do you know?" asked Sapt.

I told him what I knew of the lady, and how I knew it. He nodded.

"It's true that she's had a great row with Michael," said he thoughtfully. "I believe, though, that Michael wrote that letter."

"So do I, but I mean to know for certain. I shall go, Sapt."

"I'm hanged if you shall! I shall go!"

I rose and leaned my back against the mantelpiece.

"Sapt, I believe in that woman. I either go to the summer house or back to England," said I.

Sapt began to know exactly how far he could lead or drive, and when he must follow.

"We're playing against time," I added. "Every day I masquerade like this there is fresh risk for the King. Sapt, we must play high; we must force the game."

"So be it," he said with a sigh.

To cut the story short, at half past eleven that night Sapt and I mounted our horses. It was a very dark night. I wore no sword, but I carried a revolver, a long knife and a bull's-eye lantern. We arrived outside the gate. I dismounted. Sapt held out his hand.

"I shall wait here," he said. "If I hear a shot I'll—"

"Stay where you are; it's the King's only chance. You mustn't come to grief too."

"You're right, lad. Good luck!"

I pressed the little gate. It yielded, and I found myself in a wild sort of shrubbery. There was a grass-grown path and turning to the right as I had been bid, I followed it cautiously. Presently a large dark object loomed out of the gloom ahead of me. It was the summer house. Reaching the steps, I mounted them and found myself confronted by a weak, rickety door, which hung upon the latch. I pushed it open and walked in. A woman flew to me and seized my hand.

"Shut the door," she whispered.

I obeyed and turned my lantern on her. She was in evening dress, arrayed very sumptuously, and her dark striking beauty was marvelously displayed in the glare of the bull's-eye. The summer house was a bare little room, furnished only with a couple of chairs and a small iron table, such as one sees in a tea garden or an open-air café.

"Don't talk," she said. "We've no time. Listen! I know you, Mr. Rassendyll. I wrote that letter at the duke's orders. In twenty minutes three men will be here to kill you."

"Three—*the* three?"

"Yes. You must be gone by then. If not, you'll be killed."

"Or they will."

"Listen, listen! When you're killed, your body will be taken to a low quarter of the town. It will be found there. Michael will at once arrest Colonel Sapt and Captain von Tarlenheim, proclaim a state of siege in Strelsau and send a messenger to Zenda. The other three will murder the King in the castle, and the duke will proclaim either himself or the princess. Anyhow, he'll marry her, and become king in fact, and soon in name. Do you see?"

"It's a pretty plot. But why, madame, do you—"

"Say I'm a Christian—or say I'm jealous. My God! Shall I see him marry her? Now go; but remember that never, by night or by day, are you safe. Three men follow you as a guard. Is it not so? Well, three follow them; Michael's three are never two hundred yards from you. Your life is not worth a moment if ever they find you alone. The gate will be guarded by now. Go down softly, go past the summer house, on for a hundred yards, and you'll find a ladder against the wall. Get over it and fly for your life."

"And you?" I asked.

"If the duke finds out what I have done we shall not meet again. If not I may yet— But never mind. Go at once."

"But what will you tell him?"

"That you never came—that you saw through the trick."

I took her hand and kissed it.

"Madame," said I, "you have served the King well tonight. Where is he in the castle?"

"Across the drawbridge you come to a heavy door; behind that lies— Hark! What's that?"

There were steps outside.

"They're coming! They're too soon! Heavens, they're too soon!" and she turned pale as death.

"They seem to me," said I, "to be in the nick of time."

"Close your lantern. See, there's a chink in the door. Can you see them?"

I put my eye to the chink. On the lowest step I saw three dim figures. I cocked my revolver. A voice came from outside—a voice that spoke perfect English.

"Mr. Rassendyll," it said, "we want to talk to you. Will you promise not to shoot till we've done?"

"Have I the pleasure of addressing Mr. Detchard?" I said.

"Never mind names."

"Then let mine alone."

"All right, *sire*. I've an offer for you."

I still had my eye to the chink. The three had mounted two steps more; three revolvers pointed full at the door.

"Will you let us in? We pledge our honor to observe the truce."

"Don't trust them," whispered Antoinette.

"We can speak through the door," said I.

A sudden idea struck me. I considered it for a moment. It seemed feasible.

"I give my honor not to fire before you do," said I; "but I won't let you in. Stand outside and talk."

"That's sensible," Detchard said; and the three mounted the last step.

"Well, gentlemen, what's the offer?"

"A safe-conduct to the frontier and fifty thousand pounds English."

"No, no," whispered Antoinette. "They are treacherous."

"That seems handsome," said I, reconnoitering through the chink. They were close together, just outside the door. I had probed the hearts of the ruffians, and I did not need Antoinette's warning. They meant to rush me as soon as I was engaged in talk.

"Give me a minute to consider," said I.

I turned to Antoinette. "Stand up close to the wall, out of the line of fire from the door," I whispered.

I took up the little iron table. It was not very heavy for a man of my strength, and I held it by the legs. The top, protruding in front of me, made a complete screen for my head and body. I fastened my closed lantern to my belt and put my revolver in a handy pocket.

I drew back as far as I could from the door, holding the table in the position that I have described. Then I called out:

"Gentlemen, I accept your offer, relying on your honor. If you will open the door—"

"Open it yourself," said Detchard.

"It opens outward," said I. "Stand back a little, gentlemen, or I shall hit you when I open it."

I went and fumbled with the latch. Then I stole back to my place on tiptoe.

"I can't open it!" I cried. "The latch has caught."

"Tut! I'll open it!" cried Detchard.

I smiled to myself. An instant later the door was flung back. The gleam of a lantern showed me the three close together outside, their revolvers leveled. With a shout I charged at my utmost pace across the summer house and through the doorway. Three shots rang out and battered into my shield. Another moment, and I leaped out and the table caught them full and square, and in a tumbling, swearing, struggling mass they and I and that brave table rolled down the steps of the summer house to the ground below. Antoinette de Mauban shrieked, but I rose to my feet, laughing aloud.

De Gautet and Bersonin lay like men stunned. Detchard was under the table, but as I rose he pushed it from him and fired again. I raised my revolver and took a snap shot; I heard him curse, and then I ran like a hare, laughing as I went. I heard steps behind me, and turning round I fired again for luck. The steps ceased.

"Please God," said I, "she told me the truth about the ladder!" for the wall was high and topped with iron spikes.

Yes, there it was. I was up and over in a minute. Doubling back, I saw the horses; then I heard a shot. It was Sapt. He had heard us and was battling and raging with the locked gate, hammering it and firing into the keyhole like a man possessed. He had quite forgotten that he was not to take part in the fight. Whereat I laughed again, and said, as I clapped him on the shoulder:

"Come home to bed, old chap. I've got the finest tea-table story that ever you heard!"

He started and cried, "You're safe!" and wrung my hand. But a moment later he added, "And what the devil are you laughing at?"

"Four gentlemen round a tea table," said I, laughing still, for it had been uncommonly ludicrous to see the formidable three altogether routed with no more deadly weapon than that.

Moreover, you will observe that I had honorably kept my word and not fired till they did.

CHAPTER X

A Great Chance for a Villain

IT WAS THE CUSTOM THAT THE prefect of police should send me every afternoon a report on the condition of the capital, which included an account of the movements of any persons whom the police had received instructions to watch. The day after my adventure in the summer house Sapt came in as I was playing a hand of écarté with Fritz von Tarlenheim.

"The report is rather full of interest this afternoon," he observed, sitting down. "First, this: 'His Highness the Duke of Strelsau left the city, accompanied by several of his household. His destination is believed to be the Castle of Zenda. Messieurs De Gautet, Bersonin and Detchard followed an hour later, the last-named carrying his arm in a sling. The cause of his wound is not known, but it is suspected that he has fought a duel, probably incidental to a love affair.'"

"That is remotely true," I observed, very well pleased to find that I had left my mark on the fellow.

"Then we come to this," pursued Sapt: "'Madame de Mauban left by train at midday. She took a ticket for Dresden—'"

"It's an old habit of hers," said I.

"'The Dresden train stops at Zenda.' An acute fellow, this. And finally listen to this: 'The King is much criticized in the city' (you know, he's told to be quite frank) 'for taking no steps about his marriage. Princess Flavia is believed to be deeply offended by the remissness of His Majesty. The common people are coupling her name with that of the Duke of Strelsau, and the duke gains much popularity from the suggestion. I have caused the announcement that the King gives a ball tonight in honor of the princess to be widely diffused, and the effect is good.'"

"That is news to me," said I.

"Oh, the preparations are all made!" laughed Fritz. "I've seen to that."

Sapt turned to me and said in a sharp, decisive voice:

"You must make love to her tonight, you know."

"I think it is very likely I shall if I see her alone," said I.

Fritz whistled a bar or two; then he said: "You'll find it only too easy. The Countess Helga told me that the princess had become most attached to the King since the coronation. It's quite true that she is deeply wounded by the King's apparent neglect."

"Here's a kettle of fish!" I groaned.

"I suppose you've made pretty speeches to a girl before now," said that cold-blooded old Sapt. "I think, then, that you'd better make your offer tonight."

"Good Heavens!"

"Or, at any rate, go near it; and I shall send a 'semiofficial' to the papers."

"I'll do nothing of the sort—no more will you!" said I. "I utterly refuse to take part in making a fool of the princess."

Sapt looked at me with his small keen eyes. A slow cunning smile passed over his face.

"All right, lad, all right," said he. "We mustn't press you too hard. Soothe her down a bit, if you can, you know."

Why did Sapt urge me so little about the princess? Because he knew that her beauty and my ardor would carry me further than all his arguments. He must have seen the unhappiness he might bring on the princess; but that went for nothing with him. Can I say, confidently, that he was wrong? If the King were restored the princess must turn to him, either knowing or not knowing the change. And if the King were not restored to us? It was a subject that we had never yet spoken of. But I had an idea that, in such a case, Sapt meant to seat me on the throne of Ruritania for the term of my life. He would have set Satan himself there sooner than Black Michael.

The ball was a sumptuous affair. I opened it by dancing a quadrille with Flavia; then I waltzed with her. Curious eyes and eager whispers attended us. We went in to supper; and halfway through I—half mad by then, for her glance had answered mine—rose in my place before all the brilliant crowd, and taking the Red Rose that I wore, flung the ribbon with its jeweled badge round her neck. In a tumult of applause I sat down. I saw Sapt smiling over his wine, and Fritz frowning. The rest of the meal passed in silence; neither Flavia nor I could speak. Fritz touched me on the shoulder, and I rose, gave her my arm, and walked down the hall into a little room, where coffee was served to us. We were alone.

The little room had French windows opening on the gardens. The night was fine, cool and fragrant. Flavia sat down, and I stood opposite her. I was struggling with myself; if she had not looked at me I believe that even then I should have won my fight. But suddenly, involuntarily, she gave me one brief glance of question, hurriedly turned aside. Ah, if you had seen her! I forgot the King in Zenda. She was a princess and I an impostor. Do you think I remembered that? I threw myself on my knee and seized her hands in mine. I said nothing. The soft sounds of the night set my wooing to a wordless melody as I pressed my kisses on her lips.

She pushed me from her, crying suddenly:

"Ah, is it true? Or is it only because you must?"

"It's true," I said in low smothered tones, "true that I love you more than life —or truth—or honor!"

She set no meaning to my words, treating them as one of love's sweet extravagances. She came close to me, and whispered:

"Oh, if you were not the King! Then I could show you how I love you! How is it that I love you now, Rudolf, and never did before?"

Pure triumph filled me. It was I—Rudolf Rassendyll—who had won her! I caught her round the waist.

"You didn't love me before?" I asked.

She looked up into my face, smiling, as she whispered, "You speak as if you would be pleased to hear me say 'Yes' to that."

"Would 'Yes' be true?"

"Yes," I just heard her breathe.

"If I were not the King," I began, "if I were only a private gentleman—"

Before I could finish her hand was in mine. "If you were a convict in the prison of Strelsau you would be my king," she said.

Under my breath I groaned, "God forgive me!" But there was yet a chance for me. Summoning up what honor and conscience her beauty and the toils I was in had left me, I took my hands off her and stood a yard or two away. I remember now the note of the wind in the elm trees outside.

"Flavia," I said in a strange, dry voice that seemed not my own, "I am not—"

As I spoke—as she raised her eyes to me—there was a heavy step on the gravel outside, and a man appeared at the window. My half-finished sentence died on my lips. Sapt stood there, bowing low.

"A thousand pardons, sire," said he, "but His Eminence the Cardinal has waited this quarter of an hour to offer his respectful adieu to Your Majesty."

I met his eye full and square; and I read in it an angry warning. How long he had been a listener I knew not; but he had come in upon us in the nick of time.

"We must not keep His Eminence waiting," said I.

But Flavia, in whose love there lay no shame, with radiant eyes and blushing face held out her hand to Sapt. She said nothing, but no man could have missed her meaning who had ever seen a woman in the exultation of love. There was tenderness in the old soldier's voice as, bending to kiss her hand, he said, "In joy and sorrow, in good times and bad, God save Your Royal Highness!"

He paused and added, glancing at me and drawing himself up to military erectness:

"But before all comes the King—God save the King!"

We went into the ballroom again. Forced to receive adieus, I was separated from Flavia; everyone, when they left me, went to her. When at last I handed Flavia down the broad marble steps and into her carriage there was a great crowd awaiting us, and we were welcomed with deafening cheers. What could I do? Had I spoken then, they would have refused to believe that I was not the King; they might have believed that the King had run mad. By Sapt's devices and my own ungoverned passion I had been forced on, and the way back had closed behind me. I faced all Strelsau that night as the King and the accepted suitor of the Princess Flavia.

At last, at three in the morning, when the cold light of dawn began to steal in, I was in my dressing room, and Sapt alone was with me. I sat like a man dazed, staring into the fire; he puffed at his pipe. On the table by me lay a rose; it had been in Flavia's dress, and as we parted she had kissed it and given it to me.

Sapt advanced his hand toward the rose, but, with a quick movement, I shut mine down upon it.

"That's mine," I said, "not yours—nor the King's either."

"We struck a good blow for the King tonight," said he.

I turned on him fiercely.

"What's to prevent me striking a blow for myself?" I said.

He nodded his head. "I know what's in your mind," he said. "Yes, lad; but you're bound in honor."

"Have you left me any honor?"

"Oh, come, to play a little trick on a girl—"

"Colonel Sapt, if you would not have me utterly a villain—if you would not have your King rot in Zenda, while Michael and I play for the great stake outside— You follow me?"

"Ay, I follow you," he answered, frowning heavily.

"Well, leave me here for a week—and there's another problem for you. We must act, and quickly! You saw tonight—you heard tonight—"

"I did," said he.

"Then, in God's name," I cried, stretching out my hands to him, "let us go to Zenda and crush this Michael, and bring the King back to his own again."

The old fellow stood and looked at me for full a minute.

"And the princess?" he said.

I bowed my head to meet my hands, and crushed the rose between my fingers and my lips.

I felt his hand on my shoulder, and his voice sounded husky as he whispered low in my ear:

"Before God, you're the finest Elphberg of them all. But I am the King's servant. Come, we will go to Zenda!"

And I looked up and caught him by the hand. And the eyes of both of us were wet.

CHAPTER XI

Hunting a Very Big Boar

IT WAS A FINE BRIGHT MORNING when I walked, unattended, to the princess' house, carrying a nosegay in my hand. I found Fritz's inamorata, the Countess Helga, gathering blooms in the garden for her mistress' wear, and prevailed on her to take mine in their place. The girl was rosy with happiness, for Fritz, in his turn, had not wasted his evening.

We were walking on a broad terrace that ran along the back of the house, and a window above our heads stood open.

"Madame!" cried the countess merrily, and Flavia herself looked out. I bared my head and bowed. She wore a white gown, and her hair was loosely gathered in a knot. She kissed her hand to me, crying:

"Bring the King up, Helga; I'll give him some coffee."

The countess, with a gay glance, led the way into Flavia's morning room. Left alone, we greeted one another as lovers are wont. Then the princess laid two letters before me. One was from Black Michael—a most courteous request that she would honor him by spending a day at his Castle of Zenda, as had been her custom once a year when the gardens were in the height of their great beauty.

"I don't know who the other comes from," said Flavia. "Read it."

I knew in a moment. There was no signature at all this time, but the handwriting was Antoinette de Mauban's. It ran as follows:

I have no cause to love you, but God forbid that you should fall into the power of the duke. Accept no invitations of his. Go nowhere without a large guard. Show this to him who reigns in Strelsau.

"Why doesn't it say 'the King'?" asked Flavia, leaning over my shoulder, so that the ripple of her hair played on my cheek. "Is it a hoax?"

"As you value life, my queen," I said, "obey it to the very letter. See that you do not go out unless well guarded."

"An order, sire?" she asked, a little rebellious.

"Yes, an order, madame—if you love me."

"Ah!" she cried; and I could not but kiss her.

"You know who sent it?" she asked.

"I guess," said I. "It is from a good friend. You must be ill, Flavia, and unable to go to Zenda. Make your excuses as cold and formal as you like."

"So you feel strong enough to anger Michael?" she said, with a proud smile.

"I'm strong enough for anything, while you are safe," said I.

Soon I tore myself away from her, and then, without consulting Sapt, I took my way to the house of Marshal Strakencz. I had seen something of the old general, and I liked and trusted him. As things were now I had more work than Sapt and Fritz could manage, for they must come with me to Zenda, and I wanted a man to guard what I loved most in all the world.

The marshal received me with most loyal kindness. I charged him with the care of the princess, and bade him let no one from her cousin the duke approach her, unless he himself were there and a dozen of his men with him.

"You may be right, sire," said he, shaking his gray head sadly. "I have known better men than the duke do worse things for love."

I could quite appreciate the remark, but I said:

"There's something beside love, marshal. Love's for the heart; is there nothing my brother might like for his head?"

"I pray that you wrong him, sire."

"Marshal, I'm leaving Strelsau for a few days. Every evening I will send a courier to you. If for three days none comes you will publish an order which I will give you, depriving Duke Michael of the governorship of Strelsau and appointing you in his place. You will declare a state of siege. Then you will send word to Michael that you demand an audience of the King— You follow me?"

"Ay, sire."

"—In twenty-four hours. If he does not produce the King then the King is dead, and you will proclaim the Princess Flavia. And swear to me, on your faith and honor, and by the fear of the living God, that you will stand by her to the death, and kill that reptile, and seat her where I sit now."

"On my faith and honor, and by the fear of God, I swear it! And may Almighty God preserve Your Majesty, for I think that you go on an errand of danger."

"I hope that no life more precious than mine may be demanded," said I, rising. Then I held out my hand to him.

"Marshal," I said, "in days to come it may be that you will hear strange things of the man who speaks to you now. What say you of the manner in which he has borne himself as King in Strelsau?"

The old man, holding my hand, spoke to me, man to man.

"I have known many of the Elphbergs," said he, "and I have

seen you. You have borne yourself as a wise King and a brave man; ay, and you have proved as courteous a gentleman and as gallant a lover as any that have been of the House."

I was much moved, and the marshal's worn face twitched. I sat down and wrote my order. "I can hardly yet write," said I; "my finger is stiff still." It was, in fact, the first time that I had ventured to write more than a signature.

"Indeed, sire," he said, "it differs a little from your ordinary handwriting. It is unfortunate, for it may lead to a suspicion of forgery."

"Marshal," said I, with a laugh, "what use are the guns of Strelsau if they can't assuage a little suspicion?"

He smiled grimly and took the paper.

"Colonel Sapt and Fritz von Tarlenheim go with me," I continued.

"You go to seek the duke?" he asked in a low tone.

"Yes, the duke, and someone else who is at Zenda," I replied.

"I wish I could go with you," he cried, tugging at his white mustache. "But I will deliver the princess to you safe and sound, and failing that, I will make her queen."

We parted, and I returned to the palace and told Sapt and Fritz what I had done. Sapt had a few faults to find. This was merely what I had expected, for Sapt liked to be consulted beforehand, not informed afterward; but his spirits rose high as the hour of action drew nearer and nearer. Fritz, too, was ready; though he, poor fellow, risked more than Sapt did, for he was a lover, and his happiness hung in the scale. Yet how I envied him! For the triumphant issue which would crown him with happiness and unite him to his mistress meant to me sorrow more certain and greater than if I were doomed to fail.

Our plans were now all made. The next morning we were to start on the hunting excursion. I had made all arrangements for being absent, and now there was only one thing left to do—the hardest, the most heartbreaking. As evening fell I drove to Flavia's residence. In spite of my depression I was almost amused at the coolness and delicate hauteur with which my sweet lover received me. She had heard that the King was leaving Strelsau on a hunting expedition.

"I regret that we cannot amuse Your Majesty here in Strelsau," she said, tapping her foot lightly on the floor. "I would have offered you more entertainment, but I was foolish enough to think that just for a day or two after— after last night—you might be happy without much gaiety"; and she turned pettishly from me, as she added, "I hope the boars will be more engrossing."

"I'm going after a very big boar," said I; and, because I could not help it, I began to play with her hair, but she moved away.

"Are you offended with me?" I asked in feigned surprise.

"What right have I to be offended? True, you said last night that every hour away from me was wasted. But a very big boar! That's a different thing."

"Perhaps the boar will hunt me," I suggested. "Perhaps, Flavia, he'll catch me."

She made no answer.

"You are not touched even by that danger?"

Still she said nothing; and I, stealing round, found her eyes full of tears. With a sudden great groan I caught her to my heart.

"My darling," I cried, forgetting everything but her, "did you dream that I left you to go hunting?"

"What then, Rudolf? Ah, you're not going—?"

"Well, it is hunting. I go to seek Michael in his lair."

She had turned very pale.

"So you see, sweet, I was not so poor a lover as you thought me. I shall not be long gone."

"You will write to me, Rudolf?"

I was weak, but I could not say a word to stir suspicion in her.

"I'll send you all my heart every day," said I.

"And when will you be back? Ah, how long it will be!"

"God knows, my darling. But if never—"

"Hush, hush!" and she pressed her lips to mine.

"If never," I whispered, "you must take my place; you'll be the only one of the House then. You must reign, and not weep for me."

For a moment she drew herself up like a very queen.

"Yes, I will!" she said. "I will reign. I will do my part. Though all my life will be empty and my heart dead, yet I'll do it!"

She paused, and sinking against me again, wailed softly:

"Come soon! Come soon!"

Carried away, I cried loudly:

"As God lives, I will see you once more before I die!"

"What do you mean?" she exclaimed with wondering eyes; but I had no answer for her. I dared not ask her to forget; she would have found it an insult. I could not tell her then who and what I was. She was weeping, and I had but to dry her tears.

"Shall a man not come back to the loveliest lady in all the wide world?" said I. "A thousand Michaels should not keep me from you!"

She clung to me, a little comforted.

"You won't let Michael hurt you, or keep you from me?"

"No, sweetheart."

"Nor anyone else?"

And again I answered, "No, sweetheart."

Yet there was one—not Michael—who, if he lived, must keep me from her; and for whose life I was going forth to stake my own. And his figure—the lithe, buoyant figure I had met in the woods of Zenda—the dull, inert mass I had left in the cellar of the hunting lodge—seemed to rise, double-shaped, before me, and to come between us, thrusting itself in even where she lay, pale, exhausted, fainting, in my arms, and yet looking up at me with those eyes that bore such love as I have never seen, and haunt me now, and will till the ground closes over me—and (who knows?) perhaps beyond.

CHAPTER XII

I Receive a Visitor and Bait a Hook

ABOUT FIVE MILES FROM ZENDA, on the opposite side from that on which the castle is situated, there lies a large tract of wood. It is rising ground and on the top of the hill stands a fine modern château, the property of a distant kinsman of Fritz's, the Count Stanislas von Tarlenheim. He seldom visited the house, and had, on

Fritz's request, very courteously offered me its hospitality for myself and my party. This, then, was our destination; chosen ostensibly for the sake of the boar hunting, really because it brought us within striking distance of the duke's more magnificent dwelling on the other side of the town. A large party of servants, with horses and luggage, started early in the morning; we followed at midday, traveling by train for thirty miles, and then mounting our horses to ride the remaining distance to the château.

We were a gallant party. Besides Sapt and Fritz, I was accompanied by ten gentlemen: every one of them had been carefully chosen by my two friends, and all were devotedly attached to the King. They were told a part of the truth: the attempt on my life in the summer house was revealed to them as a spur to their loyalty and an incitement against Michael. They were also informed that a friend of the King's was suspected to be forcibly confined within the Castle of Zenda. His rescue was one of the objects of the expedition. Young, well bred, brave and loyal, they asked no more; they were ready to prove their dutiful obedience, and prayed for a fight as the best and most exhilarating mode of showing it.

Thus the scene was shifted from Strelsau to the Château of Tarlenheim and Castle of Zenda, which frowned at us across the valley. I tried to forget my love and to bend all my energies to the task before me. It was to get the King out of the castle alive. Force was useless: in some trick lay the chance; and I had already an inkling of what we must do.

Michael knew of my coming, of course. I had not been there an hour when an imposing embassy arrived from him. He had sent the other three of his famous Six—the Ruritanian gentlemen—Lauengram, Krafstein and Rupert Hentzau. A fine, strapping trio they were, splendidly horsed and admirably equipped. Young Rupert, who looked a daredevil, and could not have been more than twenty-two or twenty-three, took the lead, and made us the neatest speech, wherein my devoted subject and loving brother, Michael of Strelsau, prayed me to pardon him for not paying his addresses in person, and, further, for not putting his castle at my disposal; the reason being that he and several of his servants lay sick of scarlet fever, and were in a very infectious state. So declared young Rupert, an insolent smile curling his lip—he was a handsome villain. For my part, if a man must needs be a knave I would have him a debonair knave, and I liked Rupert Hentzau better than his long-faced, close-eyed companions.

"If my brother has scarlet fever," said I, "he is nearer my complexion than he is wont to be, my lord. I trust he does not suffer?"

"He is able to attend to his affairs, sire."

"I hope all beneath your roof are not sick. What of my good friends De Gautet, Bersonin and Detchard? I heard the last had suffered a hurt."

Lauengram and Kraftstein looked glum and uneasy, but young Rupert's smile grew broader.

"He hopes soon to find a medicine for it, sire," he answered.

And I burst out laughing, for I knew what medicine Detchard longed for—it is called Revenge.

"You will dine with us, gentlemen?" I asked.

Young Rupert was profuse in apologies, saying that they had urgent duties at the castle; and he strode past Sapt with such jeering scorn on his face that I saw the old fellow clench his fist and scowl black as night.

Now it was a curious thing that on this first night, instead of eating the excellent dinner my cooks had prepared for me, I must needs leave my gentlemen and Sapt to eat it alone, and ride myself with Fritz to the town of Zenda and a certain little inn that I knew of. There was little danger in the excursion, for the road this side of Zenda was well frequented. So off we rode, with a groom behind us. I muffled myself up in a big cloak.

"Fritz," said I as we entered the town, "there's an uncommonly pretty girl at this inn."

"How do you know?" he asked.

"Because I've been there," said I.

"But they'll recognize you."

"Well, of course they will. Now don't argue, my good fellow, but listen to me. We're two gentlemen of the King's household, and one of us has a toothache. The other will order a private room and dinner, and, further, a bottle of the best wine for the sufferer. And if he be as clever a fellow as I take him for, the pretty girl and no other will wait on us."

We were at the inn. Nothing of me but my eyes was visible as I walked in. The landlady received us; two minutes later my little friend made her appearance. Dinner and the wine were ordered. I sat down in the private room. A minute later Fritz came in. "She's coming," he said.

"If she were not I should have to doubt the Countess Helga's taste."

She came in. I gave her time to set the wine down—I didn't want it dropped. Fritz poured out a glass and gave it to me.

"Is the gentleman in great pain?" the girl asked sympathetically.

"The gentleman is no worse than when he saw you last," said I, throwing away my cloak.

She started with a little shriek. Then she cried:

"It was the King, then! I told mother so the moment I saw his picture. Oh, sir, forgive the things we said!"

"I forgive them for the thing you did."

"I must go and tell mother."

"Stop," said I, assuming a graver air. "We are not here for sport tonight. Bring dinner, and not a word of the King being here."

She came back in a few minutes, looking grave.

"Well, how is Johann?" I asked, beginning my dinner.

"Oh, that fellow, sir—my lord King, I mean!"

"'Sir' will do, please. How is he?"

"We hardly see him now, sir. I told him he came too often, sir," said she, tossing her head.

"But you could bring him back?" I suggested with a smile.

"Perhaps I could," said she.

"I know your powers, you see," said I, and she blushed with pleasure.

"It's not only that, sir, that keeps him away. He's very busy at the castle. He's in charge of the house."

"Poor Johann! He must be overworked. Yet I'm sure he could find half an hour to come and see you."

"It would depend on the time, sir, perhaps."

"Do you wish to serve the King?" I asked.

"Yes, sir."

"Then tell him to meet you at the second milestone out of Zenda tomorrow evening at ten o'clock. Say you'll be there and will walk home with him."

"Do you mean him harm, sir?"

"Not if he will do as I bid him. But I think I've told you enough, my pretty maid. See that you do as I bid you. And, mind, no one is to know that the King has been here."

I spoke a little sternly, for there is seldom harm in infusing a little fear into a woman's liking for you, and I softened the effect by giving her a handsome present.

After we had dined, I wrapped my cloak about my face and, with Fritz leading the way, we went downstairs to our horses. We jogged gently through the town, but set our horses to a sharper pace when we reached the open country.

We reached the avenue of the château, and were soon at the house. As the hoofs of our horses sounded on the gravel Sapt rushed out to meet us. "Thank God, you're safe!" he cried. "Have you seen anything of them?"

"Of whom?" I asked, dismounting.

He drew us aside, that the grooms might not hear.

"Lad," he said to me, "you must not ride about here unless with half a dozen of us. You know among our men a tall young fellow, Bernenstein by name?"

I knew him. He was a fine, strapping young man, almost of my height, and of light complexion.

"He lies in his room upstairs, with a bullet through his arm."

"The deuce he does!"

"After dinner he strolled a mile or so into the wood; and as he walked he thought he saw three men among the trees; and one leveled a gun at him. He had no weapon, and he started at a run back toward the house. But one of them fired, and he was hit, and had much ado to reach here before he fainted."

He paused and added:

"Lad, the bullet was meant for you."

"Very likely," said I, "and it's first blood to brother Michael."

"I wonder which three it was," said Fritz.

"Well, Sapt," I said, "I went out tonight for no idle purpose, as you shall hear. But there's one thing in my mind."

"What's that?" he asked.

"Why, this," I answered. "That I shall ill requite the very great honors Ruritania has done me if I depart from it leaving one of those Six alive—neither, with the help of God, will I."

And Sapt shook my hand on that.

CHAPTER XIII

An Improvement on Jacob's Ladder

IN THE MORNING OF THE DAY after that on which I swore my oath against the Six I gave certain orders, and then rested in greater contentment than I had known for some time. I was at work; and work, though it cannot cure love, is yet a narcotic to it; so that Sapt marveled to see me sprawling in an armchair in the sunshine. Thus was I engaged when young Rupert Hentzau, who feared neither man nor devil, and rode through the demesne—where every tree might hide a marksman, for all he knew—as though it had been the park at Strelsau, cantered up to where I lay, bowing with burlesque deference, and craving private speech with me in order to deliver a message from the Duke of Strelsau. I made all withdraw, and then he said, seating himself by me:

"Come, we are alone. Rassendyll—"

I rose to a sitting posture.

"What's the matter?" he asked.

"I was about to call one of my gentlemen to bring your horse, my lord. If you do not know how to address the King, my brother must find another messenger."

"Why keep up the farce?" he asked, negligently dusting his boot with his glove.

"Because it is not finished yet; and meanwhile I'll choose my own name."

"Oh, so be it! Yet I spoke in love for you; for indeed you are a man after my own heart."

"What's the message?" I asked curtly.

"The duke offers you more than I would," he growled. "A halter for you, *sire*, was my suggestion. But he offers you safe-conduct across the frontier and a million crowns."

"I prefer your offer, my lord, if I am bound to one."

"You refuse?"

"Of course."

"I told Michael you would"; and the villain gave me the sunniest of smiles. "The fact is, between ourselves," he continued, "Michael doesn't understand a gentleman."

I began to laugh. "And you?" I asked.

"I do," he said. "Well, well, the halter be it."

"I'm sorry you won't live to see it," I observed.

"Has His Majesty done me the honor to fasten a particular quarrel on me?"

"I would you were a few years older, though."

"Oh, God gives years, but the devil gives increase." He laughed. "I can hold my own."

"How is your prisoner?" I asked.

"The K—?"

"Your prisoner."

"I forgot your wishes, sire. Well, he is alive."

He rose to his feet; I imitated him. Then, with a smile, he said:

"And the pretty princess? Faith, I'll wager the next Elphberg will be red enough, for all that Black Michael will be called his father."

I sprang a step toward him, clenching my hand. He did not move an inch, and his lip curled in insolent amusement.

"Go, while your skin's whole!" I muttered.

Then came the most audacious thing I have known in my life. My friends were some thirty yards away. Rupert called to a groom to bring him his horse, and dismissed the fellow with a crown. The horse stood near. Rupert then suddenly turned to me, his left hand resting in his belt, his right outstretched. "Shake hands," he said.

I bowed, and did as he had foreseen—I put my hands behind me.

Quicker than thought, his left hand darted out at me, and a small dagger flashed in the air; he struck me in the left shoulder—had I not swerved it had been my heart. With a cry I staggered back. Without touching the stirrup, he leaped upon his horse and was off like an arrow, pursued by cries and revolver shots—the last as useless as the first—and I sank into my chair, bleeding profusely, as I watched the devil's brat disappear down the long avenue. My friends surrounded me, and then I fainted.

It was night when I awoke and found Fritz beside me. I was weak and weary, but he bade me be of good cheer, saying that my wound would soon heal, and that meanwhile all had gone well, for Johann the keeper had fallen into the snare we had laid for him, and was even now in the house.

I ordered him to be brought in at once. Sapt conducted him, and set him in a chair by my bedside. He was sullen and afraid; but, to say truth, after young Rupert's exploit we also had our fears, and Sapt kept him as far as he could from me. Moreover, when he came in his hands were bound, but that I would not suffer.

I need not stay to recount the safeguards and rewards we promised the fellow—all of which were honorably observed and paid, so that he lives now in prosperity (though where I may not mention). We soon learned that he was rather a weak man than a wicked, and had acted throughout this matter more from fear of the duke than for any love of what was done. But he had persuaded all of his loyalty; and was, by his knowledge of their dispositions within the castle, able to lay bare before us the very heart of their devices. And here, in brief, is his story:

Below the level of the ground in the castle, approached by a flight of stone steps which abutted on the end of the drawbridge, were situated two small rooms, cut out of the rock itself. The outer of the two had no windows, but was always lighted with candles; the inner had one square window, which gave upon the moat. In the outer room there lay always, day and night, three of the Six; and the instructions of Duke Michael were that on any attack being made on the outer room the three were to defend the door of it so long as they could without risk to themselves. But so soon as the door should be in danger of being forced, then Rupert Hentzau or Detchard (for one of these two was always there) should leave the others to hold it as long as they could, and himself pass into the inner room, and without more ado kill the King, who lay there with his arms confined in fine steel chains, which did not allow him to move his elbow more than three inches from his side. Thus, before the outer door were stormed, the King would be dead. And his body? For his body would be evidence as damning as himself.

"Nay, sir," said Johann, "His Highness has thought of that. While the two hold the outer room the one who has killed the King unlocks the bars in the square window (they turn on a hinge). The mouth of the window is choked by a great pipe of earthenware; and this pipe, which is large enough to let pass through it the body of a man, passes into the moat, coming to an end immediately above the surface of the water, so that there is no perceptible interval between water and pipe. The King being dead, his murderer swiftly ties a weight to the body, and dragging it to the window, raises it by a pulley till it is level with the mouth of the pipe. He inserts the feet in the pipe, and pushes the body down. Silently, without splash or sound, it falls into the water and thence to the bottom of the moat, which is twenty feet deep thereabouts. This done, the murderer cries loudly, 'All's well!' and himself slides down the pipe; and the others, if they can and the attack is not too hot, run to the inner room and bar the door, and in their turn slide down. And though the King rises not from the bottom, they rise and swim round to the other side, where the orders are for men to await them with ropes to haul them out, and horses. And here, if things go ill, the duke will join them and seek safety by riding; but if all goes well, they will return to the castle, and have their enemies in a trap.

"That, sir, is the plan of His Highness for the disposal of the King in case of need. But it is not to be used till the last; for he is not minded to kill the King unless he can, before or soon after, kill you also, sir. Now, sir, I have spoken the truth, as God is my witness, and I pray you to shield me from the vengeance of

Duke Michael; for if, after he knows what I have done, I fall into his hands, I shall pray for one thing out of all the world—a speedy death, and that I shall not obtain from him!"

The fellow's story was rudely told, but our questions supplemented his narrative. What he had told us applied to an armed attack; but if there came overwhelming force—such, for instance, as I, the King, could bring—the idea of resistance would be abandoned; the King would be quietly murdered and slid down the pipe. And—here comes an ingenious touch—one of the Six would take his place in the cell, and on the entrance of the searchers loudly demand release and redress; and Michael, being summoned, would confess to hasty action, but he would say the man had angered him by seeking the favor of a lady in the castle (this was Antoinette de Mauban), and he had confined him there, as he conceived he, as Lord of Zenda, had a right to do. But he was now, on receiving his apology, content to let him go, and so end the gossip which, to His Highness' annoyance, had arisen concerning a prisoner in Zenda, and had given his visitors the trouble of this inquiry.

Sapt, Fritz, and I in my bed looked round on one another in horror and bewilderment at the cruelty and cunning of the plan. Whether I went in peace or in war, openly at the head of a corps, or secretly by a stealthy assault, the King would be dead before I could come near him. If Michael were stronger and overcame my party, there would be an end. But if I were stronger, I should have no way to punish him, no means of proving any guilt in him without proving my own guilt also. At the worst he would stand as well as he had stood before I crossed his path—with but one man between him and the throne, and that man an impostor; at best there would be none left to stand against him.

"Does the King know this?" I asked.

"I and my brother," answered Johann, "put up the pipe, under the orders of my Lord of Hentzau. He was on guard that day, and the King asked my lord what it meant. 'Faith,' he answered, with his airy laugh, 'it's a new improvement on the ladder of Jacob, whereby, as you have read, sire, men pass from earth to Heaven.

We thought it not meet that Your Majesty should go by the common route. So we have made you a pretty private passage where the vulgar cannot stare at you or incommode your passage. That, sire, is the meaning of that pipe.' And the King, though he is a brave man, grew red and then white as he looked on the pipe and at the merry devil who mocked him. Ah, sir," (and the fellow shuddered) "it is not easy to sleep quiet in the Castle of Zenda, for all of them would as soon cut a man's throat as play a game at cards; and my Lord Rupert would choose it sooner for a pastime than any other—ay, sooner than he would ruin a woman, though that he loves also."

The man ceased, and I bade Fritz take him away and have him carefully guarded; and turning to him, I added:

"All my promises will not save you if any man here learns from you the truth as to the prisoner in Zenda. I'll kill you like a dog if the thing be so much as breathed within the house!"

Then, when he was gone, I looked at Sapt.

"It's a hard nut!" said I.

"So hard," said he, shaking his grizzled head, "that, as I think, this time next year is like to find you still King of Ruritania!" and he broke out into curses on Michael's cunning.

"There seem to me," I observed, "to be two ways by which the King can come out of Zenda alive. One is by treachery in the duke's followers."

"You can leave that out," said Sapt.

"I hope not," I rejoined, "because the other I was about to mention is—by a miracle from Heaven!"

CHAPTER XIV

A Night Outside the Castle

IT WOULD HAVE SURPRISED the good people of Ruritania to know of the foregoing talk; for, according to the official reports, I had suffered a grievous hurt from an accidental spear thrust, received in the course of a boar hunt. I caused the bulletins to be of a very serious character, and created great public excitement, whereby three things occurred: first, I gravely offended the medical faculty of Strelsau by refusing to summon to my bedside any of them save a young man, a friend of Fritz's, whom we could trust; secondly, I received word from Marshal Strakencz that my orders seemed to have no more weight than his, and that the Princess Flavia was leaving for Tarlenheim under his unwilling escort (news whereat I strove not to be glad and proud); and thirdly, my brother, the Duke of Strelsau, although too well informed to believe the account of the origin of my sickness, was yet persuaded by the reports and by my seeming inactivity that I was in truth incapable of action, and that my life was in some danger. This I learned from the man Johann, whom I was compelled to trust and send back to Zenda, where, by the way, Rupert Hentzau had him soundly flogged for daring to smirch the morals of Zenda by staying out all night in the pursuits of love.

On Flavia's arrival I cannot dwell. Her joy at finding me up and well, instead of on my back and fighting with death, makes a picture that even now dances before my eyes. In truth, to have her with me once more was like a taste of Heaven to a damned soul, the sweeter for the inevitable doom that was to follow; and I rejoiced in being able to waste two whole days with her.

The stroke was near now. For Sapt and I had resolved that we must risk a blow, our resolution being clinched by Johann's news that the King's health was breaking down under his rigorous confinement. That made prompt action advisable in the interests of the King; from my own point of view it grew more and more necessary. For Strakencz urged on me the need of a speedy marriage, and my own inclinations seconded him with such terrible insistence that I feared for my resolution.

When I look back on the time I seem to myself to have been half mad. Sapt has told me that if ever a King of Ruritania ruled like a despot I was, in those days, the man. Look where I would I saw nothing that made life sweet to me, and I took my life in my hand and carried it carelessly as a man dangles an old glove. At first they strove to guard me, to persuade me not to expose myself; but when they saw how I was set, there grew up among them a feeling that

Fate ruled the issue, and that I must be left to play my game with Michael my own way.

Late next night I rose from table, where Flavia had sat by me, and conducted her to the door of her apartments. There I kissed her hand, and bade her sleep sound. Then I changed my clothes and went out. Sapt and Fritz were waiting for me with six men and the horses. Over his saddle Sapt carried a long coil of rope, and both he and Fritz were heavily armed. I had with me a short stout cudgel and a long knife. Making a circuit, we avoided the town, and in an hour found ourselves slowly mounting the hills that led to the Castle of Zenda. The night was dark and very stormy; gusts of wind and spits of rain caught us as we breasted the incline, and the great trees moaned and sighed. When we came to a thick clump, about a quarter of a mile from the castle, we bade our six friends hide there with the horses. Sapt had a whistle, and they could rejoin us in a few moments if danger came. I hoped that Michael was still off his guard, believing me to be safe in bed. However that might be, we gained the top of the hill without accident, and found ourselves on the edge of the moat. A tree stood on the edge of the bank, and Sapt silently and diligently set to make fast the rope. I stripped off my boots, loosened the knife in its sheath and took the cudgel between my teeth. Then I shook hands with my friends and laid hold of the rope. I was going to have a look at "Jacob's ladder."

Gently I lowered myself into the water. Though the night was wild, the day had been warm and bright and the water was not cold. I struck out and began to swim round the great walls which frowned above me. I could see only three yards ahead; I had then good hopes of not being seen. There were lights from the new part of the castle on the other side, and now and again I heard laughter and merry shouts. If Johann's description were right I must be near the window now. Very slowly I moved; and out of the darkness ahead loomed a shape. It was the pipe, curving from the window to the water: it was big round as two men. I was about to approach it when I saw something else, and my heart stood still. The nose of a boat protruded beyond the pipe on the other side;

and listening intently, I heard a slight shuffle—as of a man shifting his position. Who was the man who guarded Michael's invention? I felt my knife and trod water; as I did so I found bottom under my feet. The foundations of the castle extended some fifteen inches, making a ledge; and I stood on it, out of water from my armpits upward. Then I crouched and peered through the darkness under the pipe.

There was a man in the boat. A rifle lay by him—I saw the gleam of the barrel. Here was the sentinel! He sat very still. I listened: he breathed heavily, regularly, monotonously. By Heaven, he slept! Kneeling on the shelf, I drew forward under the pipe till my face was within two feet of his. He was a big man, I saw. It was Max Holf, the brother of Johann. I drew out my knife. Of all the deeds of my life I love the least to think of this. I said to myself: "It is war—and the King's life is at stake." And I raised myself from beneath the pipe and stood up by the boat, which lay moored by the ledge. Holding my breath, I marked the spot and raised my arm. The great fellow stirred. He opened his eyes— wide, wider. He gasped in terror at my face and clutched at his rifle. I struck home.

Leaving him where he lay, a huddled mass, I turned to Jacob's ladder. My time was short. This fellow's watch might be over directly, and relief would come. Leaning over the pipe, I examined it, from the end near the water to the topmost extremity where it seemed to pass through the masonry. There was no break in it, no chink. Dropping on my knees, I tested the underside. And my breath went quick and fast, for on this lower side, where the pipe should have clung close to the masonry, there was a gleam of light! That light must come from the cell of the King! I set my shoulder against the pipe and exerted my strength. The chink widened a very, very little, and hastily I desisted; I now knew that the pipe was not fixed at the lower side.

Then I heard a voice—a harsh, grating voice:

"Well, sire, if you have had enough of my society I will leave you to repose; but I must fasten the little ornaments first."

It was Detchard! I caught the English accent in a moment.

"Have you anything to ask, sire, before we part?"

The King's voice followed. It was faint and hollow.

"Pray my brother," said the King, "to kill me. I am dying by inches here."

"The duke does not desire your death, sire—yet," sneered Detchard; "when he does, behold your path to Heaven!"

The King answered, "So be it! And now, pray leave me."

"May you dream of paradise!" said the ruffian.

The light disappeared. I heard the bolts of the door run home. And then I heard the sobs of the King. He was alone, as he thought. Who dares mock at him?

I did not venture to speak to him. The risk of some exclamation escaping him in surprise was too great. I dared do nothing that night; and my task now was to get myself away in safety, and to carry off the dead man. To leave him there would tell too much. Casting loose the boat, I got in. The wind was blowing a gale now, and there was little danger of oars being heard. I rowed swiftly round to where my friends waited, and hailed Sapt in a low tone. The rope came down. I tied it round the corpse, and then went up it myself.

"Whistle for our men," I whispered, "and haul in the line."

They hauled up the body. Just as it reached the road three men on horseback swept round from the front of the castle. We saw them; but, being on foot ourselves, we escaped their notice. We heard our men coming up with a shout.

"The devil, but it's dark!" cried a ringing voice.

It was young Rupert. A moment later shots rang out. Our people had met them. I started forward at a run, Sapt and Fritz following me.

"Thrust, thrust!" cried Rupert, and a loud groan following told that he himself was not behindhand.

"I'm done, Rupert!" cried a voice. "They're three to one. Save yourself!"

I ran on, holding my cudgel in my hand. Suddenly a horse came toward me. A man was on it, leaning over his shoulder.

I sprang to the horse's head. It was Rupert Hentzau.

"At last!" I cried.

For we seemed to have him. He had only his sword in his hand. My men were hot upon him; Sapt and Fritz were running up, and if they got close enough to fire he must die or surrender.

"It's the playactor!" cried he, slashing at my cudgel. He cut it clean in two; and judging discretion better than death, I ducked my head and (I blush to tell it) scampered for my life. The devil was in Rupert Hentzau; for, turning to look, I saw him ride, full gallop, to the edge of the moat and leap in, while the shots of our party fell thick round him like hail. With one gleam of moonlight we should have riddled him with balls; but in the darkness he won to the corner of the castle, and vanished from our sight.

"The deuce take him!" Sapt grinned.

Lauengram and Krafstein lay dead; and concealment being no longer possible, we flung them, with Max, into the moat; and rode off down the hill. And in our midst went the bodies of three gallant gentlemen. Thus we traveled home, heavy at heart for the death of our friends, and cut to the quick that young Rupert had played yet another winning hand with us.

For my own part I was vexed and angry that I had killed no man in open fight, but only stabbed a knave in his sleep. And I did not love to hear Rupert call me a playactor.

CHAPTER XV

I Talk with a Tempter

DUELS IN RURITANIA WERE FREQUENT among all the upper classes, and private quarrels between great men had the old habit of spreading to their friends and dependents without much public notice being attracted. Nevertheless, after the affray which I have just related, such reports began to circulate that I felt it necessary to issue a stern order, declaring that dueling had attained unprecedented license, and forbidding it save in the gravest cases. I sent a public and stately apology to Michael, and he returned a deferential and courteous reply to me; for our one point of union was that we could neither of us afford to throw our cards

on the table. Unfortunately, however, the necessity for concealment involved the necessity of delay: and the King might die in
his prison. For a little while I was compelled to observe a truce,
and my only consolation was that Flavia most warmly approved
of my edict against dueling.

Not the least peculiar result of the truce and of the secrecy which
dictated it was that the town of Zenda became a sort of neutral
zone, where both parties could safely go; and I, riding down one
day with Flavia and Sapt, had an encounter with an acquaintance
which presented a ludicrous side, but was at the same time embar-
rassing. As I rode along I met a dignified-looking person driving
in a two-horsed carriage. He stopped his horses, got out and approached me, bowing low. I recognized the head of the Strelsau
police.

"What brings you to Zenda, prefect?" I asked.

"Why, sire, I am here to oblige the British ambassador."

"What's the British ambassador doing *dans cette galère?*" said
I carelessly.

"A young countryman of his, sire—a man of some position—is
missing. His friends have not heard from him for two months, and
there is reason to believe that he was last seen in Zenda."

Flavia was paying little attention. I dared not look at Sapt.

"What reason?"

"A friend of his in Paris—a certain Monsieur Featherly—has
given us information which makes it possible that he came here,
and the officials of the railway recollect his name on some luggage."

"What was his name?"

"Rassendyll, sire," he answered; and I saw that the name meant
nothing to him. "It is thought that he may have followed a lady
here. Has Your Majesty heard of a certain Madame de Mauban?"

"Why, yes," said I, my eye involuntarily traveling toward the
castle.

"She arrived in Ruritania about the same time as this Rassendyll."

I caught the prefect's glance; he was regarding me with inquiry
writ large on his face. "Sapt," said I, "I must speak a word to the

prefect. Will you ride on a few paces with the princess?" And I added to the prefect, "Come, sir, what do you mean?"

He drew close to me, and I bent in the saddle.

"If he were in love with the lady?" he whispered. "Nothing has been heard of him for two months"; and this time it was the eye of the prefect which traveled toward the castle.

"Yes, the lady is there," I said quietly. "But I don't suppose Mr. Rassendyll—is that the name?—is."

"The duke," he whispered, "does not like rivals, sire."

"You're right there," said I, with all sincerity. "But surely you hint at a very grave charge?"

He spread his hands out in apology. I whispered in his ear:

"This is a grave matter. Go back to Strelsau, tell the ambassador that you have a clue, but that you must be left alone for a week or two. Meanwhile I'll charge myself with looking into the matter."

"The ambassador is very pressing, sire."

"You must quiet him. We can have no scandal. Mind you return tonight."

He promised to obey me, and I rode on to rejoin my companions, a little easier in my mind. Inquiries after me must be stopped at all hazards for a week or two. Heartily did I curse George Featherly for not holding his tongue.

"Well," asked Flavia, "have you finished your business?"

"Most satisfactorily," said I. "Come, shall we turn round? We are almost trenching on my brother's territory."

We were, in fact, at the extreme end of the town, just where the hill begins to mount toward the castle. We cast our eyes up, admiring the massive beauty of the old walls, and we saw a cortège winding slowly down the hill.

There came first two mounted servants in black uniforms, relieved only by a silver badge. These were followed by a carriage drawn by four horses: on it, under a heavy pall, lay a coffin; behind it rode a man in plain black clothes, carrying his hat in his hand. Sapt uncovered, and we stood waiting, Flavia keeping by me and laying her hand on my arm.

I beckoned to a groom.

"Ride and ask whom they escort," I ordered.

He rode up to the servants, and I saw him pass on to the gentleman who rode behind.

"It's Rupert of Hentzau," whispered Sapt.

Rupert it was, and directly afterward he trotted up to me. He wore an aspect of sadness, and he bowed with profound respect. Yet suddenly he smiled, and I smiled too, for old Sapt's hand lay in his left breast pocket, and Rupert and I both guessed what lay in the hand inside the pocket.

"Your Majesty asks whom we escort," said Rupert. "It is my dear friend, Albert of Lauengram."

"Sir," said I, "no one regrets the unfortunate affair more than I. My ordinance, which I mean to have obeyed, is witness to it."

"Poor fellow!" said Flavia softly, and I saw Rupert's eyes flash at her. Whereat I grew red; for if I had my way Rupert Hentzau should not have defiled her by so much as a glance.

"Your Majesty's words are gracious," he said. "I grieve for my friend. Yet, sire, others must soon lie as he lies now."

"It is a thing we all do well to remember, my lord," I rejoined.

"Even kings, sire," said Rupert in a moralizing tone; and old Sapt swore softly by my side.

I bowed; and Rupert, bowing lower, backed his horse to rejoin his party. With a sudden impulse I rode after him. He turned swiftly, fearing that, even in the presence of the dead, I meant him mischief.

"You fought as a brave man the other night," I said. "If you will deliver your prisoner alive to me you shall come to no hurt."

"Look here," he said, "I made you a proposal from the duke once."

"I'll hear nothing from Black Michael," said I.

"Then hear one from me." He lowered his voice to a whisper. "Attack the castle boldly. Let Sapt and Tarlenheim lead. Arrange the time with me."

"I have such confidence in you, my lord!"

"Tut! I'm talking business now. Sapt there and Fritz will fall; Black Michael will fall, like the dog he is; the prisoner, as you call him, will go by Jacob's ladder—ah, you know that? Two men will be left—I, Rupert Hentzau, and you, the King of Ruritania."

He paused, and then, in a voice that quivered with eagerness, added, "Isn't that a hand to play? A throne and your princess! And for me, say a competence and Your Majesty's gratitude."

"Surely," I exclaimed, "while you're above ground hell wants its master!"

"Well, think it over," he said. "And, look you, it would take more than a scruple or two to keep me from yonder girl," and his evil eye flashed again at her I loved.

"Get out of my reach!" said I; and yet in a moment I began to laugh for the very audacity of it.

"Would you turn against your master?" I asked.

He swore at Michael for being what the offspring of a legal, though morganatic, union should not be called, and said:

"He gets in my way, you know. He's a jealous brute! Faith, I nearly stuck a knife into him last night; he came most cursedly *mal à propos!*"

My temper was under control now; I was learning something.

"A lady?" I asked negligently.

"Ay, and a beauty," he nodded. "But you've seen her."

"Ah! Was it at a tea party, when some of your friends got on the wrong side of the table?"

"What can you expect of fools like Detchard and De Gautet?"

"And the duke interferes?"

"Well," said Rupert meditatively, "that's hardly a fair way of putting it, perhaps. I want to interfere."

"And she prefers the duke?"

"Ay, the silly creature! Ah, well, you think about my plan," and, with a bow, he pricked his horse and trotted after the body of his friend.

I went back to Flavia and Sapt, pondering on the wickedness of the man.

"He's very handsome, isn't he?" said Flavia.

Well, I was put out, for I thought his bold glances would have made her angry. But my dear Flavia was a woman, and so—she was not put out. On the contrary, she thought young Rupert very handsome—as, beyond question, the ruffian was.

"And how sad he looked at his friend's death!" said she.

"He'll have better reason to be sad at his own," observed Sapt, with a grim smile.

As for me, I grew sulky; unreasonable it was, perhaps, for what better business had I to look at her with love than had even Rupert's lustful eyes? And sulky I remained till we rode up to Tarlenheim, Sapt having fallen behind in case anyone should be following us, and Flavia, riding close beside me, said softly:

"Unless you smile, Rudolf, I cry. Why are you angry?"

"It was something that fellow said to me," said I, but I was smiling as we reached the door and dismounted.

There a servant handed me a note; it was unaddressed. I tore it open.

> Johann carries this for me. I warned you once. In the name of God, and if you are a man, rescue me from this den of murderers!
>
> A. de M.

I handed it to Sapt; but all that the tough old soul said in reply to this piteous appeal was:

"Whose fault brought her there?"

Nevertheless, not being faultless myself, I took leave to pity Antoinette de Mauban.

CHAPTER XVI

A Desperate Plan

TIME RAN ON IN INACTIVITY, when every moment was pressing; for not only was I faced with the new danger which the stir about my disappearance brought on me, but great murmurs had arisen in Strelsau at my continued absence from the city. They had been greater but for the knowledge that Flavia was with me. As a final blow nothing would content Strakencz and the chancellor save that I should appoint a day for the public solemnization of my betrothal. And this—with Flavia sitting by me—I was forced to do, setting a date a fortnight ahead, and appointing the cathedral in Strelsau as the place. And this formal act, being published far and wide, caused great joy throughout the kingdom.

I heard something of the way the news was received in the castle; for, after an interval of three days, the man Johann, greedy for more money, though fearful for his life, again found means to visit us. He had been waiting on the duke when the tidings came. Black Michael's face had grown blacker still, and he had sworn savagely.

This was the lighter side of the fellow's news; but more serious came behind, and it was plain that, if time pressed at Tarlenheim, it pressed none the less fiercely at Zenda. For the King was very sick: Johann had seen him, and he was wasted and hardly able to move. So alarmed were they that they had sent for a physician from Strelsau. He had come forth from the King's cell pale and trembling, and urgently prayed the duke to let him go back and meddle no more in the affair; but the duke would not, and held him there a prisoner, telling him his life was safe if the King lived while the duke desired and died when the duke desired. The King's life hung in the balance; and I was still strong and whole and free. Wherefore great gloom reigned at Zenda; and save when they quarreled, to which they were very prone, they hardly spoke.

Thus Johann told his tale and seized his crowns. Yet he besought us to allow him to stay with us in Tarlenheim; but I prevailed on him by increased rewards to go back and carry tidings to Madame de Mauban that I was working for her, and that, if she could, she should speak one word of comfort to the King.

"And how do they guard the King now?" I asked, remembering that two of the Six were dead, and Max Holf also.

"Detchard and Bersonin watch by night, Rupert Hentzau and De Gautet by day, sir," he answered.

"Only two at a time?"

"Ay, sir; but the others rest in a room just above, and are within sound of a cry or a whistle."

"In a room just above? I didn't know of that. Is there any

communication between it and the room where they watch?"

"No, sir. You must go down a few stairs and through the door by the drawbridge, and so to where the King is lodged."

"And that door is locked?"

"Only the four lords have keys, sir."

I drew nearer to him. "And have they keys of the grating?" I asked in a low whisper.

"I think, sir, only Detchard and Rupert."

"Where does the duke lodge?"

"In the château, on the first floor. His apartments are on the right as you go toward the drawbridge."

"And Madame de Mauban?"

"Just opposite, on the left. But her door is locked after she has entered."

"And the duke, I suppose, has the key?"

"Yes. And the drawbridge is drawn back at night, and of that too the duke holds the key, so that it cannot be run across the moat without application to him."

"And where do you sleep?"

"In the entrance hall of the château, with five servants."

"Armed?"

"They have pikes, sir, but no firearms. The duke will not trust them with firearms."

Then at last I took the matter boldly in my hands. I had failed once at Jacob's ladder; I should fail again there. I must make the attack from the other side.

"I have promised you twenty thousand crowns," said I. "You shall have fifty thousand if you will do what I ask of you tomorrow night. But, first, do those servants know who your prisoner is?"

"No, sir. They believe him to be some private enemy of the duke's."

"Look to this, then. Tomorrow, at two in the morning exactly, fling open the front door of the château. Don't fail by an instant."

"Shall you be there, sir?"

"Ask no questions. Do what I tell you. Say the hall is close, or what you will. That is all I ask of you."

"And may I escape by the door, sir, when I have opened it?"

"Yes, as quick as your legs will carry you. One thing more. Carry this note to madame and charge her, for the sake of all our lives, not to fail in what it orders."

The man was trembling, but I had to trust to what he had of courage and to what he had of honesty.

When the fellow was gone I called Sapt and Fritz to me, and unfolded the plan that I had formed.

"Why can't you wait?" asked Sapt.

"The King may die."

Suddenly Fritz von Tarlenheim laid his hand on my shoulder.

"Let us go and make the attempt," said he.

"I mean you to go—don't be afraid," said I.

"Ay, but do you stay here and take care of the princess."

A gleam came into old Sapt's eye.

"We should have Michael one way or the other then," he chuckled; "whereas if you go and are killed with the King, what will become of those of us who are left?"

"They will serve Queen Flavia," said I, "and I would to God I could be one of them."

A pause followed.

"You shall go, lad," said Sapt, finally.

Here is the plan I had made. A strong party under Sapt's command was to steal up to the door of the château. If discovered prematurely they were to kill anyone who found them—with their swords, for I wanted no noise of firing. If all went well they would be at the door when Johann opened it. They were to rush in and secure the servants if their mere presence and the use of the King's name were not enough. At the same moment—and on this hinged the plan—a woman's cry was to ring out loud and shrill from Antoinette de Mauban's chamber. Again and again she was to cry: "Help, help! Michael, help!" and then to utter the name of young Rupert Hentzau. Then, as we hoped, Michael, in fury, would rush out of his apartments opposite, and fall alive into the hands of Sapt. Still the cries would go on; and my men would let down the drawbridge; and it would be strange if Rupert, hearing his name thus taken in vain, did not descend from where he slept and seek to cross. De Gautet might or might not come with him: that must be left to chance.

And when Rupert set his foot on the drawbridge? There was my part: for I was minded for another swim in the moat; and, lest I should grow weary, I had resolved to take with me a small wooden ladder, on which I could rest my arms in the water. I would rear the ladder against the wall just by the bridge; and when the bridge was across I would stealthily creep onto it—and then if Rupert or De Gautet crossed in safety it would be my misfortune, not my fault. They dead, two men only would remain; and for them we must trust to the confusion we had created and to a sudden rush. We should have the keys of the door that led to the all-important rooms. Perhaps they would rush out. If they stood by their orders, then the King's life hung on the swiftness with which we could force the outer door; and I thanked God that not Rupert Hentzau watched, but Detchard. For though Detchard was a cool man, relentless and no coward, he had neither the dash nor the recklessness of Rupert.

So I planned—desperately. And, that our enemy might be the better lulled to security, I gave orders that our residence should be brilliantly lighted from top to bottom, as though we were engaged in revelry; and should so be kept all night, with music playing and people moving to and fro. Strakencz would be there, and he was to conceal our departure, if he could, from Flavia. And if we came not again by the morning he was to march in force to the castle and demand the person of the King; if Black Michael were not there the marshal would take Flavia with him, as swiftly as he could, to Strelsau, and there proclaim Black Michael's treachery and the probable death of the King, and rally all that there was honest and true round the banner of the princess. And, to say truth, this was what I thought most likely to happen. For I had great doubts whether either the King or Black Michael or I had more than a day to live.

It was late when we rose from conference, and I betook me to the princess' apartments. She was pensive that evening; yet when

I left her she flung her arms about me and grew, for an instant, bashfully radiant as she slipped a ring on my finger. I was wearing the King's ring; but I had also on my little finger a plain band of gold engraved with the motto of our family: *Nil Quae Feci*. This I took off and put on her, and signed her to let me go. And she, understanding, stood away and watched me with dimmed eyes.

"Wear that ring, even though you wear another when you are queen," I said.

"Whatever else I wear, this I will wear till I die and after," said she as she kissed the ring.

CHAPTER XVII

Young Rupert's Midnight Diversions

THE NIGHT CAME FINE AND CLEAR. I had prayed for dirty weather, such as had favored my previous voyage in the moat, but Fortune was this time against me. Still I reckoned that by keeping close under the wall and in the shadow I could escape detection from the windows of the château. If they searched the moat, indeed my scheme must fail; but I did not think they would. They had made Jacob's ladder secure against attack. Johann had himself helped to fix it closely to the masonry on the underside, so that it could not now be moved from below any more than from above. What harm, then, could a man do in the moat? I trusted that Black Michael, putting this query to himself, would answer confidently, "None."

Dearly would Sapt have liked to come with me had I not utterly refused to take him. One man might escape notice, to double the party more than doubled the risk.

At twelve o'clock Sapt's command left the Château of Tarlenheim and struck off to the right, riding by unfrequented roads, and avoiding the town of Zenda. If all went well they would be in front of the castle by about a quarter to two. Leaving their horses half a mile off, they were to steal up to the entrance and hold themselves in readiness for the opening of the door. If the door were not opened by two they were to send Fritz round to the other side of the castle. I would meet him there if I were alive, and we would consult whether to storm the castle or not. If I were not there they were to return with all speed to Tarlenheim, rouse the marshal, and march in force to Zenda. For if not there I should be dead; and I knew that the King would not be alive five minutes after I had ceased to breathe.

I must now leave Sapt and his friends, and relate how I myself proceeded on this eventful night. I went out on the good horse which had carried me, on the night of the coronation, back from the hunting lodge to Strelsau. I carried a revolver in the saddle and my sword. I was covered with a large cloak, and under this I wore a warm, tight-fitting woolen jersey, a pair of knickerbockers, thick stockings and light canvas shoes. I had rubbed myself thoroughly with oil, and I carried a large flask of whisky. The night was warm, but I might probably be immersed a long while, and it was necessary to take every precaution against cold. Also I tied round my body a length of thin but stout cord, and I did not forget my ladder. I, starting after Sapt, took a shorter route, skirting the town to the left, and found myself in the outskirts of the forest at about half past twelve. I tied my horse up in a thick clump of trees, leaving the revolver in its pocket in the saddle—it would be no use to me—and, ladder in hand, made my way to the edge of the moat. Here I unwound the rope from about my waist, bound it securely round the trunk of a tree on the bank and let myself down. The castle clock struck a quarter to one as I felt the water under me and began to swim round the keep, pushing the ladder before me, and hugging the castle wall. Thus voyaging, I came to my old friend Jacob's ladder, and felt the ledge of the masonry under me. I crouched down in the shadow of the great pipe and waited.

The drawbridge was still in its place. I saw its airy, light framework above me, some ten yards to my right, as I crouched with my back against the wall of the King's cell. I made out a window two yards my side of it and nearly on the same level. That, if Johann spoke true, must belong to the duke's apartments; and on the other side must be Madame de Mauban's window. Women are careless, forgetful creatures. I prayed that she might not forget that she was to be the victim of a brutal attempt at two o'clock.

Suddenly the duke's window grew bright. I cautiously raised myself till I stood on tiptoe, and thus placed, my range of sight embraced a yard or more inside the window, while the radius of light did not reach me. The window was flung open and someone looked out. I marked Antoinette de Mauban's graceful figure, and though her face was in shadow, the fine outline of her head was revealed against the light behind. A moment later a man came up and stood by her. He tried to put his arm round her waist, but with a swift motion she sprang away and leaned against the shutter. I made out who the newcomer was: it was young Rupert. A low laugh from him made me sure, as he leaned forward toward her.

"Gently, gently!" I murmured. "You're too soon, my boy!"

His head was close to hers. I suppose he whispered to her, for I saw her point to the moat and say:

"I had rather throw myself out of this window!"

He came close up to the window and looked out.

"It looks cold," said he. "Come, Antoinette, are you serious?"

She made no answer so far as I heard; and he, smiting his hand petulantly on the windowsill, went on:

"Hang Black Michael! Isn't the princess enough for him? Is he to have everything? What the devil do you see in Black Michael?"

"If I told him what you say—" she began.

"Well, tell him," said Rupert carelessly; and catching her off her guard, he sprang forward and kissed her, laughing, and crying, "There's something to tell him!"

If I had kept my revolver with me I should have been very sorely tempted. Being spared the temptation, I merely added this new score to his account.

"Though, faith," said Rupert, "it's little he cares. He's mad about the princess, you know. He talks of nothing but cutting the playactor's throat. And if I do it for him what do you think he's promised me?"

The unhappy woman raised her hands, in prayer or in despair.

I saw that Rupert was about to lay his hand on her again when there was a noise of a door in the room opening, and a harsh voice cried, "What are you doing here, sir?"

Rupert turned his back to the window, bowed low, and said in his loud, merry tones, "Apologizing for your absence, sir. Could I leave the lady alone?"

The newcomer must be Black Michael. I saw him directly, as he advanced toward the window. He caught Rupert by the arm.

"The moat would hold more than the King!" said he.

"Does Your Highness threaten me?" asked Rupert.

"A threat is more warning than most men get from me."

"Yet," observed Rupert, "Rudolf Rassendyll has been much threatened, and yet lives!"

"Am I in fault because my servants bungle?" asked Michael scornfully.

"Your Highness has run no risk of bungling!" sneered Rupert.

It was telling the duke that he shirked danger as plain as ever I have heard a man told. Black Michael had self-control. His voice was even and calm as he answered:

"Enough, enough! We mustn't quarrel, Rupert. Are Detchard and Bersonin at their posts?"

"They are, sir."

"Pray, sir, leave us," said Michael impatiently. "In ten minutes the drawbridge will be drawn back, and I presume you have no wish to swim to your bed."

Rupert's figure disappeared. I heard the door open and shut again. Michael and Antoinette de Mauban were left together. They stood talking for a moment or two. Antoinette shook her head, and he turned impatiently away. The door sounded again, and Black Michael closed the shutters.

"De Gautet, De Gautet, man!" sounded from the drawbridge. "Unless you want a bath before your bed, come along!"

It was Rupert's voice. A moment later he and De Gautet stepped out on the bridge. As they reached the middle Rupert detained his companion and leaned over. I dropped behind the shelter of Jacob's ladder.

Then Master Rupert had a little sport. He took from De Gautet a bottle which he carried, and put it to his lips.

"Hardly a drop!" he cried, and flung it in the moat.

It fell, as I judged from the sound, within a yard of the pipe. And Rupert, taking out his revolver, began to shoot at it. The first two shots missed the bottle, but hit the pipe. The third shattered the bottle. I hoped that the young ruffian would be content; but he emptied the other barrels at the pipe, and one, skimming over the pipe, whistled through my hair as I crouched on the other side.

"'Ware bridge!" a voice cried, to my relief.

Rupert and De Gautet cried, "A moment!" and ran across. The bridge was drawn back, and all became still. The clock struck a quarter past one. I rose and stretched myself and yawned.

I think some ten minutes had passed when I heard a slight noise to my right. I peered over the pipe, and saw a dark figure standing in the gateway that led to the bridge. By the careless, graceful poise I guessed it to be Rupert again. He held a sword in his hand, and he stood motionless for a minute or two. Wild thoughts ran through me. On what mischief was the young fiend bent now? Then he turned his face to the wall, took a step in my direction, and to my surprise began to climb down the wall. In an instant I saw that there must be steps in the wall. They were cut into the wall at intervals of about eighteen inches. Rupert set his foot on the lower one. Then he placed his sword between his teeth, turned round, and noiselessly let himself down into the water. Dearly would I have loved to fight it out with him then and there—with steel, on a fine night and none to come between us. But there was the King! I restrained myself, but I watched him with the intensest eagerness.

He swam leisurely and quietly across. There were more steps up on the other side, and he climbed them. When he set foot in the gateway he felt in his pocket and took something out. I heard him unlock the door. I could hear no noise of its closing behind him. He vanished from my sight.

Abandoning my ladder—I saw I did not need it now—I swam to the side of the bridge and climbed halfway up the steps. There I hung, with my sword in my hand, listening eagerly. The duke's room was shuttered and dark. There was a light in the window on the opposite side of the bridge. Not a sound broke the silence, till half past one chimed from the great clock in the tower of the château.

There were other plots than mine afoot in the castle that night.

CHAPTER XVIII

The Forcing of the Trap

THE POSITION WHEREIN I STOOD does not appear very favorable to thought; yet for the next moment or two I thought profoundly. Be Rupert Hentzau's errand what it might, and the villainy he was engaged on what it would, I had scored one point. He was on the other side of the moat from the King. I had three left to deal with: two on guard and De Gautet in his bed. Ah, if I had the keys! But I was powerless. I must wait till the coming of my friends enticed someone to cross the bridge—someone with the keys. And I waited, as it seemed, for half an hour, really for about five minutes, before the next act in the rapid drama.

All was still on the other side. The duke's room remained inscrutable behind its shutters. The light burned steadily in Madame de Mauban's window. Then I heard the faintest sound from behind the door which led to the drawbridge on the other side of the moat. It but just reached my ear, yet I could not be mistaken as to what it was. It was made by a key being turned very carefully and slowly. Who was turning it? And of what room was it the key?

I was soon to be enlightened, for the next moment—before my friends could be near the château door—before Johann the keeper would have thought to nerve himself for his task—a cry rang out, shrill in the night, "Help, help! Michael, help!" and was followed by a shriek of utter terror.

I was tingling in every nerve. I stood on the topmost step, holding my sword at the ready. Suddenly I perceived that the gateway was broader than the bridge; there was a dark corner on the opposite side where a man could stand. I darted across and stood there. Thus placed, I commanded the path, and no man could pass between the château and the old castle till he had tried conclusions with me.

There was another shriek. Then a door was flung open and clanged against the wall, and I heard the handle of a door savagely twisted. "Open the door! In God's name, what's the matter?" cried a voice—the voice of Black Michael himself.

He was answered by the very words I had written in my letter: "Help, Michael—Hentzau!"

A fierce oath rang out from the duke, and with a loud thud he threw himself against the door. At the same moment I heard a window above my head open, and a voice cried, "What's the matter?" and I heard a man's hasty footsteps. I grasped my sword. If De Gautet came my way the Six would be less by one more.

Then I heard the clash of swords and a tramp of feet, and—I cannot tell the thing so quickly as it happened, for all seemed to come at once. There was an angry cry from madame's room; the window was flung open; young Rupert stood there sword in hand. He turned his back, and I saw his body go forward to the lunge.

"Ah, Johann, there's one for you! Come on, Michael!"

Johann was there, then—come to the rescue of the duke! How would he open the door for me? For I feared that Rupert had slain him.

"Help!" cried the duke's voice, faint and husky.

I heard a step on the stairs above me; and I heard a stir down to my left, in the direction of the King's cell. But before anything happened on my side of the moat, I saw five or six men round young Rupert in the embrasure of madame's window. Three or four times he lunged with incomparable dash and dexterity. For an instant they fell back, leaving a ring round him. He leaped on the parapet of the window, laughing as he leaped, and waving his sword in his hand. He was drunk with blood, and he laughed again wildly as he flung himself headlong into the moat.

What became of him then? I did not see: for as he leaped, De Gautet's lean face looked out through the door by me, and I struck at him with all the strength God had given me and he fell dead in the doorway without a word or a groan. I dropped on my knees by him. Where were the keys? I found myself muttering, "The keys, man, the keys!" as though he had been yet alive and could listen. At last I had them. There were but three. Seizing the largest, I felt the lock of the door that led to the cell. I fitted in the key. The lock turned. I drew the door close behind me and locked it as noiselessly as I could, putting the key in my pocket.

I found myself at the top of a flight of steep stone stairs. An oil lamp burned dimly in the bracket. I took it down and held it in my hand; and I stood and listened.

"What in the devil can it be?" I heard a voice say.

It came from behind a door at the bottom of the stairs.

And another answered, "Shall we kill him?"

I strained to hear the answer, and could have sobbed with relief when Detchard's voice came, grating and cold:

"Wait a bit. There'll be trouble if we strike too soon."

There was a moment's silence. Then I heard the bolt of the door cautiously drawn back. Instantly I put out the light I held, replacing the lamp in the bracket.

"It's dark. Have you a light?" said the other voice—Bersonin's.

It was come to the crisis now, and I rushed down the steps and flung myself against the door. Bersonin had unbolted it and it gave way before me. The Belgian stood there, sword in hand, and Detchard was sitting on a couch at the side of the room. In astonishment at seeing me, Bersonin recoiled; Detchard jumped to his sword. I rushed madly at the Belgian; he gave way before me, and I drove him up against the wall. He was no swordsman, though he fought bravely, and in a moment he lay on the floor before me. I turned—Detchard was not there. Faithful to his orders, he had not risked a fight with me, but had rushed straight to the door of the King's room, opened it and slammed it behind him. Even now he was at his work inside.

And surely he would have killed the King, and perhaps me also, had it not been for one devoted man who gave his life for the King. For when I forced the door the sight I saw was this: the King stood in the corner: broken by his sickness, he could do nothing; his fettered hands moved uselessly up and down, and he was laughing horribly in half-mad delirium. Detchard and the doctor were together in the middle of the room; and the doctor had flung himself on the murderer, pinning his hands to his sides for an instant. Then Detchard wrenched himself free from the feeble grip, and as I entered drove his sword through the hapless man.

Then he turned on me, crying, "At last!"

We were sword to sword. By blessed chance neither he nor Bersonin had been wearing their revolvers. I found them afterward, ready loaded, on the mantelpiece of the outer room, but my sudden rush in had cut off access to them. We began to fight, silently, sternly and hard. Yet I remember little of it, save that the man was my match—nay, and more, for he knew more tricks than I; and that he forced me back against the bars that guarded the entrance to Jacob's ladder. And I saw a smile on his face, and he wounded me in the left arm.

No glory do I take for that contest. I believe that the man would have mastered me and slain me, and then done his butcher's work, for he was the most skillful swordsman I have ever met; but even as he pressed me hard the half-mad, wasted, wan creature in the corner leaped high in lunatic mirth, shrieking, "It's cousin Rudolf! I'll help you, cousin Rudolf!" and catching up a chair in his hands (he could but just lift it from the ground and hold it uselessly before him) he came toward us. Hope came to me.

"Come on!" I cried. "Come on! Drive it against his legs."

With an oath Detchard skipped back, and before I knew what he was doing had turned his sword against the King. He made one fierce cut at the King, and the King, with a piteous cry, dropped where he stood. The stout ruffian turned to face me again. But in turning he trod in the pool of blood that flowed from the dead physician. He slipped; he fell. Like a dart I was upon him. I caught him by the throat and drove my point through his neck, and with a stifled curse he fell across the body of his victim.

Was the King dead? It was my first thought. I rushed to where he lay. Ay, it seemed as if he were dead, for he had a great gash across his forehead, and he lay still in a huddled heap on the floor. I dropped on my knees and leaned my ear down to hear if he breathed. But before I could, there was a loud rattle from the out-side. The drawbridge was being pushed out. A moment later it rang home on my side of the moat. I should be caught in a trap and the King with me, if he yet lived. I took my sword, and passed into the outer room. Who had the drawbridge out—my men? If so, all was well. My eye fell on the revolvers, and I seized one; and paused to listen in the doorway of the outer room. As I stood listening I tore my shirt and twisted a strip of it round my bleeding arm. I would have given the world to hear Sapt's voice. For I was faint, spent and weary. And that wildcat Rupert Hentzau was yet at large in the castle. Yet, because I could better defend the narrow door at the top of the stairs than the wider entrance to the room, I dragged myself up the steps and stood behind it, listening.

What was the sound? Again a strange one for the place and the time. An easy, scornful, merry laugh—the laugh of young Rupert Hentzau! I could scarcely believe that a sane man would laugh. Yet the laugh told me that my men had not come; for they must have shot Rupert ere now if they had come. And the clock struck half past two! My God! The door had not been opened! They had gone to the bank! They had not found me! They had gone by now back to Tarlenheim, with the news of the King's death—and mine. Well, it would be true before they got there. Was not Rupert laughing in triumph? For a moment I sank, unnerved, against the door.

Then I started up alert again, for Rupert cried scornfully:

"Well, the bridge is there! Come over it! And in God's name, Black Michael, come and fight for her!"

If it were a three-cornered fight I might yet bear my part. I turned the key in the door and looked out.

CHAPTER XIX

Face-to-Face in the Forest

FOR A MOMENT I COULD SEE NOTHING for the flare of lanterns and torches. But soon the scene grew clear. At the far end of the bridge stood a huddled group of the duke's servants; two or three carried the lights which had dazzled me, three or four held pikes in rest.

They looked in as arrant a fright as I have seen men look, and they gazed apprehensively at a man who stood in the middle of the bridge, sword in hand. Rupert Hentzau was in his trousers and shirt; the white linen was stained with blood. There he stood, easy and buoyant, holding the bridge against them and daring them to come on; or, rather, bidding them send Black Michael to him; and they, having no firearms, cowered before the desperate man and dared not attack him.

By marvelous chance I was master. The cravens would oppose me no more than they dared attack Rupert. I had but to raise my revolver, and I sent him to his account with his sins on his head. He did not so much as know that I was there. I did nothing—why, I hardly know to this day. Villain as the man was, I did not relish being one of a crowd against him—perhaps it was that. But also I felt a curiosity and a fascination which held me spellbound, watching for the outcome of the scene.

"Michael, you dog! Michael! If you can stand, come on!" cried Rupert; and he advanced a step, the group shrinking back a little before him. "Michael, you bastard! Come on!"

The answer to his taunts came in the wild cry of a woman:

"He's dead! My God, he's dead!"

"Dead!" shouted Rupert. "I struck better than I knew!" and he laughed triumphantly. Then he went on, "Down with your weapons there! I'm your master now! Down with them, I say!"

I believe they would have obeyed, but as he spoke came new things. First, there came shouts and knockings from the other side of the château. My heart leaped. It must be my men, come by a happy disobedience to seek me. The noise continued, but none seemed to heed it. Their attention was chained by what now happened before their eyes. The group of servants parted and a woman staggered onto the bridge. Antoinette de Mauban was in a loose white robe, her dark hair streamed over her shoulders, her face was ghastly pale and her eyes gleamed wildly in the light of the torches. In her shaking hand she held a revolver, and as she tottered forward she fired it at Rupert Hentzau. The ball missed him and struck the woodwork over my head.

"Faith, madame," laughed Rupert, "had your eyes been no more deadly than your shooting I had not been in this scrape—nor Black Michael in hell—tonight!"

She took no notice of his words. Very slowly and deliberately she began to raise her arm again, taking most careful aim. Before she had got her aim he bowed in his most graceful fashion, cried, "I can't kill where I've kissed," laid his hand on the parapet of the bridge and lightly leaped into the moat.

At that very moment I heard a rush of feet, and a voice I knew—Sapt's—cry, "God! It's the duke—dead!" Then, throwing down my revolver, I sprang out on the bridge. There was a cry of wild wonder, "The King!" and then I, like Rupert Hentzau, sword in hand, vaulted over the parapet, intent on finishing my quarrel with him where I saw his curly head fifteen yards off in the water.

He swam swiftly and easily. I was weary and half crippled with my wounded arm. I could not gain on him. He was under the bank now, searching, as I guessed, for a spot that he could climb. I knew there to be none—but there was my rope, which would still be hanging where I had left it. Perhaps he would miss it—perhaps he would find it. I put forth all my remaining strength. At last I began to gain on him; for he, occupied with his search, unconsciously slackened his pace.

Ah, he had found it! A low shout of triumph came from him. He laid hold of it and began to haul himself up. I was at the rope, and he, hanging in midair, saw me.

"Hallo! Who's here?" he cried in startled tones.

For a moment I believe he took me for the King, but an instant later he cried, "Why, it's the playactor! How came you here, man?"

And so saying he gained the bank.

I laid hold of the rope, but I paused. He stood on the bank, sword in hand, and he could cut my head open or spit me through the heart as I came up. I let go the rope.

"Never mind," said I, "but as I am here I think I'll stay."

Suddenly the great bell of the castle started to ring furiously, and a loud shout reached us from the moat.

Rupert smiled and waved his hand to me.

"I should like a turn with you, but it's a little too hot!" said he, and he disappeared from above me.

In an instant I laid my hand to the rope. I was up. I saw him thirty yards off, running like a deer toward the shelter of the forest. For once Rupert Hentzau had chosen discretion for his part. I rushed after him, calling to him to stand. He would not. Unwounded and vigorous, he gained on me at every step; but I pressed on, and soon the forest of Zenda engulfed us both, pursued and pursuer.

It was three o'clock now, and day was dawning. I was on a long, straight, grass avenue, and a hundred yards ahead ran young Rupert, his curls waving in the fresh breeze. A moment later he turned sharply to the right and was lost from my sight.

I thought all was over, and in deep vexation sank on the ground. But I was up again directly, for a woman's scream rang through the forest. Putting forth the last of my strength, I ran on and, turning right where he had turned, I saw him again. But alas! I could not touch him. He was in the act of lifting a small girl down from her horse, a peasant's daughter, probably on her way to the early market at Zenda. Her horse was a stout, well-shaped animal. Master Rupert lifted her down amid her shrieks—the sight of him frightened her; but he treated her gently, laughed, kissed her and gave her money. Then he jumped on the horse, sitting sideways like a woman; and then he waited for me. I, on my part, waited for him.

Presently he rode toward me, keeping his distance, however. He lifted up his hand, saying:

"What did you in the castle?"

"I killed three of your friends," said I.

"What! You got to the cells?"

"Yes."

"And the King?"

"He was hurt by Detchard before I killed Detchard, but I pray that he lives."

"You fool!" said Rupert pleasantly.

"One thing more I did."

"And what's that?"

"I spared your life. I was behind you on the bridge, with a revolver in my hand."

"No? Faith, I was between two fires!"

"Get off your horse," I cried, "and fight like a man."

Then, in my rage, hardly knowing what I did, I rushed at him. I seized the bridle and I struck at him. He parried and thrust at me. I fell back a pace and rushed in at him again; and this time I reached his face and laid his cheek open, and darted back before he could strike me. He seemed almost mazed at the fierceness of my attack; otherwise I think he must have killed me. I sank on my knee, panting, expecting him to ride at me. And so he could have done, and then and there, I doubt not, one or both of us would have died; but at the moment there came a shout from behind us, and looking round I saw, just at the turn of the avenue, a man on a horse. He was riding hard, and he carried a revolver in his hand. It was Fritz von Tarlenheim, my faithful friend. Rupert saw him, and knew that the game was up. Flinging his leg over the saddle, he tossed his hair off his forehead and smiled, and said:

"Au revoir, Rudolf Rassendyll!"

Then, with his cheek streaming blood, but his lips laughing and his body swaying with ease and grace, he bowed to me and to the farm girl, who had drawn near in trembling fascination. Fritz, who was just within range, let fly a shot at him. The ball came nigh doing its work, but it struck the sword he held, and he dropped the sword with an oath and rode away at a gallop.

As I watched him go down the long avenue, he turned to wave his hand, and then was lost from our sight. Thus he vanished—reckless and wary, graceful and graceless, handsome, debonair, vile and unconquered. And I flung my sword passionately on the ground and cried to Fritz to ride after him. But Fritz stopped his horse, and leaped down and ran to me, and knelt, putting his arm about me. And indeed it was time, for the wound that Detchard had given me was broken forth afresh and my blood was staining the ground.

"Then give me the horse!" I cried, staggering to my feet and throwing his arms off me. And the strength of my rage carried me so far as where the horse stood, and then I fell prone beside it.

"Fritz!" I said.

"Ay, friend—dear friend!" he said, tender as a woman.

"Is the King alive?"

He knelt beside me again, took his handkerchief and wiped my lips, and bent and kissed me on the forehead.

"Thanks to the most gallant gentleman that lives," said he softly, "the King is alive!"

The little farm girl stood by us, weeping for fright and wide-eyed for wonder; for she had seen me at Zenda: and was not I, pallid, dripping, foul and bloody as I was—yet was not I the King?

And when I heard that the King was alive I strove to cry "Hurrah!" But I could not speak, and I laid my head back in Fritz's arms and closed my eyes, and I groaned; and then, lest Fritz should do me wrong in his thoughts, I opened my eyes and tried to say "Hurrah!" again. But I could not. And being very tired, and now very cold, I huddled myself close up to Fritz, to get the warmth of him, and shut my eyes again and went to sleep.

CHAPTER XX

The Prisoner and the King

FOR A FULL UNDERSTANDING of what had occurred in the Castle of Zenda it is necessary to supplement my own account of that night by relating briefly what I afterward learned from Fritz and Madame de Mauban. The story told by the latter explained clearly how it happened that the cry which I had arranged had come before its time, and had thus, as it seemed at the moment, ruined our hopes, while in the end it had favored them. The unhappy woman, fired, I believe, by a genuine attachment to the Duke of Strelsau, had followed him at his request from Paris to Ruritania. He was a man of strong passions, but of stronger will, and his cool head ruled both. He was content to take all and give nothing. When she arrived she was not long in finding that she had a rival in the Princess Flavia; rendered desperate, she stood at nothing which might give her power over the duke. Simultaneously Antoinette found herself entangled in his audacious schemes. Unwilling to abandon him, bound to him by the chains of shame and hope, yet she would not, at his bidding, lure me to death. Hence the letters of warning she had written. When the duke went to Zenda she accompanied him; and here for the first time she learned the full measure of his cruelty, and was touched with compassion for the unfortunate King. From this time she was with us; yet, from what she told me, I know that she still loved Michael, and trusted to gain his life, if not his pardon, from the King as the reward for her assistance. His triumph she did not desire, for she loathed his crime, and loathed yet more fiercely what would be the prize of it—his marriage with his cousin, Princess Flavia.

At Zenda new forces came into play—the lust and daring of young Rupert. He was caught by her beauty, perhaps; perhaps it was enough for him that she belonged to another man. For many days there had been quarrels and ill will between him and the duke, and the scene which I had witnessed in the duke's room was but one of many. On this night, then, Rupert had determined to have his will. When she had gone to her room he, having furnished himself with a key to it, had made his entrance. Her cries had brought the duke, and there in the dark room the men had fought; and Rupert, having wounded his master with a mortal blow, had, on the servants rushing in, escaped through the window as I have described. The duke's blood, spurting out, had stained his opponent's shirt; but Rupert, not knowing that he had dealt Michael his death, was eager to finish the encounter. Antoinette, left alone with the duke, had tried to stanch his wound, and thus was she busied till he died; and then, hearing Rupert's taunts, she had come forth to avenge him.

The same moment found my friends on the scene. They had reached the château in due time, and waited by the door. But Johann, swept with the rest to the rescue of the duke, did not open it. Till nearly half past two Sapt waited; then, following my orders, he had sent Fritz to search the banks of the moat. I was not there. Hastening back, Fritz told Sapt; and Sapt was for following orders still, and riding at full speed back to Tarlenheim; while Fritz would not hear of abandoning me, let me have ordered what I would. On this they disputed some few minutes; then Sapt, persuaded by Fritz, detached a party to gallop back to Tarlenheim and bring up the marshal, while the rest fell to on the great door of the château. For several minutes it resisted them; then, just as Antoinette de Mauban fired at Rupert Hentzau on the bridge, they broke in, eight of them in all: and the first door they came to was the door of Michael's room; and Michael lay dead across the threshold, with a sword thrust through his breast. Sapt cried out at his death, as I had heard, and Antoinette flung herself, weeping, at Sapt's feet. And all she cried was that I had been at the end of the bridge and had leaped off. "What of the prisoner?" asked Sapt; but she shook her head. Then Sapt and Fritz, with the gentlemen behind them, crossed the bridge, warily and without noise; and Fritz stumbled over the dead body of De Gautet in the doorway.

Then they consulted, listening eagerly for any sound from the cells below; but there came none, and they were greatly afraid that the King's guards had killed him, and having pushed his body through the great pipe, had escaped the same way themselves. Going back to Michael's body they found a key to the door which I had locked, and opened the door. The staircase was dark, but soon Fritz cried, "The door down there is open! See, there is light!" When they came to the outer room and saw the Belgian, Bersonin, lying dead, they thanked God, Sapt saying, "Ay, he has been here." Then rushing into the King's cell, they found Detchard lying dead across the dead physician, and the King on his back with his chair by him. And Fritz cried, "He's dead!" and Sapt knelt down by the King; and having learned more of wounds and the sign of death than I, he soon knew that the King was not dead, nor, if properly attended, would die. And they covered his face and carried him to Duke Michael's room, and laid him there; and Antoinette bathed the King's head and dressed his wounds, till a doctor came. And Sapt, seeing I had been there, and having heard Antoinette's story, sent Fritz to search the moat and then the forest. Then, as I have told, he found me, guided by the shout with which I had called on Rupert to stop and face me. And I think a man has never been more glad to find his own brother alive than was Fritz to come on me; so that, in love and anxiety for me, he thought nothing of a thing so great as would have been the death of Rupert Hentzau.

The enterprise of the King's rescue being thus prosperously concluded, it lay on Colonel Sapt to secure secrecy as to the King's ever having been in need of rescue. Antoinette de Mauban and Johann the keeper were sworn to reveal nothing. The metamorphosis had happened; and the King, wounded almost to death by the attacks of the jailers who guarded his friend, had at last overcome them, and rested now, wounded but alive, in Black Michael's own room in the castle. There he had been carried, and thence orders issued that if his friend were found he should be brought directly to the King, and that meanwhile messengers should ride at full speed to Tarlenheim to tell Marshal Strakencz to assure the princess of the King's safety, and to come himself with all speed to greet the King. The princess was enjoined to remain at Tarlenheim, and there await his further injunctions. Thus the King would come to his own again, having wrought grave deeds, and escaped, almost by a miracle, the treacherous assault of his unnatural brother.

This ingenious arrangement of my long-headed old friend prospered in every way, save where it encountered a force that often defeats the most cunning schemes. I mean nothing less than the pleasure of a woman. For, let her cousin and sovereign send what command he chose, the Princess Flavia was in no way minded to rest at Tarlenheim while her lover lay wounded at Zenda; and when the marshal, with a small suite, rode forth from Tarlenheim on the way to Zenda the princess' carriage followed immediately behind, and in this order they passed through the town, where the report was already rife that the King, going the night before in all friendliness to remonstrate with his brother, for that he held one of the King's friends in confinement, had been most traitorously set upon; that there had been a desperate conflict; that the duke was slain with several of his gentlemen; and that the King, wounded as he was, had seized and held the Castle of Zenda.

Thus the Princess Flavia came to Zenda. And as she drove up the hill, with the marshal still imploring her to return in obedience to the King's orders, Fritz von Tarlenheim, with the prisoner of Zenda, came to the edge of the forest. I had revived from my swoon, and walked, resting on Fritz's arm; and looking out from the cover of the trees, I saw the princess. Suddenly understanding from a glance at my companion's face that we must not meet her, I sank on my knees behind a clump of bushes.

But there was one whom we had forgotten, but who followed us, and was not disposed to let slip the chance of earning a smile and maybe a crown or two; and while we lay hidden, the little farm girl ran to the princess, curtsying and crying, "Madame, the King is here—in the bushes! May I guide you to him, madame?"

"Nonsense, child!" said old Strakencz. "The King lies wounded in the castle."

"Yes, sir, he's wounded, I know; but he's there. He pursued a gentleman, and they fought till Count Fritz came; and the other gentleman took my father's horse and rode away; but the King is here with Count Fritz. Why, madame, is there another man in Ruritania like the King?"

"No, my child," said Flavia softly (I was told it afterward), and she smiled and gave the girl money. "I will go and see this gentleman," and she rose to alight from the carriage.

But at this moment Sapt came riding from the castle, and seeing the princess, made the best of a bad job, and cried to her that the King was in the castle, well tended and in no danger.

"But this girl says he is yonder—with Count Fritz," said Flavia.

Sapt turned his eyes on the child with an incredulous smile. "I'll ride myself and see this man," said he hastily.

"Nay, I'll come myself," said the princess.

"Then come alone," he whispered.

And she, obedient to the strange hinting in his face, prayed the marshal and the rest to wait; and she and Sapt came on foot toward where we lay. And when I saw them coming I buried my face in my hands.

"Speak low, whatever you say," I heard Sapt whisper as they

came up; and the next thing I heard was a low cry—half of joy, half of fear—from the princess, "It is he! Are you hurt?"

And she fell on the ground by me and gently pulled my hands away; but I kept my eyes to the ground.

"It is the King!" she said. "Pray, Colonel Sapt, tell me where lay the wit of the joke you played on me?"

We answered none of us: we three were silent before her. Regardless of them, she threw her arms round my neck and kissed me. Then Sapt spoke in a low, hoarse whisper:

"It is not the King. Don't kiss him; he's not the King."

She drew back for a moment; then, with an arm still round my neck, she asked in superb indignation:

"Do I not know my love? Rudolf, my love!"

"It is not the King," said old Sapt again; and a sudden sob broke from tenderhearted Fritz.

It was the sob that told her no comedy was afoot.

"He is the King!" she cried. "It is the King's face—the King's ring—my ring! It is my love!"

"Your love, madame," said old Sapt, "but not the King. The King is there in the castle. This gentleman—"

"Look at me, Rudolf! Look at me!" she cried, taking my face between her hands. "Why do you let them torment me? Tell me what it means!"

Then I spoke, gazing into her eyes.

"God forgive me, madame!" I said. "I am not the King!"

I felt her hands clutch my cheeks. She gazed at me as never man's face was scanned yet. And I, silent again, saw wonder born, and doubt grow, and terror spring to life as she looked. And very gradually the grasp of her hands slackened; she turned to Sapt, to Fritz and back to me. Then suddenly she reeled forward and fell in my arms; and with a great cry of pain I gathered her to me and kissed her lips.

Sapt laid his hand on my arm. I looked up in his face. And I laid her softly on the ground, and stood up, looking on her, cursing Heaven that young Rupert's sword had spared me for this sharper pang.

CHAPTER XXI

If Love Were All!

IT WAS NIGHT, AND I WAS in the cell wherein the King had lain in the Castle of Zenda. The great pipe that Rupert of Hentzau had nicknamed Jacob's ladder was gone, and the lights in the room across the moat twinkled in the darkness. All was still; the din and clash of strife were gone. I had spent the day hidden in the forest from the time when Fritz had led me off, leaving Sapt with the princess. Under cover of dusk, muffled up, I had been brought to the castle and lodged where I now lay. I had thrown myself on a pallet by the window, and was looking out on the black water; Johann the keeper had brought me supper. He told me that the King was doing well, that he had seen the princess; that she and he, Sapt and Fritz had been long together. Black Michael lay in his coffin, and Antoinette de Mauban watched by him; had I not heard, from the chapel, priests singing Mass for him?

Outside there were strange rumors afloat. Some said that the prisoner of Zenda was dead; some, that he had vanished yet alive; some, that he was a friend who had served the King well in some adventure in England; others, that he had discovered the duke's plots, and had therefore been kidnaped by him. One or two shrewd fellows shook their heads and said only that they would say nothing, but they had suspicions that more was to be known than was yet known, if Colonel Sapt would tell all he knew.

Thus Johann chattered till I sent him away and lay there alone, thinking, not of the future, but—as a man is wont to do when stirring things have happened to him—rehearsing the events of the past weeks. And above me, in the stillness of the night, I heard the standards flapping against their poles, for Black Michael's banner hung there half-mast high, and above it the royal flag of Ruritania. Habit grows so quick that only by an effort did I recollect that it floated no longer for me.

Presently Fritz von Tarlenheim came into the room. He told me briefly that the King wanted me, and together we crossed the drawbridge and entered the room that had been Black Michael's.

The King was lying there in bed; our doctor from Tarlenheim was in attendance on him. The King held out his hand and shook mine. Fritz and the doctor withdrew to the window.

I took the King's ring from my finger and placed it on his.

"I have tried not to dishonor it, sire," said I.

"I can't talk much to you," he said in a weak voice. "I have had a great fight with Sapt and the marshal—for we have told the marshal everything. I wanted to take you to Strelsau and keep you with me, and tell everyone of what you had done; and you would have been my best and nearest friend, cousin Rudolf. But they tell me I must not, and that the secret must be kept—if kept it can be."

"They are right, sire. Let me go. My work here is done."

"Yes, it is done, as no man but you could have done it. When they see me again I shall have my beard on; I shall—yes, faith, I shall be wasted with sickness. They will not wonder that the King looks changed in face. Cousin, I shall try to let them find him changed in nothing else. You have shown me how to play the King."

"Sire," said I, "I can take no praise from you. It is by the narrowest grace of God that I was not a worse traitor than your brother."

He turned inquiring eyes on me; but a sick man shrinks from puzzles, and he had no strength to question me. His glance fell on Flavia's ring, which I wore. I thought he would question me about it; but after fingering it idly, he let his head fall on his pillow.

"I don't know when I shall see you again," he said faintly.

"If I can ever serve you again, sire," I answered.

His eyelids closed. Fritz came with the doctor. I kissed the King's hand, and let Fritz lead me away. I have never seen the King since.

Outside Fritz turned, not to the right, back toward the drawbridge, but to the left, and through a corridor in the château.

"Where are we going?" I asked.

Looking away from me, Fritz answered:

"She has sent for you. When it is over come back to the bridge. I'll wait for you there."

"What does she want?" said I, breathing quickly.

He shook his head.

"Does she know everything?"

"Yes, everything."

He opened a door, and gently pushing me in, closed it behind me. I found myself in a drawing room, small and richly furnished. The light that came from a pair of shaded candles on the mantelpiece was very dim, but presently I discerned a woman's figure standing by the window. I knew it was the princess, and I walked up to her, fell on one knee and carried the hand that hung by her side to my lips. She neither moved nor spoke. I rose to my feet, and piercing the gloom with my eager eyes, saw her pale face and the gleam of her hair, and before I knew, I spoke softly, "Flavia!"

She trembled a little, and looked round. Then she darted to me.

"Don't stand! You're hurt! Sit down—here, here!"

She made me sit on a sofa, and put her hand on my forehead.

"How hot your head is," she said, sinking on her knees by me. Then she laid her head against me, and I heard her murmur, "My darling, how hot your head is!"

Somehow love gives even to a dull man the knowledge of his lover's heart. I had come to humble myself and pray pardon for my presumption; but what I said now was:

"I love you with all my heart and soul!"

For what troubled and shamed her? Not her love for me, but the fear that I had counterfeited the lover as I had acted the King.

"With all my life and heart," said I, as she clung to me. "Always, from the first moment I saw you in the cathedral! There has been but one woman in the world to me—and there will be no other. But God forgive me the wrong I've done you!"

"They made you do it!" she said quickly; and she added, raising her head and looking in my eyes, "It might have made no difference if I'd known it. It was always you, never the King!"

"I meant to tell you," said I. "I was going to on the night of the ball in Strelsau, when Sapt interrupted me. After that I couldn't— I couldn't risk losing you before—before—I must! My darling, for you I nearly left the King to die!"

"I know, I know! What are we to do now, Rudolf?"

I put my arm round her and held her up while I said:

"I am going away tonight."

"Ah, no, no!" she cried. "Not tonight!"

"I must go tonight, before more people have seen me."

"I could come with you!" she whispered very low.

"My God," said I roughly, "don't talk about that!" and I thrust her a little back from me.

"Why not? I love you. You are as good a gentleman as the King!"

Then I was false to all that I should have held by. For I caught her in my arms and prayed her, in words that I will not write, to come with me, daring all Ruritania to take her from me. And for a while she listened, with wondering eyes. But as her eyes looked on me I grew ashamed, and my voice died away in broken murmurs.

She drew herself away from me and stood against the wall, while I sat on the edge of the sofa, trembling in every limb, knowing what I had done—loathing it, obstinate not to undo it.

"I am mad!" I said sullenly, at last.

"I love your madness, dear," she answered.

Her face was away from me, but I caught the sparkle of a tear on her cheek. I clutched the sofa and held myself there.

"If love were the only thing," she said in low, sweet tones, "I would follow you—in rags, if need be—to the world's end; for you hold my heart in the hollow of your hand! But is love the only thing?"

I made no answer. It gives me shame now to think that I would not help her.

She came near me and laid her hand on my shoulder. I put my hand up and held hers.

"I know people write and talk as if it were. Perhaps, for some, Fate lets it be. Ah, if I were one of them! But if love had been the only thing, you would have let the King die in his cell."

I kissed her hand.

"Honor binds a woman too, Rudolf. My honor lies in being true to my country and my House. I don't know why God has let me love you; but I know that I must stay."

Still I said nothing; and she, pausing a while, then went on:

"Your ring will always be on my finger, your heart in my heart, the touch of your lips on mine. But you must go and I must stay. Perhaps I must do what it kills me to think of doing."

I knew what she meant, and a shiver ran through me. But I could not utterly fail beside her. I rose and took her hand. "Do what you will or what you must," I said. "I think God shows His purposes to such as you. My part is lighter; for your ring shall be on my finger and your heart in mine, and no touch save of your lips will ever be on mine. So, may God comfort you, my darling!"

There struck on our ears the sound of singing. The priests in the chapel were singing Masses for the souls of the dead. They seemed to chant a requiem over our buried joy, to pray forgiveness for our love that would not die. The soft, sweet, pitiful music rose and fell as we stood opposite one another, her hands in mine.

"My queen and my beauty!" said I.

"My lover and true knight!" she said. "Perhaps we shall never see one another again. Kiss me, my dear, and go!"

I kissed her as she bade me; but at the last she clung to me, whispering nothing but my name, and that over and over again—and again—and again; and then I left her.

Rapidly I walked down to the bridge. Sapt and Fritz were waiting for me. Under their directions I changed my dress, and muffling my face, as I had done more than once before, I mounted with them at the door of the castle, and we three rode through the night and on to the breaking day, and found ourselves at a little roadside station just over the border of Ruritania. The train was not quite due, and I walked with them in a meadow by a little brook while we waited for it. They promised to send me all news; they overwhelmed me with kindness—even old Sapt was touched to gentleness, while Fritz was half unmanned. I listened in a kind of dream to all they said. "Rudolf! Rudolf! Rudolf!" still rang in my ears—a burden of sorrow and of love. At last they saw that I could not heed them, and we walked up and down in silence, till Fritz touched me on the arm, and I saw, a mile or more away, the blue smoke of the train. Then I held out a hand to each of them.

"We are all but half men this morning," said I, smiling. "But we have been men, eh, Sapt and Fritz, old friends? We have run a good course between us."

"We have defeated traitors and set the King firm on his throne," said Sapt.

Then Fritz von Tarlenheim suddenly, before I could discern his purpose, uncovered his head and bent as he used to do, and kissed my hand; and as I snatched it away he said, trying to laugh:

"Heaven doesn't always make the right men kings!"

Old Sapt twisted his mouth as he wrung my hand.

"The devil has his share in most things," said he.

The people at the station looked curiously at the tall man with the muffled face. I stood with my two friends and waited till the train came up to us. Then we shook hands again, saying nothing; and both this time—and, indeed, from old Sapt it seemed strange—bared their heads, and so stood still till the train bore me away from their sight. So that it was thought some great man traveled privately for his pleasure from the little station that morning; whereas, in truth, it was only I, Rudolf Rassendyll, an English gentleman, a cadet of a good house, but a man of no wealth or position, nor of much rank. They would have been disappointed to know that. Yet, had they known all, they would have looked more curiously still. For, be I what I might now, I had been for three months a king, which, if not a thing to be proud of, is at least an experience to have undergone. Doubtless I should have thought more of it had there not echoed through the air, from the towers of Zenda that we were leaving far away, into my ears and my heart the cry of a woman's love—"Rudolf! Rudolf! Rudolf!" Hark! I hear it now!

Epilogue

SINCE ALL THESE EVENTS whose history I have set down happened, I have lived a very quiet life at a small house which I have taken in the country. Lady Burlesdon now utterly despairs of me, although her reception of me on my return was not so alarming as I had feared, arriving as I did with neither notes nor observations to justify my Tyrol holiday. For it turned out that I had done, not, certainly, what Rose wished, but—the next best thing—what she had prophesied.

For the rest, the ordinary ambitions and aims of men in my position seem to me dull and unattractive. I have little fancy for the whirl of society, and none for the jostle of politics, and my neighbors think me an indolent, dreamy, unsociable fellow. Yet I am a young man; and sometimes I have a fancy that my part in life is not yet altogether played; that, someday, I shall mix again in great affairs, I shall again match my wits against my enemies', brace my muscles to fight a good fight and strike stout blows. Whether the fancy will be fulfilled I cannot tell, yet I love to see myself once again in the crowded streets of Strelsau, or beneath the frowning keep of the Castle of Zenda.

Thus led, my broodings leave the future, and turn back on the past. Shapes rise before me in long array—the wild first revel with the King, the rush with my brave tea table, the night in the moat, the pursuit in the forest: my friends and foes, the people who learned to love and honor me, the desperate men who tried to kill me. And, from amid these last, comes one who alone of all of them yet moves on earth, yet plans (as I do not doubt) wickedness, yet turns women's hearts to softness and men's to fear and hate. Where is young Rupert of Hentzau—the boy who came so nigh to beating me? When his name comes into my head I feel my hand grip and the blood move quicker through my veins; and the hint of Fate seems to grow stronger, and to whisper insistently in my ear that I have yet a hand to play with young Rupert.

One break comes every year in my quiet life. Then I go to Dresden, and there I am met by my dear friend and companion, Fritz von Tarlenheim. Last time his pretty wife Helga came, and a lusty crowing baby with her. And for a week Fritz and I are together, and I hear all of what falls out in Strelsau; and in the evenings, as we walk and smoke together, we talk of Sapt, and of the King, and often of young Rupert; and, as the hours grow small, at last we speak of Flavia. For every year Fritz carries with him to

Dresden a little box; in it lies a red rose, and a slip of paper with the words written: *Rudolf—Flavia—always*. And the like I send back by him. That message, and the wearing of the rings, are all that now bind me and the Queen of Ruritania. For—nobler, as I hold her, for the act—she has followed where her duty to her country and her House led her, and is the wife of the King, uniting his subjects to him by the love they bear to her, giving peace to thousands by her self-sacrifice. There are moments when I dare not think of it, but there are others when I rise in spirit to where she ever dwells; then I can thank God that I love the noblest lady in the world, the most gracious and beautiful, and that there was nothing in my love that made her fall short in her high duty.

Shall I see her face again—the pale face and the glorious hair? Of that I know nothing; Fate has no hint, my heart no presentiment. I do not know. In this world, perhaps—nay, it is likely— never. And can it be that somewhere, in a manner whereof our flesh-bound minds have no apprehension, she and I will be together again, with nothing to come between us, nothing to forbid our love? That I know not, nor wiser heads than mine. But if it be never—if I can never hold sweet converse again with her, or look upon her face, or know from her her love—why, then, this side the grave, I will live as becomes the man whom she loves; and for the other side I must pray a dreamless sleep.